150 Years of British Psychiatry, 1841–1991

Edited by
GERMAN E. BERRIOS
HUGH FREEMAN

150 Years of British Psychiatry, 1841–1991

GASKELL

ISBN 0 902241 36 2

Gaskell is an imprint of the Royal College of Psychiatrists,
17 Belgrave Square, London SW1

Distributed in North America
by American Psychiatric Press, Inc.
ISBN 0 88048 603 1

British Library Cataloguing in Publication Data
150 years of British psychiatry, 1841–1991.
1. Great Britain. 2. Psychiatry. History.
I. Berrios, G. E. (German Elias) II. Freeman, Hugh
616.8900941
ISBN 0-902241-36-2

Phototypeset by Dobbie Typesetting Limited, Tavistock, Devon
Printed in Great Britain

Contents

Part III. People

Contributors

P. H. Allderidge, Archivist and Curator, The Bethlem Royal Hospital, Monks Orchard Road, Beckenham, Kent BR3 3BX

A. L. Ashworth, Curator, Stephen G. Beaumont Museum, Stanley Royd Hospital, Aberford Road, Wakefield, West Yorkshire WF1 4DQ

D. H. Bennett, Emeritus Psychiatrist, Maudsley and Bethlem Royal Hospital, London

G. E. Berrios, University Lecturer and Consultant Psychiatrist, University of Cambridge

A. Beveridge, Consultant Psychiatrist, West Fife District General Hospital, Whitefield Road, Bellyeoman, Dunfermline KY12 0SU

W. F. Bynum, Wellcome Institute for the History of Medicine, 183 Euston Road, London NW1 2BN

K. Day, Consultant Psychiatrist, Northgate Hospital, Morpeth, Northumberland NE61 3BP

W. Ernst, Department of History, Victoria University of Wellington, PO Box 600, Wellington, New Zealand

H. L. Freeman, Editor, *British Journal of Psychiatry*, Honorary Professor, University of Salford, and Honorary Consultant Psychiatrist, Salford Health Authority

M. Finnane, Senior Lecturer, Division of Humanities, Griffith University, Nathan, Brisbane, Queensland, Australia 4111

M. G. Gelder, Professor, Department of Psychiatry, University of Oxford, Warneford Hospital, Oxford OX3 7JX

D. Healy, Academic Sub-Department of Psychological Medicine, University of Wales College of Medicine, Denbigh, Clwyd LL16 5SS

R. D. Hinshelwood, Consultant Psychotherapist, St Bernard's Hospital, Southall, Middlesex

J. G. Howells, formerly Director, Institute of Family Psychiatry, Ipswich Hospital, Suffolk

J. Jancar, Stoke Park Hospital, Stapleton, Bristol BS16 1QU

F. A. Jenner, Department of Psychiatry, Royal Hallamshire Hospital, Glossop Road, Sheffield S10 2JF

K. Jones, Emeritus Professor of Social Policy, Department of Social Policy and Social Work, University of York, Heslington, York YO1 5DD

H. Merskey, Professor, London Psychiatric Hospital, 850 Highbury Avenue, PO Box 2532, London, Ontario N6A 4H1, Canada

M. Pines, The Group-Analytic Practice, 88 Montague Mansions, London W1H 1LF

E. Renvoize, Department of Public Health Medicine, University of Leeds, 32 Hyde Terrace, Leeds LS2 9LN

H. R. Rollin, Emeritus Consultant, Horton Hospital, Epsom, Surrey, and Quondam Librarian, Royal College of Psychiatrists

R. Smith, Department of History, University of Lancaster, Lancaster LA1 4YG

D. Tantam, Professor of Psychotherapy, Department of Psychology and School of Postgraduate Medicine, University of Warwick, Coventry CV4 7AL

J. Todd, formerly Consultant Psychiatrist, High Royds Hospital, Menston, Yorkshire

T. H. Turner, Consultant Psychiatrist, Department of Psychological Medicine, St Bartholomew's Hospital, West Smithfield, London EC1A 7BE

T. Walmsley, Consultant Psychiatrist, Knowle Hospital, Fareham, Hants PO17 5NA

C. J. Wardle, Consultant and Clinical Tutor in Child and Adolescent Psychiatry, Devon

C. Webster, All Souls College, Oxford OX1 4AL

Introduction

GERMAN E. BERRIOS and HUGH FREEMAN

Of not many countries can it be said, as it can of Great Britain and Ireland, that the history of their psychiatry matches so well the history of only one professional institution. Since its foundation in 1841, the Association of Medical Officers of Asylums and Hospitals for the Insane (and its successors) has both influenced and reflected the way in which psychiatric disorder has been conceived and managed in the British Isles. Its role can best be described as that of a broker between four main influences: popular and official sentiments, the national progress of medical and psychological sciences, ideas from abroad, and the notions and desires of the profession itself. For good or ill, the Association was the main caretaker of the forum in which much of this 19th-century debate took place.

For a previously long-neglected subject, the history of society's relationship to insanity has made remarkable progress during the past 20 years, but there is no privileged historical window from which this entire process can be observed: each provides a clear view only of some events. This book puts together vistas obtained from many such vantage points, some well known, others new; but the final product must depend on individual perceptions. The professional historians here may stand out by virtue of their steady eye and steadier pen; the others, though perhaps less neat and secure in their vision, are all members of the Royal College of Psychiatrists – the 20th-century version of the body whose origin is being commemorated here. The freshness of their outlook and, even more important, their knowledge of the clinical issues involved – both mental and physical – will, the editors believe, add a new dimension to the historiography of British psychiatry. Much of its 'revisionist' history is lacking in any real understanding of the nature of psychiatric disorders or of the practical, everyday decisions that faced those responsible for the care of the mentally ill and mentally retarded in earlier periods – or indeed that face them today. Labels such as 'presentism' have been attached to the historical studies of psychiatrists, but it is the revisionists themselves who often apply late 20th-century value judgements to the activities of doctors, relatives, administrators, or politicians in the totally different conditions of the past. What is more, the adverse comments made on the psychiatry of different periods in the last 150 years often have no specific relevance; they would apply equally to medicine in general then, and often to other activities such as education or the penal system.

In the 1960s, the very existence of mental illness – a phenomenon that has been recognised throughout all human societies and recorded eras – was at the same time both widely denied and, with little consistency, attributed to a specific set of social, political, and economic circumstances usually labelled as 'late capitalism'. R. D. Laing, for instance, claimed that madness was not really illness, because it could be understood as a reaction to environmental events, yet the sociologist Joan Busfield (1987) pointed out that, "it is the nature and consequences, not the causes of the condition that lead to the designation 'illness' ". She saw psychiatry's ideological framework as that of medicine in general – the liberal-scientific tradition deriving from the Enlightenment – and acknowledged that the early lunacy reformers were mostly religious dissenters, whose motive was not merely economic exploitation, as the chapter here on Samuel Gaskell illustrates. From a Marxist viewpoint, Scull (1977) claimed that in the early 19th century, the notion of insanity had been broadened in a conspiratorial way, so that those who were of no economic value to industrial capitalism could be removed from the arena of work. The reality, though, as Cooper & Sartorius (1977) first pointed out, was that industrialisation with its accompanying urbanisation had brought people together in unprecedented numbers; since migration had separated many of these from their extended families, since their homes were often severely overcrowded, and since most adults now worked long hours away from there, it was far more difficult for them than before to care for a relative with either acute or chronic psychiatric illness. This added up to a burgeoning and unprecedented level of demand for publicly provided care.

Every social problem in 19th-century Britain, though, was overshadowed by the effects of the Poor Law Amendment Act 1834, which set the institutional solution above all others. There were already some public asylums, such as the one at Wakefield described in Chapter 25, but with the new absence of domiciliary help, they were now located firmly within the Poor Law system as institutions of last resort, to be used only when family care had become impossible. Their purpose, though, remained a humane one: far from practising medical imperialism, the doctors working in asylums found themselves faced with ever larger numbers of clinically varied but mostly destitute cases, and this required their view of which were relevant to their work to be constantly enlarged. Quite apart from any psychiatric disorder, a large proportion of these incoming people were suffering from serious physical illness or neglect: Chapter 25 here again provides evidence. With their medical training, today's psychiatrists may on the whole be better equipped to interpret these events than the majority of historians and sociologists: to understand what went on then can be as much a matter of epidemiology as of social policy.

The revisionist school draws its inspiration mainly from the work of Michel Foucault, who provided a fertile source of new intellectual approaches but who, as a historian, was economical with the facts. Whether or not a 'great confinement' occurred in France in the 17th century (Foucault, 1967), there was certainly none in England or most other European countries then. Foucault's theory of a general normative 'discipline', developing at the end of the 18th century as a characteristic of bourgeois civilisation and underlying the techniques and buildings of several public organisations, carries rather more credibility, though. The asylums, hospitals, prisons, and orphanages may indeed have formed the material basis then for new conceptions of social relations, both among those confined and with those set above them (Donnelly, 1986). But with growing scientific and technical sophistication, a reaction to the insanitary chaos of 18th-century life was hardly surprising; whether or not that constituted "bourgeois discipline", as Donnelly suggests, is largely a matter of ideology. Foucault's Gallocentrism led to his failure to appreciate the central position in English lunacy reform of evangelical religion – a role it played in most of the moves around 1800 towards a more rational and humane social policy. It was central mainly through forming the basis of moral treatment, which was the critical concept in the process of transition to the modern era. To discard the locks, chains, and brutality of the Georgian madhouse required the paternal physician to have an alternative world-view of insanity; it was his example that would appeal to the human spirit still present beneath the cloak of madness, and his direction of the asylum regime that was to guide troubled minds back to sanity. Without such a moral foundation himself, the physician would have been served by nothing but a vaguely humane pragmatism, which in the intellectual climate of the time would have carried no conviction – to either patients or society in general. In revolutionary France, Pinel might move in a similar direction with more secular impulses, but unreconstructed British society would have made little response to such a tendency, without the legitimacy conferred on it by religion, even though this was pre-eminently of minorities such as the Quakers and Unitarians.

Scull (1989) continues to insist that the previously received analysis of the history of psychiatric care is fundamentally flawed, and that whatever people's intentions may have been, actual practice was almost always morally inadequate and characterised by cruelty and neglect. In particular, he has sought to reduce to the level of myths three principles of the Whiggish interpretation: the humanitarianism of the asylum, the effectiveness of psychological medicine, and the validity of 'community care' as a non-institutional alternative. It is true, as he maintains, that ideals are the engines of change, whatever the extent to which these ideals may be related to empirical data or experience, or be rationalisations of the self-interest of any group. That there is a dynamic interplay between professional practice on the one hand, and beliefs and social structure on the other, is equally acceptable wisdom; that the ruling ideas of any period need to be constantly exposed to critical thinking is axiomatic to most psychiatrists of today, if not always to those who came before them. Yet in spite of this intellectual common ground, the general message which emerges from Scull's work, as from much other revisionist writing by sociologists and historians, is primarily a confrontational one of condemnation, if not ridicule. At the first European Conference on the History of Psychiatry & Mental Health Care, Scull appeared to be particularly dismissive of those psychiatrists who try to explore the past of their own profession, as 'amateur' historians; if they were retired clinicians, this was said to be even worse.

The revisionists, though, mostly ignore the fact that medicine's role in society is a mainly instrumental one: it is charged with the task of performing certain functions – largely practical – which are regarded culturally as important, and which therefore tend to be generously rewarded. Doctors perform this task as well as they can, on the basis of current knowledge and resources, and within the prevailing cultural, political, and economic framework; it is not their professional business to change society, other than by giving advice as to how such changes might be beneficial to health. In the case of psychiatry, though, there is an extra task – to take charge of those whose behaviour breaks society's basic rules, apparently through illness or inherent defect, rather than through their rational decisions. In doing so, it must to some extent expect the role of scapegoat, since part of the rejection felt towards the mentally deviant will inevitably stick to those who provide care for them. There is profound ambivalence in most societies' views on this question, causing psychiatry and its allied professions to experience strongly contrasting social attitudes from one period to the next: in Britain, for instance, general approbation in the 1950s was followed by odium and rejection in the mid-1960s. Yet throughout these fluctuations of public sentiment, the instrumental tasks must be carried on: the caring professions can neither take a sabbatical nor transfer their attention to some intellectually more satisfying topic.

The revisionists' other main target is that school of history, predominantly based on the tradition of social administration, that is described as 'Whiggish' because it finds an unbroken thread of progress in the story – at least, up to the mid-1980s. Yet without this work – notably by Kathleen Jones in Britain and Gerald Grob in the United States – there would simply be no basis of factual data on which varying interpretations could be constructed. To deny the existence of such an entity as 'factual data', as some revisionists have done, is to move from sophistication to absurdity: either there was an act of Parliament of 1845 or there was not, although evaluation of these data is open to all. Before Kathleen Jones's pioneering work, collected in her *History of the Mental Health Services* (1972), such basic knowledge was inaccessible to most people, and there was certainly no coherent narrative. But what of its 'Whiggishness'?

Grob (1985) pointed out that the limitations and imperfections of 19th-century mental hospitals were little different from those of most other contemporary human institutions: in England, the developing public schools are an obvious example. A common-sense view, which a professional with experience of responsibility for psychiatric care might be very likely to take, is that comparing the average situation for a patient of 1790 with the average 200 years later, a fairly straight upward trend of improvement can be seen. There would be some fluctuations – for instance, a sharply upward slope in the early 19th century, for some individuals at least, followed by a downturn – but the general direction would follow that form. In the professional lifetime of today's senior psychiatrists in Britain, average standards of treatment and care have improved greatly in all respects, related partly to the creation of a well-trained and now fairly numerous profession. If local horror stories are quoted to the contrary, it has to be said again that such exceptions are true of every kind of human service activity, but these are not a valid basis for general statements.

The revisionists, though, are vulnerable to the rigorous examination of their own assumptions and data, and this has resulted in Scull's Marxist-based historical sociology being hoist with its own petard (Grob, 1990). Since the validity of his interpretation rests upon a particular view of society and of human behaviour, does not this direct his choice of data and his interpretation, as much as anyone else's? "Because the underlying rhetoric is clothed with the language of the social sciences," the underlying act of faith, which denies all alternative ideologies, is concealed (Grob, 1990, p. 228). "It is inconsistent to insist on the primacy of impersonal forces and yet condemn the results as immoral", since moral systems must assume a degree of freedom of action. Furthermore, once Scull's verbal pyrotechnics have been penetrated, the underlying data look more than shaky. Grob points out that before 1880, the proportion of chronic patients in American mental hospitals was relatively low – and the same may be said of Britain. This proportion then rose, for a variety of reasons, but many of the new residents were aged or paretic, needing custodial and general medical care; where else were they to get this, except in the worse conditions of the workhouse? Similarly, when the 'decarceration' that began in the mid-1950s is examined, Scull's emphasis on reductions in total numbers fails to take account of the increases in admissions and acute care. "The result", Grob (1990, p. 231) concludes, "is a profoundly ahistorical treatment . . . analysis of the process of change is absent . . . negative or undesirable outcomes must be *ipso facto* the deliberate end product of a calculating behaviour."

A constant theme of revisionists has been the 'failure' of the asylum in the 19th century, related to a falling rate of 'cures', after the initial period. Both these concepts are in fact naive, showing up egregiously the lack of clinical and epidemiological understanding on the part of those who make such statements. In the first place, what was the 'success' of any kind of hospital at that time? There is no clear answer, nor is there one even in relation to the hospitals of today – certainly not in terms of the crude percentages which are generally used in such discussions. To put the question more clearly, what were the proportions of patients admitted to an institution in any period who left either dead, unchanged, improved, or free of symptoms? A supplementary question is how do these proportions for asylum patients compare with those for medical, surgical, or any other category of patients admitted then to other institutions? Yet another question should ask how these proportions compared, in turn, with the outcome for sufferers from the same conditions who remained at home, as the majority probably did. The answers depend on a whole variety of factors, which include: the number of places available, accessibility of the institution (in geographical, administrative, and financial terms), criteria of selection for admission, staffing levels, prevalence of intercurrent infections, hygiene and nutrition, the physical state on admission of psychiatric patients, and the suitability of outside accommodation for those discharged. It is clear that any or all of these may vary over time, usually for reasons outside the control of the institution itself, and consequently affecting overall outcome for successive cohorts of admitted patients.

To be more specific, the early small asylums would be likely to receive a fairly high proportion of cases of acute psychosis, many of which would have a relatively good prognosis, at least in the short term. This was because they were new institutions, which would be seen as particularly appropriate for this socially prominent type of case. However, with the passage of time, the asylums would be affected by three processes. Firstly, some of those admitted would fail to recover sufficiently to be discharged; however few, they would accumulate over the years. Secondly, because of the success of the asylums in dealing with acute psychoses, they would be pressed to take other cases, of worse prognosis, such as chronic psychoses, mental retardation, addictions, dementia, or epilepsy. Thirdly, the more established the asylum, the more widely known would its facilities become, and the greater would be the demands on it to admit cases which hitherto had been managed – though with much difficulty – elsewhere, for example by families, in workhouses, or in small private establishments. The combined effect of all these factors would be to reduce steadily the proportion of acute recoverable cases in successive admission cohorts, and thus the crude rate of 'cure'. Additional processes tending in the same direction were, firstly, an inevitable erosion of the initial optimism (itself a therapeutic factor) of the asylum staff, as their population became more chronic, and secondly, an inevitable failure of the funding authorities (granted the prevailing parsimonious philosophy of public expenditure) to increase staff or maintain standards in proportion to these growing numbers. An institution with 2000 beds is a very different commitment from one with 200.

It is remarkable that a century later, the same evangelical optimism was being expressed by new services, set up in response to what was perceived as the failure of the mental hospital (e.g. Silverman, 1968), or by services for new communities in which there had not been time for cases of chronic, disabling conditions to accumulate (Taylor & Chave, 1964). Even with the availability of present-day treatment methods, conclusions about the 'success' of a service must remain tentative until information is available about *all* cases derived from a defined population, and these data have been followed for some years (Wooff *et al*, 1983). There is little evidence that either revisionist historians or sociological critics have given serious thought to considerations such as these. In the same way, exciting initiatives such as the scientific and academic work of the Wakefield asylum (Chapter 25) or Dr Thomas Beaton's integrated service at Portsmouth in the 1930s (Freeman, 1962) might have flowered and withered, mainly because they were too far ahead of their contemporaries. Awareness of the whirligig of time should lead to greater caution in condemning individuals who or institutions which, on the whole, were doing their best according to their lights.

As editors, it is not our intention here either to summarise the main parts of each chapter, in a kind of promotional brochure, or to give our own condensed account of the whole 150 years; the contributors' work can stand well enough on its own. Inevitably, though, a book of this nature must be incomplete, and the editors are painfully aware of some of its gaps. Most noticeable among these topics are the role of the European *émigrés*, Jaspersian ideas, and (except briefly) the influence of the Cambridge School of Psychopathology on British views of mental disorder. The histories of some treatments such as drugs and the convulsive therapies, mental nursing, occupational therapy, and clinical psychology also remain unreported. There are two main reasons for these omissions. The first was the constraint of time, since it would have undermined the book's purpose if it had not been published at the time of the anniversary it marks. The second was that of space: the book is longer than originally intended, and to include everything would have made it an impractical enterprise.

The gaps, furthermore, may stimulate others later to have their say, so that there could be a successor volume. The intention of this book was, in fact, more commemorative than one of full stock-taking. When in 1881 Daniel Hack Tuke assessed the first 40 years of the Medico-Psychological Association (MPA), he did not feel unduly pessimistic about the state of psychological medicine "throughout the Kingdom", and rightly saw the evolution of the latter as intimately associated with the work of the MPA. He concluded by specifying the order in which the three functions of the Association might be evaluated in the future: "first in relation to insanity and the insane; secondly, in relation to its members; thirdly, in relation to the public" (Tuke, 1882, p. 496). This book includes chapters on all three functions, and more or less starts where Tuke left off.

One does not need to hold a 'Whiggish', accumulative, or merely linear view of history, nor ignore the contribution of those who have rightly criticised some aspects of British psychological medicine, to say that current members and fellows of the Royal College of Psychiatrists have reason to feel proud of the progress shown by the profession since its formal organisation began. They might even feel immodest enough to accept that something of what Tuke said in 1881 might apply to them now: "And may the Medico-Psychological Association . . . be about to enter, after its wanderings . . . a land flowing with milk and honey, won by conquest over ignorance, superstition, and cruelty – the triumphs of the application of humanity and medical science to the relief of mental weakness and suffering."

References

BUSFIELD, J. (1987) *Managing Madness*. London: Hutchinson.

COOPER, J. & SARTORIUS, N. (1977) Cultural and temporal variations in schizophrenia: a speculation on the importance of industrialization. *British Journal of Psychiatry*, **130**, 50.

DONNELLY, M. (1986) *Managing the Mind*. London: Tavistock.

FOUCAULT, M. (1986) *Madness & Civilization*. London: Tavistock.

FREEMAN, H. L. (1962) The Portsmouth mental health service 1926–52. *The Medical Officer*, **107**, 149–151.

GROB, G. (1985) *Mental Illness & American Society 1875–1940*. Princeton, NJ: Princeton University Press.

—— (1990) Marxian analysis and mental illness. *History of Psychiatry*, **1**, 223–232.

JONES, K. (1972) *History of the Mental Health Services*. London: Routledge & Kegan Paul.

SCULL, A. (1977) *Decarceration: Community Treatment and the Deviant – A Radical View*. Englewood Cliffs, NJ: Prentice-Hall.

—— (1989) *Social Order/Mental Disorder: Anglo-American Psychiatry in Historical Perspective*. Berkeley, CA: University of California Press.

SILVERMAN, M. (1968) A comprehensive department of psychological medicine. *British Medical Journal*, **114**, 493.

TAYLOR, S. & CHAVE, S. W. P. (1964) *Mental Health & Environment*. London: Longmans.

TUKE, D. H. (1882) Progress of psychological medicine during the last forty years: 1841–1881. In *Chapters in the History of the Insane in the British Isles*, pp. 443–505. London: Kegan Paul, Trench.

WOOFF, K., FREEMAN, H. L. & FRYERS, T. (1983) Psychiatric service use in Salford: a comparison of point-prevalence ratios 1968 and 1978. *British Journal of Psychiatry*, **142**, 588–597.

I. Institutions

1 ''Not worth powder and shot'': the public profile of the Medico-Psychological Association, c. 1851–1914

TREVOR TURNER

In 1858 the first editor of the *Journal of Mental Science* (*JMS*), John Bucknill, felt compelled to write an article entitled ''The newspaper attack on private lunatic asylums'' (Bucknill, 1858). This was in reaction to the 'lunacy panic' of that year which arose from public concern over the inappropriate incarceration of alleged lunatics. A proposed Bill to introduce 'medical examiners' had alarmed the Association (of Medical Officers of Asylums and Hospitals for the Insane) to such an extent that ''committees were appointed, resolutions passed, reports drawn up, amidst a flurry of special meetings, a deputation to the Home Secretary and a petition to Parliament'' (McCandless, 1974). Bucknill had in fact addressed the 'Select Committee on Lunatics' (*Lancet*, 1860, vol. ii, p. 268) in his capacity as President of the Association, warning that their proposals would drive ''all respectable physicians out of the lunacy specialty''. But if the opposition of the alienists did not convince the Committee of the impracticability of the measure, the testimony of Lord Shaftesbury certainly seems to have killed it. As a result, it was the Board of Commissioners that ended up with more responsibility, and more power.

This affair, one of the first public tests of the fledgling Association's usefulness as a body, may not be a fair example of the work for which it was designed or of the methods by which it would generally proceed. But it does demonstrate several key factors in its ability to act as a public pressure group of respectable opinion. For a start, the issue involved *private* asylums, whereas the increasing number of public institutions was soon to provide the majority of the members of the Medico-Psychological Association (MPA), and tensions seem to have flourished between these two groups. Secondly, it was Shaftesbury, representing the Commissioners in Lunacy, who actually won the day, while thirdly, the demand for, and actual holding of, a public inquiry into lunacy practice was the central theme of the event. By and large, this was to be the pattern repeated (via Mr Dilwyn's 1877 Select Committee and Mr Brudenell Carter's 1889 London County Council Special Committee) throughout the century. In other words, the MPA acted as a secondary and defensive body, its disparate members (from both the public and private sectors) hanging together for support, while popular concerns about illegal detention, asylum mismanagement or excuse-mongering for criminals washed around what Blustein (1985) has termed the ''hollow square of psychological science''.

In this chapter, I try to portray some of the problems encountered by the MPA in having a public profile, as well as the related difficulties in researching this field. It is likely that the two phenomena *are* related, in that the stigma attached to alienists and their business during the period in question was surely immense. Today's dismissive term is 'shrinks'. Yesterday's was 'mad-doctors', reduced to the "Mad Ox" by the "lusty eloquence" of Charles Reade's sensible (because not an alienist) physician-hero, Dr Sampson. Of course, *Hard Cash*, Reade's 1863 novel which was most celebrated for its vituperative assault on "psychological science", is hardly a fair standard to go by, but other similar works are not uncommon (e.g. *Valentine Vox* (1854) by Henry Cockton and *The Bastilles of England* (1883) by Louisa Lowe) and criticism of the fledgling psychiatric profession from within its own ranks is also not difficult to find. Furthermore, it was constantly squeezed by other medical groups (one of which nearly swallowed it up) – in particular the British Medical Association (BMA) with its Psychological Section – as well as being dominated both legally and practically by the Commissioners in Lunacy. Thus, while individual MPA members may have dabbled in them, there is very little apparent evidence of a consistent role for the Association (or even a desire for a role) in public campaigns against, for example, prostitution, alcoholism or opiate abuse. Though only a painstaking review of, say, a decade of national and local newspapers could clarify this point, the better-documented periodicals give little grounds for hope that such evidence could be found.

Sources

The basis for any evaluation must be the *JMS*. As Henry Maudsley pointed out at the Annual Meeting in 1870, "The Medico-Psychological Society [*sic*] of this country is known in England and in all parts of the world by reason of the Journal" (*JMS*, 1870/71, vol. 16, p. 453). From its pages, both the spoken attitudes and implicit assumptions of MPA members can be gleaned: meetings minuted in detail, a "Notes and News" section, and "Occasional" pieces combine to provide a substantial resource. These writings can be supplemented by reviewing the *Lancet* and *British Medical Journal* (*BMJ*) for news about the Association, albeit from a general medical viewpoint.

Beyond such internal, professional sources there are the serious periodicals, from quarterly to weekly, so beloved of the Victorian public (to judge by their immoderate growth). Those most involved in the lunacy debate were the *Westminster Review*, the *Edinburgh Review*, the *Nineteenth Century*, and the *Fortnightly Review*, but even in these journals the number of relevant articles is in single figures. At a more populist level, one can also explore the pages of *Punch* and the *Illustrated London News*. The former consistently mocks the aspirations of doctors in general, especially their interest in money, while the illustrations of the wards at Bethlem in 1860 in the latter are a common adornment of modern psychiatric history books. Again, though, it is difficult to obtain a view of the Association as a coherent body: aspects of lunacy (the asylums, the language, individual 'medical men') are profiled but not a small, perhaps rather obscure, society. There are several lively pieces in the *Saturday Review*, and the editors of the *JMS* were not averse to publishing material directly from it. However, when in 1889 (vol. 67, pp. 599, 633) this same weekly chose to print a pair of articles on the medical profession, outlining the nuts and bolts of training, expenses, career patterns and financial prospects, there is no mention whatsoever of 'medico-psychology'.

Two other broad areas remain. Daily and local newspapers have already been mentioned, and would require a specific research project. There is also a range of books, written by or about the medical profession, in the form of memoirs, stories (e.g. Conan Doyle's *Round the Red Lamp* (1894)), or novels of varying popularity. Sir James Crichton-Browne, doyen in the 1870s of the West Riding Asylum and blessed with remarkable longevity, produced several volumes of personal notes (e.g. *Victorian Jottings* (1926), *What the Doctor Thought* (1928)), and L. Forbes Winslow (son of the founder of the *Journal of Psychological Medicine*) wrote his *Recollections of Forty Years* (1910). Again, the MPA is notable by its absence from these works: while there may have been isolated events or campaigns that temporarily brought it some public notice, the general perspective lacks any obvious image or attitude. Just as Aubrey Lewis (1951) found Henry Maudsley a "shadowy figure", so his Association emerges as a shadowy society, playing second, or even third fiddle to the dominant leads of the Commissioners, the BMA, and individual doctors.

The modern secondary literature about Victorian medical practice is equally bare, the MPA at most being mentioned as an example of professional specialisation. Many of the 19th-century attitudes to mental illness were in fact generated by events in the law courts and subsequent legislation - an area not germane to this review. The campaign against public alcoholism developed its own organisations, under the umbrella of the Temperance Movement, such as the Society for Promoting Legislation for the Control and Cure of Habitual Drunkards (which later became the Society for the Study and Cure of Inebriety), and the Homes for Inebriates Association. The BMA was heavily involved, via its nicely named 'Habitual Drunkards Committee', and individual physicians like Dalrymple and Kerr enjoyed personal publicity in this connection (MacLeod, 1967).

In the case of suicide prevention, while one might have expected a specific role for the MPA, there is no mention of such. In her comprehensive review, Anderson (1988, p. 417) is forced to conclude that "no section of the Victorian and Edwardian medical profession ever encountered a true cross-section of the suicidal population". Another example is that of the 'Alleged Lunatics' Friend Society', which received some support from Conolly (*JMS*, 1859, vol. 5, p. 392), "but it was the Commission ultimately that the Society had to influence" (Hervey, 1986). In July 1876, at the MPA's annual meeting, John Bucknill did in fact comment on a pamphlet "purporting to have come from a Society of Supposed Lunatics, in which charges were made against many of us". But it seems that no public debate ensued, "because we all of us had sense enough to see that a clique of crazy women and their imbecile supporters were not worth powder and shot (laughter)" (*JMS*, 1876/77, vol. 22, p. 495).

Professional stigma

Perhaps one of the most important reasons for the MPA's apparent lack of profile was the alienist's own stigmatised position. Throughout the period in question, there was a stream of what might delicately be called 'negative' comments, emanating as often as not from the MPA's own ranks. In 1852, a brief piece in the *Journal of Psychological Medicine* (vol. 5, p. 160) denounced "the disreputable proceedings of a *few* [their emphasis] illiterate pseudo-medical men who have embarked in this specialty with no other object than that of self-aggrandizement". This attack was aimed at owners of private asylums pushing their wares, but a casual comment earlier in the article is arresting: "We have heard of a London physician of some standing repudiating, in indignant language, the assumption that he was 'specially engaged in the treatment of the insane;' and we heard a physician, also of position, say, that he should consider it less degrading to keep a public-house than an asylum."

It must not be forgotten that the social standing of the profession, still somewhat precarious in the years around the 1858 Medical Registration Bill, would have naturally been sensitive to the 'trade' and commercial aspects of private asylums. One of Anthony Trollope's (1870) genteel spinsters "would not absolutely say that a physician was not a gentleman, . . . but she would never allow to physic the same absolute privileges which . . . belonged to law and the church". But this formed only one source of the suspicion about mad-doctors. As President of the Association in 1860, Bucknill remarked that "The public extends its unreasonable antipathy to the insane, to all those who are connected with insanity, even to those who wrestle with the great evil" (quoted in Stern, 1961). Even the *Lancet* (1864, vol. i, p. 376) in its review of the first volume of the *Asylum Journal*, described "a class of medical men – an almost peculiar class – the medical superintendents of the public asylums". Thus, by the 1864 annual meeting, it was possible for Baron Mundy, a visiting alienist from Germany, to pronounce that "our science does not exist at all . . . every snob has now become accustomed to sneer at 'mad-doctors'" (*JMS*, 1864, vol. 10, p. 459). The taunt was not new, but when even a Lord Chancellor could use the term in Parliament (*JMS*, 1869, vol. 15, p. 331), it cannot have been easy for the MPA to assume a public stance without considerable trepidation.

Things were not all bad. After a particularly successful meeting in Edinburgh in 1866, the *JMS* (vol. 12, pp. 440–441) was able to announce that "Medico-psychology now claims a definite place among the inductive sciences, and if asked to show its credentials it points to the field which it cultivates, to the method by which it proceeds, and to the results which it has already achieved." Admittedly, things had not always been so. The article went on to decry the time "not very far distant" when a "treatise on lunacy was almost invariably a portentous cross-birth between bad metaphysics and premature physiology". But now it seems there was "never a time when so many accomplished physicians made it the business of their lives to investigate and treat the phenomenon of lunacy; and who will say that the labours of all these men have been without result?" Ending with a final eulogy to Prichard and Conolly, it is not surprising to note that the piece had been reprinted from the *Lancet* (15 August 1866). Earlier in the same year, the *JMS* (1866, vol. 12, p. 136) had chosen to include a *Times* review of Reade's *Hard Cash*, which contained the following passage:

> "The incautious reader is apt to imagine mad-doctors to be scientific scoundrels, lunatic asylums to be a refined sort of Tophet and the commissioners in lunacy and insanity justices to be a flock of sheep. This is the untruthful exaggeration of fact jumbled with fiction." ('Tophet' is a

Biblical reference (e.g. 2 Kings xxiii, 10), being a place south of Jerusalem used as a rubbish dump where bonfires were kept burning, and symbolic of the torments of hell.)

It seems that while neither article actually mentions the MPA, their inclusion in the Association's journal assumes both their relevance and their morale-boosting qualities.

If morale needed boosting in 1866, by 1869, when Thomas Laycock gave his Presidential Address at York (Laycock, 1869), it can hardly have improved. Lambasting the inadequacies of the Association (see below), he quoted Conolly's remark of 1862 that "no section of society . . . labours under more misapprehension and greater disadvantage than our section – the specialty of attending to the interests of the insane. We really may be said to be people who have no friends". Advising that they form a 'defence committee' – a parapet to hide behind, perhaps? – he suggested that the public "look upon asylums as places of detention, and on the Medical Superintendents as little better than jailers" (p. 332). Thus, "some of the best minds of the profession are thereby repelled from your department of medicine," not least because the "humane treatment of the insane which you all defend and practice" brings you "into collision with the public, whatever you do" (p. 333). Laycock concluded this section of his speech by suggesting that "we can readily understand why a chorus of vituperations of 'mad-doctors' arises from the press and the public where a cruel and ferocious murderer, albeit insane, escapes as a lunatic from public vengeance" (p. 334).

Beyond the *contagious* effects of direct involvement with 'lunatics', there were other versions of distrust. Hidden in an 1853 piece "Our pauper lunatic asylums" (*JPM*, vol. 6, pp. 409–411) is a description of "the mode of election of the medical officer". After the usual course of advertisements, testimonials and anxious interest, "the day of election arrives", but "to the surprise and vexation of three or four highly qualified candidates, a gentleman whose qualifications are of the most mediocre description is selected". It then apparently turns out that the successful candidate "is a relative, or connexion, or protege of one of the Committee, or that he possessed great private influence or local interest". The article goes on to cite the selection of "a gentleman who had no practical experience whatever", though "possessing extraordinary private influence", for a metropolitan asylum post. While the sour complaints of failed candidates continue today to echo around some selection committees, there is nevertheless a recurring hint of such practices at the time. Medical superintendencies were secure and comfortable posts, with a pension, so that local 'interests' cannot have been insignificant.

In fact, if we examine the nature of asylum work, as then understood by doctors themselves as well as the interested layman, a troubling picture emerges. In his introductory lecture on mental diseases, delivered at St Bartholomew's Hospital in the summer of 1872 (Claye Shaw, 1872), the medical superintendent of the Leavesden Asylum advised that his audience should "consider well before you undertake one of these appointments". He went on – "There is a degree of indolence begotten in many of these quiet asylum appointments that leads a man to spend his days in lotus-eating" – and described the routine producing "a listless frame of mind", the lack of competition, as well as "the certainty that at the end of a certain period the cheque will come with it''. All in all, he felt that ''few men are able to rise above the depressing atmosphere in which they live and the restraint of their responsibilities''.

Nor was this an isolated outburst. The *Edinburgh Review* of 1870 (vol. 131, pp. 418–449) had called for a ''thorough revolution'' in asylum management, because ''the spirit of Conolly is dead''. Instead, ''a miserable spirit of routine, without resource, spring or energy is sapping and destroying asylum life'', so that ''wholly fresh blood is imperatively demanded''. The article called for general physicians rather than those ''trained in all the bad traditions of asylums'', and handicapped by ''habits of mind instilled into them by a kind of Chinese practice and a reverence for old authority''. But even by 1903, the situation does not seem to have changed. Brudenell Carter in *Doctors and Their Work* (1903) lamented that ''this superintendence has been almost entirely barren as regards the advancement of science'' (p. 302). He described the asylum medical service as one in which ''men enter it early in life and grow up subject to its conditions'' (p. 305), falling into a ''groove'' that directs them from medicine to administration. ''For many years our public asylums have been conducted medically speaking under the cold shade of an experience which has become crystallised into habit'' (p. 303).

Overall, then, attitudes towards the members of the MPA, echoing through that period, were those of suspicion and denigration. Alienists were corrupt or mad or incompetent or bureaucrats, or any combination thereof. They had ''failed to stay the progress of the disease by the exercise of their art'' and had ''but partially succeeded in bringing their specialty within the pale of medical science'' (Tuke, 1889). They were also aware of ''the very great defects that exist in the state of medical education'' with regard to the study of insanity (*JMS*, 1875, vol. 21, p. 458). This was despite various pleas for an ''examination in lunacy'' to be included in the pass-paper, so that ''the public will be satisfied that in certifying insanity the practitioner is professionally competent to do so'' (*Lancet*, 1872, vol. ii, p. 269). And, of course, public disquiet at inappropriate certification by ill-trained doctors rebounded on to alienists by natural association, even though they were largely innocent receivers of the incompetent doctor's victims.

By 1914, things had reached a crisis sufficient for a committee on the 'Status of British Psychiatry' to be convened (see below). In a spirited debate on the committee's report, a range of views was presented, although it was generally agreed that the report itself reflected the true situation. However, a comment on ''the apathy of large numbers of . . . members'' of the Association (*JMS*, 1914, vol. 60, pp. 686–694) echoed the ''lotus-eating'' dullness outlined by Claye Shaw in 1872. This theme was further taken up in the new year by C. Hubert Bond (1915) in his address on the 'Position of Psychiatry'. Calling it the Cinderella of medicine, and decrying the lot of asylum medical officers, he mentioned ''the lack of sustaining interest and blind alleys where their scientific enthusiasm is chilled, and their legitimate aspirations to maintain an honourable position for themselves are disappointed''.

To what extent these professional insights were transmitted to the public perception is, of course, difficult to clarify. But the whole process is riddled with paradoxes that seemed intrinsic to the lunacy question. Alienists, while themselves seen as a bit mad, were also regarded as exemplars of dull routine. Medical men who were not specialists could sign certificates, yet there was (until 1895) no psychiatric part to the final MB examination. Scientific interest was lacking, yet the language of the specialty was in itself a riddle to unwary medical students. Thus, Geoffrey Bourne (1963), as a medical student during World War I, described Sir Robert Armstrong Jones's lectures on mental disease as fluent, "yet so incomprehensible, as indeed are apt to be those of his professional heirs and successors. . . . He might have been some eloquent foreigner, fluently discussing in his own tongue a subject the nature of which nearly became apparent but always elusively escaped" (pp. 106–107).

The Association's influence in relation to other organisations

Given that it represented a group of 'foreigners' in the eyes of other medical men as well as the public, in what way could the MPA usefully have influenced decisions about its interests and professional status? That it played little part in the various reform campaigns (e.g. the 'drink' question), at least as a coherent body, seems undoubted. This may have related to the extensive use of alcohol in asylums (Hunter & Macalpine, 1974; Turner, 1989) – to keep the inmates and attendants happy, one presumes – but it probably also reflected the nature of the MPA as a body of loosely knit individuals owing their allegiance more to the BMA, their local asylum committee, or their own specific interests. This is not to say that the Association did not try to influence public opinion, by Parliamentary pressure, the publication of the *Journal of Mental Science*, and individual activities. Whether it managed to create a distinct and effective image, however, is difficult to judge now, and there is little affirmative evidence as yet available.

An 1858 *Lancet* leader (vol. i, pp. 143–144) on "Minor Medical Societies" suggested how limited was the role of such bodies as the MPA, and helps us today to understand better what was expected of them. Outlining their meetings as "scenes in which men may meet on the common ground of scientific enquiry", the article pointed to the dreariness and "copyism" of such events, as compared with the "great societies". It also stressed the importance of social contact, an aspect reflected in the original MPA circular of 1841 as to the purpose of its foundation (i.e. for medical men connected with asylums to be better known to each other, to communicate their experiences, to co-operate in collecting information, and to assist in improving treatment). This notion was taken up by Dr Hitchman, in his address to the Association in 1855 – "It was in the beginning a social festival at which laborious men forgot for a while their anxious daily task and luxuriated in the sympathy of their brethren," but whether this kind of ambience continued is not supported by the researches of Walk & Walker (1961), but the *conversaziones* (e.g. at Crystal Palace in 1864 (*JMS*, 1864/65, vol. 10, pp. 448 *et seq.*) and at York in 1865 (*JMS*, 1869, vol. 15, pp. 474–477)) and the large gatherings at Dublin (1875) and Edinburgh (1888) do not suggest frugality.

There is also evidence, throughout the period in question, for the primacy of the BMA in setting the agenda for lunacy matters. Thus, Dr David Thomson's (1914) address to the MPA annual meeting, reviewing the "Progress of Psychiatry" over the last 100 years, paid tribute, for example, to the MPA's initiative (in 1890) in the systematised training of mental nurses (p. 561), insisting also that "we have roused the conscience of the country to give us its support legislatively and financially''. But in his very next paragraph, he deferred to ''the work being done by committees of the British Medical Association as regards 'Insanity and Crime' and 'Incipient Insanity' . . . on which Committees this Association is *represented*'' (my emphasis). An ''Occasional Note'' later in the same volume (*JMS*, 1914, vol. 60, p. 635) reinforces this deference. Discussing a special Treasury research grant, the note states that it was ''gratifying to the Association [the MPA] that the Board of Control has asked for its co-operation as to the best way in which the grant can be utilised''. The piece went on to applaud the Association's ''respectable age of 73 years'', and its work ''not only for psychiatric medicine, but in a quiet way, though none the less powerful, for the wellbeing of the public generally''. In this respect, however, things had improved to some degree in 1914, compared with the failure in 1877 to obtain government grants for ''scientific subjects in connection with lunacy'' (*JMS*, 1877, vol. 23, p. 449). Also mentioned (p. 438), was ''a proposition made by the Chairman of the Lunacy Commissioners which would most materially affect the position of all the Superintendents of County asylums.'' (This was the plan to appoint visiting physicians to oversee asylum practice to ''assure the public that no improper proceedings were going on''.) While such proposals were not adopted, perhaps because of active resistance by the MPA (although it is doubtful if the visiting physicians would have wanted the task anyway), the position of asylum doctors remained apparently marginal.

The London County Council (LCC) Committee of 1889 took evidence from 16 ''distinguished members of the profession'', only two of whom (Crichton-Browne and Batty Tuke) had ''asylum administrative experience'' (*BMJ*, 1889, vol. ii, p. 1188). In 1898, it was a ''Joint Committee of the British Medical and Medico-Psychological Associations'' that drafted a clause for insertion into the forthcoming lunacy bill, with the BMA's General Secretary actually placing the proposals before the Lord Chancellor. In the same year, a *BMJ* leader (vol. i, p. 1398) on the ''Increase of lunacy in the metropolis'' stressed that it was ''the duty of the Board, which is entrusted with the care of the insane, to see that the conditions of cure are the best attainable''. Meanwhile, the Asylum Workers Association (founded in 1895) was also trying to make its presence felt. A ''very successful meeting'' presided over by Sir James Crichton-Browne, on 28 March 1898, included the report of a petition ''setting forth the view of attendants and nurses'' (*BMJ*, 1898, vol. i, pp. 905–906).

It is not surprising, therefore, to find the MPA constantly standing in the shadows of more traditional or more powerful organisations. Maudsley helped ward off the proposed absorption of the Association into the Medico-Chirurgical Society in the 1870s, but many members would have accepted the takeover. Changing the dates of meetings so as to dovetail with those of the BMA was also mooted (*JMS*, 1883, vol. 29, p. 440) and in 1904 (*JMS*, vol. 50, p. 750) the poor attendance at the annual meeting was attributed in part to the ''specially attractive'' BMA gathering elsewhere. There were no permanent rooms or offices in which to meet, and in 1875 Hack Tuke even suggested the use of space in the Royal College of Physicians for the nucleus of a library in London. In response, Dr J. Stewart asked ''whether they might not do something for the promotion of mental science, such as the British Medical Association was doing for the profession at large''. It was resolved then to form a committee to consider devoting ''a portion of the funds [of the MPA] for the advancement of Medico-Psychology''

(*JMS*, 1875, vol. 21, pp. 457–458). However, at the same meeting, one of their number commented that it was "a melancholy thing to find intelligent men so utterly ignorant of insanity and the nervous diseases as many medical practitioners were" (p. 459), and there is little evidence to show a material improvement in the situation over the next 30 years.

Of course, there were certain advantages in this secondary position. Thus, in 1901 (*JMS*, vol. 47, pp. 112–113) the "inadequacy of the Lunacy Commission to cope with the amount of work and responsibility heaped on it" could be equated with the "anachronistic abuses which the conservatism resulting from mediaeval modes of education permits us to endure". Lambasting "red tape that goes far to paralyse asylum physicians", this article concluded with a vigorous demand for "more medicine and less law". Asylum scandal could also be blamed elsewhere. The *JMS* report (vol. 49, p. 323) on the 1903 Colney Hatch fire, in which 52 patients died in poorly designed temporary buildings (Rollin, 1989), stressed that the jury "blamed the disastrous construction equally on the London County Council, the Home Secretary and the Lunacy Commission", while exonerating "the splendid behaviour of the asylum staff, from highest to lowest". Likewise with the Horton Asylum affair, involving misappropriation of asylum supplies, the management of the LCC bore the brunt of criticism (*JMS*, 1904, vol. 50, pp. 751–756, 814–815). Even the lack of "those exact and laborious clinical studies which are to be found in the French and German psychiatric literature" could be attributed to "the unhappy system by which case-books have come to be regarded . . . as something to be compiled 'to satisfy the Commissioners'". Yet at the same time as these perhaps reasonable criticisms of official bodies were expressed, the Association proudly asserted its "growing influence and activity" in describing the number of members, communications, and discussions – not to mention the "flourishing" finances – at the annual meeting (*JMS*, 1903, vol. 49, pp. 703, 705).

Problems and weaknesses

Associated with the problems of stigma and the dominance of other organisations, there do seem to have been intrinsic differences within the MPA that are difficult to elucidate from this historical distance. Subtle nuances in attitudes and personal relationships cannot easily be extracted from the dry bones of *JMS* reports. Harrington Tuke's 1877 attack on Henry Maudsley is well documented (cf. Walk, 1976; Turner, 1988), but the "doctrines" of which he complained can only be guessed at. His outburst is also unusual in its openness, the general tone of meetings being apparently conciliatory and arranged so as to avoid clashes of principle or personality. Nevertheless, there is a consistent trail of criticism to be followed from the 1850s through to 1914, when the "frank and damning detail" (Lewis, 1969) of the report of the Status Committee was published. What cannot as yet be ascertained is the extent to which this inner disunity impeded a desired public profile, or provided the reason for actively avoiding such.

One of the earliest criticisms of the inactivity of the MPA came from Forbes Winslow, the prolific and rather idiosyncratic founder editor of the *Journal of Psychological Medicine*. In a rather bitter piece on the Association (*JPM*, 1853, vol. 6, pp. 453–455) he denigrated the methods and plans generated by

Dr Bucknill to start another journal (the *JMS*) in spite of his own organ's established position. He also castigated the MPA for having published no transactions and urged "the necessity of constituting itself into a worthy body", since "these are not the times for apathy and supineness". Contrasting the American Association, which "exercises a great influence over public opinion in America", he called on his profession to "do something collectively to advance the exalted branch of science which we cultivate". Such criticisms from such a quarter may be more indicative of that author's cantankerous nature than of the true situation, but other, later voices echoed his comments.

Perhaps most shocking was Laycock's "Anniversary Address" (1869). The "shortcomings of the Association" and its "defective organization" were said to be "numerous", and he went on to outline the "defects which render us so impotent" even though "there are many difficulties, scientific, social or political, which we could by a few discussions help to solve" (a quote from the previous year's address by Dr Sankey). He called for a more enlightened system of instruction, the reorganisation of the *JMS* ("I need hardly say it is not equal to its name"), and a committee that "might usefully take in hand the duty of incessantly bringing the weight of public opinion to bear upon the legislators in medical education". He rejected fusion with the Medico-Chirurgical Society, saying that the MPA itself needed "more publicity, freer action, and a more extended sphere of influence amongst the general public as well as the profession". He did comment, however, on the "sad cases of hitherto incurable dementia [i.e. chronic schizophrenia] which encumber the asylums by the thousands" of which alienists were "wearied and helpless spectators". And this may be a clue as to the inner dynamics of the organisation. Founded as it had been in the heyday of non-restraint, and developing in the optimistic dawn of the post-1845 era of statutory county asylums, the MPA's expectations may well have been too rudely let down by therapeutic failure. Early treatment was the continued cry of 19th-century medical psychologists, yet it proved a chimera, as did the much-vaunted promise of 'moral treatment'. Asylums grew extra wings like the classical Hydra's heads, doubling remorselessly into unwieldy, overcrowded homes for "incurables". In a letter to *The Times* in March 1878, reprinted in the *JMS* (vol. 24, pp. 161–162), Lockhart Robertson commented on "the unnecessary filling up of the wards by incurable lunatics and imbeciles from the workhouses" because of the 4 shilling subsidy given to the union (parish) authorities to do so, but his plea for a change in the system went unheeded. The MPA certainly sent a deputation on this issue, although Robertson simply signed himself as writing from the Athenaeum Club in London.

Other hints emerge as to the MPA's limitations. In 1876, Bucknill contrasted the role of clergymen in "the crusade against intemperance", wishing he could supplement it by saying that:

> "members of his [own] profession were taking a wise, patriotic and useful part in the attack upon the great vice of our age and country. But he was afraid that just now members of his profession were taking hold of the stick by the wrong end, and were considering drunkenness not as a cause of disease, but as a disease in itself . . . he looked upon inebriate asylums as an unfortunate attempt to coddle drunkenness, and patch up a wide and fruitful social mischief."

To what extent these views were representative of his fellow medico-psychologists is impossible to gauge, but there seems no doubt that within the specialty there was no consensus as to whether alcoholism was a moral vice or a medical illness, which may explain its insignificant temperance role. We can even surmise that, lacking an agreed public position, the MPA preferred to default on the matter, and the same lack of coherence may have reduced its activities on other public issues. Caught between the scientific materialism of Maudsley, Spencer, and Darwin, and the evangelical and official religion of Lord Shaftesbury and the establishment, silence may in fact have been the only public option.

As described above, by 1914, there was general agreement within the MPA that things were not going well, and the Report of the Committee re Status of British Psychiatry and of Medical Officers (1914) makes sober reading. Outlining the "grave defects in the present position", the report stressed in particular the haphazards of appointment committees and the shortage of attractive posts. For example, medical officers were "generally compelled to live in the institution, and their personal liberty [juniors were not allowed to marry] is curtailed to an extent which is sometimes needless and arbitrary". Themes from the past 70 years constantly recur, such as "the tendency of routine to kill enthusiasm", the lack of organised teaching, and the lack of provision for early treatment. An interesting comment on the report (at the prolonged discussion that took place) suggested that "the desired reform must come through the public, rather than through the medical schools", although the more lucrative career prospects of other specialties were also mentioned as militating against the asylum service. The influential Dr Hayes Newington declared that "this problem raised the whole question of psychiatry, in one way or another. It was a matter upon which this Association had the right and the experience to speak definitely, and when that was so it should speak to the best of its ability." He thought this report might be said to represent the "*real* views of the Association" (*JMS*, 1914, vol. 60, pp. 686–694). Yet only nine years earlier the same admirable physician, for many years the acknowledged "power behind the throne" of the organisation, when commenting on the Statistical Committee Report of 1905 (*JMS*, vol. 51, p. 211), had declared: "It would depress the public mind if they saw the wreckage of incurable insanity in our asylums. Therefore we thought it best to omit it" (a column in which superintendents could comment on the condition of their asylum cases!).

Conclusions

Our present state of knowledge about the 19th-century psychiatric profession remains very limited. Certain leading figures such as Conolly, Hack Tuke, Maudsley, and Bucknill led lives that were sufficiently public – in terms of both the spoken and written word – to allow some understanding of their position. But the majority of the MPA's members, their social origins, training, attitudes, and career patterns, remain obscure and little researched. Any overview of their professional organisation must therefore be fragmentary, picking up hints from comments in the *JMS* and other medical writings. Even so, it is likely that a few dominant figures may be over-represented in any portrayal of their collective ideas or *esprit de corps*. However, that same spirit was (in 1905) itself said to be "wanting" (*JMS*, vol. 51, p. 146), because MPA members had "tamely submitted to a wanton aggression on that supposed British palladium, the liberty of the subject."

The most obvious feature of the psychiatric specialty, though, is the lack of any definite impact, in terms of seriously influencing public attitudes towards mental illness. In a somewhat bitter "Occasional Note" in 1905 (*JMS*, vol. 51, pp. 144–146), entitled "The disabilities of alienist physicians", already alluded to above, the public's tendency to consult "quasi-quacks" was deplored. "If a medical man *is* consulted, care is taken, in the large majority of cases, that he is not one whose name is associated with mental diseases." Such disability, it was felt, will go on until "the public are educated into the recognition that the treatment of mental disease is not limited to Weir-Mitchelling etc . . . narcotics . . . a nursing home or . . . travelling abroad". This reflected an earlier comment in 1902 on the Warneford Asylum affair, when a discharged patient committed homicide and suicide. "The prejudices of the public mind in lunacy matters" were discussed, and the need for "evidence from the asylum" – lacking in this case because the superintendent was apparently absent from England! – to "educate the public to understand . . . such regrettable incidents must from time to time occur", was called for with some exasperation. A similar tone informed another 1902 comment on "Another Messiah", whom the "Clapton public" took "very seriously and excitably". "That the press and public are not better informed of the frequency of the Messianic delusion is also a matter for regret", stated the article, which went on to call for the "necessary statistics" (*JMS*, 1902, vol. 48, pp. 70–71, 765–766).

The stigma carried by their patients, their therapeutic difficulties despite an intensive asylum-building programme, the overarching power of the Lunacy Commission (which evolved into the Board of Control), and the likely contrast with the remarkable developments in medicine and surgery (e.g. Pasteur's inoculations, Lister's antisepsis) all seem to have forced the MPA into being an introverted body, whose members gave it only a partial allegiance. Their increasing awareness of the defects of the situation, culminating in the 1914 report, was also reflected in the efforts of Mott and Maudsley (from 1907 onwards) to establish the Maudsley Hospital. Coinciding with World War I and the new Freudian psychology, this foundation radically altered the whole conspectus.

Although increasing in numbers and more complex in organisation (it was trumpeted as "second of the medical societies of this country" in terms of its financial position in 1906 (*JMS*, vol. 52, p. 658), the MPA previously gave little sense of having a weighty effect on medical affairs. Eschewing a reformist role, probably because of its own fragmented and uncertain intellectual and psychological position, its major achievement was in remaining independent despite these internal divisions. At its core seems to have been an empirical and practical system of care for a clientele that it barely understood. Peeling off the pure neurologists (as that specialty developed in the latter half of the 19th-century), taking on research in the new bacteriology, limited (by national rivalries perhaps) in its ability to pick up the German intellectual focus, it nevertheless created a distinctively British psychiatric tradition.

Perhaps most indicative of this achievement was the superannuation question that by 1902 had been before the Parliamentary Committee "for many years past – at least ten or twelve – and the Committee thought they were gradually making headway'' (*JMS*, 1902, vol. 48, p. 197), according to Dr Hayes Newington. However, it was not until 1909 that the Asylum Officers' Superannuation Act became law, being described as ''one of the most important objects for which this Association has striven during the last thirty years''. The subsequent report of the commemorative dinner occupies nearly 10 pages of the *JMS* (1910, vol. 56, pp. 109–110, 174–183); the sheer happy relief of the participants bursts from all the toasts and speeches. The then President, Dr Bevan Lewis, summed up the occasion as one of ''the most auspicious in the history of the Association'' (p. 183). But clearly there was more to this event than security in retirement. It marked the official acceptance of asylum doctors and of their Association as an adult organisation. Staying sane while critics raved around them was the central public achievement of the pre-1914 MPA. It would provide the basis for the many therapeutic and attitudinal shifts, as much in public consciousness as in psychiatrists' self-esteem, that were to transform the profession after World War I.

References

ANDERSON, O. (1988) *Suicide in Victorian and Edwardian England*. Oxford: Clarendon Press.

BLUSTEIN, B. E. (1985) A hollow square of psychological science. In *Madhouses, Mad-Doctors and Madmen* (ed. A. Scull). Philadelphia: University of Pennsylvania Press.

BOND, C. H. (1915) The position of psychiatry. *Journal of Mental Science*, **61**, 1–17.

BOURNE, G. (1963) *We Met at Barts*. London: Frederick Mullen.

BUCKNILL, J. (1858) The newspaper attack on private lunatic asylums. *Journal of Mental Science*, **4**, 146–154.

CARTER, B. (1903) *Doctors and Their Work*. London: Smith, Elder & Co.

CLAYE SHAW, T. (1872) Introductory lecture on mental diseases. *Lancet*, *ii*, 911–912.

COMMITTEE RE STATUS OF BRITISH PSYCHIATRY (1914) Report. *Journal of Mental Science*, **60**, 667–674.

CONAN DOYLE, A. (1894) *Round the Red Lamp*. London: Methuen & Co.

CRICHTON-BROWNE, J. (1926) *Victorian Jottings*. London: Etchells and MacDonald.

—— (1928) *What the Doctor Thought*. London: Ernest Bean.

HERVEY, N. (1986) Advocating or folly: the Alleged Lunatics' Friend Society; 1845–63. *Medical History*, **30**, 245–275.

HUNTER, R. & MACALPINE, I. (1974) *Psychiatry for the Poor*. London: Dawsons.

LAYCOCK, T. (1869) The objects and organization of the Medico-Psychological Association; the anniversary address. *Journal of Mental Science*, **15**, 327–343.

LEWIS, A. (1951) Henry Maudsley – his work and influence. *Journal of Mental Science*, **97**, 259–277.

—— (1969) Edward Mapother and the making of the Maudsley Hospital. *British Journal of Psychiatry*, **115**, 1349–1366.

MACLEOD, R. M. (1967) The edge of hope: social policy and chronic alcoholism 1870–1900. *Journal of the History of Medicine and Allied Sciences*, **22**, 215–245.

MCCANDLESS, P. (1974) Insanity and society: a study of the English lunacy reform movement 1815–1870. Unpublished Doctoral thesis, University of Wisconsin, USA.

ROLLIN, H. R. (1989) The fire at Colney Hatch Lunatic Asylum, 1903, remembered. *Psychiatric Bulletin*, **13**, 188–189.

STERN, E. S. (1961) Three notable nineteenth-century psychiatrists of Warwickshire. *Journal of Mental Science*, **107**, 187–193.

THOMSON, D. (1914) The progress of psychiatry. *Journal of Mental Science*, **60**, 541–572.

TROLLOPE, A. (1870) *The Vicar of Bullhampton*. London: Bradbury and Evans. (Reprinted 1988, Oxford: Oxford University Press).

TUKE, J. B. (1889) Lunatics as patients not prisoners. *Nineteenth Century*, **25**, 595–609.

TURNER, T. H. (1988) Henry Maudsley – psychiatrist, philosopher and entrepreneur. *Psychological Medicine*, **18**, 551–574.
—— (1989) Rich and mad in Victorian England. *Psychological Medicine*, **19**, 29–44.
WALK, A. (1976) Medico-psychologists, Maudsley and The Maudsley. *British Journal of Psychiatry*, **128**, 19–30.
—— & WALKER, D. L. (1961) Gloucester and the beginnings of the R.M.P.A. *Journal of Mental Science*, **107**, 603–632.
WINSLOW, L. F. (1910) *Recollections of Forty Years*. London: John Ouseley.

2 The culture of the mental hospital

KATHLEEN JONES

In the second half of the 20th century, the mental hospital system, once so solid and seemingly inpregnable, has virtually collapsed. The hospitals were attacked in the 1960s by a series of writers, of whom Goffman (1961), Foucault (1961), and Szasz (1961) were the most prominent, on the grounds that they were "total institutions", "carceral cities", "agencies of social control" (Jones & Fowles, 1984). In the 1970s, the criticism shifted from the theoretical to the practical: allegations of cruelty and neglect against mental hospital staff were given much prominence by press and television, and many hospitals were subject to public inquiries (Beardshaw, 1981; Martin, 1984). In the 1980s, the process of decline gathered speed: in-patient populations were reduced, huge wards were left empty, and the solid Victorian buildings began to be demolished to make way for suburban housing, warehouses, or supermarkets. Although some in-patient psychiatric beds will remain in hospitals, the distinctive culture which was so violently attacked has gone.

Current anti-institutional views make it difficult to evaluate the work which mental hospitals (or, to use the older term, asylums) carried out in earlier periods; but for nearly 150 years, these institutions represented the main means of psychiatric care and treatment. It was a stigmatised and unpopular service. Asylum staff took society's rejects, and did what they could for them with the limited funds which society was prepared to provide. Their staff worked within social constructs and with social pressures very different from those of the 1990s. A historical account must get beyond prejudice, both old and new, assessing the asylum movement in the context of its own day.

There were four waves of asylum building, respectively following the County Asylums Acts of 1808 and 1828, the Lunatics Act of 1845, and the Lunacy Act of 1890. Like the great Victorian prisons, which developed in the same period, the asylums were constructed at a time when building costs were low and land was cheap – which made massive expansion possible; but they were built also at a time when the standard of living of the mass of the population was unbelievably low. The great *Report on the Sanitary Condition of the Labouring Classes* (Chadwick, 1842), with its accounts of damp and disease-ridden hovels without light or sanitation, the piles of refuse, the filthy and stinking gutters, the people "worse off than wild animals", suggests that those who were admitted to the asylums were relatively fortunate. Asylums provided better care than prisons or workhouses: patients were fed and clothed, housed in dry wards, looked after, and given medical treatment, and this was more than many of them could hope for in the world outside. The asylums were not democratic institutions; they were paternalistic and class-conscious, but so was Victorian society.

The enduring problem has been the architecture. When both social values and medical practice changed, the buildings were still there, making their outmoded statement against the skyline. Most of the old Victorian asylums still stand at the time of writing, and they bear a remarkable similarity to each other: it is as though most of them were built by the same architects and builders, with only minor variations of design, out of a common stock of materials. Where else can one find those long drives, imposing facades, mosaic-floored entrance halls, and endless echoing corridors? These were stately homes for the lower classes.

Any understanding of their work must start from some fundamental questions: how and why did the asylum system originate? What concepts and models were built into its foundation? How, and on what principles, did it operate? How did it change over time?

The foundation of the asylums

Before 1808, there were a few lunatic hospitals in the cities, of which London's Bethlem was the oldest and the best known. There were many private madhouses, for those who could pay, but the majority of mentally ill people went to the workhouses because they were destitute or to the prisons because they broke the law (including the vagrancy law, which made it an offence for people without visible means of support to be found wandering outside their parish of settlement).

The decision to set up asylums arose out of the problems of workhouses and prisons. It was not a means of incarcerating a new section of the population, but of making better provision for people who were already institutionalised, and in much less suitable conditions. The general mixed workhouses of the old Poor Law could make no special provision for lunatics, and when growing social and economic distress filled the workhouses, disruptive or irrational inmates were difficult to manage. Sometimes the overseers of the poor contracted them out to private madhouses, but since the payment was low and the madhouses often virtually unsupervised, conditions tended to be very poor there too. After 1800, the prisons had to accommodate criminal lunatics detained "during His Majesty's pleasure", so that lunatics who were minor offenders were seen as a threat to discipline.

There was a brief period of reforming government, the Ministry of all the Talents, in 1806, during a temporary break in the Napoleonic wars. In the name of humanity and good administration, the reformers argued that it was inappropriate to detain lunatics in either workhouses or prisons. A new type of institution, specifically designed for their needs, was therefore proposed (Paul, 1806). The House of Commons set up a select committee in 1807, and required a statistical return of all pauper and criminal lunatics in England from the county justices of the peace (JPs). The returns were patchy: some county JPs apparently took pride in replying that they had no lunatics at all within their borders, and some did not bother to answer. Statistical returns were not popular in 1806; but there was enough positive evidence from the returns to justify permissive legislation – the County Asylums Act 1808.

The preamble to the act stated that the practice of sending pauper lunatics to workhouses and criminal lunatics to prison was "highly dangerous and inconvenient". Justices of the peace at quarter sessions might form a committee to erect and inspect an asylum, and raise a county rate for the purpose. Each asylum was to be erected in "an Airy and Healthy Situation . . . but such as may afford a Probability of constant Medical Assistance". There were to be separate wards for males and females, wards for "Convalescents" and "Incurables", day rooms and airing grounds for the "Convalescents", and "dry and airy Cells for Lunatics of every Description".

This act established a number of important principles: it applied to people who were already stigmatised for poverty or crime, and made specialised and improved provision for them. It provided for treatment out of the rates, including the full cost of maintenance and care, medicine and clothing, long before that was possible for physical illness. It recommended that the asylums should be sited outside the towns – a wise provision in 1808, when the towns were subject to epidemic and endemic disease, and sanitary reform was still half a century ahead; but it stipulated that they should be near enough to the towns to be able to secure medical support when necessary. Since visiting doctors would have to travel on horseback or by pony and trap, that limited the distance to a few miles. If they were 'isolated' (a charge often made later, in the days of their decline), the asylums were isolated from cholera and typhus, from foul air and dirty hovels, from open cesspools and contaminated water supplies, rather than from human contact.

The first asylums

Between 1811 and 1842, 16 county asylums were set up: in Nottingham, Bedford, Norwich, Lancaster, Stafford, Wakefield, Bodmin, Lincoln, Gloucester, Chester, Dorchester, Canterbury, Leicester, and three in the Home Counties, taking inmates from north and south London. The early asylums were often given an impressive facade, to indicate that they offered a new and better status for the people who came to them from the workhouses and prisons for treatment. They were usually designed round the house of the resident physician, the wards stretching out in two wings from his private accommodation. The physician was paid by the justices' committee on a per capita basis. He was expected to manage the accounts (including his own salary and living costs), supervise the staff, control supplies, treat the inmates, and monitor their condition. Few had any relevant experience, and newly appointed physicians were sometimes sent to Bethlem or to the York Retreat (a small Quaker institution run on humane lines) for three months before taking up their duties.

Some asylums took paying patients, providing superior accommodation for them: this was a useful means of decreasing the stigma attaching to an institution catering for paupers and criminals, and a still more useful addition to financial resources, enabling the justices to avoid increases in the rates.

The distinction between the short-stay wards and the back wards seems to have started early. 'Convalescent' inmates were treated well, and allowed a certain amount of freedom: some worked in the kitchens or gardens, or followed their own trades – a cobbler or a wheelwright was useful to the asylum. There were forms of recreation – music, domestic animals, and flower growing. Life for dangerous or troublesome inmates, however, was very different: they were commonly subject to physical restraint – handmuffs, straitjackets, and leglocks. The keepers had an incentive to restrain such inmates, since the 1808 Act made no specification of standards of care, but provided that keepers would be heavily fined if inmates escaped. Some asylums had no heating on the wards, so that inmates in restraints suffered bitterly from the cold in winter, and frostbite was not uncommon. Most inmates had beds, but incontinent inmates were sometimes left to sleep on straw.

Visiting justices – usually local gentry, wealthy tradesmen, and clergy – seem to have taken very little interest in standards of care. They made their rounds, satisfied themselves that inmates were clean and fed, but rarely exerted themselves further.

After 1828, there was a minor degree of central government control: visiting justices were required to send annual returns of admissions, discharges, and deaths to the Home Department, and the Secretary of State was empowered to send a visitor to inspect any asylum where he had reason to think there was a need for improvement. However, it was not until 1842 that the Metropolitan Commissioners in Lunacy (who had been set up to inspect the many private madhouses of the metropolis) were empowered to make a national survey of all lunatics in any kind of accommodation. On the whole, the Commissioners (1844) found the county asylums to be "extremely well-conducted", but were anxious about rising costs. The move to provide special accommodation for pauper lunatics was subject to fierce criticism from the powerful Poor Law authority set up in 1834. The apostles of the new Poor Law claimed that the asylums were extravagant, and that Poor Law bodies could run them more cheaply. For much of the 19th century, the Lunacy Commissioners and the asylum authorities had to fight off the claims of a parsimonious and deterrent Poor Law, which would have destroyed their medical and rehabilitative function in the name of economy.

The period of rapid growth

In 1845, the National Lunacy Commission was set up with power to control and inspect the whole system, but even as they started work, the asylums were being swamped by numbers. The institutional population was increasing rapidly – in the first half of the 19th century, it had virtually doubled. More and more lunatics were sent from the workhouses and the prisons, and this was seen as a mark of progress, because the asylums made better provision for them. In 1827, there were 1046 persons in county asylums; by 1850, the number had increased to over 7000, and by the end of the century, it was to reach 74 000 (Lunacy Commissioners, 1900). County after county built an asylum, a second or a third asylum, and still the pressure increased. The rise in numbers of lunatics (partly due to population increase and partly to reclassification) created some public alarm, and there was much discussion of whether insanity was on the increase (Browne, 1837).

Scull (1979) discusses a number of other possible reasons for the growth of asylums in the 19th century: the development of a modern market economy; the destruction of the "traditional links between rich and poor which had characterised the old order''; the failure of family support; the desire of the asylum doctors to lay claim to a new area of expertise; and the control and repression of those posing a direct threat to social order. All these factors were no doubt involved. Though the 'control and repression' argument has been overstressed by some other writers such as Foucault and Szasz, it may have had some validity in the early days of the asylums. The visiting justices were likely to be local gentry. They welcomed the asylum doctor as an ally and a social equal, and from the evidence of many reports, were interested primarily in the orderliness and quietness of the wards, rather than in the individual welfare of the inmates. Fear of revolution certainly persisted among the upper classes, but the social-control hypothesis undervalues two great social movements of the 19th century for which there is scant sympathy among academics in the late 20th: the evangelical movement in the churches and the Benthamite movement in social and administrative reform. The evangelicals (among whom the seventh Earl of Shaftesbury, chairman of the Lunacy Commissioners for many years, was a leading figure) took the Christian social gospel seriously (Heasman, 1962). The Benthamites had an equal secular passion for 'amelioration' – for stemming the terrible waste of human life which resulted from sheer muddle and inefficiency (Mack, 1962).

Both evangelicals and Benthamites supported the asylum system quite simply because there was no viable alternative. Victorian England was slowly and painfully becoming aware of the need for that structure of health and social services which would make community care possible in the late 20th century. In an age when people could starve in the streets, though, only the institutions offered any type of sustained care: the asylum was what the term originally meant – a place of shelter from a very harsh world.

As the numbers increased, so the building programmes reached unforeseen proportions: asylums of 50 or 80 beds grew to 1000 or 2000. Inevitably, at the same time, the regimes altered: the staff increased, the administration became more complex. What had started as an extension of a gentleman's household often became more like a great landed estate, and the inmates were the peasants – increasingly regarded as a source of menial labour to keep down costs.

There were also improvements, though: mechanical restraint began to fall into disuse following the work of Dr Charlesworth and Dr Gardiner Hill at the Lincoln asylum (Hill, 1857), and Dr John Conolly extended the 'non-restraint system' to the more difficult population of the large Hanwell asylum, now St Bernard's, Southall, which admitted its inmates from the industrial slums of London. Conolly saw the implications of non-restraint – he instituted a training school for keepers and an education programme for inmates, although both schemes were defeated for a time by his committee on the grounds of economy (Conolly, 1856). The Lunacy Commissioners developed an active system of visitation, inspecting premises, heating and water supplies, facilities and amenities, checking on bathing facilities, food, exercise, and occupation; but the face-to-face relationships which had characterised the early days had become impossible. The asylums had reached the stage of what Goffman (1961) calls ''batch living'', where inmates were treated impersonally as a class, rather than as individuals.

The institutional culture

The total number of inmates continued to increase – reaching a total of over 140 000 in 1930 (Board of Control, 1931). The increasing demand on a relatively fixed stock of buildings meant that overcrowding was a constant problem. Wards built for 30 patients often took 60 or more.

The crowded asylums had a highly organised life of their own, with its own norms and its own assumptions. The physician had become the medical superintendent, with a medical staff. A clerk and steward became the head of a department responsible for supplies and accounts. There was a 'male side' run by a chief male nurse, and a 'female side' run by a matron, with often something of a polite war between the two. Most male nurses were unqualified, recruits from the forces or the ranks of the unemployed, and the main qualifications for the job up to the late 1930s were that they should be of a powerful physique and either good at cricket and football, or able to play a musical instrument. There was some scorn for the 'Nightingale' tradition of the female side, where qualified nurses were increasingly employed. The contrast was acute: the male side would often be run on the model of a barracks, and the female side like a residential home. On the male side, there would be bare boards, and bare windows, and voices barking orders. On the female side, there would be curtains and flowers, pictures on the walls, and a gentler way of handling patients. Despite the steady development of the qualification in psychiatric nursing, this basic distinction persisted in some hospitals through to the 1960s.

Most large asylums had their own farms, with pigs, cattle, and sheep, and a farm manager and a master butcher. They had their own vegetable gardens, flower gardens, orchards, and greenhouses, under the direction of the head gardener. Fresh food went to the huge Victorian kitchens, whence it would emerge, often unrecognisable, in trolleys for the long journey to the wards. There was an engineer's department, responsible for minor works, building maintenance, boilers, plumbing, carpentry, and, later, electrical work. Some asylums even had their own fire engines. The asylum world was a society within a society – busy, purposeful, encapsulated.

Inmates lived on wards, each of which consisted of a complex: dormitory, day room, dining room, offices. The outer doors were locked with a double lock, which it took some practice to master. Male inmates who were judged fit to leave the wards worked under supervision in the farms and gardens, or in gangs which did the rough work on the estate. Female inmates worked in the kitchens, in the laundry, or in staff houses. Working for the staff was a job much sought after, because it involved getting out of the hospital into an ordinary domestic atmosphere. Patients were paid with tobacco, sweets, or small amounts of pocket money. Those on closed wards left the wards only for specified activities, when they were counted out and counted in again. The jangle of keys was heard constantly, as doors were unlocked and locked again: keys were a source of power and a mark of responsibility. It was a serious matter for members of staff to lose their keys. This led to being 'sent down the drive' (i.e. dismissed) without notice. Outdoor exercise for violent inmates was provided in the airing courts – small flowerless gardens surrounded by high wire, where the inmates could be seen shambling round or sometimes (if the staff were not quick to stop them) shouting at the passers-by.

Before the introduction of the phenothiazines, the atmosphere of the more disturbed wards was bizarre at times: violence was frequent on the male wards, and not unknown on the female wards. Male nurses were expert in quickly handling an aggressive patient: pulling the coat back over his shoulders and pinioning his arms, which had to be done without injury, because every bruise or contusion had to be reported and logged. Padded cells were a kindness – at least they prevented frenzied inmates from banging their heads against the wall and injuring themselves. Schizophrenic patients hallucinated openly, talking animatedly to non-existent companions, cowering from imagined attack, or preparing to fight imaginary enemies. Delusions were common. Manic patients sang and shouted and sometimes fought. Depressed patients cried almost without remission. Obsessional patients walked carefully, avoiding the cracks on the linoleum, or stretched out hands that were red and raw from constant symbolic washing.

The ward environment attacked the senses: there was the sound of demented voices, the sight of demented people, the smell of cheap disinfectant, boiling cabbage, and boiling laundry. In contrast, the senior staff and their families led a comfortable domestic life. Their houses were provided, and cleaned by patients. Their gardens were tended by patients, with plants delivered from the hospital greenhouses. Their laundry was collected and delivered, washed and ironed in the hospital laundry (a considerable advantage in the days before domestic washing machines). They retired at 55 – five years earlier than their colleagues in general hospitals. It was a tough job, and acknowledged to be so. In exchange for their privileges, they too led an encapsulated life, living on the hospital estate, in some cases spending leisure time in the staff social club, aware of the public prejudice which separated them from the rest of society, maintaining an air of determined normality in conditions where a crisis could erupt at any moment, and nothing was 'normal'.

County mental hospitals

Asylums were not technically 'hospitals' until 1930. After the setting up of county and county borough councils in 1888, they were managed by a separate asylums committee of the local authority, which had no administrative connection with the management of general hospitals: workhouse infirmaries remained under the Poor Law guardians. Though asylum doctors had long talked of 'mental illness' and 'patients', and looked for closer contacts with general medicine, it was not until the passing of the Mental Treatment Act 1930 that the concept of mental illness as illness was cautiously accepted. That act brought about a major change in the patient population by introducing 'voluntary' status. Voluntary patients were asked to sign a form, stating that they requested treatment, and were entitled to discharge themselves after giving 72 hours' notice.

Medical superintendents and their staff took a pride in the proportion of voluntary patients admitted: this was an indication that the old prejudices associated with certification were being overcome, and that the hospital was an acceptable centre for treatment. The prevailing philosophy was that many people had been deterred from seeking early treatment by fear and misunderstanding, and that an increase in numbers indicated an active and successful mental health policy. So the hospitals increased in size again, some to more than 3000 beds.

As the voluntary patients came in, mental hospitals became more open communities. Many wards were unlocked, and patients were allowed to move about more freely on a 'parole' system (the terminology was perhaps a sign that the association with the penal services had not been entirely forgotten). There was 'hospital parole' for those who were allowed to walk about the buildings unsupervised, 'ground parole' for those who were allowed to go as far as the hospital gates, and 'town parole' (usually only on Saturday afternoons) for those who could be given a minor degree of freedom. The development of out-patient clinics made it possible to discharge patients at an earlier stage in their recovery.

The Board of Control, which had succeeded the Lunacy Commissioners in 1913, promoted positive programmes of rehabilitation. Patients were encouraged to wear their own clothes rather than the old asylum uniform. A large hospital would have an education department, with several teachers tackling anything from literacy classes to discussion groups, and possibly an art teacher, who would encourage patients to find expression through drawing and painting. Occupational therapy was introduced. Dances were frequent (with male and female patients seated on opposite sides of the hall, and supervised to prevent enthusiastic embraces). The new talking films, which the Board of Control at first thought unlikely to endure, became popular, and were screened two or three times a week. The Council for Music in Hospitals sent musicians in full evening dress to play Bach and Mozart to the patients. Perhaps more popular were the concert parties, complete with red-nosed comedian, a sing-song, and brass bands. There were whist drives, beetle drives, outings to the seaside, gymnastic sessions, exercise classes, and dancing lessons. For patients who worked during the day and were able to take part in social activities at night and at the weekends, it was a full life – often much more so than their life outside.

Sport played a considerable part in mental hospital life, particularly cricket and football, for which each hospital would have its first team, composed of younger staff and patients. The cricket team would be provided with flannels, and a cap and blazer bearing the hospital crest. The football team would have its own distinctive 'rig'. Away matches (with other mental or mental handicap hospitals) were occasions of great excitement, and long-stay patients could recite the scores from matches with this hospital or that over 10 or 20 years previously.

The hospital would have its own institutional celebrations: Christmas, with a long series of ward parties; sports day, when patients and staff would join in races and other events, the committee wives' hats would rival Ascot, and much merriment would be caused by the sight of junior doctors battling with pillows on the greasy pole, or dipping their heads into a tub for apples. If there was an element of role reversal in this, it was a healthy one.

The model had changed again – mental hospitals were learning from the holiday camps which had become popular in the 1930s, and the old hierarchical structure was beginning to dissolve. However, the position of the medical (or physician) superintendent was still one of great prestige and great authority. There were stories of superintendents of the past – this one had made his rounds in a top hat, that one had worn plimsolls to creep into the wards unheralded at night. Some ate alone in state, their food separately prepared and served, rather than joining the doctors' mess. At least one hospital had a corridor 250 yards long, built specifically so that the medical superintendent could move from his house to his office without being subject to approaches from staff or patients on the way. Dr Walter Maclay, the last Senior Medical Commissioner of the Board of Control, had a joke about an admission certificate for a patient which ran on the following lines:

> "This patient is arrogant, overbearing, and suffers from delusions of grandeur. He thinks he is a medical superintendent. In fact, he behaves just like a medical superintendent."

Despite much genuine kindness and goodwill, patients still occupied the lowest rank in the culture of the mental hospital. It was common to hear a staff member say to another "Don't do that: get a patient to do it for you". Patients provided the labour which made the whole enterprise possible, but in return, the hospital gave isolated people a certain sense of belonging, and could literally provide care from the cradle to the grave. If a woman patient had a baby, there was an arrangement with the local Registrar of Births, Marriages & Deaths that the address recorded on the birth certificate was not 'X-shire County Mental Hospital', but some innocuous agreed substitute like '4, London Road'. If a patient died without relatives, the hospital had its own sad little cemetery, and would take charge of the funeral. Patients who were discharged were encouraged to come back, like old boys and old girls of a school, to see the staff and their former comrades. Some hospitals ran clubs for ex-patients, which were well attended.

The National Health Service Act 1946 brought the mental hospitals into the same administrative framework as acute hospitals. Some psychiatric wards and units developed within general hospitals. In the mental hospitals, medical staff salaries, which had been low by comparison with those in acute hospitals, increased sharply, but staff were required to pay for those services which had previously been provided free.

Standards of equipment and ward decoration and furnishing were well below those acceptable in general hospitals, and a major programme of upgrading was undertaken by the new regional hospital boards. New medical equipment was provided, new kitchens were installed, some distressing Edwardian furniture was removed, and experimental colour schemes replaced the drab greys and dirty cream walls of the pre-war era. There was a vogue for 'colour therapy': pillar-box red and bright yellow for depressed patients, dove-grey and pale blue for manic patients; but the improvements could not make much impact on the old Victorian buildings, which became increasingly expensive to maintain and heat, and were manifestly unsuitable for the changing psychiatric practice of the post-war period.

Overcrowding became worse than ever. In the early 1950s, some hospitals had beds head-to-foot down the centre of the dormitories, and even beds in the corridors. It was in this period that the hospital authorities began, of necessity, to judge their work by the numbers of patients they could discharge rather than by the numbers they could induce to come forward for treatment.

The years of decline

Before the hospitals had fully adjusted to the changes involved in their new status, a change of even greater import occurred: the development of the phenothiazines (initially in a Paris pharmaceutical house in the winter of 1953) was to revolutionise the treatment of mental illness. Many patients were able to be treated in the community, without the necessity for mental hospital admission; others needed only to spend a short time in hospital for diagnosis and the prescription of medication (perhaps with further short periods in hospital for observation and the adjustment of the prescription). Increasingly wards began to be unlocked, and the old airing courts were turned into gardens or car parks. In 1961, the Minister of Health announced that it was expected that the mental hospital population would drop by 50% within 15 years.

The subsequent changes are surprisingly difficult to quantify, because of a variety of statistical and definitional problems (Jones & Fowles, 1983), but the number of psychiatric beds in England and Wales (including those in general hospital units) came down from a high point of 155 700 in 1959 (Ministry of Health, 1960) to 114 200 in 1970 and 79 200 in 1980 (unpublished government statistics, 1982). In 1990, it was probably well below 60 000, and falling at an accelerative rate. In these circumstances, it was to be expected that psychiatrists, armed with the new pharmacopoeia, should lose interest in the hospital as a social milieu. In practice, they came to spend less and less time there, for there were clinics to run, day hospitals and detached units to visit, and consultancy services to other agencies to maintain. The awesome medical superintendent disappeared in the early 1960s, to be replaced by a medical committee. The task of running the hospital devolved on the lay administrators, as a matter of physical planning, supplies, maintenance, and accounts.

As psychiatrists moved closer to general medicine, so psychiatric nurses moved closer to general nursing. Professional standards rose, and the sharp distinction between the 'male side' and the 'female side' disappeared. The therapeutic community movement, which had enjoyed a brief vogue in trying to mobilise the positive forces in the hospital environment and to negate the destructive ones by "flattening the authority pyramid" (Jones, 1952; Rapoport, 1961) was ultimately defeated by the fact that the hospital community was rapidly disintegrating. The principles of the therapeutic community were to have some success in other fields, such as the penal services, but short-stay psychiatric patients no longer stayed long enough to benefit from them.

Farms and gardens were sold off: industrial units, where patients carried out simple, repetitive work such as assembling electric plugs or fitting together umbrella spokes, and earned money which they could bank for the future, replaced the older, largely unpaid forms of patient labour for the institution. Television gradually took the place of the extensive education and entertainment programmes: it was cheaper, it was more convenient, and many patients liked it better than the enforced effort and relentless jollity of communal activities. The tensions of ward life receded: newly tranquillised patients sat quietly watching soap operas and comedy shows, rather than enacting their own dramas.

It was at this point, when both medical practice and official policy were phasing out the mental hospital as the main centre of treatment, and well over 90% of patients had voluntary status (informal status after the Mental Health Act 1959), that the media became alarmed at the possibilities of certification and the dangers of the abuse of staff power. Between 1969 and 1975, allegations of ill-treatment were made in almost every mental hospital in England. Press and television whipped up a "moral panic" (Cohen, 1980), and the lay public was given the impression that mental hospitals were brutal places in which human rights were ignored and scandals occurred daily. The major hospital inquiries (e.g. Committee of Inquiry into Whittingham Hospital (1972) and Warlingham Park – Kent Area Health Authority (1977)) did identify irregularities and insensitive behaviour on the part of individual staff members, but it was notable that incidents of this kind were not generic to particular hospitals: they occurred on specific (usually male) wards and on specific shifts. The main instances of cruelty and ill-treatment occurred not in mental hospitals but in mental handicap hospitals: the media repeatedly confused two very different types of institution.

The reportage of alleged scandals died out quite abruptly in about 1975, and since that time there have been no major allegations. It could be argued that the campaigns were successful, and that there have been no further incidents; or that new complaints machinery has provided an efficient means of redress; or, more probably, that media interest is inherently short term – it exaggerated the problems at the time, and has tended to ignore them since. Media attention is sporadic, but now tends to emphasise the deficiencies of community care. In 1983, the Mental Health Act strengthened the provisions protecting the rights of the small minority of compulsorily detained patients, but did little to improve either the conditions of the majority of in-patients or the low standards of community services.

In the 1980s, the movement to close the mental hospitals accelerated. Wards were emptied and many blocks reduced to rubble, for these intimidating old buildings, sturdy though they are, can mostly serve no other useful purpose; property speculators began to bid for the extensive grounds, now worth millions of pounds. Elderly patients who had been in hospital for 20 or 30 years, often highly institutionalised, have been moved – or 'decanted', to use an unfortunate phrase in vogue – to small residential homes or hostels.

Some mental hospitals will continue to exist, providing mainly short-term care for patients who need periods of observation for the prescription or adjustment of medication. One matter for concern is that some patients who would formerly have been sent to mental hospitals now have to go to prison for lack of mental hospital accommodation, which takes us back to the situation in 1806; but the asylum culture, so much a part of the Victorian age, so alien to the late 20th century, has gone for ever. In a period when no other form of care was available, and psychopharmacology undeveloped, it served its purpose, until it was defeated by sheer numbers. We need neither deny its usefulness in its own day, nor regret its passing.

References

BEARDSHAW, V. (1981) *Conscientious Objectors at Work*. London: Social Audit.

BOARD OF CONTROL (1931) *Annual Report of the Board of Control*. London: HMSO.

BROWNE, T. (1837) *What Asylums Were, Are, and Ought To Be*. Edinburgh: Black.

CHADWICK, E. (1842) *Report on the Sanitary Condition of the Labouring Population of Great Britain* (ed. M. W. Flinn, 1965) Edinburgh: Edinburgh University Press.

COHEN, S. (1980) *Folk Devils and Moral Panics*. London: Martin Robertson.

COMMITTEE OF INQUIRY INTO WHITTINGHAM HOSPITAL (1972) *Report*, cmnd 4681. London: HMSO.

CONOLLY, J. (1856) *On the Treatment of Insanity*. London: Smith.

FOUCAULT, M. (1961) *Folie et déraison: histoire de la folie à l'âge classique*. Paris: Plon. (Trans. R. Howard (1965) *Madness and Civilisation*. New York: Pantheon.)
GOFFMAN, E. (1961) *Asylums: Essays on the Social Situation of Mental Patients and Other Inmates*. New York: Anchor Doubleday.
HEASMAN, K. (1962) *Evangelicals in Action*. London: Geoffrey Bles.
HILL, R. (1857) *The Non Restraint System in Lunacy*. London: Simpkin Marshall.
JONES, K. & FOWLES, A. J. (1983) People in institutions: rhetoric and reality. In *The Year Book of Social Policy in Britain, 1982* (eds C. Jones & J. Stevenson), pp. 75–77. London: Routledge & Kegan Paul.
—— & —— (1984) *Ideas on Institutions: Analysing the Literature on Long-Term Care and Custody*. London: Routledge & Kegan Paul.
JONES, M. (1952) *Social Psychiatry*. London: Tavistock.
KENT AREA HEALTH AUTHORITY (1977) *Report of Emergency Panel on Warlingham Park Hospital*. Maidstone: Maidstone Health Authority.
LUNACY COMMISSIONERS (1900) *54th Annual Report of the Lunacy Commissioners*, Appendix A. London: HMSO.
MACK, M. (1962) *Jeremy Bentham: An Odyssey of Ideas, 1748–1792*. London: Heinemann.
MARTIN, J. P. (1984) *Hospitals in Trouble*. Oxford: Blackwell.
METROPOLITAN COMMISSIONERS IN LUNACY (1844) *Report of the Metropolitan Commissioners in Lunacy to the Lord Chancellor*, pp. 11–12, 29–30. London: HMSO.
MINISTRY OF HEALTH (1960) *Annual Report*, Part I, cmnd 1418, Appendix II, Table A, p. 166. London: HMSO.
PAUL, G. O. (1806) *Suggestions of Sir George Onesiphorus Paul, Bart, to Earl Spencer*. Published as Appendix IV to the *Report of the Select Committee on Criminal and Pauper Lunatics*, House of Commons Papers (1807). London: HMSO.
RAPOPORT, R. (1961) *Community as Doctor*. London: Tavistock.
SCULL, A. (1979) *Museums of Madness: The Social Organisation of Insanity in Nineteenth Century England*, pp. 26–48. Harmondsworth: Penguin.
SZASZ, T. S. (1961) *The Myth of Mental Illness: Foundations of a Theory of Personal Conduct*. New York: Dell.

Other sources

Where specific references are not given, this account is based on the following sources:

before 1844: reports of the Visiting Justices of County Asylums
1844–1913: annual reports of the Lunacy Commissioners
1913–59: annual reports of the Board of Control

Information was also drawn from personal experience from the early 1950s, and many discussions with psychiatrists whose experience went back to the 1920s. Of these, Dr Alexander Walk (1901–82), Librarian of the Royal College of Psychiatrists, Dr J. E. Nicole (1898–1963), Dr Rolf Strom-Olsen (1902–86) and Dr Walter Maclay (1901–64) should have special mention.

3 The Association of Medical Officers of Asylums and Hospitals for the Insane, the Medico-Psychological Association, and their Presidents

EDWARD RENVOIZE

Few doctors showed much interest in the mentally ill before the second half of the 18th century, and the day-to-day care of such patients was usually left to laymen. However, following the County Asylums Act 1808 and the Lunatics Act 1845, an increasingly well defined group of doctors specialising in mental illness (known initially as 'mad-doctors' and later as 'asylum doctors' or 'alienists') began to emerge; medical knowledge on the subject of insanity expanded, and doctors working in this area began to claim particular expertise in the diagnosis, management, and treatment of the mentally ill. The founding of the Association of Medical Officers of Asylums and Hospitals for the Insane in 1841 marked the birth of an organisation which sought to represent the professional interests of these doctors, as well as to improve the plight of the mentally ill. This Association was transformed in 1865 into the Medico-Psychological Association, which subsequently developed into the Royal College of Psychiatrists, established in 1971.

In this chapter, the background and origins of the Association of Medical Officers of Asylums and Hospitals for the Insane and its evolution into the Medico-Psychological Association are traced, and the biographies of some of the men who occupied presidential office briefly described. The annual presidential addresses frequently dealt with subjects of contemporary concern to asylum doctors, and in the final section of the chapter, some of the more common preoccupations which emerge from an analysis of addresses given in the second half of the 19th century are considered.

Before doing so, however, several points need to be emphasised. Firstly, the events to be described have become the subject of considerable controversy and differing interpretations. The old 'Whiggish' analysis, which saw the acceptance by the state of responsibility for the care of the mentally ill and for the development of asylums during the 19th century as springing from a progressive and compassionate concern for the welfare of patients and from scientific advance, has been seriously challenged. Radical writers such as Foucault (1967) and Scull (1979) have emphasised the political, social, and economic contexts in which these developments occurred, and have suggested that they represent no more than a particular example of Victorian society's coercive response to social deviance. However, more recent empirical evidence (e.g. Digby, 1985; Walton, 1985; Mackenzie, 1985; Russell, 1988; Thompson, 1988; Turner, 1990), by revealing a much more complex picture of the Victorian asylum era, has pointed to deficiencies in both these historical perspectives. Porter (1987*a*), for example, has shown that blanket condemnations of the 18th-century treatment of the insane have been oversimplified, and he suggests that the roots of much 19th-century psychiatric practice owe their origin to the experience of 'madhouse' doctors of the 18th century, rather than to any new radical thinking.

Secondly, the emergence of the asylum doctor in the 19th century has recently been examined from different perspectives by various authors (e.g. Scull, 1979; Digby, 1985; Russell, 1988). An important element in the asylum doctors' campaign to establish themselves as the sole and legitimate professional group to supervise the care of the insane was their contention that mental disease was a brain disorder, thus necessitating medical intervention. By the second half of the 19th century, the asylum doctors had essentially won their battle in this respect, although, as will be shown, a number of insecurities concerning their role remained. Scull (1979) has suggested that the latter part of the 19th century was a time in which asylum doctors consolidated their monopoly through increasing professionalisation. Seen from a sociological perspective, the formation by asylum doctors of the Association of Medical Officers of Asylums and Hospitals for the Insane and subsequently of the Medico-Psychological Association was merely an organisational strategy designed to establish their professional monopoly.

Thirdly, it is important to recognise that 19th-century asylum doctors were not a homogeneous group (Tomes, 1988). The establishment of new county asylums, following the act of 1808, led to the creation of the post of medical superintendent, which combined medical duties with supervision of the nursing and domestic staff. Initially, however, such men were not clinically autonomous, since visiting physicians continued to direct the treatment of asylum patients. However, in 1853, the post of medical superintendent was more clearly defined by the Commissioners in Lunacy in their report for 1851/52:

> "He should have paramount Authority in the Asylum, and be precluded from private Practice, and should devote his whole Time and Energies to the Duties of his Office. . . . The Commissioners consider it the preferable Arrangement that there should not be any Visiting Physician or other Medical Visitor with a Salary, but that in lieu thereof the resident Medical Superintendent should have the Power to call in Medical or Surgical Advice. . . . In the Event of the Asylum becoming full . . . it may be advisable to appoint an Assistant Medical Officer." (Hunter & Macalpine, 1963)

This report marked the formal division of doctors specialising in the treatment of mental illness into a majority group who worked within public county asylums and whose patients mainly comprised the pauper poor and the severely disturbed, and a minority group who worked in private practice and private asylums and whose patients were mainly affluent (Hunter & Macalpine, 1963). Although – faced with increasing public hostility – both public and private doctors were eventually to make common cause on many issues, early differences were evident and never completely disappeared. Tomes (1988), for example, suggests that the brief and poorly attended meetings of the Association of Medical Officers of Asylums and Hospitals for the Insane, which drew its membership from the medical staff of both public and private asylums, and its failure to play any effective role in advancing the specialty's interests in Parliament or elsewhere

(Chapter 1), stemmed partly from a lack of cohesion and identity between these two groups. Scull (1979) has suggested that the division between public and private asylum doctors diminished the effectiveness of the Association for much of the 19th century. This factionalism even surfaced in the specialty's literature, with Forbes Winslow's *Journal of Psychological Medicine*, founded in 1848 and representing the interests of private asylum doctors, having a more distinctive clinical bias, while the *Asylum Journal of Mental Science*, founded in 1853, which championed the cause of public asylum doctors, had a more practical approach, concerned with the running of public asylums (Tomes, 1988).

Bucknill (1860), in his presidential address, encouraged unity between private and public doctors by pointing out their common links:

> "I feel strongly that the welfare of the whole body of medical men practising in lunacy is intimately and indissolubly one and the same. Constant personal changes take place between the two classes, if classes they can be called; the physicians of private asylums often leave the field of professional action to take the superintendence of public asylums, so that about one-third of the latter are under the control of gentlemen who have effected an exchange, so to say, in the regiment but not in the service. Perhaps a still larger number of men have made the same change in the reverse manner, so that to assume any difference of feeling founded on personal grounds in these matters is either an error or a shallow pretence. Moreover, if these constant interchanges in the personnel of our corps did not exist, we should still be indissolubly allied by common sympathies and the common interests, and especially must our interests be intimately allied in considering the professional and social status which is attainable by physicians engaged in the care and treatment of the insane, whatever may be their particular field of practice. The Association over which I have the honour to preside is one brotherhood, devoted to a most noble, though arduous calling."

However, it is likely that differences in conceptual approaches to psychiatry remained between public and private asylum doctors. The protests from public asylum doctors at the change of emphasis in the *Journal of Mental Science* from its previous preoccupations with practical and administrative matters of relevance to public asylum management, to more esoteric and philosophical psychiatric concerns, under the editorship of Henry Maudsley (Russell, 1988; Turner, 1988) provides evidence of this. In fact, a number of the leading Victorian thinkers and writers on psychiatry, like Maudsley himself, were employed in the private sector and had little experience of the problems facing doctors who worked in the public asylums.

Political, social and medical background of the formation of the Association of Medical Officers of Asylums and Hospitals for the Insane

The coming of the Industrial Revolution had a profound impact on British society of the early 19th century. The previous agrarian economy was replaced by one based on industry and commerce (Ashton, 1988); many of the population now lived in towns and cities and were employed in the rapidly developing manufacturing industries (Briggs, 1985*a*,*b*). There was a dramatic growth in the British population, which doubled from 10½ million to 21 million between 1801 and 1851 (Walvin, 1987).

Cities expanded, and new towns sprang up especially in the north of England, the Midlands, and South Wales in response to the new industries (Briggs, 1985*a*,*b*). Such growth was usually unplanned and often associated with desperate poverty, overcrowding, slum housing, atmospheric pollution, poor sanitation, contaminated water supplies, and general squalor. Working conditions were often harsh and dangerous, while frequent epidemics of infectious diseases such as cholera and tuberculosis led to high infant mortality and early death for many of the urban poor (Smith, 1979; Wohl, 1984).

The Poor Law Amendment Act 1834 severely curtailed outdoor relief for such people as paupers, and many who had previously been supported in their own homes were now forced into the workhouse, if they were to receive help (Royle, 1987). The principle of 'less eligibility' meant that conditions in the workhouse were made as unpleasant as possible, in order to deter all but the most desperate. The workhouse came to be hated and feared by the poor, and many preferred to put up with abject poverty, rather than subject themselves and their families to the miseries of these institutions.

The wealth of the country grew fast so that by the middle of the 19th century, Britain could boast that it was the richest country in the world (Best, 1988). However this affluence was very unevenly distributed and examples of extremes of wealth and poverty could be found almost side by side in most Victorian cities and towns.

The process of industrialisation and the rapid economic growth in the early decades of the 19th century also demanded new skills and increased specialisation of the workforce. As a result, new social classes began to emerge, with membership of the 16 leading professions doubling to just under 150 000 between 1841 and 1881 (Royle, 1987). The extension of the franchise to some of the new industrial, mercantile, and professional classes as a result of the Reform Act 1832 marked the beginning of a shift in political power from the land-owning aristocracy and gentry of the countryside to the growing upper and middle classes of the urban areas (Thomson, 1986).

In mid-Victorian Britain, the medical profession in general did not enjoy a particularly high status, and the standing of doctors in society did not much improve until nearer the end of the century (Peterson, 1978). Before the Medical Registration Act 1858, the profession was poorly organised and educational standards frequently low: many bodies were entitled to grant licences to practise medicine, and their standards varied considerably. Medical training ranged from attendance at university courses and instruction in medical schools and teaching hospitals, to an apprenticeship system. Three broad groups of the medical profession were distinguishable – physicians, surgeons, and apothecaries – each of which had their own professional body. The university-educated physicians, who had the highest social prestige, ministered to the wealthier sections of society, while the least prestigious, the apothecaries, looked after the health needs of the mass of the population as best they could. By the 1840s, though, the training of doctors had become more standardised, and many students of medicine were beginning to share a similar educational experience (Peterson, 1978; Youngson, 1979). The Medical Registration Act, which formally unified the medical profession, provided both a framework for the regulation of doctors and a mechanism to exclude 'unqualified' practitioners such as medical botanists and bone-setters (Porter, 1987*b*). However, rivalries between the different groups within the profession remained.

Before the middle of the 18th century, while the socially privileged were able to exercise a degree of choice in the type of care which their relatives received, for most of the population, care of the mentally ill differed little from the experience of other disadvantaged groups such as paupers and vagrants (Scull, 1979). There were no clear central policy guidelines and the mentally ill remained within the community, unless dangerous or causing a disturbance. Specialist hospital provision was rare; it was usually left to local parishes to organise care in the form of outdoor relief or admission to a workhouse if this proved necessary.

Although most of the mentally ill continued to remain at liberty within the community, and private 'madhouses' had been a feature of English life for several centuries, such institutions became increasingly common in the 18th century (Parry-Jones, 1972, 1988). Such establishments catered both for paupers – boarded out by their parishes, which paid for their fees – as well as for the more affluent, who continued to pay for themselves. This "trade in lunacy" was run for profit by lay people such as clergymen, as well as by doctors, and such institutions ranged in size from one to over 100 patients. Accommodation was often sparse and totally unsuitable for the purpose, while patients were frequently subjected to harsh treatment and mechanical restraint. Private madhouses continued as an important though declining form of institutional care for the insane until the late 19th century, although by this time, they were fully under the control of medically qualified proprietors.

Although St Mary of Bethlem (Bedlam) in London had cared for the mentally ill since at least 1403, it was not until the 18th century that hospital facilities for the insane began to be seriously provided, and even this was on a relatively small scale. Hospital institutions were founded at Norwich in 1713, at St Luke's, London, in 1751, Manchester in 1766, Newcastle in 1767, York in 1777, and Liverpool in 1790 (Bynum, 1983). However, institutional care of the mentally ill in such asylums or private 'madhouses' was the exception rather than the rule, and most confined lunatics were to be found in workhouses, poor-houses, and prisons.

Society's attitudes towards the mentally ill, though, started to change in the latter part of the 18th century, and various factors appear to have prompted this trend. King George III's psychiatric illness (Hunter & Macalpine, 1963; Jones, 1972) showed that diseases of the mind could strike at anyone, irrespective of class or position in society, and his apparent recoveries at the hands of Dr Willis fostered a therapeutic optimism that such disorders could be treated successfully. There was also a growing humanitarian concern about the often harsh conditions in which lunatics were confined and the abuses of physical restraint to which some were exposed. The closing down of the Bethlem Hospital 'peep show' of lunatics as a holiday entertainment for the masses in 1770 was an indication of this change of mood, although the extent to which such exhibitions ever occurred seems to have been greatly exaggerated (Allderidge, 1985). The unease about the state in which many lunatics were kept also found expression in the 1774 Act, under which five commissioners from the Royal College of Physicians inspected private 'madhouses' in London, and justices visited and licensed those in the provinces (Jones, 1972). Though not successful in eliminating abuses, this act was a forerunner for the later system of inspection of asylums.

The demonstration by Philippe Pinel at the Bicêtre in Paris that asylum patients could be managed without the need for restraint pointed the way towards a more enlightened form of care. However, in Britain, it was the founding of the Retreat at York in 1796 by William Tuke, a Quaker and layman, and the pioneering there of 'moral treatment', that showed reformers that asylum patients could be cared for humanely (Jones, 1972; Digby, 1985). When Tuke's grandson published details of the institution and its methods in *A Description of the Retreat* in 1813, the concepts of moral treatment reached a wider audience. Despite its small size, its Quaker inspiration, and other atypical characteristics (Digby, 1985), the Retreat began to act as a model which many future asylums attempted to emulate. This experience convinced many psychiatric reformers that institutional care was the ideal method of treating the mentally ill, and, under an act of 1808, magistrates were allowed to build a rate-supported asylum in each county to cope with the large number of pauper lunatics (Jones, 1972). However, as the act was only discretionary, few counties availed themselves of the opportunity.

Yet interest in the plight of the mentally ill did not abate: a Parliamentary select committee of inquiry held between 1815 and 1816 found further evidence of abuse, not only in private madhouses and workhouses but also at the Bethlem Hospital and York asylum (Jones, 1972; Scull, 1979). This convinced many of the need for greater state intervention in the care of the mentally ill, and also for an improved system of inspection by a national body of premises in which lunatics were looked after, but opposition from various quarters defeated attempts to pass legislation. It was not until 1828 that legislation permitted the new Commission in Lunacy to license and supervise private madhouses in the metropolitan area, although the act did not apply to county asylums. This omission was remedied in the Lunatics Act 1845, and in the same year a further act made the building of county and borough asylums for pauper lunatics compulsory (Chapter 2).

Towards the latter part of the 18th century, some members of the medical profession were also beginning to show a greater and more active interest in the diagnostic, clinical, therapeutic, and legal aspects of the care of the insane (Bynum, 1983); the growth in medically run asylums, a developing medical literature on the subject, and medicolegal involvement in court cases testified to this. The recognition that the mind is a function of the brain enhanced this process, so that it became increasingly accepted by doctors, and to a lesser extent by the public, that mental illness was in fact a disease and therefore legitimately fell within the province of the medical profession. The latter was given an important inspection and supervisory role in relation to metropolitan private madhouses under the 1828 Act, and then under the Lunatics Act 1845. This made it mandatory that each county asylum should have a resident medical officer (Jones, 1972), giving state recognition to the dominant position of the medical profession in the sphere of diagnosis and treatment of mental illness.

The formation of the Association of Medical Officers of Asylums and Hospitals for the Insane

The early history of the Association, on which the following account is based, was chronicled by Outterson Wood (1896), who used both the detailed

Fig. 3.1. Samuel Hitch, the man who made the first steps in the founding of the Association of Medical Officers of Asylums and Hospitals for the Insane, the forerunner of the Royal College of Psychiatrists

abstracts of the minute book of the Association and the personal recollections of Bucknill to compile his record. Walk & Walker (1961) have also written an excellent history of this period.

On 19 June 1841, Dr Samuel Hitch (Fig. 3.1), Resident Physician of Gloucester General Lunatic Asylum, sent the following circular to all visiting physicians and resident medical superintendents of 26 asylums and hospitals in England, 11 in Ireland and 7 in Scotland:

> "Dear Sir,
> It having been long felt desirable that the Medical Gentlemen connected with Lunatic Asylums should be better known to each other – should communicate more freely the results of their individual experience – should co-operate in collecting statistical information relating to Insanity – and, above all, should assist each other in improving the treatment of the Insane – several Gentlemen who have the conduct of Lunatic Asylums have determined on making an attempt to form 'An Association of the Medical Officers of Lunatic Asylums'.
> For this purpose they propose to meet annually, at the time and place 'the British Association for the Cultivation of Science' shall select for holding their Meetings; and to hold a first or preliminary meeting this year, on the 29th July next, at Devonport.
> I have been requested by these Gentlemen to learn how far their brethren will co-operate with them; and I shall feel it a personal kindness therefore if you will, as soon as possible, give me your opinion upon this proposed Association, and also inform me if you will give it your support.
>
> I beg to remain, dear Sir,
> Your obedient and faithful Servant,
> Samuel Hitch,
> Resident Physician,
> Gloucester General Lunatic Asylum."

Of the 88 circulars sent out, 44 replies, including those from Monro, Conolly, Gaskell, Morison, and Browne, were received in favour of the formation of the Association and expressing their willingness to join. However, only four respondents were in favour of attending the proposed meeting at Devonport, and the preliminary meeting was instead held at the Gloucester Lunatic Asylum on 27 July 1841. Present on this historic occasion were Dr Shute, visiting physician of the Gloucester lunatic asylum and chairman of the meeting, Dr Hitch, Mr Gaskell, medical superintendent of Lancaster asylum, Mr Powell, resident medical superintendent of Nottingham asylum, Dr Thurnam, resident medical superintendent of the York Retreat, and Mr Wintle, resident medical superintendent of Oxford asylum (Warneford). The following resolutions were passed.

> "That it does not appear incumbent on those who issued the circular and convened the meeting to proceed to Devonport.
> That this meeting considers itself competent to establish the Association proposed in the circular.
> That an Association be formed of the Medical Officers attached to Hospitals for the Insane, whose objects shall be – Improvement in the management of such institutions and the treatment of the insane, and the acquirement of a more extensive and more correct knowledge of insanity.
> That the medical gentlemen attached to Hospitals for the Insane be individually addressed and requested to join the Association.
> That, by the members of this Association, the terms Lunatic and Lunatic Asylum, be abandoned, except for legal purposes, and that the terms 'Insane Person', and 'Hospital for the Insane', be substituted.

That to effect the great objects of this Association, visits be made annually to some one or more of the Hospitals for the Insane in the United Kingdom; and that the order of rotation in which such visits shall be made, be determined at the several meetings.

That the concurrence of the Governors of the several hospitals to this arrangement be solicited by the respective Medical Officers.

That at its meetings the Association ascertain and record, as far as possible, the medical and moral treatment adopted in each hospital.

That to insure a careful comparison of the results of treatment in each, it is strongly recommended that uniform registers be kept, and that tabular Statements, upon a like uniform plan, be circulated with the annual report of each hospital; or, where this be not practicable, that it be otherwise transmitted to the Association.

That, at the meetings, papers and essays be read; subjects of interest to the insane and to the Association be discussed, and the information communicated.

That, at the Annual Meetings, the Senior Medical Officer of the Hospital visited be Chairman.

That a Secretary be appointed to keep the journals, papers, etc., of the Association, and to perform the usual duties of such officer.

That the first Annual Meeting be held at Nottingham early in the month of September next, of which due notice shall be given.

That Dr. Hitch be requested to act as Secretary pro tem.

That these resolutions be printed, and a copy forwarded to every Medical Officer of the Hospitals for the Insane in Great Britain, and as far as practicable, to the Medical Officers of similar establishments on the Continent.

Signed,
Hardwicke Shute, Chairman."

As Outterson Wood later wrote, "These resolutions gave very clearly the objects and aspirations of the new Association, and to this day they remain the basis, and contain the fundamental principles upon which our present Association [Medico-Psychological Association] is established."

Owing to 'unforeseen circumstances', the first annual meeting held at the Nottingham lunatic asylum was postponed until 4 November 1841. Dr Andrew Blake, visiting physician to the Nottingham asylum, acted as chairman of the meeting, which comprised 11 asylum doctors and three visitors, including Dr Bowden from Hanwell. All of the 'Gloucester Six' attended, apart from Mr Wintle, while Dr Corsellis from Wakefield, Dr Crommelink from Belgium, Dr Prichard from Northampton, Mr Prosser from Leicester, and Mr Smith from Lincoln were also present. The meeting lasted two days and was preceded by a thorough inspection of the Nottingham asylum. The chairman pointed out that, hitherto, asylum doctors had been working in isolation, but now that the Association had been formed, this was no longer the case. The meeting was then devoted to a discussion and adoption of the rules and constitution. It was agreed that the Association would be open to doctors attached to private as well as public asylums and that prospective members would be proposed by two existing members and elected by ballot, with at least a two-thirds majority. Mr Samuel Tuke of York, Mr Farr of London, Dr Bowden of Hanwell, and Dr Guislain of Ghent were elected honorary members of the Association.

The choice of Gaskell's county asylum at Lancaster as the venue for the second annual meeting was in part dictated by its proximity to Scotland and Ireland: the first meeting had been arranged at a time of year when travel was difficult, especially for those from those two countries. At the time of the first annual meeting, about 60 medical men had written to Dr Hitch, promising to attend future meetings, so it was hoped that the choice of Lancaster would result in a much larger attendance. However, only ten asylum doctors and three visitors attended, and this pattern of low attendance was to be repeated in future years, part of the explanation being the wide geographical distribution of the members and the relatively poor communication systems at that time (it was not until after the 'railway mania' of 1845–47 that most of the major towns were connected by rail (Briggs, 1985*a*; Royle, 1987)). In addition to facing transport difficulties, asylum physicians – who usually lacked an assistant – may also have been reluctant to leave their institutions without medical supervision.

Up to 1853, the procedure at each annual meeting was similar. After the election of a chairman, who was usually the host member, a programme of events followed which included a tour of the asylum and presentation of papers relating to mental illness, asylum care, and professional matters.

The third annual meeting was held at Morley's Hotel in London, in June 1843, and participants included Dr Conolly from Hanwell and Dr Stewart from Belfast; sessions were held at Hanwell, St Luke's Hospital, and the Surrey asylum. Dr Hitch, the Secretary, reported that he had collected a considerable number of asylum reports, books, and pamphlets for the Association, had been in contact with Lord Shaftesbury on matters connected with the mentally ill, and had also approached the government about the need for each Irish district asylum to have its own resident medical officer. The meeting passed a resolution approving of what Dr Hitch had done in regard to the Irish asylums, adding that they wished to record "their opinion that nothing can be more detrimental to the comfort and welfare of the insane than confiding the entire superintendence of asylums to those who are not members of the medical profession". The meeting also agreed on the need for a more general and systematic provision for the insane poor.

For reasons unclear, following the 1844 annual meeting, in York, no further meetings were held until June 1847, when members of the Association met in Oxford at the Warneford and Littlemore asylums. Numbers were again small, but it was at this meeting that the idea of publishing a journal was first mooted, and the following resolution passed: "That it is desirable that this Association should issue from time to time, as it shall hereafter be determined, a 'Volume of Contributions relative to Insanity in particular, and to Psychology in general'." Mr Gaskell, Dr Thurnam, Mr Wintle, and Drs Williams and Hitch, now joint secretaries of the Association, were appointed to carry it out. However, an attempt to collect contributions from members of the Association elicited no response, and this particular committee met no further.

There then followed a further dormant period in the activities of the Association, and the only available record between 1847 and 1849 is a letter organised by Hitch and signed by 31 of the Association's members, congratulating Gaskell on his appointment as a Commissioner in Lunacy. The Association in fact failed to meet again until July 1851, the year of the Great Exhibition and the Crystal Palace. At least 25 members of the Association attended this meeting, held at the Freemasons' Tavern in London: members present included Conolly, Forbes Winslow, and Bucknill. A letter of resignation from his post as Secretary was read from Dr Hitch and was accepted. He was thanked for his long, continued, and valuable service, and at the same time it was resolved that he should be requested to become Treasurer of the Association. A committee including Conolly, Forbes Winslow, Bucknill, and Corsellis was appointed to examine the lunacy acts and to report thereon. A letter from Dr Williams of Gloucester, advocating the erection of a central criminal asylum, was generally supported and a petition in favour of this was ordered to be drawn up and forwarded to the Secretary of State. Sessions were held at the Asylum for Idiots at Highgate, the Surrey asylum, Colney Hatch, the Bethlem Hospital and also at Sussex House, a private asylum run by Forbes Winslow. It was also resolved that future annual meetings would be held in each July at the Freemasons' Tavern, and that quarterly meetings would also be held.

However, the seventh annual meeting was in fact held in Oxford, and proved to be the most successful so far. Outterson Wood attributes this success to Mr Ley, the medical superintendent of the Littlemore asylum, who at the meeting advocated the establishment of a journal for the use of Association members. The meeting in fact resolved that a journal should be established and that Bucknill should be appointed the editor. The *Asylum Journal of Mental Science* made its first appearance in November 1853; and gave to the Association a stability and cohesion which it had not previously had, providing as it did a means of communication between widely dispersed asylum doctors. The eighth annual meeting was held at the Freemasons' Tavern on 22 June 1854, and it was resolved that the chairman at the annual meeting would be president of the Association for the whole year. This meeting, the transactions of which were extensively reported in the *Asylum Journal* (1855*a*), also marked the ending of the long connection of Dr Hitch with the Association, as he formally resigned his post as Treasurer and apparently failed to take any further interest in the Association. A resolution was passed thanking him for "his great services in the establishment and support of the Association and in the discharge of his duties as Treasurer".

The following officers of the Association were appointed for the year 1854/55 (*Asylum Journal*, 1855*b*): President, Dr Sutherland; Treasurer, Mr Ley; Auditor, Dr Kirkman; Editor of the *Journal*, Dr Bucknill; and Honorary Secretary for Ireland, Dr Stewart. Very few Scottish asylum doctors were members of the Association, and it was therefore decided to set up a branch of the Association in Scotland to improve recruitment, with W. A. F. Browne becoming the first Scottish Secretary. The failure of the Association's special committee, set up previously to oversee lunacy legislation, to influence the new lunacy acts which passed through Parliament the previous year, encouraged the 1854 meeting to set up a permanent Parliamentary Committee to give advice on asylum legislation and oppose any which threatened to lower standards.

Discussion also took place on business matters (the Treasurer's report showed a balance of £28.16*s*. 9*d* in favour of the Association), membership of the Association, and current Parliamentary legislation relating to the care of the mentally ill. Bucknill presented two new buckles to fasten dresses or boots, for use on patients who stripped themselves, and a Dr Foote exhibited two models of the liver of a patient who had died from 'apoplexy' of the liver, and a larynx from a patient who had died suddenly in a convulsive fit with symptoms of apnoea. Following the day's proceedings, it is recorded in the *Asylum Journal* (1855*a*) that "the Members afterwards dined together, and spent a most agreeable evening". This combination of discussion of business, political, and professional matters relating to the Association, the election of president and officers, the delivery of the presidential address, clinical presentations, and social intercourse, became the pattern for future annual general meetings of the Association.

The 1854 meeting turned out to be the first of a long line of annual meetings of doctors specialising in the treatment of mental illness, which continue to the present day under the aegis of the Royal College of Psychiatrists, and the report of its proceedings in the *Asylum Journal* is the first published record of the Association's meetings. By 1854, the membership had expanded to over 120 ordinary members.

Amended rules were adopted at the 1855 annual meeting, and the objectives of the Association were declared to be "the improvement of asylums and hospitals for the insane; the acquisition and diffusion of a more extended knowledge of insanity and its treatment; and the promotion of a free communication on these subjects between the Members" (*Asylum Journal*, 1856).

In his presidential address, Bucknill (1860) summarised the origin and evolution of the Association thus:

> "The history of this Association marks its aim and object as eminently practical. Originally founded by the Superintendents of County Lunatic Asylums, for the purpose of affording themselves opportunities of social intercourse at each other's homes, and by friendly and unostentatious talk on the subjects of their calling, to gather knowledge of each other, and from each other, this worthy but limited object was soon satisfied; the few members of the Association became friends; they found that they could communicate by letter, and the meetings of the Association fell into disuse. It was in this way probably that the Association became for many years to all appearance dead. Without any of those causes which usually break up societies, without any disruption of amity or change of circumstance, all activity in the association ceased, and for many years it showed no signs of life, though in truth only dormant. This state of things continued until the year 1853 when the first step to the rejuvenescence of the Association was taken at the meeting at Oxford, under the auspices of my friend Mr. Ley, at which it was determined that efforts should be made to vivify our dormant life by the establishment of a literary organ of the Association. It would ill become me to speak of the manner in which the numbers and strength of our present Association have gathered around this centre of our vitality. I am too conscious of the errors and shortcomings of the part of the work which has been placed in my hands, not to feel gratified surprise, at the effect which this real but simple bond of interest and communion has exercised upon the members of our specialty. Infinitely more successful as it might have been as a literary enterprise, it has at least been successful beyond all our expectations as the means of vivifying and extending and uniting this Association of medical men, scattered as the members are over all parts of the United Kingdom; working as they do in every department of the special branch of medicine to which they belong; influenced by diverse interests; entertaining widely different opinions, and only united by that strong bond of sympathy which is to be found in one great common object, which to them is the welfare of the insane, and the desire to promote all legislative and scientific and social measures which are calculated to attain this object."

The formation of the Medico-Psychological Association

In 1865, under the chairmanship of Dr Wood, and apparently at the suggestion of Henry Maudsley (Turner, 1988), the Association of Medical Officers of Asylums and Hospitals for the Insane changed its name to the 'Medico-Psychological Association'. Though it had the same objectives as the previous Association (*Journal of Mental Science*, 1865), this change of title reflected a growing confidence of its membership, and a recognition that the role of the Association needed to be strengthened and its influence extended outside the confines of asylums. Membership of the Association was no longer limited to medical officers of public and private hospitals and asylums for the insane, but was extended to legally qualified medical practitioners interested in the treatment of insanity. However, a proposal by Dr Arlidge to extend membership to non-medical men interested in psychology or in the practice of lunacy was defeated by 6 votes to 12.

Officers of the Association now comprised a president, treasurer, general secretary, a secretary for Scotland and one for Ireland, the editor of the *Journal*, and two auditors, all to be elected by ballot at each annual meeting. These officers, together with eight ordinary members, now constituted the Council of the Association. Although its "infancy and childhood were . . . modest and retiring" (Whitcombe, 1891), by the end of the 19th century, the Medico-Psychological Association was to grow to a membership of almost 600, and an organisational structure which comprised three English divisions, and a division each for Scotland and Ireland.

Browne (1866) gave voice to the Association's new-found confidence and optimism in his presidential address at the first annual meeting of the Association under its new title, held in Edinburgh in 1866: The change of title, he said:

> "appears . . . auspicious both as inaugurating a more correct designation, and as pointing to a wider and more legitimate destiny. We can no longer be mistaken for a mere friendly club or a mutual defence society. We may now claim as among our objects the investigation of all subjects bearing upon the science of mind in connection with health and disease, as well as those which affect our personal interests or those committed to our charge. We claim even a wider, almost a universal range for the science of Medico-Psychology, and we claim for it a distinct position in science. The difficulty is to assign and to restrain it within limits."

Munro (1864) had previously described the Association of Medical Officers of Asylums and Hospitals for the Insane as "a very ill-used body", but it fell to Sankey (1868) to point out its faults in more detail:

> "It has appeared to me that hitherto the chief functions of this association . . . have consisted in publishing a quarterly periodical . . . I believe that it is competent to achieve much more than it has yet accomplished, and that we may look to the future as well as the past in estimating its utility."

Sankey (1868) advanced cogent reasons why doctors specialising in mental illness should join together in the Medico-Psychological Association:

> "In these days every class of men having common interests combine for mutual assistance. We have not only common interests, but our special

occupation isolates us very much, not only from the public and from the general body of the profession, so that our interests, and I may add, our grievances, at all events our duties and our studies, are all peculiar. . . . Unless we place our own case before the public it is more than probable it will remain unknown.''

Biographies of some 19th-century presidents

The offices of President of the Association of Medical Officers of Asylums and Hospitals for the Insane and the Medico-Psychological Association were occupied by some of the most eminent and influential asylum doctors of the second half of the 19th century, and the lives of some of these are now described. Henry Maudsley is the subject of Chapter 23, and so is not dealt with below.

John Conolly

John Conolly (Fig. 3.2) has been the subject of extensive biographical essays, for example by Maudsley (1866), Leigh (1961), Hunter & Macalpine (1963), and more recently by Scull (1985), and reference should be made to these for a more detailed account of Conolly's career.

John Conolly was born at Market Rasen, in Lincolnshire, in 1794. His mother's maiden name was Tennyson, and her family were distantly related to the Poet Laureate of the same name. Following the death of their Irish father at a young age, Conolly's two brothers were adopted by members of their mother's family, and he was sent away to a small grammar school in Holderness as a boarder at the age of five. He regarded his schooldays as a very miserable period of his life ''in which the semblance of learning was mechanically imparted by aid of frequent punishments'' (*Journal of Mental Science*, 1866).

On leaving school, he returned to live with his mother in Hull. She had by now remarried, her husband being an *émigré* Scot from Paris. A mutual affection grew up between Conolly and his stepfather, who taught him French and acquainted him with French literature. At the age of 18, he was commissioned into a Cambridgeshire militia regiment, and spent an enjoyable four years in Scotland and Ireland. On leaving the regiment, Conolly married at the age of 22, and he and his wife spent an idyllic year living in a cottage near Tours in France, where his brother practised as a doctor. After the birth of his first child, and when his capital began to run out, Conolly decided to study medicine in Scotland. He read the works of Pinel and Tuke as a medical student at the University of Edinburgh, and qualified in 1821, having taken insanity as the subject for his thesis. On leaving Edinburgh, Conolly went to Lewes with a view to establishing a practice, but after three months moved to Chichester with the same purpose. Here, he made a lasting friendship with Dr John Forbes, who was later to be knighted and to become one of the founders of the British Medical Association and a prominent medical journalist. Chichester was unable to support two physicians, and Conolly moved on after one year to set up in general practice in Stratford-on-Avon.

This move was more successful, and at last he started to enjoy a modest prosperity. He began to publish and establish a reputation, and was twice mayor

Fig. 3.2. John Conolly

Fig. 3.3. Forbes B. Winslow

of the town. He was said to be "a reformer by nature and a hearty liberal in politics, ardently devoted . . . to the furtherance of every measure of progress" (Maudsley, 1866). However, after five years he was appointed to the post of Professor of the Principles and Practice of Medicine at University College, London, chiefly through the influence of Lord Brougham.

Conolly's time at University College was not very successful. He failed to establish a private practice partly because there was no hospital attached to the medical school; his lectures were often vague and discursive, and therefore poorly attended; he had a series of disagreements with the university authorities, and his suggestion that medical students should have access to the London asylums for clinical instruction was turned down. However, during this appointment he published his work on *The Indications of Insanity*.

He resigned his professorial post after three years and returned to general practice in Warwick, where he remained for the next eight years. This period was marked by financial struggle, but he continued to publish articles, and with Drs Forbes and Tweedie founded the *British and Foreign Medico-Chirurgical Review*. While at Stratford-on-Avon and Warwick, Conolly also held the post of inspecting physician to the lunatic asylums of Warwickshire. Although discouraged from doing so by his friends, in 1838 he applied for the post of Resident Physician to the Hanwell asylum, but was not appointed. He moved to Birmingham, but a year later the post again became vacant, and this time, despite his lack of experience in running an asylum, his application was successful. As an obituarist put it, "now at last, after many wanderings and much suffering, he had found the true sphere of his labours" (*Journal of Mental Science*, 1866).

He was appointed Resident Physician at Hanwell asylum in June 1839, and quickly abolished all forms of mechanical restraint. In addition to being influenced by the teachings of Pinel and Tuke, Conolly had prepared himself for reform by visiting the Lincoln asylum, where restraint had been abolished three years before, and by speaking and corresponding with Drs Charlesworth and Gardiner Hill. As Maudsley (1866) made clear, Conolly never claimed to be the originator of non-restraint. However, through its successful implementation at Hanwell where there were almost 1000 patients, Conolly showed the practicability and benefit of non-restraint in large public asylums. His powerful advocacy and ability to influence leaders of public opinion were crucial in gaining general acceptance of his reforms.

In 1842, Conolly introduced clinical medical undergraduate teaching at Hanwell asylum, and one of his first students was William Gull. He resigned his appointment at Hanwell in 1843 after a threat to place the daily administration of the asylum in lay hands. However, he continued as a visiting physician until 1852. By now, Conolly had a national reputation, had established a private practice, and was a frequent expert witness in forensic cases. In order to supplement his income, he also took in a few female patients at his Lawn House residence, and acquired interests in several other small private asylums.

Along with Dr Reed, Conolly founded the Earlswood asylum, and made a strenuous but unsuccessful attempt to establish a public asylum for the middle classes near London. He was a founder member of the British Medical Association in 1832, and was Chairman of the Association of Medical Officers of Asylums and Hospitals for the Insane in 1843 and 1851, becoming President in 1858. He was an active member of various societies throughout his life, including the Society for the Diffusion of Useful Knowledge and the Warwick and Leamington Phrenological Society. A very sociable man, he enjoyed attending meetings, lecturing and writing. Among his later publications were *On the Construction and Government of Lunatic Asylums* (1847) and *The Treatment of the Insane without Mechanical Restraints* (1856). He was an ardent Shakespearian and published *A Study of Hamlet* in 1863. He received few official awards, although was presented with a testimonial consisting of a silver group of allegorical figures together with his portrait in 1852, and in the same year the honorary degree of DCL was conferred upon him by the University of Oxford.

Maudsley (1866) wrote ambivalently of Conolly: "As a practical physician, Dr. Conolly did not specially distinguish himself, either in the exact investigation of disease, or in its treatment . . . the actual practice of his profession was not agreeable to him". According to Maudsley (1866), Conolly was "by nature passionate and impetuous", but he was also described as having an "amiable disposition, courteous manners and refined culture which distinguished him through life" (*Journal of Mental Science*, 1866).

He began to suffer increasingly from ill-health, and by 1860 was forced to retire to Lawn House. Here he continued to write and was occasionally consulted in difficult psychiatric cases. In 1866 he died following a stroke. He left a son and three daughters, two of whom married the eminent psychiatrists Henry Maudsley and Harrington Tuke.

Forbes Benignus Winslow

Dr Forbes Winslow (Fig. 3.3) was born in 1810, the ninth son of a military father. He was a descendant of Edward Winslow, one of the Pilgrim Fathers who went to America in the *Mayflower* in 1620. The family had returned to England in difficult financial circumstances after supporting the Royalists in the American War of Independence, and Winslow had to show persistence and tenacity to realise his early ambition of becoming a doctor.

He received his medical education at the Middlesex Hospital and subsequently at University College, London. In 1835 he became a member of the Royal College of Surgeons, and graduated as a Doctor of Medicine at the University of Aberdeen in 1849. In the following year he became a Fellow of the Royal College of Physicians of Edinburgh and a member of the London College in 1859, in which year he also obtained the honorary degree of DCL from the University of Oxford. He was at one time President of the Medical Society of London, and became President of the Association of Medical Officers of Asylums and Hospitals for the Insane in 1857. His political views were staunchly Conservative, and on four occasions he was asked to stand for Parliament.

Winslow had prodigious energy and paid for his medical education by acting in the evenings as a House of Commons reporter for *The Times*. He had an extensive private practice and was the proprietor of two private asylums. He had a particular interest in medicolegal issues, wrote about the plea of insanity in criminal cases, and gave evidence in a number of celebrated trials, including the McNaughton case.

He was a prolific writer of articles and books on psychiatric topics from an early age. At 21 he wrote his first work on insanity, entitled *An Essay on the Application of the Principles of Phrenology to the Elucidation and the Cure of Insanity*. Among his many publications are the books entitled *Physic and Physicians* (1839), *The Anatomy of Suicide* (1840), *On the Preservation of the Health of the Body and Mind* (1842), and *On the Obscure Diseases of the Brain, Disorders of the Mind* (1860) which passed through four editions and which he considered his *magnum opus*.

However, Winslow is best remembered as the founder and driving force behind the *Journal of Psychological Medicine and Mental Pathology*, a quarterly journal which first appeared in 1848. This was the first journal in Britain to be wholly devoted to mental illness, and unlike the *Asylum Journal*, which first appeared in 1853, it had a distinct emphasis on psychology and philosophical inquiry in relation to mental disorders (Shepherd, 1986). Winslow launched the journal with £1000 of his own money, and was the sole proprietor and editor during its existence, writing many of the articles and reviews himself. The journal ceased publication after 16 years following Winslow's serious illness. The journal reappeared in 1875 under the editorship of Winslow's son, only to fold three years later.

It has been suggested that by his journal Forbes Winslow did more than anyone else at this time to popularise the term and concept of 'psychological medicine', with all the implications of a recognised medical specialty (Hunter & Macalpine, 1963). Shepherd (1986) has provided an elegant analysis of the historical importance of Winslow and his journal.

Winslow died of renal disease on 3 March 1874, and was buried in the family vault at Epping, his brother performing the burial ceremony. Obituaries appeared in both the *Journal of Mental Science* and the *British Medical Journal*.

John Charles Bucknill

John Charles Bucknill (Fig. 3.4) was born on Christmas Day 1817, at Market Bosworth in Leicestershire, where his father practised as a surgeon. He was first educated at Rugby School under Dr Arnold, and later at the local grammar school. He became a student at University College, London, in 1835 and qualified with honours in both medicine and surgery at the University of London in 1840. He subsequently became a house surgeon under Liston at University College Hospital; after leaving there, he started in medical practice in Chelsea.

Bucknill married in 1842 and had three sons, one of whom became a colonel in the Royal Engineers, and another a QC and MP. As the result of ill-health, he was advised to leave his Chelsea practice and live in a warmer climate. This no doubt determined his application for the Devon County Asylum at Exminster, where he was appointed as the first medical superintendent in 1844 and held that position for 18 years. There, he developed residences for some of the patients outside the asylum and was much praised by his own asylum committee as well as by the Commissioners in Lunacy for this action.

He became the first editor of the *Asylum Journal of Mental Science*, and continued in this and in his asylum post until 1862, when he was appointed a Lord Chancellor's Visitor. As such, "he showed himself a thorough man of business with a rare grasp of detail; it is, in fact, as an indefatigable and fearless official that he will long be remembered with feelings of gratitude" (*Lancet*, 1897*a*). In 1858, he produced in collaboration with Hack Tuke what contemporaries felt was his greatest work, *A Manual of Psychological Medicine*. In 1859 and 1860, he published books respectively on Shakespeare's psychological and medical knowledge, and became President of the Association of Medical Officers of Asylums and Hospitals for the Insane in 1860. In 1876, he resigned his post as Lord Chancellor's Visitor and commenced private consulting practice. In the late 1870s, in conjunction with Crichton-Browne, Ferrier, and Hughlings Jackson, he brought out and edited the neurological journal *Brain*.

As well as being a member of several London clubs, including the Athenaeum and the Garrick, Bucknill was also a Fellow of the Royal Society, a justice of the peace for the County of Warwick, and a governor of Bethlem Hospital. He enjoyed literature, music and the arts, and was also fond of all outdoor sports including shooting, fishing and fox hunting. He was one of the founders of the 1st Exeter and Devonshire Rifle Volunteers, and devoted himself in his spare moments to the organisation, drilling, and other activities of the regiment. He was the first recruit to be sworn in, and stuck to the ranks throughout his connection with the regiment. He was knighted in 1894, the honour being conferred as a recognition not only of his distinction within the medical profession, but also because of his services in the matter of national defence.

He was said to be a man "of most reserved habits" and "uncommunicative" about himself (Clapham, 1897). His son, Colonel Bucknill, described him as "demonstrative in wrath: but it was not so evident when he was pleased. He was a difficult man to understand" (Clapham, 1897). An anonymous obituarist in the *British Medical Journal* (1897*a*) felt that at times he was "of far too extreme views, expressed at times in language overstrained". After a long illness, Bucknill died in Bournemouth, aged 79, on 20 July 1897, and was buried near Rugby.

David Skae

Skae (Fig. 3.5) was one of two sons of an architect and was born in Edinburgh on 5 July 1814. The family moved to St Andrews when Skae's father died,

Fig. 3.4. John C. Bucknill

Fig. 3.5. David Skae

and he was educated by his uncle, the Reverend W. Lothian. At the age of 14, he began to study in the Arts Faculty of St Andrews University, but at 16 left to work as a clerk in an Edinburgh lawyer's office. He eventually gave this up to study medicine at the University of Edinburgh and, on qualifying, settled in practice in the city.

In 1836, Skae became a Fellow of the College of Surgeons of Edinburgh and began to lecture on medical jurisprudence in the Extra-Academical Medical School there. He was also appointed surgeon to the Lock Hospital, an appointment which he held for ten years and during which time he published several papers on syphilis. In 1842, he succeeded Robert Knox as an anatomy lecturer at Edinburgh University. He was a close friend of Sir James Simpson, the eminent obstetrician.

In 1846, Skae was appointed as Superintendent at the Royal Edinburgh Asylum, a position he held until his death in 1873. In this capacity he was, through his example of humanity towards the mentally ill in his charge, to influence for the good a generation of doctors who served under him and who were later to become eminent psychiatrists themselves. He believed that the asylum should be a therapeutic environment and not simply a custodial institution, that patients should be allowed maximum freedom and treated with kindness, and that they needed to be engaged in healthy activities to distract their minds from morbid thoughts. He protested against the practice of sending patients to the asylum in irons.

In his approach to mental illness, Skae was a somaticist, defining insanity as a disease of the brain affecting the mind. In his 1863 address as President of the Medico-Psychological Association (Skae, 1863), he proposed a classification of mental illness based on the natural history of the disease. His scheme was rejected by most British psychiatrists, which may partly explain the subsequent underestimation of Skae's contribution to 19th-century psychiatry. He was also interested in forensic psychiatry and, like many of his contemporaries, was dismayed at the reception of asylum doctors' opinions in the courts of law. He wrote knowledgeably on that subject, on organic mental illness, and on the antisocial personality, and was an important teacher, initiating the first course of lectures on mental diseases at the Royal Edinburgh Asylum in 1853. Thereafter, Skae continued to lecture there every year for the next 20 years.

Skae had a pleasant and approachable personality. Clouston (1873) described him as: "A stout figure, a kindly expression, ever ready to break out into a winning smile or a jovial laugh, reassuring brown eyes, a massive head, only second to Simpson's among the Edinburgh doctors, set on a strong neck and shoulders, the impression he made on a stranger was that of one who enjoyed life and wished others to enjoy it too." In his obituary in *The Scotsman* (Clouston, 1873), he was described as "one of the most kindly and genial of men, large-hearted, sympathetic and tolerant with a refined taste and most subtle humour, a singularly clear judgement and a well-balanced mind".

He died on 18 April 1873, from oesophageal cancer, leaving a widow and five sons. Three of the sons were members of the medical profession, and two of these followed in their father's footsteps as asylum superintendents.

William Alexander Francis Browne

Dr W. A. F. Browne (Fig. 3.6) was born in Stirling, Scotland, in 1805. His father, an army officer, was drowned at sea in the same year and he was brought up by his grandfather. He was educated at Stirling High School and from there went on to study medicine at the University of Edinburgh, qualifying in 1826. While in Edinburgh, he developed an interest in phrenology and became a disciple and follower of George Combe (*Lancet*, 1885).

After qualifying as a doctor, he travelled on the Continent and resided for a time in France, where he acquired a thorough knowledge of the language and studied psychology. After an absence of several years, he returned to Scotland and in about 1830 commenced medical practice in Stirling. Soon, however, he accepted the medical superintendency of Montrose asylum, where he put into practice his theories with regard to the humane care and treatment of the mentally ill.

In 1837, he published *What Asylums Were, Are and Ought To Be*, in which he described the asylum reforms based on the principles of kindness and occupation and also reaffirmed his belief in phrenology (*Journal of Mental Science*, 1885). This book came to the attention of Mrs Elizabeth Crichton, a wealthy benefactress, who was so impressed by it that she offered Browne the post of first resident physician and medical superintendent of the Crichton Institution in Dumfries. Browne accepted the position and took up his duties in 1839. He remained there for 18 years and succeeded in establishing an enviable reputation for the Crichton as a centre of excellence for the humane care of the insane, chronicled in his annual reports. As his obituarist in the *British Medical Journal* (1885) put it: "By

Fig. 3.6. William A. F. Browne

Fig. 3.7. Charles A. Lockhart Robertson

his humane and skilful treatment he founded its connection and established its fame, he husbanded and improved its resources, and he developed it, and left it as an institution which will endure as a monument of the best work of his own most useful life.'' Like Clouston, Browne sought to reach the general public and increase their acceptance of psychiatry, using his annual reports for this purpose. He insisted on patients being occupied throughout the day, and they had to adhere to a rigid daily timetable. In 1854, he instituted a course of lectures on insanity to asylum staff – the first course of lectures given to mental nurses in Scotland.

In 1857, the Scottish Lunacy Board was instituted and Browne was appointed a Commissioner in Lunacy for Scotland; he conscientiously carried out his duties of inspecting asylums and suggesting improvements in care. The Lunacy Commission reports reflect the enormous attention to detail that the Commissioners exercised in their inspections. Browne was elected a Fellow of the Royal Society of Edinburgh and became President of the Medico-Psychological Association in 1866. In 1870, he had to resign his post as Commissioner because of blindness as the result of a carriage accident, and retired to Dumfries, where he died in 1885. His eldest son, Dr (later Sir) James Crichton-Browne, also became an eminent psychiatrist.

Charles Alexander Lockhart Robertson

Lockhart Robertson (Fig. 3.7) came from a distinguished Scottish medical family, his father being an eminent surgeon and his brother, Argyll Robertson, an eminent ophthalmologist. After studying at Edinburgh and St Andrews, he went into the Army Medical Service and became assistant surgeon to the Yarmouth Army Lunatic Asylum. He remained at Yarmouth for five years, and then resumed his medical studies by entering the University of Cambridge at the age of 26. He took a medical degree there and then worked in private practice in London until 1859, when he became the first medical superintendent of the Sussex County Lunatic Asylum. Under his care, this achieved a reputation as a model institution and was frequently visited by European alienists.

Between 1855 and 1862, he was Secretary of the Association of Medical Officers of Asylums and Hospitals for the Insane, and from 1862 to 1870, was editor of the *Journal of Mental Science* with Henry Maudsley. He became President of the Medico-Psychological Association in 1867. His literary contributions were numerous and were principally devoted to practical administrative rather than academic matters.

Although not a particularly original thinker, he is best remembered as an early advocate and pioneer of non-restraint and a supporter of the Association for the After-Care of Poor Persons Discharged Recovered from Asylums for the Insane. The chaplain of the Sussex County Asylum, Henry Hawkins (1897), has left this account of Robertson's rule: "Personally he was not very much in the wards, his visits being occasional and irregular, but the establishment was maintained in good order; and even when absent, the telegraph, it has been said, conveyed his instructions."

He married quite late in life, and for many years suffered from recurrent bouts of ill-health ('neuralgias'), from time to time being constrained to take periods of rest from work. In 1867, in association with Dr Rutherford, he translated Griesinger's book, *Mental Disease*. In 1870, he became Lord Chancellor's Visitor in Lunacy, a post he held until the year before his death. He retired owing to ill-health and died on 18 May 1897 at Exmouth.

His obituary in the *British Medical Journal* (1897*b*) described him as "very definite and dogmatic in his beliefs, and . . . in the habit of expressing them without regard to consequences . . . [He was] perhaps a little intolerant of those who differed from him." Hawkins (1897) remembered that "His remarks were somewhat caustic at times, and inclined to be very aggressive." Despite this, he was said to be (*British Medical Journal*, 1897*b*):

> "benevolent and kind-hearted, though he often covered his good deeds with a cloak of cynicism. He was essentially a clubable man and few men belonged to so many clubs in all parts of the country. He had the means to enjoy learned leisure and he followed his inclination in this direction. He was very dependent on the refinements of life."

He was also described as of a "delicate sensibility" (*British Medical Journal*, 1897*b*) and "a man of much culture . . . [with] a very large circle of friends and acquaintances . . . and during his active years was a prominent figure in social life" (*Lancet*, 1897*b*).

Daniel Hack Tuke

Daniel Hack Tuke (Fig. 3.8), the youngest son of Samuel Tuke and the great grandson of William Tuke, the founder of the Retreat, was born in York in 1827. His mother died soon after his birth. His father, who was very strict in his views of conduct, was a deeply religious man and belonged, like his ancestors, to the

Society of Friends. Tuke later regretted that his childhood had not been passed in a more joyous atmosphere. He was a delicate child and his Quaker schooling was often disrupted by illness. In 1845, when his schooling was over, he was articled to a solicitor in Bradford with a view to becoming a lawyer, but appears to have quickly lost interest in this ambition. Illness threatened and his doctor advised him to leave his employment. He spent the next year recuperating in Ventnor and Clifton, during which time he read books on philosophy and poetry.

Back in York, Tuke became friendly with Dr Thurnam, the superintendent of the York Retreat, who lent him books on insanity. In 1847, he began working as a steward in the asylum and took a keen interest in the patients. He was later to say: "Actual residence in an asylum is almost essential to a thorough understanding of the life, nightly as well as daily, of the inmates" (Ireland, 1895). He remained at the Retreat for two years, when he attended lectures on chemistry and botany, and began to frequent the wards of York Hospital.

In the spring of 1850, he went to London to study medicine at St Bartholomew's Hospital, qualifying with the MRCS in 1852. In 1853, he graduated MD at Heidelberg University, and in the same year married and went abroad to visit the asylums of Holland, Germany, Austria, and France. On his return to York, Tuke set up in medical practice. He became visiting physician to the York Dispensary and to the Retreat, and also lectured in psychology at the York School of Medicine. However, he then became ill with a pulmonary haemorrhage and was forced to give up work and move south in search of a milder climate.

He settled in Falmouth, where he lived for 15 years. When his health improved, he began to busy himself with the care of the public library, schools, and working men's clubs. He also did much literary work and maintained his interest in all things relating to psychology and the insane. In 1858, he published in conjunction with Bucknill, the *Manual of Psychological Medicine*, which remained for many years the standard work on insanity. Tuke wrote the first half of the volume – on lunacy laws, and the classification and causation of insanity – while Bucknill wrote on diagnosis, pathology, and treatment.

In 1875, his health having much improved, he moved to London and became a consultant in lunacy. He made frequent visits to Bethlem Hospital and was subsequently made a governor of it. He then became the superintendent of Hanwell asylum, but also continued to journey daily to his London consulting rooms. In 1878, his book *Insanity in Ancient and Modern Life* was published, and in 1880 he became, with Dr G. H. Savage, joint editor of the *Journal of Mental Science*, remaining so until his death. In 1881, he became President of the Medico-Psychological Association, and in the following year his book, *History of the Insane in the British Isles*, was published. In 1883, his elder son, Dr William Samuel Tuke, died after a long illness, and in the following year he visited North America, subsequently writing a book on *The Insane in the United States and Canada*. However, his most ambitious literary work was the *Dictionary of Psychological Medicine*, a magnum opus for which Tuke enlisted the services of 128 contributors, including many eminent European doctors. Tuke himself contributed 68 articles, and the whole work was completed in two years. He made a special study of moral insanity, one of his contributions to medical literature being a description of Prichard and Symonds's first recognition of this disorder. Early in his career, he had also taken a particular interest in the study of hypnotism.

In the 1890s, Tuke became an examiner in mental physiology in the University of London and a lecturer on insanity at Charing Cross Hospital. He was one of the founders and subsequently chairman of the 'After-Care Association', set up in 1879 to rehabilitate female patients discharged from asylums, back into social and domestic life. On 5 March 1895, he died of a brain haemorrhage in London and was buried in Saffron Walden.

Tuke was a kindly, genial man, much liked by his contemporaries. He was described by Ireland (1895) as being "of nervous temperament" and had "a good deal of philosophical simplicity about him". He had an extraordinary capacity for work, rising early and going to bed late, and worked right up until his last days. He was a persuasive speaker and a well-known figure at medical societies. He was fond of pictures, old engravings, and literary curiosities, had a particular interest in history, and also enjoyed entertaining at his house. His surviving son became an artist.

Tuke's particular contribution lay in emphasising the humane side of treatment, but he also had the capacity to synthesise the ideas of others. Tuke's obituarist in the *British Medical Journal* (1895) summed him up thus:

> "It is hardly necessary to say more of Dr. Tuke than he was an absolutely honest worker, a man with enthusiasm, energy, kindliness, and with the deepest feeling of his responsibility to humanity in regard to his professional work. He leaves behind him the feeling of having done a splendid life's work, and leaving a gap which at present seems impossible to be filled."

Tuke's major strength was his "persistent observation with methodical recording and arranging of facts", and he was regarded more as "a receiver and a recorder than an originator. He was the cool-eyed observer of nature, and not the far-seeing prophet" (*Lancet*, 1895).

Thomas Smith Clouston

T. S. Clouston (Fig. 3.9), who was to become the doyen of British alienists of his time, was born at Nist House, Marray, Orkney, on 22 April 1840. He was educated locally at first and then at Aberdeen's West End Academy. On leaving school, he entered the University of Edinburgh and qualified in 1860, graduating MD with a gold medal for his thesis on the nervous system of the lobster in the following year. Clouston studied under Laycock, a professor of medicine who also lectured on medical psychology, and his later writings show the strong influence of Laycock's theories of the mind.

After graduation, he worked for three years as an assistant physician under Skae at the Royal Edinburgh Asylum, where one of his colleagues was David Yellowlees. At the early age of 23, he was appointed physician superintendent of the Cumberland and Westmorland Asylum at Carlisle, where he stayed for ten years, developing his administrative talents and publishing a number of clinical observations. After Skae's death in 1873, Clouston took up the post of physician superintendent at the Edinburgh Royal Asylum, Morningside, and in 1879 became the first official lecturer on mental diseases at the University of Edinburgh, holding this post until his retirement in 1908. He was a meticulous,

Fig. 3.8. Daniel H. Tuke

Fig. 3.9. Thomas S. Clouston

disciplined doctor and under his leadership, the Royal Edinburgh Asylum thrived. Clouston ensured that his junior doctors took detailed case histories and gave strict instructions as to case-note recording. He initiated the building of Craig House, a spectacular gothic building luxuriously appointed, to cater for the upper classes. At work, Clouston could be seen attired in frock coat and striped trousers, carrying a silk hat, as he made his ward rounds.

Clouston, who was a clear and lucid teacher, an original thinker, a masterful clinician, an excellent administrator, and a prolific writer, was to have a major influence on many alienists who later achieved professional distinction in their own right. He became editor of the *Journal of Mental Science* and his *Clinical Lectures on Mental Diseases* went through six editions between 1883 and 1904. These lectures reflected Clouston's somaticist views on the nature of mental illness and theories of treatment.

Clouston was also a great populariser, seeking to reduce the stigma of mental illness and to educate the public with such books as *The Hygiene of Mind* (1906) and *Unsoundness of Mind* (1911), in which he advocated self-discipline and moderation to avert mental disintegration. Clouston methodically kept newspaper cuttings of references to asylum care, and it is obvious that he was very sensitive to the public perception of psychiatry. His annual asylum reports were regularly reviewed in the press, and Clouston sought to make the accounts both readable and instructive. He was also interested in the moral and social issues of the day, taking a prominent part in the establishment of a council of public morals in Scotland, and an interest in the questions of eugenics, marriage, education, and alcoholism. He received many honours during his lifetime, becoming President of the Medico-Psychological Association in 1888, being given the freedom of the Royal Burgh of Kirkwall in Orkney in 1908, and receiving a knighthood in 1911. He died in 1915, leaving a widow, two sons (one of whom was a humorous writer), and one daughter.

We can gain some impression of Clouston from the comments of his colleagues:

> "Clouston was a fluent and forcible speaker, often the more forcible the less sure he was of his own view, but he could always differ pleasantly and without shadow of offence. He did not suffer fools gladly." (Yellowlees, 1915)

> "No man ever lectured in a more forceful and interesting way and threw himself more zealously into this work." (Robertson, 1915)

> "Full to overflowing of facts and experience, hard perhaps to persuade, but convinced, he was ready to accept the new position. A ready writer, his tendency was perhaps to too frequent appeals to the public, but he was so fully persuaded that he had a very important message to deliver that he was bound to write." (Savage, 1915)

> "He found his life's work in combating an attitude of pessimism and agnosticism towards mental diseases which was too all prevalent, even among a large section of alienists. His method of warfare was the 'gospel of work' indefatigably pursued in the clinical study of his patients." (Macpherson, 1915)

> "The thing that struck one most was his enormous capacity for work." (Hayes Newington, 1915)

> "In private life his intimate friends were not numerous, but those admitted to his friendship generally continued in it. There was that aloofness of disposition often characteristic of greater minds which repelled mere acquaintances rather than attracted them within the sphere of intimate friendship." (*Journal of Mental Science*, 1915)

William Julius Mickle

After a distinguished career as a medical student, William Julius Mickle (Fig. 3.10) graduated MD at Toronto University in 1867. He then came to England, studied at St Thomas' Hospital and took the diplomas of MRCS and LSA in 1869. He was elected to membership of the Medico-Psychological Association in 1871, and worked as an assistant physician at Derby and Warwick asylums. It was then that he first recognised the importance of syphilis in the production of organic disease of the nervous system, and in 1876/77 he published a paper entitled "Syphilis and insanity".

In 1879, he became a member of the Royal College of Physicians and afterwards was appointed medical superintendent of Grove Hall Asylum at Bow in east London. Grove Hall was an unusual asylum with an atypical clientele, being really a private asylum that had been taken over by the East India Company for soldiers and employees of the company. The patients were chiefly old soldiers who had served abroad and who were suffering from brain disease due to syphilis, tropical diseases, or sunstroke.

Fig. 3.10. William J. Mickle

Fig. 3.11. George H. Savage

Mickle's original interest in syphilis and brain disease was further developed at Grove Hall, and resulted in a series of papers and a book on general paralysis of the insane (GPI), in which he pointed out the close relationship between this condition and syphilis. He was regarded as "a careful and reliable observer" (Mott, 1918) and his published works were described as "encyclopaedic" (Savage, 1918). His book was the most complete collection of all facts on GPI recorded by English and foreign observers up to 1886, but he also contributed to Hack Tuke's *Dictionary of Psychological Medicine* on such subjects as the use of digitalis in insanity, the treatment of acute mania, and traumatic factors in mental illness. Mickle was also interested in the relationship of mental illness to disorders of circulation and catatonia, and for many years lectured at University College and the Middlesex Hospital, London.

Mickle was described as being "very formally courteous in manner, but distant, and not given to any wide social life . . . a self-contained man" (Savage, 1918). Unmarried, and with no particular hobbies, Mickle led a busy professional life. He was an active member of the British Medical Association and of its Parliamentary Bills and Lunacy Laws Committees, became President of the Medico-Psychological Association in 1896, and later of the Neurological Society. He remained at Bow until he retired when Grove Hall closed, in 1908. After living for some years in Bayswater, he returned to stay with his sister in Canada, when his general health began to fail. He died in November 1918.

Savage (1918) summarised Mickle's contribution to psychological medicine thus:

> "Mickle was a careful observer and a most indefatigable collector and recorder, but his collection of facts was so general as to be rather a heap than an arranged group. He toiled but he hardly constructed. And now he has left very many valuable collections, from which others may select."

More charitably, Mott (1918) described Mickle as "a pioneer in recognizing the association between syphilitic lesions of the aorta and general paralysis".

George Henry Savage

George Henry Savage (Fig. 3.11) was born in 1842. His father, a Yorkshireman, ran a successful chemist's business in Brighton, and also became an alderman and a justice of the peace. Savage Senior also had a keen appreciation of science and was a regular attender at the meetings of the British Association. Savage's mother, a deeply religious woman of Scottish descent, was a keen botanist and transmitted her enthusiasm for the subject to her son.

Savage was educated in Brighton and on leaving school, went to work in his father's business. However, this type of work was not to his liking and after working as a pupil for two years at the Sussex County Hospital, he entered Guy's Hospital as a medical student in October 1861. There, he won the Treasurer's Gold Medal and graduated MB in the University of London in 1865, proceeding MD two years later. After house appointments at Guy's Hospital and the Sussex County Hospital, he worked for four years as a medical officer for a lead-mining company in Cumberland. He married in 1868, but in the following year his wife died from a pulmonary embolism, a few days after giving birth to a daughter. He remarried in 1882, and had a son.

He was appointed resident assistant medical officer to the Bethlem Royal Hospital in 1872, having previously worked at this hospital for six months in 1866 as a resident student. He became lecturer on insanity at Guy's Hospital soon after his appointment, and in 1873 was elected a member of the Medico-Psychological Association. In 1879, he was promoted to the post of physician superintendent of Bethlem, a post he held for ten years. "He was well and widely read in the literature . . . was a shrewd and careful observer . . . endowed with much common sense, and had a genial open manner, totally free from pomposity, so that he was socially one of the most popular of men" (*British Medical Journal*, 1921*a*). A popular lecturer, he wrote widely on a variety of subjects including marriage and mental illness, general paralysis of the insane, and medicolegal psychiatry. He was also a frequent contributor to the journal *Brain* and communicated regularly with neurologists such as Hughlings Jackson, Ferrier, and Bristowe. The first edition of his popular textbook *Insanity and Allied Neuroses* was published in 1884, and he wrote no less than 20 of the articles in Tuke's *Dictionary of Psychological Medicine*.

Savage was one of the earliest to recognise that general paralysis of the insane was the result of structural changes in the nervous system, and during his time at Bethlem insisted on the dictum, "show me a case of general paralysis and I shall show you a case of syphilis" (*Lancet*, 1921*b*). An avid reader, he was familiar with most British and Continental literature on insanity, kept personal notes of all cases, and made microscopic preparations of morbid material. Special features of his time at the Bethlem were his Sunday-morning ward rounds and his encouragement and close interest in the careers of his junior colleagues (Percy Smith, 1921).

He retired from Bethlem in 1889 and developed a thriving consulting practice, being frequently approached by the Home Office for an opinion on difficult psychiatric cases. He became a member of the governing body of Bethlem, and took an active interest in this institution until the end of his life. For many years, he was also a consulting physician to the Royal Institution for the Mentally Deficient at Earlswood, the Priory, Roehampton, and Chiswick House.

He was a regular attender at the meetings of many of the London medical societies and was active in the British Medical and the Medico-Psychological Associations. He was appointed co-editor of the *Journal of Mental Science* in 1878 and continued in this role until 1894. He became President of the Medico-Psychological Association in 1886, and for many years took an active role in the After-Care Association. He was also an early advocate of the cause of medical education for women. In 1912, in belated recognition of a remarkable career, he received a knighthood, and in the same year also became the first president of the newly formed Section of Psychiatry of the Royal Society of Medicine.

Savage's chief characteristics were said to be a "widespread interest, abundant energy, intense sociability, transparent candour, and whimsical humour . . . his mental activity was only equalled by his bodily activity" (Champneys, 1921). His interests included walking, mountaineering (he was Vice-President of the Alpine Club), gardening, botany, mineralogy, fishing, fencing, golf, cycling, and tennis. He was also a highly clubbable man who enjoyed entertaining and dining out, and was in great demand as an after-dinner speaker. He died on 5 July 1921, at the age of 78, following a stroke.

David Yellowlees

David Yellowlees (Fig. 3.12) was born in 1837, brought up in Stirling, and graduated in medicine at the University of Edinburgh in 1857. After an appointment as house surgeon at the Edinburgh Royal Infirmary and a period of study in Paris, he returned to the Edinburgh Royal Infirmary as an assistant to the physician Sir William Gairdner.

His first appointment in psychiatry was as assistant to Dr Skae at the Edinburgh Royal Asylum, remaining there until 1863. In that year, he became superintendent of the Glamorgan County Asylum, where he stayed for 12 years. During this period, he built up a reputation as an excellent administrator and clinician.

In 1874, Yellowlees was appointed to the post of physician superintendent of the Royal Glasgow Asylum, Gartnavel. Under him, "Gartnavel became a keen centre of psychiatric thought. His physical energy and enthusiasm, combined with a radiant optimism, infected his assistants, as well as in some measure the patients and their friends" (*Lancet*, 1921*b*). During his tenure, he lectured on insanity at the University of Glasgow and was active in a variety of medical bodies.

Yellowlees became a member of the Association of Medical Officers of Asylums and Hospitals for the Insane in 1862, and was a regular attender at its meetings, where "he generally spoke briefly and to the point, and he always carried weight" (Savage, 1921). He became president of the Medico-Psychological Association in 1890 and of the Faculty of Physicians and Surgeons of Glasgow between 1892 and 1894, and was elected honorary member of a number of foreign medical societies, including the American Medico-Psychological Association and the Moscow Society of Neurological and Mental Diseases.

Fig. 3.12. David Yellowlees

Yellowlees had a high sense of public duty, which seemed to spring from his deep religious convictions, and he took a leading part in the philanthropic life of Glasgow. He was one of the founders of the Glasgow Association for the Care of Defective and Feeble-minded Children, and was active on the board of the Association for the Relief of Incurables and Consumptives. He was a keen supporter of the Glasgow Medical Missionary Society and of rights for women and children.

Yellowlees retired from Gartnavel in 1901 because of failing eyesight. He continued to live in Glasgow until 1919, when he returned to Edinburgh to spend the last 18 months of his life. He died on 19 January 1921, in his 85th year. Menzies (1921) described Yellowlees as "a man who was imbued with all that was best in the specialty, a man of great breadth of sympathy, of high character, of great professional attainments, of social qualifications beyond the ordinary, and whose whole life was spent in doing good". The *British Medical Journal* (1921*b*) concurred: "He was highly esteemed for his strong common sense and his high sense of duty by all who knew him in connexion with public affairs, while his deep religious convictions moulded and coloured his whole life." His two sons also became distinguished psychiatrists.

Presidential themes

The presidential addresses delivered at the annual meetings of the Association of Medical Officers of Asylums and Hospitals for the Insane and the Medico-Psychological Association marked "the progress of psychiatry periodically and definitely" (Urquhart, 1898) throughout the second half of the 19th century. Such addresses allowed eminent practitioners to communicate their ideas on a variety of topics relating to mental illness, and were also a forum to discuss the major issues of the day facing asylum doctors. These published addresses thus allow important insights to be gained into the major preoccupations of the psychiatric profession during this period, and have been drawn on in the following discussion.

Challenges to the role of asylum doctors and medical recognition of the failure of asylums to live up to their early promise

The early Victorian period was a time of therapeutic optimism that the newly established public asylums, imbued with the principles of moral therapy and non-restraint which asylum doctors now claimed as their own, would inevitably lead to major improvements in the care and treatment of the mentally ill. The 1845 Act gave the medical profession a central role in this new order, and, inevitably, asylum doctors became identified with the institutions in which they worked. Thus, their inability to implement moral therapy in public asylums because of the increasing numbers of patients being admitted, combined with a lack of effective treatments, inadequate and insufficient asylum staff, and an increasing public suspicion concerning wrongful confinement, began to undermine the authority and credibility of asylum doctors.

Some presidents attempted to redress the balance by re-emphasising the importance of the asylum doctor. Laycock (1869), for example, reminded his audience that 'mad-doctors' had been instrumental in many of the improvements achieved in the treatment of the insane. Duncan (1875) reiterated this claim and, along with others such as Needham (1887) and Hayes Newington (1889), asserted that as insanity was clearly a disease, it needed to be treated by doctors on the same principles as those which regulated practice in other branches of medicine.

However, other presidents were highly critical of the way public asylums were developing, and were well aware that their early promises were not being fulfilled. There were criticisms about the pressures exerted on medical superintendents to continually expand the numbers of asylum patients. Conolly (1858), for example, complained about:

> "the Visiting Magistrates of the county of Middlesex, who are enlarging their already far too large asylums, adding wing to wing, and storey to storey, and thus constantly accumulating impediments to any proper system being pursued in them. The works, now in progress will make efficient inspection impossible, and leave the patients exposed to violences and accidents which, in turn, will become the pretexts for the revival of strait-waistcoats, and straps, and chains, and gags, and all the horrors of times thought to have gone by."

He went on to predict that the overcrowding and the poor physical conditions in such "monster asylums" would become a disgrace and that the huge size of these institutions would "inevitably lead to the frequent neglect of the attentions required by a houseful of helpless people, whose various troubles require various aid at all hours of the day and of the night". He blamed the visiting magistrates of asylums for this sorry state, whose main concern was economy, and exonerated the Commissioners in Lunacy and asylum doctors whose opinions on these matters were usually ignored.

Similarly, although Lockhart Robertson (1867) was in no doubt of the superiority of public asylums to workhouses and private dwellings for the insane poor, he advocated that asylums should accommodate no more than 800 patients, and that auxiliary asylums of an intermediate character between the workhouse and asylum should be built; he also suggested that about a quarter of asylum patients could be safety transferred to local workhouses with benefit, and that about 15% of asylum patients "might, with increased enjoyment of life, be restored to their own families, were suitable provision made for their care and maintenance". Indeed, anticipating 'community care', Lockhart Robertson felt sure that future progress in the treatment of the insane lay in the direction of increasing their liberty and home treatment.

By the mid-Victorian period, there was a clear recognition among some of the leaders of the profession that the original therapeutic aims of the public asylums had been lost and that a system of institutional psychiatry was now being practised. Boyd (1870) voiced such concern when he complained that asylums were "gradually becoming places of detention for confined lunatics rather than hospitals for the cure of the insane, which they were intended to be". Boyd suggested that whether an individual pauper was lodged in a workhouse or an asylum seemed to depend principally on the workhouse officials and on the relative costs of the two types of maintenance. Rogers (1874) also spoke out against the demands made on asylums to admit "chronic and incurable cases, and imbeciles" who were currently living in workhouses; and Parsey (1876) complained of the increasing pressures on asylums to admit "the large number of persons of diseased mind that have become a burden on the community . . . though their mental condition does not warrant so costly a form of management".

There was also an appreciation of the disadvantages of the county asylum system, and of the need for alternative services to complement it. Maudsley (1871), for example, although accepting that some patients needed to be treated in asylums, suggested that most could be managed outside. He pointed out that asylum care had a major disadvantage: "the patient's individuality is little considered; he becomes one of a crowd, the majority of whom are not expected ever to get well, and his moral treatment is little more than the routine of the establishment and the dictatorship of an attendant". Furthermore, "the confinement, the monotony, the lack of interest and occupation, the absence of family relations . . . do, after a certain time in some cases, more than counterbalance the benefit of the seclusion".

Although accepting the need for asylums, Sir James Coxe (1872), in his presidential address the following year, returned to the theme of the disadvantages of asylums. He admitted that the early hope that the establishment of asylums would produce a reduction of insanity had not been realised, and even questioned whether recoveries from mental illness which took place in these institutions resulted from treatment or occurred because of natural processes. He also questioned the propriety of detaining patients with milder forms of insanity in asylums, as the latter often had features which reinforced such illnesses, and concluded: "an asylum in itself possesses no special virtue; nor am I inclined to ascribe any particular influence to anything special in the treatment pursued in it". Rogers (1874) also warned that the bad architectural arrangements in asylums almost neutralised treatment, and suggested that less overcrowding and more "elbow room" for patients was a more effective tranquilliser than any sedative drug. Other presidents (e.g. Rayner, 1884; Hayes Newington, 1889;

Whitcombe, 1891; Baker, 1892) proposed new models for the hospital care of the mentally ill, including the provision of voluntary admission and out-patient departments.

Why did the number of asylum patients increase in the second half of the 19th century?

The reasons for the rise in the number of county asylum beds during the 19th century – from 5500 to 26 000 in England and Wales between 1847 and 1867 – exercised the minds of a number of presidents and asylum doctors, as well as the press and public, during the second half of the century. Lockhart Robertson (1867), Sir James Coxe (1872), and Rayner (1884) believed that this was not due to any actual increase of insanity, but to factors such as the transfer of patients from private dwellings, where their existence was not officially known, to public establishments where they were registered and reported, to population growth, and to the excess of asylum admissions over discharges and deaths. Sir James Coxe (1872) also suggested the following:

> ''there must be taken into consideration all the different influences which in modern society lead to persons being reckoned as lunatics, and removed as such from home. Chief among these are the facilities afforded by the poor-law for the gratuitous disposal of indigent patients in asylums; and next to these the opportunities which asylums afford of getting quit of persons who from temper, disease, vice, intemperance, or old age, have become troublesome or expensive inmates at home. Under such influences the definition of lunacy has expanded, and many a one is accordingly now treated as a lunatic who formerly would not have been regarded as coming within the meaning of the term.''

Hayes Newington (1889) agreed, and argued that the chief cause for the rise in the number of asylum patients was ''the sending to us for treatment of a number of brains that are already dead in intellect, and an equally large number of brains that are foreordained to such death, in spite of any amount of skill that the most sanguine may desire us to possess.''

The comments of Coxe and Hayes Newington give some credence to Scull's (1979) contention that ''insanity was such an amorphous, all-embracing concept, that the range of behaviour it could be stretched to encompass was almost infinite''. However, Scull's (1979) assertion that asylum doctors were reluctant to narrow the concept of insanity and were ''impelled to seek out still more cases'' in order to increase their prestige and importance, and substantiate their claims for extra resources, is more questionable. Such a hypothesis ignores the external pressure on asylums to admit patients from an increasingly complex industrial society, which Scull admits was becoming less tolerant of its more awkward and inconvenient members.

Other presidents (e.g. Harrington Tuke, 1873; Duncan, 1875; Eames, 1885) were unconvinced that factors such as the transfer of people from workhouses and more complete registration accounted for the rise in the asylum population, and advanced the theory that the incidence of insanity was truly on the increase because of stresses associated with Victorian 'civilisation'. Harrington Tuke (1873) suggested that ''higher wages, and the consequent means of undue indulgence'' as well as ''poverty and the absence of mental training'' among some of the working classes were responsible. Duncan (1875) attributed the apparent increase to a variety of factors associated with the 'New Age', including the weakening of parental authority and the loosening of the family bond. However, in Duncan's view, the evil of intemperance was the greatest cause of the increase, and he called for government legislation to reduce the number of public houses, shorten their opening hours, and force them to close on Sundays. Crichton-Browne (1878) also referred to the pressures of modern life on the human nervous system, which might predispose to all kinds of nervous disorders, as well as adversely affect the reproductive centres, resulting in the propagation of mental illness to future generations. Over a century later, Hare (1983) suggested that the rise in the asylum population might have resulted from a true increase in the incidence of schizophrenia.

Professional and public pressures on asylum doctors

Little is known about the social and professional backgrounds of most asylum doctors of the 19th century. However, Turner (1958) implies that the possibility of physical attack and the unusual stresses of asylum life meant that medical posts in asylums were far from popular with newly qualified doctors, and were not particularly well paid or regarded.

Authority and the style of management within the asylum rested firmly with the medical superintendent, who during the early Victorian period was often single handed. His role was essentially that of an administrator, and day-to-day clinical contact with his ever-expanding number of patients was inevitably limited. Medical superintendents were held accountable for everything within the confines of the asylum, and Hayes Newington (1889) suggested that one of the sources of stress on the asylum physician was the all-pervading element of responsibility for patients, ''even down to such mundane details as seeing that they have proper food, clothing and exercise''. Norman (1894) agreed:

> ''Our calling is in its nature a depressing and trying one. . . . The constant tension, the continual feeling of responsibility under which we ourselves work, are wearing on all, exquisitely so on some. The routine nature and the seeming triviality of much of our labour . . . weary us. The peculiar combination of worry and monotony which characterize asylum life often torture us. . . .''

Medical superintendents were generally required to live within the asylum grounds as part of their conditions of service, a factor conducive to both physical and social isolation from the outside world. Bucknill (1860) spoke of the sacrifice which asylum doctors made by consenting to spend their lives in asylums, ''in a morbid atmosphere of thought and feeling, a perpetual 'Walpurgis Night' of lurid delusion, the perils of which he, who walks through even the most difficult paths of sane human effort, can little appreciate''. Concern was repeatedly expressed (Bucknill, 1860; Wood, 1865; Sankey, 1868; Hack Tuke, 1881; Clouston, 1888; Hayes Newington, 1889; Norman, 1894) that such association with patients in relative seclusion imposed a severe and continuous strain on asylum doctors, and also rendered them more susceptible to mental illness.

A further cause for disquiet among these doctors was the interference by lay persons in the running of asylums. Conolly (1858) was highly critical of the governing bodies of the large county asylums, complaining that:

> "they discourage and, as far as they can, repudiate the aid of the medical officers, and disregard their advice, restricting their duties and their influence with an apparent want of discrimination between the requirements of the insane and those of mere paupers, or of prisoners in jails. . . . One result of this kind of government of lunatic asylums will, I fear, be that the best educated men of our profession will be found less and less willing to devote themselves to duties which, although among the highest that can devolve upon medical men, are not appreciated."

Sankey (1868) also complained of "the complete irresponsibility of the governing bodies of the public asylums. The Committees of Visitors, it is well known, are virtually self-elected, and have absolute and uncontrolled power over everything connected with the asylum". Crichton-Browne (1878) warned that the "presence of Poor Law Guardians on Visiting Committees will render Lunatic Asylum service more distasteful than it is now to cultivated medical men, so that the tone and status of those engaged in this service will undergo gradual deterioration".

Asylum doctors were often regarded as lowly by the public and also by some members of the medical profession. Winslow (1857) identified three factors which accounted for this low status: "The conduct of a few narrow-minded and ignorant men, who have improperly had the care of the insane, and who have, by their very questionable proceedings, in a measure degraded us all to their own ignoble level"; the law which permitted non-professional persons to have charge of the care of the insane, and which also operated prejudicially to the interests of psychological doctors; and the erroneous picture of insanity held by the public, and fostered by poets, dramatists, and novelists.

Scull (1979) has suggested a further explanation: "Close and unremitting contact with the stigmatized and powerless carries its own peculiar reward – a share of their stigma and marginality". A number of presidents recognised this point. Bucknill (1860) bemoaned:

> "Do we not sacrifice the good-will of the community, not so much for the short-comings, which in our great task are inevitable, but because the public extends its unreasonable antipathy to the insane, to all those who are connected with insanity. . . . We are part of a disagreeable subject, which the public, except when frightened from its propriety, is too happy to ignore and to forget. Our very merits place us in taboo."

Wood (1865) suggested that the reasons for the low public esteem of asylum doctors included:

> "prejudices and mistaken notions, which are, in fact, the remnants of superstition and ignorance. The ideas of former times still prevail to a great extent throughout society, nor are the members of our own profession entirely free from them."

Sankey (1868) warned:

> "There are but few rewards and distinctions within the reach of our specialty. In connecting ourselves with lunacy we are almost compelled to share the seclusion of our patients. Certainly we have to renounce our chances of many posts of professional distinction."

Laycock (1869) asserted that many people still regarded asylums as places of detention and medical superintendents as little better than gaolers, and that such popular beliefs even put off "some of the best minds of the [medical] profession" from specialising in asylum care. Even 20 years later, Hayes Newington (1889) lamented that the public perception of asylum doctors was that despite having all the facilities needed at their disposal, they had made little progress in the understanding of the nature of insanity, and had only "partially succeeded in bringing their specialty within the pale of medical science". As was pointed out by Munro (1864) and Rogers (1874), such apparent public hostility provided all the more reason to support the Association, to establish a united front among asylum doctors and to obtain for the Association "the position to which it is entitled, to be the exponent of all matters relating to our specialty" (Rogers, 1874).

Some of the presidential addresses touched on the feeling experienced by many asylum doctors of being professionally isolated from the other branches of medicine. Sankey (1868), for example, complained bitterly that: "We seem to be very Levites among our medical brethren. We cannot look to them for support, for they do not understand us." Duncan (1875) stressed the importance of maintaining a close connection between asylum doctors and other branches of scientific medicine, and Crichton-Browne (1878) suggested that collaborative research would be one method of achieving this. Despite Hack Tuke's (1881) reassurance that "medical psychology is less and less regarded as a fragment detached from the general domain of medicine", Gairdner (1882) – a professor of medicine made president of the Medico-Psychological Association – warned his audience that there was a danger of their specialty becoming "wholly divorced from the progress of medical science and of the medical act". Some 16 years later, Urquhart (1898) returned to this theme, urged that there should be closer links with other branches of the medical profession, and looked "with great hopefulness to the results of that closer contact with general hospitals which we should endeavour to bring about".

The pressures of asylum life, coupled with professional isolation, may partly explain why some of the leaders of the psychiatric profession, for example Bucknill and Maudsley, appear to have become disenchanted with such work, and sought more interesting and lucrative employment opportunities outside these institutions.

The need to improve the professional status, salaries, and conditions of service of asylum doctors and attendants

Compared with most other groups within the medical profession, and even with the relatively few alienists in private practice, asylum doctors suffered the triple penalties of low social status, financial insecurity, and poor conditions of service. Issues such as security of tenure, terms and conditions of service, and salaries and pensions of its members therefore regularly appeared in presidential addresses (e.g. Conolly, 1858; Bucknill, 1860; Kirkman, 1862; Sankey, 1868; Duncan, 1875; Crichton-Browne, 1878; Hack Tuke, 1881; Rayner, 1884; Needham, 1887). Crichton-Browne (1878) perhaps summed up the general demands of asylum doctors when he declared that: "Independence of action, fixity of tenure, and security of pension are what asylum medical officers are entitled to ask, not only with a view to their own comfort, but with an eye to the welfare of their patients and the claims of science".

Despite these demands, the professional and financial status of asylum doctors does not appear to have materially improved by the end of the 19th century, and they remained a relatively stigmatised medical group. The decline in the private 'trade in lunacy' from around the middle of the century reduced opportunities for public asylum doctors to transfer to the more lucrative and tranquil pastures of the private sector, and very few could hope to aspire to the post of Commissioner in Lunacy (Bynum, 1983). Indeed, Russell (1988) paints a dreary picture of demoralisation and isolation: medical superintendents who had reached an impasse in their careers, from which most were unable to extricate themselves; and other asylum doctors – some very experienced – who were poorly paid and with only slender hopes of advancement, spending their days fruitlessly dissecting post-mortem brains and administering routine medication.

Some presidents also spoke out on behalf of asylum attendants, and the need to improve their wages and conditions of service (Conolly, 1858; Lalor, 1861; Hack Tuke, 1881; Eames, 1885). Such demands were perhaps dictated not only by altruism, but also by the realisation that the smooth and efficient running of a large asylum required the co-operation of a well disciplined and motivated work force of attendants. Turnover of attendants in asylums was in fact often rapid (Russell, 1988), no doubt because of the arduous nature of the work, the long and unsocial hours, and the poor pay. However, Murray Lindsay (1893) was highly critical of the Association for not having done more on behalf of asylum attendants:

> "But what, I may ask, is the Association doing to improve their position and emoluments? Very little, it seems to me. I am well aware that the . . . wages of attendants have here and there gone up, but without much encouragement or help from the Association."

Beveridge Spence (1899) returned to this theme when he contrasted the unfavourable pay, poor pensions, and inferior prospects for advancement of asylum attendants with those of prison warders.

There were also frequent calls for an expansion of the numbers of asylum medical and attendant staff to keep pace with the growth in the asylum population, and also to allow doctors more time for scientific research into the causes of mental illness and its treatment (Duncan, 1875; Rayner, 1884; Eames, 1885; Yellowlees, 1890; Murray Lindsay, 1893; Beveridge Spence, 1899).

Law and psychiatry

During the 19th century, the interface between the law and psychiatry was an area of considerable friction between lawyers, journalists, and the public on the one hand, and asylum doctors on the other (Smith, 1981). Medicolegal concerns which frequently surfaced in presidential addresses were: issues of wrongful confinement, procedures of certification, and the lack of conformity between doctors and lawyers in the legal definition of insanity, particularly in relation to the insanity plea and the boundary between mental illness and criminal responsibility. Kirkman (1862) protested against "hazy legislation" in the area of the lunacy laws, "which would hazardously interfere in purely medical questions and encroach upon the full prerogative of medical men to judge of mental sanity," and Laycock (1869) perhaps expressed the general feeling of asylum doctors about their vulnerable position when he declared that:

> "Whether you restrain the personal freedom of the insane in the interests of society, or plead for a kindly and charitable consideration of them in the interests of justice and mercy, you are held to be equally in the wrong."

The threat of wrongful confinement was an abiding Victorian fear and was the subject of novels such as *Hard Cash*, written by Charles Reade, a friend and collaborator of Charles Dickens, and published in 1863 (Beveridge & Renvoize, 1988). Most cases of alleged wrongful confinement involved the affluent, and critics therefore tended to concentrate their attacks on private asylums and doctors, whereas public asylums were frequently ignored (McCandless, 1981). A number of presidents (Hastings, 1859; Bucknill, 1860; Munro, 1864; Wood, 1865; Rogers, 1874; Fielding Blandford, 1877; Crichton-Browne, 1878; and Lush, 1879) attempted to allay this public fear by denying that wrongful confinement was common. Wood (1865) also complained that public suspicion about the motives of asylum doctors often resulted in their reluctance to diagnose and treat patients showing early signs of mental illness, to the detriment of the patients and also their families.

Sir Charles Hastings (1859) expressed criticism about the way the law impeded early treatment of the mentally ill by not permitting voluntary admission to asylums. Boyd (1870) and Rogers (1874) agreed, Boyd (1870) pointing out that by the time asylum patients were admitted, they had passed the acute and most curable stage of the disorder, and were often in a very feeble and bad state of health, usually attributable to neglect and improper treatment. Rayner (1884) was also critical of the system of certification, which frequently led to delays in the admission of mentally ill patients to asylums, even occasionally resulting in suicides, homicides, and other criminal acts, he claimed.

However, legal and public concerns about wrongful confinement and certification procedures found expression in the Lunacy Act 1890, which tightened even more the legal framework in which asylum doctors worked. This "triumph of legalism" (Jones, 1972) emphasised custodialism and imposed a rigid system of certification, which discouraged early diagnosis and treatment.

Although the number of such cases was relatively small, perhaps the greatest medicolegal concern of asylum doctors in the second half of the 19th century was the question of crime in relation to insanity. As Smith (1981) has described, the newly emerging psychiatric profession was at a considerable disadvantage in a court-room, compared with lawyers, when dealing with the issue of criminal responsibility. Asylum doctors had no agreed conceptual framework for the diagnosis and classification of mental illness and were unable to demonstrate any underlying physical basis to the conditions which they described in court. They were thus open to the accusation of being biased in favour of diagnosing mental illness when it did not exist, and also of being deceived by simulation. Also, public court-room disagreements between asylum doctors on whether or not mental illness was present in the accused inevitably undermined the credibility of these 'expert' witnesses. The language and milieu of the court-room was that of the lawyer and not the doctor, and asylum doctors consequently had considerable difficulty in communicating their ideas in this formidable setting. Finally, few doctors had sufficient training and experience to cope with counsel's incisive cross-examination of their evidence. Any rejection of individual medicopsychological evidence also had the unfortunate effect of appearing to undermine asylum doctors' professional expertise in other areas of mental illness.

Sir Charles Hastings (1859) admitted that the connection between crime and insanity was intricate to unravel, that knowledge on the subject was imperfect, and that there were sometimes ambiguities in the medical testimony in such cases, which led the public to place less reliance on medical evidence than it deserved. Sir James Coxe (1872) succinctly summed up the dilemma, as seen by most asylum doctors:

> "It is a matter of extreme difficulty to determine where sanity ends and insanity begins; and it is remarkable that, although it is generally considered to be the duty of the physician to fix that point, it is, nevertheless, the lawyer who decides the question whenever anything more than the mere liberty of the patient is involved. In fact, the lawyer then sits in judgement on the physician, and determines, or directs the jury to determine, whether the acts of the patient, as observed and reported by the physician, afford proof of sanity or insanity."

Rogers (1874) concurred: "the diagnosis and definition of insanity, instead of being treated as a purely medical question, has been a sort of battle field, or at least neutral ground, between the lawyers and doctors".

Skae (1863) advocated that members of the Association should use all their energies and influence to bring about a revision of the law regarding insanity, so as to get the distinctions and definitions of lawyers in conformity with theirs, that is, "in conformity with nature and facts". Rogers (1874) agreed: "It is time that we made an effort to claim for the profession of medicine the right to determine what does and what does not constitute insanity, whilst we leave to the lawyers the legal questions affecting the insane". Sankey (1868) also proposed that doctors should be exempt from cross-examination in the witness box because: "It is well known . . . that the whole process of cross-examination is mere trickery, a carefully laid pitfall; it cannot elicit truth, and is as often intended to confound it". Similar sentiments were expressed almost 20 years later by Needham (1887), who suggested that part of the explanation for the continuing low esteem of asylum doctors was that in court they were frequently "brow-beaten by opposing counsel and depreciated by the bench and juries".

The use of such severe language directed against the judiciary may have been prompted not only by feelings of injustice on behalf of the mentally ill found guilty of crime, but also by frustration at the complete lack of autonomy afforded to asylum doctors as medical witnesses in the court-room, which appeared to confirm their inferior status compared with doctors in other branches of medicine (Smith, 1981).

Medical education

Few mid-19th-century doctors – even those employed in the newly established county asylums – had received any formal undergraduate or postgraduate training in psychiatry, and one of the aims of the Medico-Psychological Association was the need to remedy this situation. By such educational initiatives, it was hoped that general knowledge of insanity and standards of clinical practice would improve, and no doubt it was also believed that both the status of asylum doctors and recruitment into the new specialty would be enhanced.

Thus, Conolly (1858) supported "the desirableness of affording opportunities of clinical instruction to medical students in all our large asylums, during some portion of each year", a recommendation endorsed by Lalor (1861) and by Wood (1865). Some early progress was in fact made in respect of undergraduate teaching: for example, Maudsley persuaded the Senate of the University of London to allow medical students to attend recognised asylums in London for three months' clinical instruction on a voluntary basis, and several of the larger medical schools appointed lecturers in the subject. However, Sankey (1868) demanded that attendance of medical students at such lectures should be compulsory, and that asylum doctors should give the lectures. Laycock (1869) returned to this theme, suggesting the establishment of an educational committee of the Association to press for inclusion of the study of "mental medicine" in the medical undergraduate curriculum.

Rogers (1874) reasoned that the establishment of asylums as "schools for the clinical study of insanity" would be "the best way of admitting light" into such institutions, and the presence of medical students would also encourage asylum doctors to strive for high standards of practice. Duncan (1875) pointed out the inconsistency of allowing registered doctors to be legally entitled to sign 'certificates of insanity', irrespective of their knowledge of the subject. Crichton-Browne (1878) suggested that the conversion of "asylums into clinical schools to a far greater extent than has yet been attempted" would reduce the estrangement between asylum doctors and the rest of the medical profession, and that the adoption of a more scientific approach to teaching would result in the asylum wards being "thronged with eager students". The importance of the *Journal of Mental Science* in bringing scientific work before asylum doctors was acknowledged by Hack Tuke (1881), but he also spoke of the need for the Association to enlighten the public about mental illness as well.

The need for the compulsory inclusion of lectures on mental illness at medical undergraduate level was further emphasised by Eames (1885), Needham (1887), Hayes Newington (1889), and Yellowlees (1890). However, by the time of Whitcombe's address in 1891, this particular battle had been won, as the General Medical Council (GMC) began to include psychological medicine in the list of compulsory subjects for education and examination. Whitcombe hoped that the GMC's decision would "result in an increasing supply of ardent workers in the specialty, some of whom may possibly attempt to allay the thirst which is arising for more scientific knowledge in our department".

Conolly (1858) had recommended in his address that candidates for a medical appointment in an asylum should have attended a course of instruction on the subject of insanity, and have received a certificate of attendance. In 1885, the Association instituted an examination for a Certificate of Efficiency in

Psychological Medicine which asylum doctors were encouraged to sit, and medical superintendents of the future tended to be recruited from successful candidates. Murray Lindsay (1893) could later confidently claim that:

> "[whereas] formerly it was not an unusual thing to hear ourselves sneeringly called 'mad doctors', who in the opinion of an ignorant and prejudised public were considered a set of specialists only half-educated . . . I venture without fear of contradiction to assert that there is no public service . . . which contains a higher or even so high a proportion of men who have distinguished themselves. This should, once and for all, dispose of the taunt occasionally thrown at us that our specialty is filled and recruited by inferior men."

However, Norman (1894) was much less confident about the status of asylum doctors, and suggested that the specialty would not

> "acquire its due authority until it insists upon the thorough education of its members and till it enforces proper qualifications for the holders of important lunacy appointments. . . . Asylums should be officered, in the first instance, by highly-qualified young men well grounded in the most modern methods of research, and these men should be kept up to their work by examinations through which it would be necessary to pass before attaining a higher grade. The result of this would be to weed out insufficient men if such got into the service, and to prevent men who did not take enough interest in their specialty to work at it thoroughly from rising to the best positions through mere seniority. It would make promotion a question of capacity, not of chance. The work of education in psychiatry is the most useful object to which our Association can devote itself."

This constant reference to men reflected the fact that the asylum medical profession remained almost exclusively male until the end of the 19th century, and within the asylum, as in most other areas of Victorian society, women were expected to assume a more subordinate role as the superintendent's wife, matron, or nursing attendant. Showalter (1981) has explored how this male dominance may have affected the perception of asylum doctors towards mental illness in women during this period.

As mentioned above, there was also a growing recognition that the Association had a responsibility for improving the education of asylum attendants. This was partly out of self-interest, for as Munro (1864) pointed out, asylum doctors were:

> "very much the victims of the conduct of attendants. Inquests and trials now and then occur at which we find ourselves in that position, and I think it would be a great gain for us, as well as a great mercy for our poor patients, if we could, in some way or other, raise the standard of attendants."

Almost 30 years later, Whitcombe (1891) had to admit that "every medical man will, I think, acknowledge that good nursing is his chief agent in the treatment of disease". The introduction in 1891 by the Association of an examination to test the proficiency of asylum nurses gave tangible evidence of the importance which this body attached to the professional education of this group of asylum staff. In the first year of the examination certificates were granted to 106 nurses, but this figure had risen to 594 in 1898. However, Beveridge Spence (1899) expressed concern about the difficulties of recruiting "the right sort of persons'' to become asylum nurses and also of keeping them in service once they were trained. He suggested improved pension schemes and gratuities for nurses ''as an inducement to enter and remain in the asylum service''.

Treatment

The accumulation of patients with chronic disorders, combined with overcrowding and staff shortages, effectively precluded the application of the principles of moral treatment within the public asylums, and led to a growing reliance on the use of drugs. Their use may also have been partly dictated by the need for asylum doctors to establish their scientific credentials with the rest of the medical profession and the public at large. However, examination of the presidential addresses reveals that, by the 1870s, leaders of the asylum doctors were fairly sceptical of the efficacy of chemotherapy in the treatment of psychiatric illness.

Maudsley (1871), in particular, expressed considerable caution:

> ''it seems to me that we are yet grievously in want of exact information with regard to the real value of sedatives in the treatment of insanity. . . . In all cases my aim is to dispense with sedatives as far as I can; and it often seems to me that the patient begins to improve when he begins to do without them and not in consequence of them.''

Maudsley called for more ''exact observation'' on the use of drugs in the treatment of the insane, and suggested that ''no one so far as I know has ever yet tried the experiment of treating one case of acute insanity without giving any sedative whatever, and of treating another case, as nearly like it as possible, with sedatives, and of observing the results''. Rayner (1884) concurred, admitting that: ''Our progress in treatment . . . would appear to have been more conspicuous on the negative than the positive side'', and pointed to the serious side-effects of many drugs in psychiatric use. Sir James Coxe (1872) was also doubtful about the value of drugs in promoting cures, and, along with Rogers (1874), stressed the importance of moral treatment in the management of the mentally ill.

As well as casting doubt on the value of the newer drugs such as bromide, Hack Tuke (1881) also questioned the effectiveness of other treatments such as electricity, the Turkish bath, and the wet pack. He admitted: ''It must be frankly granted that Psychological Medicine can boast, as yet, of no specifics, nor is it likely, perhaps, that such a boast will ever be made.'' He warned that:

> ''the humane treatment of the insane may have its ebb as well as its flow; that so far from its being true that there is a constant and certain tendency to humanity, there is also a strange tendency to relapse into inhuman ways. Vigilance is and always will be required, for if it be allowed to slumber, we but too well know that there is only one direction in which things will go when left to themselves – and that is down hill.''

Even those with more enthusiasm for the use of drugs recognised their limitations. Browne (1866), for example, advocated an eclectic approach: ''the man of one remedy or class of remedies, or who elects such to the undue disparagement or disuse of others, is nearly as rash and in as great danger of defeat as he who fights his antagonist with one hand, or as the physician with no remedy at all''. Harrington Tuke (1873) admitted that ''the indiscriminate administration of medicine is useless. Medical treatment is only valuable, when based upon sound reasoning, conjoined with prolonged experience''. Needham (1887), although stressing the advantages of drugs, particularly in the control of excitement, also recognised the importance of moral treatment. Yellowlees (1890) concurred: ''the medicinal and the moral treatment must go together, else the patient is culpably maltreated''; and he concluded that ''the majority of [asylum] patients require no medicinal treatment''.

Research

The early Victorian era was a time of immense confidence that medical science would soon unravel the causes of disease, and asylum doctors were no less imbued with this spirit of optimism than those in other disciplines. Indeed, the belief of asylum doctors that insanity, like other diseases, had an underlying physical aetiology, and that they alone were competent to diagnose, treat, and investigate mental illness, was fundamental to their claim to be the supreme authority in this field.

Asylum doctors spent considerable time and effort in performing post mortems in the hope of identifying the structural lesions underlying mental illness (Russell, 1988). Savage (1886), for example, had spent 14 years persistently examining pathological sections, and ''Without wishing to discourage younger men from following up this line of work,'' he admitted that:

> ''without learning very much from the sections, I think I have learnt a good deal while cutting them, and thinking over them, and the cases from which they were derived. . . . We are groping in the dark for what we do not yet know. . . . There is at present a very deep ditch of ignorance between us and the true pathology, and for that matter, physiology of mind.''

Such research approaches were indeed ultimately to prove sterile, and disenchantment began to set in when the immense efforts were not rewarded with success. Part of the explanation for this failure lay in the professional isolation of asylum doctors, who, although working assiduously in remote institutions, were cut off from scientific research centres and cross-fertilisation of ideas. Whereas in Germany and Austria, psychiatry and neurology were to meet in the mid-19th century to form the rich neuropsychiatric tradition of Griesinger, Wernicke, Krafft-Ebing, Meynert, and Korsakoff (Bynum, 1985), no such fusion of ideas occurred in Britain. The one creative link between neurologists, physiologists, and psychiatrists – at the West Riding Lunatic Asylum of the 1860s and 1870s, under the leadership of James Crichton-Browne (Chapter 25) – was eventually broken, and neurology and psychiatry went their separate ways (Bynum, 1985).

This pattern of early optimism, followed by the realisation that scientific progress in psychiatry would be slow, is reflected in some of the presidential addresses. Browne (1866), referring to the newly inaugurated Medico-Psychological Association, confidently asserted that:

> "We can no longer be mistaken for a mere friendly club or a mutual defence society. We may now claim as among our objects the investigation of all subjects bearing upon the science of mind in connection with health and disease."

Sir Charles Hastings (1859) expressed confidence that knowledge of mental illness would grow in the future:

> "The brain being the instrument by which all mental manifestations are displayed, we are led to the anticipation, that ultimately, by aid of the microscope, we may be able to trace changes in its minute structure, which may lead to further advances in the pathology of this disease."

He also suggested that the possible aetiological role in mental illness of such factors as intemperance, tobacco, and poverty, the relationship between crime and insanity, and the development of statistical inquiries into both the causes and treatment of these disorders, would be suitable topics for scientific examination. He believed that such studies might be fit subjects for reports by committees of the Association.

However, Maudsley (1871) was much more cautious and suggested that the proper function of mental science "for some time to come must be to learn rather than to teach, to practise observation until it has acquired much more exact data than it is yet in possession of". He warned that "it is to be feared that rather loose assertions are sometimes made confidently, as if they were well-established facts of observation, when they perhaps have no better foundation than conjecture". Crichton-Browne (1878) also had to admit that scientific progress in the field of mental illness was sluggish compared with that in other areas of medicine, and that the Association should "by all means at its power, promote scientific research". What was needed, according to Crichton-Browne, was "the fusion of the two great elements recognised in the name of this Association, the medical and the psychological . . . [and advance] on both these lines of study . . . if we are to attain to greater precision and success in the diagnosis, prognosis and treatment of insanity."

A few presidents suggested ways in which research could be encouraged. As Laycock (1869), Duncan (1875), and Crichton-Browne (1878) pointed out, although the public asylums had the necessary facilities for the scientific study of mental illness, there was an obvious lack of asylum doctors scientifically trained for the task. Crichton-Browne's answer was that asylum and other appropriately trained doctors should collaborate on research, and that the Association should not only provide a medium through its journal for the publication of results, but should also sponsor research from its own funds, or seek funding for researchers from other sources. Hayes Newington (1889) also advocated the development of small specialised ("educational") hospitals for the mentally ill linked to medical schools, in which "the advance of science shall be the guiding principle".

However, by the last decade of the century, there was a recognition of the immensity of the task confronting the researcher into mental illness. Yellowlees (1890) suggested that the failure of asylum doctors to cure many of their patients and to discover the causes of insanity resulted not from "neglect or incapacity, but from the very nature of the malady''. Similarly, although advocating the appointment of full-time researchers into mental illness, McDowall (1897) uttered a cautious and realistic note about the likely results of such work: ''The subject is so vast, and the difficulties are so overwhelming, that only at long intervals of time can we expect very brilliant results. . . . We must not expect too much; we must not be over sanguine''. He warned that the application of scientific methods to mental illness often led to disappointing results; thus asylum doctors ''came in time to place no reliance on reported discoveries . . . and in our disappointment we are apt to run to the extreme of renouncing belief in any kind of scientific work''.

Prevention of mental illness

The lack of effective treatments and the failure of research efforts to identify the underlying causes of mental illness encouraged some asylum doctors to look away from asylum-based solutions and more towards the possible prevention of these disorders. Sir James Coxe (1872), for example, suggested that asylums were the antidote provided by the state ''to neutralise the effects of its neglect'', and that these institutions had done nothing to reduce insanity. He also complained that members of the Association had concentrated too much on providing asylum care and not enough on prevention of mental illness through improved education of the public, with greater emphasis on moral and physical training. This educational approach was supported by Harrington Tuke (1873) and by Duncan (1875), who also advocated government legislation to limit the number of licensed public houses and their opening hours, to overcome ''the master evil of intemperance''. Crichton-Browne (1878) asserted that:

> ''the medical psychologist of the future cannot be confined to his asylum wards. It must be his to walk abroad and anticipate disease by throwing the weight of his experience and wisdom into the scales in favour of purity and truth in all questions of personal and social ethics.''

Rayner (1884) also advised that efforts in the direction of the prevention of insanity ''should be recognised as a fundamental duty by every alienist physician'', and Whitcombe (1891) advocated a health educational approach to forestall mental illness.

However, other presidents (e.g. Bucknill, 1860) were more doubtful about the effectiveness of prevention. Maudsley (1871) concluded that the subject ''is so wide and so beset with difficulties, as to render it a hard matter to treat it with the exactness which would give scientific value to the discussion''. However, this did not prevent him from suggesting that those with an inherited predisposition to insanity should be encouraged to develop will-power and self-control, and should be taught that ''moral laws are laws of nature'' which cannot be broken without disastrous consequences. Although agreeing that some cases of mental illness might be preventable, Clouston (1888) suggested that this was impossible in other cases because their ancestry had ''transgressed the laws of nature in their modes of life or in their sexual unions, and the progeny must pay the penalty of mental death to stop a bad mental stock''. This later emphasis on the role of heredity in the aetiology of mental illness also provided a plausible scientific hypothesis to explain why the asylum system and asylum doctors had apparently failed to achieve much progress in the subject.

Hayes Newington (1889) also sounded a cautionary note when he warned his audience:

> "It is not exactly our business to go further than we have done in the direction of preventing the spread of insanity in the population as a whole. We have lifted our voices in serious warning, and have denounced certain risks; but while the public will persist in intermarrying, in marrying and giving in marriage individuals who either in person or by heredity are in danger of handing on insanity; while the public persists in straining the endurance of frail and unstable brains, by over-indulgences in every direction, we can do but little more."

However, he did advocate the large-scale development of out-patient departments to encourage people with early psychiatric symptoms to seek speedy treatment so that any illness could be prevented from passing beyond the initial stages.

Conclusions

How far had the original aims of the Association of Medical Officers of Asylums and Hospitals for the Insane and the Medico-Psychological Association been met, by the end of the 19th century? Sadly, analysis of the presidential addresses suggests that two of the three objectives – those of improvement of asylums and hospitals for the insane, and of acquisition and diffusion of a more extended knowledge of insanity and its treatment – were not achieved.

The presidential addresses document a declining standard of care within the public asylums. The early optimism and confidence following the 1845 Act gradually faded, and British psychiatry took on an increasingly institutional and bureaucratic form of custodial care. Attempts to implement moral therapy and non-restraint were defeated by the inexorable rise in the asylum population, the accumulation of chronic cases who were beyond any form of therapeutic help, and the lack of sufficient numbers of medical and attendant staff.

The main body of the psychiatric profession came to be identified with the remote institutions in which they worked. Their isolated base inevitably bred a degree of insularity and limitation of vision, but also effectively cut off asylum doctors from the rest of the medical profession and from the potential influence of fresh ideas. For the most part, asylum doctors concentrated on practical and administrative matters, and eschewed new research possibilities and psychological theories. Asylum research focused almost exclusively on patho-anatomical studies, and there were few attempts to integrate psychiatry with the fast developing disciplines of neurology, neurophysiology, and psychology. Those new medical treatments which were in fact introduced proved to be ineffective.

Although the Medico-Psychological Association played an important role in establishing the study of psychiatry within the undergraduate medical curriculum, public knowledge of insanity remained low and its attitude towards the mentally ill unenlightened. The public, and even some members of the medical profession, continued to be suspicious of the motives of asylum doctors and retained a peculiar fear of most things psychiatric.

Thus, at the end of the 19th century, British psychiatry had reached a low ebb in its history. It would be simplistic, though, to ascribe this state of affairs solely to the failure of asylum doctors and the Medico-Psychological Association. As Bucknill (1860) had observed, Victorian society was content to ignore the problem of mental illness once the public asylum system had been established. Furthermore, both authority and the public at large seemed impervious to the unique professional pressures exerted on asylum doctors and attendants.

It would also be misleading to assume that all asylum doctors were complacent and accepting of the Victorian asylum system. As the presidential addresses show, there was a growing recognition of the deficiencies of these institutions as well as suggestions for their improvement. Possible psychiatric initiatives outside the asylums also began to be advocated. Indeed, it is ironic that a preventative approach to mental illness, which some 19th-century asylum doctors recommended but which for so long has been derided and neglected by British psychiatrists, should now be the subject of re-examination (e.g. Newton, 1988; Cooper & Helgason, 1989).

Acknowledgement

I am very grateful to Dr A. W. Beveridge for his helpful comments on the manuscript.

References

ALLDERIDGE, P. (1985) Bedlam: fact or fantasy? In *The Anatomy of Madness, Volume II, Institutions and Society* (eds W. F. Bynum, R. Porter & M. Shepherd), pp. 17–33. London: Tavistock.

ASHTON, T. S. (1988) *The Industrial Revolution 1760–1830*. Oxford: Oxford University Press.

ASYLUM JOURNAL OF MENTAL SCIENCE (1855*a*) Transactions of the Annual Meeting of the Association of Medical Officers of Asylums and Hospitals for the Insane, held at Freemasons' Tavern, June 22nd, 1854. *Asylum Journal of Mental Science*, **1**, 83–88.

—— (1855*b*) Officers for the Year 1854–55. *Asylum Journal of Mental Science*, **1**, 223–224.

—— (1856) Rules of the Association of Medical Officers of Asylums & Hospitals for the Insane, Adopted at the Annual Meeting, 19th July, 1855. *Asylum Journal of Mental Science*, **2**, 124–126.

BAKER, R. (1892) Presidential Address. *Journal of Mental Science*, **38**, 487–493.

BEST, G. (1988) *Mid-Victorian Britain 1851–75*. London: Fontana.

BEVERIDGE, A. & RENVOIZE, E. (1988) The presentation of madness in the Victorian novel. *Psychiatric Bulletin*, **12**, 411–414.

BEVERIDGE SPENCE, J. (1899) Presidential address. *Journal of Mental Science*, **45**, 635–657.

BOYD, R. (1870) Presidential address. *Journal of Mental Science*, **17**, 315–320.

BRIGGS, A. (1985*a*) *A Social History of England*. Harmondsworth: Penguin.

—— (1985*b*) *Victorian Cities*. Harmondsworth: Penguin.

BRITISH MEDICAL JOURNAL (1874) Obituary of Forbes Winslow. *British Medical Journal*, *i*, 366.

—— (1885) Obituary of W. A. F. Browne. *British Medical Journal*, *i*, 568–569.

—— (1895) Obituary of D. H. Tuke. *British Medical Journal*, *i*, 565–566.

—— (1897*a*) Obituary of Sir John Charles Bucknill. *British Medical Journal*, *ii*, 255.

—— (1897*b*) Obituary of C. A. L. Robertson. *British Medical Journal*, *i*, 1385–1386.

—— (1921*a*) Obituary of Sir George Savage. *British Medical Journal*, *ii*, 98–99.

—— (1921*b*) Obituary of David Yellowlees. *British Medical Journal*, *i*, 177.

BROWNE, W. A. F. (1866) Presidential address. *Journal of Mental Science*, *12*, 309–327.

BUCKNILL, J. C. (1860) Presidential address. *Journal of Mental Science*, **7**, 1–23.

BYNUM, W. F. (1983) Psychiatry in its historical context. In *Handbook of Psychiatry, Volume 1, General Psychopathology*, (eds M. Shepherd & O. L. Zangwill), pp. 11–38. Cambridge: Cambridge University Press.

—— (1985) The nervous patient in eighteenth- and nineteenth-century Britain: the psychiatric origins of British neurology. In *The Anatomy of Madness, Volume I, People and Ideas* (eds W. F. Bynum, R. Porter & M. Shepherd), pp. 89–102. London: Tavistock.
CHAMPNEYS, F. (1921) Obituary of Sir George Savage. *British Medical Journal*, *ii*, 174.
CLAPHAM, C. (1897) Obituary of Sir John Charles Bucknill. *Journal of Mental Science*, **43**, 885–889.
CLOUSTON, T. S. (1873) Obituary of David Skae. *Journal of Mental Science*, **19**, 323–324.
—— (1888) Presidential address. *Journal of Mental Science*, **34**, 325–348.
CONOLLY, J. (1858) Presidential address. *Journal of Mental Science*, **5**, 71–78.
COOPER, B. & HELGASON, T. (1989) *Epidemiology and the Prevention of Mental Disorders*. London: Routledge.
COXE, J. (1872) Presidential address. *Journal of Mental Science*, **18**, 311–333.
CRICHTON-BROWNE, J. (1878) Presidential address. *Journal of Mental Science*, **24**, 345–373.
DIGBY, A. (1985) *Madness, Morality and Medicine. A Study of the York Retreat 1796–1914*. Cambridge: Cambridge University Press.
DUNCAN, J. F. (1875) Presidential address. *Journal of Mental Science*, **21**, 313–338.
EAMES, J. A. (1885) Presidential address. *Journal of Mental Science*, **31**, 315–327.
FIELDING BLANDFORD, G. (1877) Presidential address. *Journal of Mental Science*, **23**, 309–324.
FOUCAULT, M. (1967) *Madness and Civilization: A History of Insanity in the Age of Reason*. London: Tavistock.
GAIRDNER, W. T. (1882) Presidential address. *Journal of Mental Science*, **28**, 321–332.
HACK TUKE, D. (1881) Presidential address. *Journal of Mental Science*, **27**, 305–342.
HARE, E. (1983) Was insanity on the increase? *British Journal of Psychiatry*, **142**, 439–455.
HARRINGTON TUKE, T. (1873) Presidential address. *Journal of Mental Science*, **19**, 327–340.
HASTINGS, C. (1859) Presidential address. *Journal of Mental Science*, **6**, 3–13.
HAWKINS, H. (1897) A reminiscence of the late Dr. C. Lockhart Robertson. *Journal of Mental Science*, **43**, 677–678.
HAYES NEWINGTON, H. (1889) Presidential address. *Journal of Mental Science*, **35**, 293–315.
—— (1915) Obituary of Sir Thomas Smith Clouston. *Journal of Mental Science*, **61**, 495–496.
HUNTER, R. & MACALPINE, I. (1963) *Three Hundred Years of Psychiatry, 1535–1860*. London: Oxford University Press.
IRELAND, W. W. (1895) Obituary of D. H. Tuke. *Journal of Mental Science*, **41**, 377–386.
JONES, K. (1972) *A History of the Mental Health Services*. London: Routledge & Kegan Paul.
JOURNAL OF MENTAL SCIENCE (1865) Rules of the Medico-Psychological Association. *Journal of Mental Science*, **11**, 396–397.
—— (1866) Obituary of Dr. J. Conolly. *Journal of Mental Science*, **12**, 147–149.
—— (1874) Obituary of Forbes Benignus Winslow. *Journal of Mental Science*, **20**, 165–166.
—— (1885) Obituary of W. A. F. Browne. *Journal of Mental Science*, **31**, 149–150.
—— (1915) Obituary of Sir Thomas Smith Clouston. *Journal of Mental Science*, **61**, 333–338.
KIRKMAN, J. (1862) Presidential address. *Journal of Mental Science*, **8**, 311–321.
LALOR, J. (1861) Presidential address. *Journal of Mental Science*, **7**, 318–325.
LANCET (1885) Obituary of W. A. F. Browne. *Lancet*, *i*, 499.
—— (1895) Obituary of D. H. Tuke. *Lancet*, *i*, 718–719.
—— (1897*a*) Obituary of Sir John Charles Bucknill. *Lancet*, *ii*, 228–229.
—— (1897*b*) Obituary of C. A. L. Robertson. *Lancet*, *i*, 1568.
—— (1921*a*) Obituary of Sir George Henry Savage. *Lancet*, *ii*, 155.
—— (1921*b*) Obituary of David Yellowlees. *Lancet*, *i*, 301–302.
LAYCOCK, T. (1869) Presidential address. *Journal of Mental Science*, **15**, 327–343.
LEIGH, D. (1961) *The Historical Development of British Psychiatry, Volume I, 18th and 19th Century*. Oxford: Pergamon Press.
LOCKHART ROBERTSON, C. A. (1867) Presidential address. *Journal of Mental Science*, **13**, 289–306.
LUSH, J. A. (1879) Presidential address. *Journal of Mental Science*, **25**, 309–314.
MACKENZIE, C. (1985) Social factors in the admission, discharge, and continuing stay of patients at Ticehurst Asylum, 1845–1917. In *The Anatomy of Madness, Volume II, Institutions and Society* (eds W. F. Bynum, R. Porter & M. Shepherd), pp. 147–174. London: Tavistock.
MACPHERSON, J. (1915) Obituary of Sir Thomas Smith Clouston. *British Medical Journal*, *i*, 745.
MAUDSLEY, H. (1866) Memoir of the late John Conolly. *Journal of Mental Science*, **12**, 151–174.
—— (1871) Presidential address. *Journal of Mental Science*, **17**, 311–334.
MCCANDLESS, P. (1981) Liberty and lunacy: the Victorians and wrongful confinement. In *Madhouses, Mad-Doctors, and Madmen. The Social History of Psychiatry in the Victorian Era* (ed. A. Scull), pp. 339–362. Philadelphia: University of Pennsylvania Press.
MCDOWALL, T. W. (1897) Presidential address. *Journal of Mental Science*, **43**, 683–702.
MENZIES, W. F. (1921) Obituary references. *Journal of Mental Science*, **67**, 256.

MOTT, F. W. (1918) Obituary of William Julius Mickle. *British Medical Journal*, *i*, 102–103.
MUNRO, H. (1864) Presidential address. *Journal of Mental Science*, **10**, 448–449.
MURRAY LINDSAY, J. (1893) Presidential address. *Journal of Mental Science*, **39**, 473–491.
NEEDHAM, F. (1887) Presidential address. *Journal of Mental Science*, **33**, 343–363.
NEWTON, J. (1988) *Preventing Mental Illness*. London: Routledge & Kegan Paul.
NORMAN, C. (1894) Presidential address. *Journal of Mental Science*, **40**, 487–498.
OUTTERSON WOOD, T. (1896) The early history of the Medico-Psychological Association. *Journal of Mental Science*, **42**, 241–260.
PARRY-JONES, W. Ll. (1972) *The Trade in Lunacy. A Study of Private Madhouses in England in the Eighteenth and Nineteenth Centuries*. London: Routledge & Kegan Paul.
——— (1988) Asylum for the mentally ill in historical perspective. *Psychiatric Bulletin*, **12**, 407–410.
PARSEY, W. H. (1876) Presidential address. *Journal of Mental Science*, **22**, 343–361.
PERCY SMITH, R. (1921) Obituary of Sir George Henry Savage. *Journal of Mental Science*, **67**, 393–404.
PETERSON, M. J. (1978) *The Medical Profession in Mid-Victorian London*. Berkeley: University of California Press.
PORTER, R. (1987*a*) *Mind Forged Manacles*. London: Athlone Press.
——— (1987*b*) *Disease, Medicine and Society in England 1550–1860*. London: Macmillan.
RAYNER, H. (1884) Presidential address. *Journal of Mental Science*, **30**, 337–353.
ROBERTSON, G. M. (1915) Obituary of Sir Thomas Smith Clouston. *British Medical Journal*, *i*, 787.
ROGERS, T. L. (1874) Presidential address. *Journal of Mental Science*, **20**, 327–351.
ROYLE, E. (1987) *Modern Britain. A Social History 1750–1985*. London: Edward Arnold.
RUSSELL, R. (1988) The lunacy profession and its staff in the second half of the nineteenth century, with special reference to the West Riding Lunatic Asylum. In *The Anatomy of Madness, vol. 3, The Asylum and its Psychiatry* (eds W. F. Bynum, R. Porter & M. Shepherd), pp. 297–315. London: Routledge.
SANKEY, W. H. O. (1868) Presidential address. *Journal of Mental Science*, **14**, 297–304.
SAVAGE, G. H. (1886) Presidential address. *Journal of Mental Science*, **32**, 313–331.
——— (1915) Obituary of Sir Thomas Smith Clouston. *Journal of Mental Science*, **61**, 495.
——— (1918) Obituary of Julius Mickle. *Journal of Mental Science*, **64**, 111–114.
——— (1921) Obituary of David Yellowlees. *Journal of Mental Science*, **67**, 271.
SCULL, A. T. (1979) *Museums of Madness*. London: Allen Lane.
——— (1985) A Victorian alienist: John Conolly, FRCP, DCL (1794–1866). In *The Anatomy of Madness, vol. 1, People and Ideas* (eds W. F. Bynum, R. Porter & M. Shepherd), pp. 103–150. London: Routledge.
SHEPHERD, M. (1986) Psychological medicine redivivus: concept and communication. *Journal of the Royal Society of Medicine*, **79**, 639–645.
SHOWALTER, E. (1981) Victorian women and insanity. In *Madhouses, Mad-Doctors, and Madmen, The Social History of Psychiatry in the Victorian Era* (ed. A. Scull), pp. 313–336. Philadelphia: University of Pennsylvania Press.
SKAE, D. (1863) Presidential address. *Journal of Mental Science*, **9**, 309–319.
SMITH, F. B. (1979) *The People's Health 1830–1910*. London: Croom Helm.
SMITH, R. (1981) *Trial By Medicine*. Edinburgh: Edinburgh University Press.
THOMPSON, M. S. (1988) The wages of sin: the problem of alcoholism and general paralysis in nineteenth-century Edinburgh. In *The Anatomy of Madness, vol. 3, The Asylum and its Psychiatry* (eds W. F. Bynum, R. Porter & M. Shepherd), pp. 316–341. London: Routledge.
THOMSON, D. (1986) *England in the Nineteenth Century*. Harmondsworth: Penguin.
TOMES, N. (1988) The great restraint controversy: a comparative perspective on Anglo-American psychiatry in the nineteenth century. In *The Anatomy of Madness, vol. 3, The Asylum and its Psychiatry* (eds W. F. Bynum, R. Porter & M. Shepherd), pp. 190–225. London: Routledge.
TURNER, E. S. (1958) *Call the Doctor: A Social History of Medical Men*. London: Michael Joseph.
TURNER, T. (1988) Henry Maudsley: psychiatrist, philosopher and entrepreneur. In *The Anatomy of Madness, vol. 3, The Asylum and its Psychiatry* (eds W. F. Bynum, R. Porter & M. Shepherd), pp. 151–189. London: Routledge.
——— (1990) Rich and Mad in Victorian England. In *Lectures on the History of Psychiatry* (eds R. M. Murray & T. H. Turner), pp. 170–193. London: Gaskell/Royal College of Psychiatrists.
URQUHART, A. R. (1898) Presidential address. *Journal of Mental Science*, **44**, 673–693.
WALK, A. & WALKER, D. L. (1961) Gloucester and the beginnings of the R.M.P.A. *Journal of Mental Science*, **107**, 603–632.
WALTON, J. K. (1985) Casting out and bringing back in Victorian England: pauper lunatics, 1840–70. In *The Anatomy of Madness, vol. 2, Institutions and Society* (eds W. F. Bynum, R. Porter & M. Shepherd), pp. 132–146. London: Tavistock.
WALVIN, J. (1987) *Victorian Values*. London: André Deutsch.

WHITCOMBE, E. B. (1891) Presidential address. *Journal of Mental Science*, **37**, 501–514.
WINSLOW, F. (1857) Presidential Address. *Asylum Journal of Mental Science*, **4**, 4–16.
WOHL, A. S. (1984) *Endangered Lives*. London: Methuen.
WOOD, W. (1865) Presidential address. *Journal of Mental Science*, **11**, 384–389.
YELLOWLEES, D. (1890) Presidential address. *Journal of Mental Science*, **36**, 473–489.
—— (1915) Obituary of Sir Thomas Smith Clouston. *Journal of Mental Science*, **61**, 494–495.
YOUNGSON, A. J. (1979) *The Scientific Revolution in Victorian Medicine*. London: Croom Helm.

4 The foundation of the Maudsley Hospital

PATRICIA ALLDERIDGE

The Maudsley Hospital was founded somewhere between 1907 and 1923. It would be difficult to identify more precisely the exact point at which 'foundation' might be deemed to have occurred, though it could certainly be said that conception took place in 1907 and, while both the gestation and labour were more than a little protracted, birth had undoubtedly been achieved by 1923. But in any case the story must be taken considerably further back than either of these events, to what can with hindsight be recognised as voices crying in the wilderness to foretell the eventual coming.

The origin of the Maudsley is, in one sense, implicit in the very beginnings of the county-asylum movement in the early 19th century, or at least in the second wave of asylum building which began in the mid-century: for the explicit need for a small acute hospital of the type which eventually came into existence was created by the obvious failures and inadequacies of the asylum system itself, and in particular of those gigantic institutions which were built mainly after the passing of the Lunatic Asylums Act 1845.

Rumblings of dissatisfaction with the asylums and proposals displaying proto-Maudsley characteristics of one sort or another can be traced throughout the second half of the century. Walk (1976) opted for Dr J. G. Davey as the first proponent of "what we should now call a Maudsley-type hospital"; and although new ideas rarely turn out on examination to be so new as they first appeared, it may be that this one *was* having its first recognisable public airing when Davey, a former medical officer of Colney Hatch Asylum, read his paper "On the insane poor of Middlesex" to the Medico-Psychological Association in 1867. In it, he contended that the great asylums should be regarded as places for care and protection only, and that what London needed was "a hospital for the insane poor, one of the most approved construction and embracing all the means essential to the relief and cure of the disordered mind"; and one, moreover, restricted to 250 beds, otherwise it would be no hospital. He had apparently proposed this to the committee of Colney Hatch as long ago as 1851, and had been met with laughter and impatience.

Another concept which eventually came to fruition in the Maudsley Hospital, that of an out-patient department, emerged in the discussion following this paper. Dr Belgrave, formerly of the Lincoln asylum, stated that "In this large metropolis there is no institution where the poor may in their incipient condition

---

This chapter originated as a paper given at a symposium on "Henry Maudsley and his Contribution to Psychiatry" at Robinson College, Cambridge, on 6 October 1988, under the title "Maudsley and the Foundation of the Maudsley Hospital".

apply to receive advice and relief. I suggest that some of us should establish a dispensary or hospital for diseases of the brain or nervous system.''

The idea behind Davey's scheme was, of course, that of separate establishments for curable and incurable cases: the large asylum for incurables, the small hospital for curables. This latter was, in fact, what Bethlem Hospital had been throughout the centuries, and managed to remain even while the asylums were gradually shifting the emphasis away from cure and towards custody and long-term maintenance. But Bethlem had recently ruled itself out of this particular argument with the decision to stop taking pauper patients, though it continued as a public charitable hospital for the poor: and in any case Bethlem had its own governors and its own way of doing things. The institution now under consideration was intended to be an integral part of the asylum system.

An earlier scheme had, indeed, been that the Middlesex County Asylum at Hanwell should become such a hospital, reserved for recent cases in which cure might be hoped for, while the quiet, chronic incurables would be looked after in a separate and more economical establishment. The Lunacy Commissioners had favoured this approach, in the 1840s. John Conolly, then superintendent of Hanwell, had opposed it, as had the Middlesex justices, though probably for different reasons. Conolly was against the whole notion of a first-class establishment for cure and a second-class one for care, where, he had no doubt, neglect would become endemic and the inmates would be condemned to a life without hope: the justices' arguments were probably more to do with money. The outcome, in any case, was to enlarge Hanwell but otherwise leave it alone, and build an even bigger asylum for 1250 patients at Colney Hatch to serve the other end of Middlesex.

The idea of the hospital within the asylum system came up again in the medical press in the 1880s, though doubtless it had been kept gently on the boil in the interim: and again, it appeared with variations. One proposal was for small hospitals of about 30 beds to be built in connection with each asylum, having their own autonomy and admitting curable cases only, somewhat along the lines of the villas which were later to be sprinkled around the grounds of asylums but which never really fulfilled this function. The idea of a 'receiving' or 'reception house' for each county was also mooted, where all patients would be sent in the first instance, until it was seen how the case would develop.

Meanwhile in London, the ground was being more actively prepared for the coming of the Maudsley by a series of changes and chances. In 1889, under the newly formed London County Council (LCC), responsibility for the former Surrey and Middlesex asylums at Banstead, Cane Hill, Colney Hatch and Hanwell was taken over by the Council's Asylums Committee, together with completion of a fifth asylum, of which the foundations had already been laid, at Claybury in Essex.

The Asylums Committee (whose work, incidentally, must command a good deal of respect from anyone acquainted with it) was already, in its first report, referring to the probable need to build a sixth asylum in the near future. At the same time in the LCC itself one of its members, Brudenell Carter, an ophthalmic surgeon, had proposed that a committee should be appointed ''to inquire and report on the advantages which might be expected from the establishment, as a complement to the asylum system, of a hospital with a visiting medical staff for the study and curative treatment for insanity''. The committee was duly set up with Carter himself as chairman, and duly came to a conclusion in favour of such a hospital. The LCC then referred Carter's report to its Asylums Committee, which concluded that "a special Hospital for the treatment of the Insane was a matter beyond the immediate province of this Committee or of the Council, such a Hospital affecting national rather than metropolitan interests", and suggested that the report should be forwarded to the Lunacy Commissioners.

Carter's scheme was in fact, according to Walk (1976), very ill-thought out, though whether this is why the Asylums Committee rejected it is another matter. The fact that they were still only in their second year of operation, and were just getting to grips with the large and growing shortfall of beds which they had taken on along with five big pauper lunatic asylums, probably had much to do with their unwillingness at this stage to become involved with something which could legitimately be regarded as someone else's business. For the time being they got on with advertising for a site for another asylum of 1000 beds (which, by the time the land at Bexley was acquired, had risen to 2000), and with getting Claybury finished.

By 1892, however, the Asylums Committee was showing its ability to rise to a really suitable challenge, and it spawned a special subcommittee which was to have far-reaching consequences. Set up to consider the need for pathological research, and whether a pathologist should be appointed for each asylum or whether a central service should be established, this subcommittee obtained information on the state of pathological investigation not only from the medical officers of the LCC's own asylums but, through the assistance of the Foreign Office, from no less than 94 asylums and hospitals in Belgium, Denmark, France, Germany, Holland, Italy, Norway, Portugal, Russia, Spain, Sweden, Switzerland, and the United States (Austria–Hungary alone sent regrets at being unable to help), all of which evidence was published as an appendix to the Asylum Committee's annual report for 1894. The subcommittee's conclusion was that "the advantages in favour of appointing one pathologist available to all the county asylums far outweigh any that can be suggested in favour of one pathologist to each asylum", and that a pathologist "of standing and position" should be appointed and provided with a laboratory closely associated with one of the asylums so that he could also engage in clinical study. He should have access to material from all the asylums, and should direct and encourage research among the younger staff in their separate outposts.

Claybury, where building work was still in progress, was felt to be a suitable location for this central laboratory and by 1895 a separate building had been completed and equipped there, and Frederick Mott was appointed as the first pathologist to the LCC asylums and director of their laboratories. The Asylums Committee had got it right again: they could not have made a better choice than Mott. Alfred Meyer (1973) describes in detail the impressive range and originality of Mott's work at the LCC laboratories, which attracted visitors from all over the world and eventually won him a knighthood in 1919. It also won him that rather more elusive accolade, the approval of Dr Henry Maudsley: and something else which clearly won Maudsley's approval was Mott's campaign for the establishment of a London mental hospital with teaching facilities.

Mott, who was strongly influenced by the Continental psychiatric clinics attached to universities, had aired the subject in 1903, when he wrote in support of the LCC's intention to set up receiving houses (an intention which was only frustrated by the annual failure of Parliament to find time to pass the necessary bill); and in 1907 he returned to the attack in the preface to the third volume of the *Archives of Neurology* (which he himself had founded and published from Claybury). This time he was more specific about the type of hospital which he envisaged: "The LCC scheme for Receiving Houses," he wrote, "would probably include the establishment of an acute hospital to which a clinic might with advantage be attached," and he pointed out that "if suitable postgraduate training in medico-psychology and neuropathology were established, doubtless the University and licensing bodies might be induced to establish a diploma along the lines of the DPH."

Maudsley's own views on the hospital versus asylum issue do not seem to have emerged during the 1867 discussions, but Walk (1976) states that for many years he favoured the treatment of early or mild cases in private houses, or in villas in the grounds or neighbourhood of asylums. In this he would have been in accord with the early views of his father-in-law, John Conolly, though Conolly later came round to a wholly pro-asylum stance. Maudsley had, however, made clear in the 1860s his view that the last thing that London needed was a mental hospital: or rather, the last thing a mental hospital needed was London. In the course of a debate about whether or not Bethlem Hospital should be moved into the country, he had questioned:

> "Can a hospital for mental diseases in a large town be a hospital for that purpose? Does it not rather become a prison? Are not intercourse with nature and employment absolutely necessary? We should not be discussing whether patients should be confined in a large town. A 'hospital' for mental diseases so situated is surely miscalled."

(It is interesting to note, incidentally, that in 1865 Maudsley actually applied for the vacant post of resident physician to Bethlem Hospital: and even more interesting to speculate on the implications for either Bethlem or the Maudsley, or indeed for Henry Maudsley himself, if he had got it.)

That Maudsley should think differently 40 years later should come as no surprise, for he considered changing one's mind to be a positive virtue, a fact which is not always fully appreciated (in either sense of the word) by those who try to pin down his views on any particular subject. "It is," he wrote in his autobiographical note, "a narrow and barren mind which does not expand and develope with changing circumstances. Consistency signifies prejudice and stagnation." One matter on which he had long been consistent, however, was the need for better education in the study and treatment of mental disorders, and in this he was in complete agreement with Conolly.

Conolly had also advocated a system in which the entire care and treatment of lunatics should be administered by the state, whether in state-owned institutions or outside them, even though he himself had been obliged for financial reasons to go into private practice, and even to set up his own private licensed house. It is ironic that Maudsley's principal material inheritance from the man who had been so passionate an advocate of state care should have been a private asylum; and Maudsley had, of course, spent most of his own working life in private practice. Nevertheless, when it came to the point it was the public and not the private sector in which he chose to embody his beliefs about the future of psychiatry, and this in the very heart of the very largest of the large towns which he had once thought so unsuitable: a fine example of allowing the mind to expand and develop with changing circumstances.

It was also a fine example of striking while the iron was hot, and Frederick Mott was the man who was just then heating up the iron. Whether his article arrived on Maudsley's breakfast table in March 1907 like a bolt from the blue, or whether it might even have been a piece of subtle coat-trailing for a scheme which they were already working out together, there is no doubt that they made common cause from that time on. By early July Mott had already communicated to the Asylums Committee, via its finance subcommittee, "a proposal in connection with the treatment and study of insanity", which was referred to the Special (Housing and Treatment of Lunatics) Sub-Committee on 16 July. The statement which Mott read on this occasion is clearly the product of careful collusion.

> "*Proposed Hospital for the Care and Treatment of Acute Recoverable cases of Mental Disease, with due Provision for Clinical and Pathological Research.*
>
> The main object of this Institution will be the *early* treatment of acute cases of mental disorder, with a view, so far as possible, to prevent the necessity of sending them to the County Asylums; to promote exact scientific research into the causes of insanity and to acquire knowledge that shall tend to its decrease and to the better treatment of the insane. In order that such an institution may be established the Donor offers to the London County Council the sum of £30,000 on the following conditions:-
>
> (1) The Hospital to be for early and acute cases only.
>
> (2) The Hospital to have an out-patient department.
>
> (3) The Hospital to be equipped for 75 to 100 patients; 50 to 75 pauper patients and the remainder paying patients.
>
> (4) The Hospital to be in a central position, and within three to four miles of Trafalgar Square.
>
> (5) Due provision to be made for clinical and pathological research. It is suggested that this would be accomplished most economically by the removal of the staff and equipment of the Claybury Laboratory to the new institution if it should be so desired. It has been ascertained that the present building could be easily adapted to other purposes of the Claybury Asylum without much cost.
>
> (6) The Hospital, Laboratory and teaching side of the institute to be recognised as a school of the University of London for the study of mental diseases and neuropathology.
>
> (7) The London County Council to have entire charge, control, maintenance and upkeep of the institution, excepting in the case of the appointing of Medical Officers, and in matters relating to education and research, when it is suggested that three nominees of the London University shall be co-opted with the Asylums Sub-Committee of Management of the Institution.
>
> (8) Only cases certified as insane or convalescent after cure of insanity, or cases brought by practitioners for advice and treatment are to be received at the institution.
>
> (9) The Donor states that if the Hospital be conducted on such lines he may ultimately make a further contribution."

There then followed a three-page statement by Mott, putting forward the arguments in favour of the scheme (one of which was that it would be decidedly more convenient for everyone to have his laboratories in London, than stuck out in Essex two miles from the station). Though he began by listing the benefits to patients in terms of improved treatment, he left no doubt that the most important consideration was "the acquisition and spread of knowledge of the causes and treatment of insanity", which would come about through the provisions for clinical and pathological research and the association with university teaching. He ended:

> "The strongest testimony, however comes from the distinguished alienist who, by his knowledge of mental diseases and his writings on the physiology and pathology of the mind, has gained a world wide reputation and is prepared to back his opinion as to the desirability of an acute hospital for mental diseases established on the lines indicated above by a gift (during his lifetime) of £30,000."

How much of the detail originated with Maudsley and how much with Mott we may never know, but there is no doubt that both must have been in full sympathy with all the proposals. Maudsley was backing them with £30 000, and Mott had to steer them through the shoal-filled waters of the LCC and its committees and subcommittees, neither being an undertaking to appeal to the half-hearted. Mott was, in fact, to carry out all the public negotiations for the next seven months, while Maudsley remained as the anonymous 'donor' whose name would only be disclosed if the offer was accepted. Even while in Devon for "a little rest and amusement" in August, Mott was busy promoting the scheme in a letter to the clerk to the Asylums Committee, and setting out his intention to visit clinics and hospitals at Munich, Berlin, Halle, Heidelberg, and other university towns in Germany, "so that I may learn and adapt such information & knowledge as I may be able to obtain for the erection & equipment of an Acute Hospital for mental diseases". At the same time he recommended an article in the *British Medical Journal* (from August 1907) about "an Acute Hospital & Clinic for Mental Diseases based upon the German system" shortly to be erected in New York, which he suggested should be copied and sent to every member of the Council, "as I think it is a clear indication that we are on the right lines".

All this might have suggested that the details were, indeed, Mott's, and that Maudsley was merely supporting them, but events of December 1907 show otherwise. In the intervening months, costings had been prepared for the relevant committees. The estimated total now stood at £60 000, comprising anything from £10 000 to £20 000 for a site, £30 000 for the building, and a further £10 000 for equipment, all of which the Asylums Committee was nobly prepared to accept, but some of the conditions presented genuine difficulties in relation to the Council's legal powers. The Lunacy Act 1890, for example, defined 'hospital' and 'asylum' in such a way that the Council could set up and run as many huge asylums as it could cram into the surrounding countryside (and by now it had 10 and was contemplating an 11th) but would be *ultra vires* should it think of erecting even the smallest hospital. Another problem was that the Asylums Committee could not co-opt people who were not members of the Council, even for the purpose of appointing medical officers: another was the treatment of uncertified patients and out-patients, neither of which appeared to be permissible under the act.

On 9 December the chairman of the LCC, accompanied by the respective chairmen of the General Purposes, Asylums, and Finance Committees, along with Sir John McDougall, Dr Mott, and the clerk of the Asylums Committee, therefore held a conference with the still anonymous donor to discuss these and other matters. If nothing else, this must have convinced the donor that giving away £30 000 is an arduous business; but it also shows that the scheme was at least as much Maudsley's as Mott's, and that he was the only one who could vary it in any way.

The report of the conference reinforces this view. It began with Maudsley recapitulating the arguments in favour of such a hospital, in respect of early treatment (and he particularly cited cases of puerperal insanity), teaching, and research (and here he instanced Mott's work on neurosyphilis in the Claybury laboratory). The conditions were then discussed item by item. Maudsley was particularly anxious that the hospital should not be either called or known as an asylum, but a "Hospital for Mental Disorders". However, he appreciated the Council's difficulty, and accepted their slightly devious solution that it should be *called* a hospital, even though it might occasionally have to appear in official documents as an asylum. He appears to have dispelled their fears that there might be difficulty in selecting early and acute cases, and was emphatic about the need for an out-patient department, where people who believed that they might be becoming insane, and those discharged from asylums, could obtain the expert medical advice which was not available from general practitioners. Despite some suggestions, however, there seem to have remained unresolved anxieties about the Council's lack of powers to treat uncertified cases.

Maudsley also attached importance to the hospital's being as central as possible, but did not object to the out-patient department's being sited somewhere else, possibly at a general hospital such as Charing Cross. In discussing the conditions relating to teaching, "The Donor was of opinion that the presence of students would bring to the hospital an atmosphere of sanity as compared with the atmosphere of insanity in the County Asylums." This pronouncement so appealed to the Asylums Committee that they were to quote it (fully attributed) in two later reports of their own. There was also a problem over the Council's inability to fund clinical teaching, and Maudsley later wrote to say that he thought the students might be asked to pay for clinical instruction. On the appointment of medical staff, it was agreed that the three advisory nominees of the University of London would only be consulted, and not co-opted onto the committee. There would be visiting physicians for purposes of consultation, and Maudsley appears to have requested that a specialist in women's diseases should be appointed. After the meeting, he communicated his further opinion that the medical officer in charge should not engage in private practice of any sort, nor appear as a lunacy expert in any legal trial unless it involved the hospital's own patients. Finally, he agreed that the hospital itself could go ahead forthwith, leaving the out-patient department to be developed later as might seem convenient.

Another document in the same file indicates that the donor had been approached "with a view to inducing him to waive some of the conditions imposed by him". A retrospective reading of the report suggests that the donor did not give any more ground than would be expected by anyone who knew him: and that, indeed, he seems to have taken the opportunity to add a few new safeguards against potential backsliding.

On St Valentine's day 1908 (surely only a happy coincidence?) Maudsley wrote a formal letter in his own name to the chairman of the LCC, summarising the proposals and asking the Council to accept his money. *Inter alia* he stated:

> "As a physician who has been engaged in the study and treatment of mental diseases for more than half-a-century I have been deeply impressed with the necessity of a hospital, the main object of which would be (1) the early treatment of cases of acute mental disorder, with the view, so far as possible, to prevent the necessity of sending them to the county asylums; (2) to promote exact scientific research into the causes and pathology of insanity, with the hope that much may yet be done for its prevention and successful treatment; and (3) to serve as an educational institution in which medical students might obtain good clinical instruction."

On the latter point he commented that "as an educational institution the hospital would be, I think, of almost inestimable value", providing a supply of trained medical officers to fill the posts in the large asylums, "men furnished with the requisite instruction and imbued, one may hope, with the earnest spirit of scientific observation and enquiry". The letter ended:

> "I will only add, in conclusion, the expression of my belief that the establishment of such a hospital, in vital touch with the general hospitals and the University of London, would do much to break down the unfortunate isolation from general medical knowledge and research in which the study and treatment of insanity remains; and it is not perhaps too much to hope that in the end it might save to the rates some of the prolonged expense of chronic and incurable insanity."

It is hard not to see the hand of Mott, the experienced local government officer, in this final sentence. "Just add something about its being a saving on the rates", I hear him say, as he and Maudsley settle down to an evening of strategic planning and Maudsley hands him the draft for comment: "That always goes down well."

The Council at last took decisive action. They thanked Maudsley for his letter, and referred it to the Asylums Committee for consideration and report. The Asylums Committee, which had been considering the scheme almost non-stop for the past seven months, dutifully buckled down and considered it again, leaving no doubts about their enthusiasm: and finally, on 31 March, the full Council accepted Maudsley's offer and thanked him for his generous gift. The members of the Asylums Committee were almost jubilant in their annual report for that year. They were going to get the hospital which, in their own words, they had long desired, and they repeated, endorsed, and occasionally expanded all Maudsley's arguments in favour of it. They were convinced that Dr Maudsley's gift would "confer a great and lasting benefit on a class of sufferers, the effectual assistance of whom has hitherto been amongst the most difficult of social problems."

Three years later, a site had only just been acquired to build it on (though an earlier purchase had fallen through at the last minute when the vendor withdrew). Maudsley says in his memoir that he grew so tired of the delays that he threatened to withdraw his offer in a public letter, and that is what forced the business through: and although much of what he says in the memoir about these delays is exaggerated and some of it frankly untrue, it does seem likely that such a threat would have helped to concentrate the Council's corporate mind. It could also have had some influence on their decision to name the new institution the Maudsley Hospital, which was agreed in 1911 as soon as the 4½-acre site in Denmark Hill was purchased and Maudsley's money safely in the bank.

The architect of the buildings was the LCC's asylums engineer, William Charles Clifford Smith, who worked in consultation with both Maudsley and Mott. As previously mentioned, Mott had already visited Germany to gather information from the university clinics, and in 1909 the architect and two members of the Asylums Committee visited Kraepelin's clinic at Munich, on Maudsley's suggestion that "hints as to design, staffing and administration might be obtained there". In 1912 Clifford Smith called on Maudsley with plans and elevations for alternative schemes for 76 and 108 beds, which Maudsley examined in some detail, approving of everything except the lack of relief to the roofs of the ward blocks. He was particularly pleased with the single-room accommodation, and was emphatic that the 108-bed scheme, which allowed room for private patients, was the only satisfactory one. (By the time the hospital was finally opened, the numbers had been brought up to 157.)

In 1913 the contract went out to tender, but construction work was soon halted by a building strike, and after that came the war. The army coveted the nearly finished hospital, and with Maudsley's agreement the buildings were handed over, as completed, to the Royal Army Medical Corps for use as the Maudsley Neurological Clearing Hospital. Mott moved the laboratories in from Claybury in 1916, and Henry Maudsley was able to see his hospital do valuable work on the treatment of shell-shock, before his death in 1918. After the war the Ministry of Pensions took over for a while, and then three years were spent in reinstating the buildings and arguing over dilapidations. Finally the hospital opened as originally intended, under the administration of the LCC, in 1923. It was a hospital, not an asylum; it took voluntary patients only, the Council having put a bill through Parliament for this purpose in 1915, and subsequently decided to admit no certified cases at all; it had research and teaching facilities; and it had an out-patient department. Maudsley's arguments had won the day.

The buildings themselves were very different from the asylum architecture which had for so long dominated English psychiatry, though perhaps it is not surprising that a post-war description in *The Architect* (22 June 1923, p. 426) did not mention the German prototypes which had influenced their style. They consisted of two ward blocks, each of three stories, behind an administrative building with an elevation onto Denmark Hill and designed in "a free treatment of English Renaissance", in Portland stone and red brick. The ward blocks, whose sleeping accommodation was mainly in small dormitories of six or eight, with some single rooms, had gardens on the south side with ground-floor verandas, and were connected by a main corridor to all other departments. The administrative building contained offices, quarters for resident officers, and the out-patient department on the ground floor, with the laboratories and further staff accommodation above. A laundry and stores were on the lower ground floor.

The rapid rise during the 1920s and '30s of this small local-authority hospital to a position of international prestige, particularly in the field of education and research, is another story, part of which has already been told by Sir Aubrey Lewis (1969) in his lecture "Edward Mapother and the making of the Maudsley Hospital". It is certainly true that Mapother, its first medical superintendent, *was* the making of the Maudsley, backed by the willing if sometimes slightly bemused support of the former Asylums Committee, now reborn as the Mental Hospitals Committee. Not only did he bring his almost superhuman determination to bear in promoting its physical growth and development: it was Mapother more than any other person who put together the heady mix of scepticism, eclecticism, experimentalism, and pragmatism which came to be widely recognised as 'the Maudsley tradition', and which must have been an exhilarating atmosphere to breathe after nearly a century in the stifling air of the asylum tradition.

Henry Maudsley might be considered exceptionally lucky, in that the hospital which carried his name into the future of psychiatry should have fallen into the hands of men who took it so faithfully in the direction which he had intended, and so much further than he could ever have dared to hope: but this would suggest too great an element of chance. His own foresight had ensured that all the essentials were in place, and a pioneering enterprise will attract like-minded pioneers to its service. It may be that even without his intervention some similar institution would eventually have come into existence, possibly under the auspices of the LCC: but it would not have had precisely those features, and above all that potential, which Maudsley had so opportunely and so insistently imposed on the less resolute minds around him. It might be as difficult to say precisely who was the founder of this hospital as it is to specify the exact date of its foundation, but there can be no doubt that it has the right name over the door: and although much emphasis is (rightly) placed on Maudsley's personal pessimism, it would be hard not to see the Maudsley Hospital itself as a final gesture of defiant optimism.

References

LEWIS, A. (1969) Edward Mapother and the making of the Maudsley Hospital – the first Mapother Lecture. *British Journal of Psychiatry*, **115**, 1349.

MEYER, A. (1973) Frederick Mott, founder of the Maudsley Laboratories. *British Journal of Psychiatry*, **122**, 497–517.

WALK, A. (1976) Medico-psychologists, Maudsley and the Maudsley. *British Journal of Psychiatry*, **128**, 19–39. (This paper is the source of much of the pre-history of the Maudsley, including the discussions in 1867 and the 1880s.)

Other sources

Annual Reports, Asylums Committee of the London County Council, 1892–1914.

Archives of the Maudsley Hospital, particularly LCC file G.7–01 entitled "The Maudsley Bequest", now preserved in the archives department of the Bethlem Royal Hospital and the Maudsley Hospital. This file contains most of the papers used to trace the progress of Maudsley's proposal after its first communication to the LCC in 1907.

Maudsley, Henry, autobiographical sketch, archives of the Bethlem Royal Hospital and the Maudsley Hospital.

5 Law and mental health: sticks or carrots?

KATHLEEN JONES

The history of the psychiatric services in England and Wales over the past 150 years is marked by six major pieces of legislation: the Lunatics Act 1845, the Lunacy Act 1890, the Mental Treatment Act 1930, the National Health Service Act 1946, the Mental Health Act 1959, and the Mental Health Act 1983. Each of these statutes embodies a different philosophy, reflecting the practice of a different period; but the six statutes also reflect long-term differences between lawyers and doctors about what the law can and should do.

The legal approach is characterised by Dicey's classic study of *The Law of the Constitution*, which rests on two basic principles: reverence for the rule of law, and the sovereignty of Parliament in making law. To Dicey, law is what is laid down by statute, and this is binding on all citizens. Whatever the law forbids incurs penalties. What is not forbidden is permissible. "In England, no man can be made to suffer punishment or to pay damages for any conduct not definitely forbidden by law" (Dicey, 1915, p. xviii).

In mental health law, the legal profession has traditionally been most closely concerned with the issue of the liberty of the subject, with prescribing in detail the circumstances under which individuals may be deprived of their liberty, institutions penalised for not observing the regulations, or doctors and nurses held culpable for abuse or neglect. The paradigm is that of the criminal law. Major questions of care and treatment have been held to be matters of no legal significance, provided that the law was observed.

The medical profession has maintained a very different frame of reference. Doctors, in particular psychiatrists and their predecessors the asylum doctors, have looked for law which would provide a framework for the care of all patients, place no obstacles in the way of early treatment, enable medical decisions to be made in the best interests of the patient without hampering legal requirements, support practitioners in a difficult and taxing area of work, and give them some protection against vexatious litigation. The contrast between the quest for prescriptive law – precise, detailed, minimalist, focused on concepts of offence and punishment – and the quest for normative law – setting standards and providing guidance for the operation of a good service – has led to many heated interprofessional debates. As the American sociologist of jurisprudence, Donald Black (1976) makes clear, law is not immutable: law *behaves*. It is subject to many societal and political pressures, and particular statutes illustrate the relative strengths of the legal and medical representations made during their passage through Parliament.

The question raised in the following discussion relates to a basic issue in jurisprudence: what kind of law has reached the statute book in different periods, and how have medical and legal interests interacted in framing it? It is not concerned with the detailed provisions of mental health law, except where these have some particular significance in the legal–medical debate; nor is it concerned with the particularly difficult issues relating to forensic psychiatry. It is the style of law which is in question – whether, in Black's terms, the emphasis is 'penal' or 'therapeutic'.

Early legislation

The law has traditionally been much more concerned about property than about personal liberty. Kittrie (1971) based a complicated argument for exercise by the state of paternal power over the lunatic on *parens patriae*, a doctrine derived from the statute (*De Praerogativa Regis* of Edward II. Even a superficial examination of this statute is sufficient to indicate that it related primarily to 'lands and tenements', and that the modern American use of the term to refer to an infraction of personal liberty is quite unhistorical. Ideas of human rights in the modern sense did not begin to be evolved until the 17th century (Jones & Fowles, 1984, pp. 137–141).

Vagrancy laws of 1714 and 1744 contained minor provisions to the effect that vagrant lunatics should be "safely locked up in some secure place" and there "kept, maintained and cured". Since the only secure place available was usually the county gaol, and there were no provisions for treatment, it is unlikely that their custody varied much from that meted out to beggars, poachers, gypsies, and other deviants covered by the acts. The first 18th-century statute specifically relating to lunatics was primarily directed to people of property, and had a clearly prescriptive emphasis. It was designed to regulate a situation in which relatives and the proprietors of private madhouses could collude to 'put away' a wealthy patient.

The traditional reliance on habeas corpus to free such patients was proving ineffectual by the late 18th century. There was no obligation on madhouse proprietors to keep records; patients could have their names changed to conceal their presence, or be moved from one madhouse to another. The subject was a difficult one, because many of the private madhouses were in London, some contained patients from distinguished families, and some were directed by eminent members of the medical profession. Though some seem to have been of a good standard (Parry-Jones, 1972), there is evidence that substantial abuses did occur, particularly in those houses which took pauper patients contracted out from workhouses (House of Commons Select Committee, 1816, 1827). After some 11 years of discreet inquiry and still more discreet discussion, the Madhouses Act 1774 was eventually passed.

This Act proposed two systems: one for the metropolis, and one for the provinces. In "the cities of London and Westminster and within seven miles of the same, and in the county of Middlesex", responsibility for licensing and visiting madhouses was placed in the hands of the medical profession. The Royal College of Physicians (RCP) was to elect five of its number as commissioners, who were to meet annually, and to visit all madhouses, between the hours of

9 a.m. and 5 p.m. If any madhouse proved deserving of "Censure or Animadversion", they were to make a report which would be posted in the RCP, and might be read by any interested parties. In the county areas, the justices of the peace at quarter sessions were to undertake similar duties. The reason for the different procedure in the counties was that there was no recognised medical organisation outside London, and over 80 years before the Medical Qualifications Act 1858, the standard of medical practice outside the metropolis was of very variable quality. Justices of the peace were usually local gentry – landlords of large estates who could be relied on to know what was going on in their districts.

The Madhouses Act remained almost a dead letter. The RCP and the justices of the peace had no incentive to take their duties very seriously. Though they granted licences, they had no power to revoke them. In 1827, a House of Commons Select Committee heard an RCP Commissioner, Dr Alexander Frampton, say that he had never visited Bethlem, or any other asylum to make a comparison with the conditions he found in private madhouses. He seldom visited any madhouse more than once a year. Though there was evidence of appalling conditions in the White House at Hoxton, Dr Frampton thought it "excellently regulated – a very good house" (House of Commons Select Committee, 1827). It seems likely that his inspection did not lead him to visit the back wards, where violent and incontinent patients were left chained in cribs, unattended from Saturday to Monday, and had the excrement washed off with a mop and a bucket of cold water.

The Madhouse Act 1828 improved procedure by setting up the Metropolitan Commissioners in Lunacy – a statutory body for the London area consisting of 11 Members of Parliament (a group of members of the House of Commons had taken a leading part in investigating the evils of the London madhouses) and five medical practitioners. The Commissioners were to visit every madhouse in the metropolis four times a year. They could visit without notice, and by night if malpractice was alleged on oath by an informant. They were appointed by the Secretary of State for the Home Department, and though they had no power of their own to revoke licences, they could recommend revocation by the Secretary of State. Most importantly, they could order the immediate release of any patient whom they found to be wrongly confined.

The legal establishment evidently had second thoughts about leaving this procedure in the hands of medical men and laymen. In 1828, they evinced no great interest, but in 1832 there was a further Act specifying that two of the Commissioners must be barristers. Except for the period 1959–83, the task of inspecting conditions for mentally ill people in institutions has involved joint action by the two professions ever since.

The 1828 Act was primarily a prescriptive Act, laying down rules and penalties for infringement. It had to be, because it was dealing with the private sector, where there was no general power of regulation. The County Asylums Act of 1808 and 1828 (see Chapter 2) were by contrast normative acts, facilitating the creation of a network of asylums to be paid for out of public funds, and concerned with the care and maintenance of pauper lunatics. Though there were regulations concerning admissions, discharges, and deaths, and the local justices made statutory visitations, administration was left very much in medical hands.

In the first four decades of the 19th century, lunatics were scattered in many different settings. After the passing of the first County Asylum Act, Parliamentary reformers were working towards a comprehensive lunacy law, and a Parliamentary inquiry (House of Commons Select Committee, 1816) revealed widespread abuses: in Bethlem, London's old asylum; in workhouses; in gaols; and in private madhouses. There was good practice in some of the small subscription hospitals, like the York Retreat, and in the developing county asylums, but legislation was delayed by a long period of socially repressive government (this was the period of Peterloo and the Tolpuddle Martyrs) and by legal reluctance to intervene. Lord Eldon's famous dictum that "there could not be a more false humanity than an over-humanity with regard to persons afflicted with insanity" appears to have summed up the views of the Lord Chancellor's Department. The old group of reforming MPs – George Rose, Whitbread, Romilly, Williams-Wynn – disintegrated, and the reform movement had to await a new champion.

Lord Ashley (after 1851 the Earl of Shaftesbury) became a Metropolitan Commissioner in Lunacy in 1828, at the age of 26. His views carried great influence, first as chairman of the Metropolitan Commissioners, and then of the national Lunacy Commission which succeeded it, until his death in 1884. As a good Parliamentarian – a member first of the House of Commons, then of the House of Lords when he succeeded to the earldom – he believed as firmly as Dicey in the sovereignty of Parliament, and in the importance of statute law; but in lunacy law, as in the other fields of social reform with which his name is connected such as factory reform, education, and public health, he looked to the law to promote, not merely to prohibit. He believed that the detection of abuse could be better carried out through a discretionary body like the Commission than through the application of penalties by the courts, but inspection should be subordinated to positive guidance and the setting of standards of good practice. The Metropolitan Commissioners developed their own standards, and ensured that they were observed. It was largely due to Ashley's efforts that they were empowered in 1842 to undertake a national inspection of all places where lunatics might be found. Their report, a massive undertaking (Metropolitan Commissioners in Lunacy, 1844), led to the first comprehensive mental health law.

The Lunatics Act 1845

The 1845 Act set up the powerful central Lunacy Commission, on an administrative model very similar to that of the Poor Law Commission of 1834 and the Factory Commission of 1833. The Commissioners, based in London, had jurisdiction over the whole country. There were five laymen, including the chairman; three medical Commissioners; and three legal Commissioners: a delicate balance. The medical and legal Commissioners were salaried (at the then quite generous rate of £1500 a year). They were responsible for visiting both county asylums and private madhouses, and were to work in tandem, one doctor and one lawyer forming a team. A significant change was that the Commission was to report to the Lord Chancellor's Department rather than to the Home Office. Thus, the legal element was stronger than it had been, but as long as Shaftesbury remained as chairman, it was unlikely to become dominant.

Documentation was regarded as the primary safeguard against bad practice. There was an elaborate medical certification procedure involving two doctors. Establishments were to keep five different sets of detailed records including medical case records, which could be inspected and checked. Details of admission, discharge or death, escape or transfer, restraint, seclusion, and injury were all to be kept. But the Commissioners were not only interested in records. Their reports show that they were interested in the positive aspects of care – in architecture, in farms and gardens, in the employment and exercise of patients, in staff recruitment and training, and above all in human relations.

The private madhouses were dwindling in number, and patients were being brought into the county asylums from prisons and workhouses. The system relied primarily on the growing expertise of the Lunacy Commissioners and on the probity of the asylum doctors. By 1868, the President of the Medico-Psychological Association, Dr C. Lockhart Robinson, was able to record with satisfaction that beds in county asylums had increased from 5500 to 26 000 in the first 20 years of the Act's operation, and that considerable progress had been made.

Paradoxically, it was at this time, when the worst abuses of the private madhouses had been dealt with and the Lunacy Commissioners were convinced that 20 years' hard work had brought the problems under control (House of Commons Select Committee, 1877), that the general public became alarmed at the state of the lunacy laws. Perhaps this was a matter of cultural lag: the horrifying conditions which the reformers had been trying to publicise for half a century may have only just percolated through to the popular consciousness. Certainly, some of the evidence produced in the 1860s and 1870s was distinctly dated. Charles Reade's *Hard Cash* (1863), a popular novel of the day, included material taken from the evidence to the Select Committee on Madhouses of 1816, almost word for word, and without acknowledgement, apology, or any indication that the law had changed in nearly 50 years. Shaftesbury had to defend the Lunacy Commission before select committees of the House of Commons in 1859 and 1877 – to find, like many another pioneer, that the system he had created was now under attack by a new generation with different ideas.

As Dr Daniel Hack Tuke (editor of the *Journal of Mental Science* for some years, and President of the Medico-Psychological Association in 1881) wrote philosophically, "Waves of suspicion and excitement occasionally pass over the public mind in regard to the custody of the insane"; Hack Tuke, a member of a well-known Quaker family devoted to the humane treatment of the insane, had been accused in the press of using a horsewhip on a patient (Tuke, 1882).

The asylum doctors were well aware that prejudice against insanity – a taboo subject in Victorian England – was only too easily transferred from the patient to his physician. Like Shaftesbury, they argued that the major needs of asylums were not for tighter law but for greater public support – better staff and better training – but the attacks proceeded with unremitting hostility. They came at a time when the first cheap newspapers became popular, and sensations were much in demand by the reading public. The spearhead of this Victorian protest movement was the Alleged Lunatics' Friend Society. The chairman was an admiral with a distinguished record, and the secretary was a solicitor. This group, which contained a number of former asylum patients, was not concerned with the welfare of lunatics, but with how to keep people out of asylums. They campaigned ceaselessly and with much publicity for additional legal safeguards against illegal detention, in particular for a magistrate's order to supplement the two medical certificates required. They were openly hostile to the asylum doctors, and spent their time in attempting to 'rescue' patients from their clutches.

On two occasions, in 1859 and 1877, agitation reached the point where select committees of the House of Commons were appointed to consider the state of the lunacy laws. On each occasion, they were satisfied by Shaftesbury's patient explanations of the Lunacy Commissioners' work, and the evidence of progress being made, but in the early 1880s, matters were brought to a head by a series of legal cases instituted by Mrs Georgiana Weldon. Had Mrs Weldon not been spirited, attractive, well connected, and wealthy, her activities would probably not have become a *cause célèbre*; but she was a red-headed beauty with a mind of her own, her husband was a minor official in the royal household, and she could afford to sue. Her many cases occupied the legal columns of *The Times* and the minds of the legal establishment for several years.

Whether Mrs Weldon was mentally ill was a matter for medical disagreement. She dabbled in spiritualism, had advanced ideas on education and ladies' dress, and could not get on with her husband, who tried to have her certified and committed to a private asylum. One of the doctors involved was the eminent Dr Forbes Winslow, a former President of the Medico-Psychological Association, who had a private asylum in Hammersmith. The door was barred, and he had to force an entry. The secretary of the Alleged Lunatics' Friend Society, a former mental patient, helped Mrs Weldon to escape, dressed as a nun. Mrs Weldon then embarked on a flurry of litigation in which she sued everybody involved, including her husband, Dr Forbes Winslow and the other certifying doctor, the editors of several newspapers, and the composer Gounod (for charging her too much when she hired the Covent Garden Opera House for a protest meeting) (*The Times*, 1883–84).

Prominent barristers clashed in court; prominent psychiatrists gave evidence, and disagreed about Mrs Weldon's condition. Was she, as Dr Forbes Winslow contended, incoherent and deluded, or was she merely eccentric, and entitled to be so? The cases dragged on, and cost a small fortune; but in the end, Forbes Winslow lost, and had to pay £500 damages. An eminent judge, Baron Huddleston, made the celebrated "crossing-sweeper judgement" to the effect that if two crossing-sweepers cared to put someone into a private lunatic asylum, they had only to find "two medical men who had never had a day's practice in their lives" and who would "for a small sum of money grant their certificates" (*Standard*, 1884). This was an inexact statement of the state of the law, but the phrase stuck.

The Lunacy Commission and the asylum doctors protested that the procedure involved in a magistrate's order, as advocated by the Alleged Lunatics' Friend Society, would delay treatment: patients would be deterred from seeking help by its formality and the judicial deprivation of liberty. The progressive move would be towards less formality, to enable early treatment to be given on an informal basis. The *Lancet* set up a commission on the subject (Granville, 1877), and there was much medical support for that commission's view that patients should be admitted to asylums with as little fuss as patients admitted to ordinary hospitals, rather than being subjected to a stigmatising and threatening form of detention. It was another half century before that became legally possible.

So the hunt was up. Before Shaftesbury died in 1884, he took part in the House of Lords in a debate on the motion (proposed by Lord Milltown, an Irish barrister) "that the existing state of the Lunacy Laws is unsatisfactory, and constitutes a serious danger to the liberty of the subject". The motion was eventually withdrawn in deference to the aged Shaftesbury, who rallied his failing powers to make a long speech (House of Lords Debates, 1884; Hodder, 1887); but not before the motion had attracted some strong support, and the Lord Chancellor had promised action. Lord Stanley of Alderley dismissed Shaftesbury's arguments:

> "It had been said that insanity could be more easily cured in its initial stage, but it was also true that the despair caused to inmates of asylums on finding themselves hopelessly locked up . . . would increase slight derangement into raving madness." (House of Lords Debates, 1884)

It took another five years and two more Lords Chancellor (Herschell and Halsbury) before the Lunacy Acts Amendment Bill of 1889, which included all the legal profession's many safeguards against illegal detention, was passed against considerable medical opposition. By that time, Shaftesbury was dead. Though the Medico-Psychological Association had strong reservations, its objections were deflected by the inclusion of clause 330, which was designed to protect members against court actions of the Weldon v. Winslow variety. (In fact, it did little to stem the flow of vexatious actions, and it was not until the Mental Treatment Act 1930 that more adequate protection for decisions made in good faith became part of the law.) In the following year, the Lunacy Act consolidated the law on the subject.

The Lunacy Act 1890

The 1890 Act is the prime example of a 'close-textured' statute in which everything is prescribed in great detail, and nothing is left to chance or to professional discretion. It ran to 342 sections. It prescribed methods of admission, including the controversial magistrate's order. It specified the duration of treatment under different kinds of order, it prohibited certain degrees of relationship between certifying doctors, doctors and patient, and doctors and manager of the institutions to which the patient was being sent, and had a whole section on "escape and recapture" which dealt with "escaped lunatics" travelling to or from Scotland or Ireland, which had different jurisdictions. It multiplied the already heavy burden of documentation and the procedure for visitation to establishments of different kinds. A whole section of the Act was devoted to "penalties and misdemeanours", the penalties for non-compliance or obstruction being set in precise terms: £10 for failing to send in a required document, £20 for "conniving" at an escape, £50 for obstructing a Commissioner, and between £2 and £20 for ill-treating a patient: an interesting scale of values.

From the legal point of view, the 1890 Act was a thoroughly satisfactory document, with every eventuality set down in cold print. 'Knowing the Act' became a virtue, an exercise in rule observance and proper procedure. Psychiatric treatment became a last resort, and every obstacle was placed in the way of treating it as an offer of help. From the medical point of view, the Act set the treatment of mental illness back for many decades.

The Act was to remain on the statute-book until 1959. It had created a good deal of controversy and absorbed a good deal of Parliamentary time. Successive administrations were not anxious to disturb a piece of legislation so monumental, so legally watertight, so apparently definitive. Debates on mental health are not well attended in the House of Commons or the House of Lords. The subject had become highly technical, and technicalities are wearisome in debate, so that it is not surprising that for the next 69 years, legislation went round the Act rather than tackling it head on.

Circumventing the 1890 Act

Three main changes occurred in the law between the two major Acts of 1890 and 1959: the removal of mentally handicapped people from the operation of the Act in 1913; the introduction of voluntary treatment and an out-patient clinic system in 1930; and the integration of the mental health services into the National Health Service in 1946. Through all these changes, the 1890 Act survived – frequently amended, but never abolished. By the early 1950s, the only way of understanding its provisions was to refer, not to the Act itself, but to Matthews' *The Mental Health Services* (1948), a book which became the mental welfare officers' bible. This indispensable publication gave the original text with outdated sections deleted and later provisions inserted in italics. Since the terminology had changed, the agencies had changed, and the shape of the services had changed; what remained was barely comprehensible, and whole sections were in italics.

The Mental Treatment Act 1930 represented a marked change from a legal to a medical perspective. This was particularly remarkable, since the Royal Commission (1926) which preceded it and framed the recommendations (in the Macmillan report) had six eminent lawyers among its members, and the Lord Advocate for Scotland as its chairman. There were only two medical members, Sir Humphrey Rollestone, President of the Royal College of Physicians, and Sir David Drummond, Professor of Medicine at the University of Durham, and neither was a psychiatrist; but their conversion of their colleagues to a medical perspective may have been helped by the fact they both came from mainstream medicine rather than from the less prestigious tributary of psychiatry, and both held legal as well as medical qualifications. Whatever the internal dynamics of the Commission, its members were not anxious to stir up the hornets' nest of 'the liberty of the subject' again, and they commented that the evidence received from the National Society for Lunacy Reform (a successor to the Alleged Lunatics' Friend Society) was likely to encourage "recrimination and controversy". They took the view that the best policy for patients' liberty was not to increase legal provisions against illegal detention, but to introduce voluntary treatment and discharge, and to promote the work of out-patient clinics. The 1890 Act could be left on the statute-book, to fall into disuse in the course of time.

The Commission started its report with a firm statement that mental illness was "essentially a public health problem, to be dealt with on public health lines":

mental illness was often accompanied by physical symptoms; physical illness was often accompanied by emotional or intellectual disturbance. Mental illness should be treated as far as possible on the same terms as other illnesses; the old stigmatising terms 'lunatic', 'attendant', and 'asylum' should be abandoned.

The 1930 Act was strongly normative, clearing away (at least for voluntary patients, who gradually became the most numerous group) a mass of legal technicalities. As the number of certified patients dwindled over the years, the scope of the 1890 Act diminished, and the use of a general medical terminology – 'patient', 'doctor', 'nurse', 'hospital' – became accepted. The way was paved for the integration of the mental health services into the general structure of health provision.

This nearly failed to happen. In 1943, the Ministry of Health announced that the mental health services would not be included in the new National Health Service (NHS) (House of Commons Debate, 1943), but the decision was rescinded in the following year. The 1944 white paper on the NHS specifically included these services; though the Macmillan report was 20 years old, it was quoted in the white paper. By 1944, the enhanced prestige of psychiatrists, due to some outstanding work in the forces in World War II (Ahrenfeld, 1958) and some intensive lobbying from what was now the Royal Medico-Psychological Association (RMPA), had produced a change of heart in the government. The RMPA's own publication on the issue (1945) set out the argument for "treating psychiatry in all essential respects like other branches of medicine", in order to improve the services and reduce the stigma which still attached to psychiatric treatment.

The Mental Health Act 1959

The old 1890 Act was still on the statute-book – "a good Act", according to many a mental welfare officer, because it provided for every practical contingency, and allowed for no discretion. However, the medical view of mental illness had by now superseded the legal view, and the next step was clearly to bring the confused mass of mental health law into line with general health service law.

Although 13 years separates them in time, the 1959 Act was the logical corollary of the National Health Service Act, part of the post-war 'welfare state' legislation. The Percy Commission recommended the abolition of much of the special legislation and procedure (Royal Commission, 1957), while the Board of Control recommended its own abolition: the task of visiting all the hospitals and scrutinising all the documents had grown to mammoth proportions, and it was felt that much of this work could be delegated to the regional hospital boards (now regional health authorities). Designated patients would no longer go into designated beds in designated hospitals: the whole system would be freed, so that the services could respond to changing needs and changing circumstances. Most importantly, the clause requiring a magistrate's order for compulsory detention was to go at last. Witnesses before the Percy Commission had described it as one of the main causes of the stigma attaching to psychiatric treatment (Royal Commission, 1957).

The 1959 Act, like the Mental Treatment Act 1930 and the National Health Service Act 1946, is a normative Act – relatively brief, non-prescriptive, and concentrating on the principles of good service rather than on offences and penalties. The Minister of Health, Derek Walker-Smith, called the existing state of mental health law "a mosaic" to be replaced by "a single contemporary design" (House of Commons Debates, 1959). The new Act repealed more than 70 other Acts in whole or in part, and amended more than 60 more. The main concern in the House of Commons was with the workability of the proposals for community care, rather than with the liberty of the subject. The new mental health review tribunals, where a legal member, a medical member, and a lay member would sit together to determine appeals concerning detention, were thought likely to be adequate to ensure the protection of civil rights. In the House of Lords, the Lord Chancellor, Lord Kilmuir, introduced the bill, commending it as a progressive measure, and expressing no legal reservations. It seemed that the 'liberty of the subject' issue was finally extinct.

Yet after nearly half a century in which the legalistic view of mental illness had been little more than a hindrance to good practice and an embarrassment to good practitioners, the scene again changed radically. The 1959 Act was not yet fully in force when the antipsychiatry and anti-institutional movements began (Laing, 1960; Goffman, 1961; Foucault, 1961; Szasz, 1961; Laing & Esterson, 1964; Scheff, 1966). The new libertarians learned from the United States, importing the methods of the American Civil Liberties Union (ACLU) into a campaign marked by the sophisticated use of the media. The ACLU was (and is) an organisation dedicated to the principles of 'due process', which involve the introduction into the mental health field of the practices of the criminal courts – presumption of innocence, exclusion of hearsay evidence, and above all legal representation (American Civil Liberties Union, 1973). In the United States, its campaign was given point by the fact that most patients in mental hospitals were still under compulsory detention. This was not the case in Britain, but public alarm was fuelled by two new sets of problems: the hospital scandals of the early 1970s, which received considerable publicity (Chapter 2), and the growing potential of psychiatric treatment, both psychopharmacology and psychosurgery, for modifying individual behaviour.

At one level, the new movement was quasipolitical. 'Bourgeois psychiatry' (Leonard, 1985, p. xii) was attacked from a number of different perspectives – Marxist, feminist, race relations (Sedgwick, 1982; Banton *et al*, 1985). The central theme of the attack was that 'madness', as it was now again termed, does not reside in the individual. It is the result of pressures by society, by governments, by the capitalist system. The 'medical model' was rejected, and psychiatrists regarded as 'agents of social control'. Anthony Clare's *Psychiatry in Dissent* (1976) is a thoughtful analysis of a very confusing debate in which there were some useful new insights, but the emotional force of the attack offered little possibility of synthesis with past experience.

The National Association for Mental Health, a voluntary organisation formed in 1946 out of smaller mental health associations, changed its name and its purpose. Renamed MIND, it abandoned the long-standing partnership with the statutory services in which it had provided mental health training and consultation, and became a pressure group, devoted to civil liberties and with a more confrontational role. Larry Gostin, a young American lawyer with civil rights experience, became MIND's Legal and Welfare Rights Officer, and began to press for changes in the law, in particular the limitation of the powers of the medical profession. Gostin's (1975) *A Human Condition* carried a foreword by Louis Blom-Cooper QC and Professor Margot Jeffreys which expressed the changing perspective on mental health law:

> "the willingness to leave so much power in the hands of the medical profession was the result of a general wave of optimism about the capacity of mankind to solve most of its age-long problems of poverty, ignorance, squalor, disease and deviance. . . . Our recent failures to achieve the most modest social welfare objectives has forced us to re-examine even those policies and practices that seemed least controversial and open to criticism. Optimism has given way to scepticism, if not pessimism. . . . Certainly any earlier complacency about the provisions of the Mental Health Act 1959 has evaporated."

Gostin's detailed analysis concentrated on the traditional legal issues – procedure for compulsory admission, access to the courts, secure hospitals, the position of the abnormal offender – but it also contained a critique of the work of mental health review tribunals, and a chapter on "treatment as a modifier of behaviour" which criticised the "coercive power" of the state as exercised by the psychiatrist. Gostin's solution was the creation of a corps of trained advocates (the "Committee on the Rights and Responsibilities of Staff and Residents in Psychiatric Hospitals", or CORR) which would inspect and supervise the work of mental hospitals, advising patients of their legal rights and vetting 'suspect' treatments.

While this proposal was not acceptable in its original form, the idea of instituting some new form of protection for the civil rights of patients was well received. In the 19th century, when the numbers of patients were much smaller, the Lunacy Commission had fulfilled this role, but its successor, the Board of Control, had been defeated by the sheer weight of documentation. Since the abolition of the Board of Control in 1959, there had been no independent statutory body with a direct interest in patients' rights. It was also widely agreed that new and drastic kinds of treatment should be brought under some form of public control, rather than being left to the individual doctor's decision.

The Mental Health Act 1983

Unlike the 1930 and 1959 Acts, the Mental Health Act 1983 was not preceded by a royal commission. In the confused and rather heated state of public discussion, this procedure might have been valuable in enabling experts with conflicting views to come together and to hammer out their differences; but no such royal commissions have been appointed since 1979. The debate was pursued by pressure groups, lobbying, and media publicity. The focus was once more on the control and limitation of psychiatric practice in relation to patients who are legally of detained status. The 1983 Act contains no new statements of general principle, no extension of services, and has little relevance to patients (some 95% of the total in hospital) who are not legally detained, even though some of them are '*de facto* detained', that is, unable to leave hospital, either because they are not capable of making a choice or because they have nowhere to go. Once again we have 'close-textured' prescriptive law, characterised by prohibitions and penalties. The "single contemporary design" of 1959 had been replaced by an updated version of the 1890 Act in which it is again necessary for practitioners to 'know their sections' and to operate according to the letter of the law.

The 1983 Act put considerable responsibility (though little power) in the hands of the Mental Health Act Commission (MHAC). This interdisciplinary body, proposed by the Royal College of Psychiatrists, has been allotted the watch-dog role once carried out by the Lunacy Commissioners and the Board of Control, but with important differences. It is technically a 'special health authority', and reports to the Minister of Health, not to the Lord Chancellor. There are some 90 members from all parts of England and Wales. In addition to medical, legal, and lay members, there are members from the other health professions – nurses, social workers, psychologists, pharmacists, and health service administrators; appointment is part-time, and the membership changes frequently. The chairman is an eminent lawyer.

Teams from the MHAC make regular visits to hospitals to ensure that patients are informed of their civil rights, and any detained patient has a right to an interview in private. Medical Commissioners, and others in some circumstances, are also involved in elaborate 'consent to treatment' proceedings:

> "the nature of the authority that should be provided in new legislation has been the subject of fierce debate. . . . On one side it was argued that decisions about competency are entirely legal matters, outside the province of doctors who prescribe treatment. The medical profession, on the other hand, considered that only doctors are professionally equipped, as a result of their training, to make a comprehensive evaluation of the patient's mental state." (Bluglass, 1983, p. 77)

The complexities of assessing 'informed consent' for different kinds of treatment and of dispensing with it for different categories of patients are considerable. The Commission was also charged under the Act with the task of compiling a code of practice, but its efforts to do so resulted in a document so lengthy, and leaving so little room for professional discretion that the first version was quietly dropped in response to opposition from medical and nursing organisations. A new version was approved in 1990.

The Commission differs in constitution from the Mental Welfare Commission in Scotland, which is a small, permanent, and professional body, able to build up an expertise in inquiry and advice which the more diffuse MHAC may find it hard to match.

The 1983 Act may not have said the last word on the subject of the human rights of mentally ill people. It was introduced in an atmosphere of controversy, and the professional debate was confrontational rather than consensus-seeking. The procedures are cumbersome, unwieldy, and expensive. They apply only to a small – and decreasing – number of detained patients in hospital, and it is doubtful whether elaborate schemes of ward notices, leaflets about civil rights, and formal visits by short-term Commissioners really lead to greater freedom for these patients. There have been too many cases in which the civil-rights leaflets have been found neatly filed away in the patients' dossiers, and the patients disappointed with the results of interviews, because the Commissioners have no power of release.

The future

'Liberty' is a complex concept, as a growing body of human-rights literature testifies (Brownlie, 1973; Davies, 1988). The history of law and mental health suggests that efforts to preserve liberty by the imposition of legal penalties and detailed legal prescription are often self-defeating. A survey of the attempts to frame law for mental illness raises a series of questions for future discussion.

(a) What is the role of Parliament? Over the last two centuries, Parliament has made a major contribution to improving conditions, but this has often been achieved by the mechanism of select committees and the appointment of royal commissions, or by open inquiry and debate, rather than by statutory prohibition. In the 1980s, it was significant that new House of Commons committees undertook some of the review functions of select committees and royal commissions in the past. The House of Commons Social Services Committee (1985) produced a report which has much to say about the inadequacies of community care for mentally ill people: it looks to executive action rather than to statute law for improvement of a situation that raised serious concern.

(b) Could penalties for abuse and neglect be dealt with by more general legislation which protects all patients, and not only those who are technically subject to compulsion? If Britain adopted a human-rights charter into domestic law, would this provide a sufficient basis for the protection of all citizens through the courts, whether mentally ill or not?

(c) Could inspection and professional support (with the emphasis on the latter) be better provided by a small, permanent, full-time team of mental health professionals than by the Mental Health Act Commission as at present constituted?

(d) Could practice issues, including consent to treatment, be dealt with adequately by the Royal College of Psychiatrists and the British Medical Association, as matters of medical discipline?

Conditions for compulsory detention do require legal definition and an appeals mechanism; but, those issues apart, we may be suffering from too much law, in the wrong places, and of the wrong type. The true liberty of psychiatric patients has often been better served by improvements in care and treatment for all who need it (in and out of hospital) than by penal rules to protect the minority. Normative law, which deals primarily with the basic principles of good practice and frees the professionals to regulate their operation, may in the long run prove preferable to prohibition and detailed regulation.

References

AHRENFELD, R. H. (1958) *Psychiatry in the British Army in the Second World War*. London: Routledge & Kegan Paul.

AMERICAN CIVIL LIBERTIES UNION (1973) *The Rights of Mental Patients*. New York: Avon.

BANTON, R., CLIFFORD, P., FROSH, S., *et al* (1985) *The Politics of Mental Health*. London: Macmillan.

BLACK, D. (1976) *The Behavior of Law*. New York: Academic Press.

BLUGLASS, R. (1983) *A Guide to the Mental Health Act 1983*. London: Churchill Livingstone.

BROWNLIE, I. (ed.) (1973) *Basic Documents in Human Rights*. Oxford: Clarendon Press.

CLARE, A. (1976) *Psychiatry in Dissent*. London: Tavistock.

DAVIES, P. (ed.) (1988) *Human Rights*. Oxford: Clarendon Press.

DICEY, A. V. (1915) *The Law of the Constitution* (8th edn). London: Macmillan.
FOUCAULT, M. (1961) *Folie et déraison: histoire de la folie à l'âge classique*. Paris: Plon. (Trans. R. Howard (1965) *Madness and Civilisation*. New York: Pantheon.
GOFFMAN, E. (1961) *Asylums: Essays on the Social Situation of Mental Patients and Other Inmates*. New York: Doubleday.
GOSTIN, L. O. (1975) *A Human Condition*. London: MIND.
GRANVILLE, J. M. (1877) *The Care and Cure of the Insane. Report of the Lancet Commission*. London: Croft.
HOUSE OF COMMONS DEBATES (1943) *House of Commons Debates*, vol. 338, col. 1401, 15 April.
——— (1959) *House of Commons Debates*, vol. 598, col. 704, 26 January.
HOUSE OF COMMONS SELECT COMMITTEE (1816) *Report of the Select Committee on Madhouses*. Parliamentary Papers vol. 104, pp. 1, 317, 321. London: HMSO.
——— (1827 *Report of the Select Committee on Pauper Lunatics in the County of Middlesex, and on Lunatic Asylums*. Parliamentary Papers, vol. 235, p. 73. London: HMSO.
——— (1877) *Report of the Select Committee on the Operation of the Lunacy Laws*. Parliamentary Papers, 373, xiii. London: HMSO.
HOUSE OF COMMONS SOCIAL SERVICES COMMITTEE. *Second Report of the Social Services Committee, Session 1984–5, Community Care, with Special Reference to Adult Mentally Ill and Mentally Handicapped People, vol. 1*. London: HMSO.
HOUSE OF LORDS DEBATES (1884) *House of Lords Debates*, vol. 287, cols 1268–1291, 5 May.
HODDER, E. (1887) *The Life and Work of the Seventh Earl of Shaftesbury, K.G.* London: Cassell.
JONES, K. & FOWLES, A. J. (1984) *Ideas on Institutions*. London: Routledge & Kegan Paul.
KITTRIE, N. N. (1971) *The Right to be Different: Deviance and Enforced Therapy*. Baltimore: Johns Hopkins University Press.
LAING, R. D. (1960) *The Divided Self*. London: Tavistock.
——— & ESTERSON, A. (1964) *Sanity, Madness and the Family*. London: Tavistock.
LEONARD, P. (1985) Editor's Introduction. In *The Politics of Mental Health* (eds K. Banton *et al*) London: Macmillan.
MATTHEWS, F. B. (1948) *Mental Health Services*. London: Shaw & Sons.
LOCKHART ROBINSON, C. (1868) *Journal of Mental Science*, **14**, 583.
METROPOLITAN COMMISSIONERS IN LUNACY (1844) *Report to the Lord Chancellor*. London: HMSO.
PARRY-JONES, W. Ll. (1972) *The Trade in Lunacy*. London: Routledge.
ROYAL COMMISSION (1907) *Report of the Royal Commission on the Care of the Feeble-Minded* (the Radnor Report). London: HMSO.
——— (1926) *Report of the Royal Commission on Lunacy and Mental Disorder* (the Macmillan Report). London: HMSO.
——— (1957) *Report of the Royal Commission on Mental Illness and Mental Deficiency* (the Percy Report). London: HMSO.
ROYAL MEDICO-PSYCHOLOGICAL ASSOCIATION (1945) *Report of Medical Planning Committee: A Memorandum on the Future Organisation of the Psychiatric Services*. London: RMPA.
SCHEFF, T. J. (1966) *Being Mentally Ill*. London: Weidenfeld & Nicolson.
——— (ed.) (1977) *Mental Illness and Social Processes*. London: Harper & Row.
SEDGWICK, P. (1982) *Psycho Politics*. London: Pluto Press.
SZASZ, T. S. (1961) *The Myth of Mental Illness: Foundations of a Theory of Personal Conduct*. New York: Deel.
TUKE, D. H. (1882) *Chapters in the History of the Insane in the British Isles*. London: Kegan Paul.

6 Psychiatry and the early National Health Service: the role of the Mental Health Standing Advisory Committee

CHARLES WEBSTER

This chapter sets out the problems of psychiatry and the mental health services before 1960 as they were perceived by the Mental Health Standing Advisory Committee (MHSAC), the expert body appointed to advise on mental health and mental handicap under the National Health Service (NHS) (Cuthbert, 1967). Inevitably, the MHSAC does not provide an exact mirror either of the profession or the service, but it is a useful vehicle for reflecting issues of high priority within the new health service.

The MHSAC was merely one of a dozen standing advisory committees (SACs) operating under the umbrella of the Central Health Services Council. At the insistence of the medical profession, this advisory machinery was designed to play a vital strategic role in the NHS, but these expectations were not fulfilled (Webster, 1988). Neither the profession nor the government departments were willing to delegate real responsibility to the SACs. Also, the elaborate consultative procedures allowed the various committees to cancel out one another. Consequently, the cumbersome advisory machinery was easily marginalised, and arguably it played only a token part in the development of the health service.

The MHSAC was something of an exception. Most of the advisory committees were controlled by medical politicians, and the MHSAC contained this element, but it also possessed figures of genuine standing and commitment. This committee made a determined attempt to influence events. While many SACs virtually lapsed soon after their inception, the MHSAC was active for more than five years, and thereafter it maintained a discreet and regular presence. Initially, the Committee pushed its remit to an extreme. As an independent, critical voice, its probings and conclusions frequently disconcerted officials. The MHSAC, at least for the first phase in its existence, was the only part of the advisory system to give the impression of coming to terms with the central problems of its sector.

Although this degree of intelligent initiative reflects the intellectual calibre of the Committee, it also indicates that the mental health services were the part of the NHS facing the most acute crisis. The MHSAC could scarcely remain insensitive to the manifold difficulties afflicting the services for which it was responsible; it oscillated between anger and frustration at the failure of the administration of the NHS to respond appropriately to its advice. Its interventions were unwelcome and embarrassing at a time when the new health service was beset by difficulties on all fronts, largely associated with resource constraints. Issues such as prescription charges, the cost of the dental service, waiting lists in acute hospitals, doctors' pay, or lack of capital for new hospitals, monopolised the headlines. Services for the chronically sick attracted little attention. At least before 1960, the MHSAC and the lobbies associated with mental health failed to establish a place on the political agenda for the desperate problems with which they were confronted.

The NHS was launched in 1948 with high expectations on all fronts. Bevan's campaign to 'universalise the best' was designed to bring about a transformation of services, and the mental health services were expected to become major beneficiaries of change. The inception of the NHS indeed marked one of the major organisational turning points in the history of the mental health services in Britain: the changes that were introduced represented the most substantial reform since the development of the county lunatic asylum, 100 years earlier. The new arrangements were calculated to bring the advantages of planning and advanced standards to the health services as a whole. The NHS marked the end of a 25-year campaign to end separate administration of mental health services: this 'isolation' was thought to have impeded progress. 'Integration' was seen as the key to modernisation and to the development of services freed from the taint of the Poor Law and lunacy code. However, the major loose end that was left by the NHS was reform of the law relating to lunacy, and this was duly undertaken in 1959, following the Royal Commission on the Law relating to Mental Illness and Mental Deficiency (1954–57) (see Unsworth, 1987). The Mental Health Act 1959 therefore completed a process of modernisation begun by the National Health Service Act 1946.

As already indicated, the transformation of the mental health services was not as successful or complete as the architects of the NHS had intended. Resource constraints were not the only problem: assimilation of the mental health sector into the NHS was not accomplished without difficulty. Indeed, before 1946, there was little expectation of the inclusion of mental health and mental handicap services in the new health service, and therefore little planning. The Board of Control was taken by surprise and it was subsumed into the NHS structure as an unwilling and inferior partner. Although nominally committed to integration, the Board of Control fought a rearguard action, attempting as far as possible to maintain the autonomy and separate identity of mental health administration (Webster, 1988). These policies were pursued from the best of motives, but they proved damaging to the status of the mental health sector within the regional system of hospital administration adopted under the NHS. Also, the tripartite organisation adopted for the new service was subversive to unified planning of mental health services, and, in this respect, the NHS was at a disadvantage compared with the local-authority administration of mental health services that existed before 1948. From the outset, the mental health sector occupied a weak position within the regional hospital framework. There was a danger of drifting into the worst of both worlds, with the mental health services remaining isolated and not deriving benefits from integration, while risking decline in their share of financial and material resources, owing to the superior influence of other sections of the hospital service.

Although the mental health sector was isolated and disregarded, its problems were massive. At the outset of the NHS, the beds provided in mental hospitals and mental handicap institutions by local authorities (169 000) exceeded the total bed provision in acute hospitals, which had previously been voluntary or operated by local authorities. In 1946, there were 147 000 mental patients, and 53 000 mental handicap patients under institutional care, as well as 47 000 mentally handicapped people in the community, about 5000 of whom were awaiting admission. These numbers were swelled by the inmates of Poor Law institutions: "when the Workhouses are abolished, questions will arise as to the disposal of patients detained in them under Sections 24 and 25, as well as to the disposal of the nondescript medley of uncertified but mentally enfeebled persons now usually to be found in them." It was calculated that workhouses contained 10 000 persons of unsound mind, 10 000 mentally handicapped, and a much greater number of enfeebled elderly.

Hospitals housing mental patients were generally unsuited to modern hospital purposes: they were old, physically inappropriate, poorly provided with amenities, geographically isolated, and mostly too large. The 'desirable maximum' number of beds in a mental hospital accepted within the MHSAC was 1000, yet the Leeds and Manchester regional health boards (RHBs) between them had seven mental hospitals with more than 2000 patients, while the South West Metropolitan RHB itself had seven institutions of this size. Sixty-seven of the 140 mental hospitals housed more than 1000 patients.

The pressures faced by the mental sector had been made worse by World War II, when 35 000 beds had been requisitioned for the Emergency Medical Services, and the ejected patients risked becoming displaced persons. As the pressures on accommodation mounted, especially owing to the virtual doubling of admissions of voluntary patients between 1947 and 1950, the RHBs housing patients evacuated from such areas as London and the Home Counties became increasingly restive. In order to relieve pressure on their accommodation, such regions as Oxford and South Western urged the metropolitan regions to take back such patients. Inevitably, the hard-pressed regions of origin refused, with the result that the patients were exposed to all the hazards associated with overcrowding in humiliating conditions.

In the London area, many mental hospitals also suffered bomb damage, and after the war there were long delays before accommodation was restored to its former use, thus adding to an already serious problem of overcrowding. Even when requisitioned property was returned, the hospital authorities often lacked the finance or nursing staff to be able to restore services. In anticipation of the loss of their mental services, local authorities ceased to invest in maintenance and improvement. The NHS therefore inherited an unsuitable and partly derelict hospital stock, already overcrowded, and each year subjected to ever-increasing demand for treatment, due to such factors as the growth in the population of the elderly, the easing of legal obstacles to access to mental hospitals, and the increased scope of modern psychiatry.

These factors give some impression of the magnitude of the task undertaken by a new health service, which did not possess the resources, the organisation, or an effective scale of priorities needed to effect the modernisation of the mental health sector.

First meetings and personnel of the MHSAC

This was the situation faced by the MHSAC when it first met in March 1949. This was not a particularly prompt start, since preparations for the new health service had begun in earnest in 1946. The main memorandum of guidance to regional hospital boards (RHB(47)13) was dated November 1947 and the appointed day for the new service was 5 July 1948. The MHSAC was therefore not able to participate in the vital planning stages.

Some 30 individuals were involved with the MHSAC before 1960, and the meetings were generally attended by about 15 members, about half of whom were medically qualified, but not all of these were drawn from the field of psychological medicine. However, the latter were the most active members of the Committee. Especially dominant before 1960 was Aubrey Lewis, the outstanding intellect of British psychiatry of the time, and Clinical Director of the Maudsley Hospital since 1936. His aggressive and acerbic style was irritating to many officials, but others, such as George (later Sir George) Godber, the Deputy Chief Medical Officer, appreciated his intellectual qualities. Barter complained that Lewis had been "at times . . . inimical to the Board of Control", and he was also described as "difficult" and "apt to make mischief". Selection as chairman of the MHSAC did little to moderate Lewis's approach. In 1959, he complained that his committee was not being properly consulted by the Ministry. John Bowlby, Director of the Child Guidance Department of the Tavistock Clinic, was also uncongenial to the officials, who resented his campaigning approach. He was described as "a 'live' member, with embarrassing enthusiasm for his own speciality. An advanced theorist who does not always give the weight to practical considerations."

Officials better appreciated W. Gordon Masefield, Medical Superintendent of Brentwood Mental Hospital, Essex, a veteran who had been a prominent figure in the Royal Medico-Psychological Association (RMPA), and its Honorary General Secretary from 1936 to 1945. The officials also liked Desmond Curran and T. P. Rees. Curran, who taught at St George's Hospital, was joint author of a standard textbook, and he was a member of the RMPA Council. Rees was Medical Superintendent of Warlingham Park Hospital, Surrey, and a prominent figure in the World Federation of Mental Health. N. H. M. Burke, the Medical Superintendent of the Cell Barnes Mental Deficiency Colony, near St Albans, was another active member of the Committee, before his retirement in 1958; he was a member of the Council and Education Secretary of the RMPA. Useful recruits in the late 1950s were T. M. Cuthbert, Physician-Superintendent of St Luke's Mental Hospital, Middlesbrough, and D. H. H. Thomas, Burke's successor at Cell Barnes. Besides the above-mentioned involvement in the RMPA, Burke, Masefield, and Rees were members of the Psychological Medicine Group Committee of the British Medical Association (BMA). Therefore, the MHSAC contained some of the leading politicians of psychological medicine, besides including the academic distinction of Bowlby and Lewis.

Neurology was initially represented by the distinguished Russell Brain, but he resigned almost immediately, when monthly meetings were in prospect. He was replaced by the London neurologist Denis Williams. General practitioners were first represented by W. S. MacDonald of Leeds, and by the much more active C. A. H. Watts, who provided a link with the College of General Practitioners. The Society of Medical Officers of Health (SMOH) was first represented by Sir Allen Daley, the experienced Medical Officer of Health to the London County Council (LCC), and therefore, before 1948, the administrator in general charge of the largest mental hospital organisation in the world.

After Daley's retirement, a succession of chairmen of SMOH represented the public health interest during the 1950s.

Nurses and laypersons on the MHSAC made a relatively small contribution, and many of them were poor attenders. The British Psychological Society was first represented by Professor P. E. Vernon, but there was then difficulty in finding a successor. Professor Oliver Zangwill, the Cambridge psychologist, refused to serve; the Board of Control wanted the controversial Hans Eysenck, but this was generally unacceptable. Finally, Miss M. A. Davidson was selected; she had worked as an educational psychologist in Oxford, before transferring to the Warneford Hospital. The most active and respected layperson was Sir Cecil Oakes, Deputy Chairman of the East and West Suffolk Quarter Sessions. Also influential was C. F. Comer, General Secretary of the Confederation of Health Service Employees (COHSE), although he was not entirely popular with officials on account of his vigorous trade union approach. Comer's successor, Claude Bartlett, also an influential figure in COHSE, proved to be more pliable.

Of those mentioned above, Brain, Daley, Lewis, Masefield, and Oakes were also members of the Central Health Services Council. Bartlett, Oakes, and Rees served on the 1954–1957 Royal Commission.

The character of the MHSAC was much influenced by its chairmen. Daley, the first chairman, enjoyed the confidence of the Ministry of Health, with whose officers he had worked amicably for many years. A replacement was needed in 1952, when Daley retired from the LCC and embarked on an extended visit to America. Records of the discussions concerning the choice of a successor are instructive. Percy Barter, Chairman of the Board of Control, strongly advocated the appointment of a layman as MHSAC chairman, arguing that it was "not desirable to have a psychiatrist". For Barter, a layperson experienced in mental administration was the next best thing to a public health official, since, to him, psychiatrists made poor bureaucrats and their judgement was inclined to be suspect. Oakes was a natural choice, but he declined because of quarter sessions duties. In the absence of another layperson of Oakes' standing, it was necessary to turn to a medical man. The reaction to this is again instructive: a psychiatrist was again avoided, in favour of a neurologist. The officials favoured inviting Brain to return to the MHSAC as chairman, but this plan was abandoned because it would have involved premature replacement of Williams. With some reluctance, but without any strong inhibitions, the officials turned at last to the psychiatrist Masefield, who had served as vice-chairman to Daley. Masefield was chairman from 1952 until 1955, with Oakes as vice-chairman. There was again in 1955 a preference among officials for Oakes as chairman, but on this occasion the psychiatrists Rees and Burke were seriously considered. On the advice of George Godber, the more adventurous choice of Lewis was made, again with Oakes as vice-chairman until his death in 1959, when he was replaced by Cuthbert.

The MHSAC almost compares with the Medical SAC and Nursing SAC in its levels of activity during the early years of the NHS, and before 1955 it was arguably the most controversial of the SACS. However, it is important not to exaggerate the scale of its performance. Initially, it was intended to hold monthly meetings, but this objective was achieved only in 1949; in 1950, the meetings were bimonthly and in 1951 and 1952 they were quarterly. Between 1953 and 1960, the meetings were held between twice and four times a year.

This diminished frequency was to some extent compensated for by subcommittees, but after an exhilarating start, the MHSAC drifted into a more routine mode of operation, its leading members participating less actively. By 1960, the MHSAC was no longer seen as a major forum for initiative.

The first meeting of the MHSAC, on 2 March 1949, provides a useful insight into the issues of the day as they were perceived by officials and their advisers. The uppermost problem for officials was the seemingly unremitting expansion of the mental hospital in-patient population; this was an unwelcome development, in view of concern over the escalating costs of the new hospital service. Because elderly patients were accounting for much of this expanded demand in mental hospitals, the MHSAC was asked to provide advice on the mental health problems of the elderly. This was the first initiative under the NHS concerning the health of the elderly, and it provides a foretaste of concerns which have become ever more pressing as the century has progressed.

The Committee raised a variety of issues. Curran asked for information on the supply of psychiatric social workers, a request which was easily met because the Department of Health had, in 1948, appointed a working party to investigate the question. Lewis pressed for discussion of a memorandum on selection and training in the field of child psychiatry that had been produced by the National Association for Mental Health (NAMH). The NAMH urged a national training scheme, which, to Lewis, looked likely to cut across the Diploma of Psychological Medicine. Officials saw this as a potentially embarrassing conflict, because the NAMH had not consulted the Department before circulating the memorandum to RHBs, and Lewis was privately persuaded not to pursue this issue further. Interventions by the NAMH were not universally welcomed, and it is noticeable that proposals to include NAMH representatives on the MHSAC met with considerable hostility. Lewis again intervened to ask for information on the supply of nurses, and he also wanted to know about the likely impact of the new nursing legislation on this supply. As indicated below, Lewis was raising one of the most intractable problems of the mental health services, upon which he led the Committee into confrontation with the line advocated by the Ministry. Finally, Rees asked for information on differences in the organisation of mental health services in the various regions. This was embarrassing to officials, because there was less uniformity than they wanted. Rees was therefore warned that such questions lay outside the scope of the committee, because they related to the "scrutiny of details of administration". Nevertheless, the Committee persisted and the information was supplied. As noted below, during the early years, other attempts were made to constrain the discussions of the Committee on the ground that it was exceeding its remit, but few of these efforts at restriction were successful.

Issues for the Committee

It is appropriate to mention briefly the range of topics which came to the attention of the MHSAC, before dealing with issues which predominated at the meetings. Even issues which were not explored in depth tended to expose points of embarrassment. It has already been noted that the Committee at its first meeting pressed for information about regional organisation, and inquiries showed that the Board of Control's recommendations concerning a uniform regional pattern had not been followed. In 1949, four regions had avoided appointing regional psychiatrists, and the regional mental health committees generally lacked the status and influence wanted by the Board of Control. Furthermore, the Birmingham region had flouted fundamental precepts by amalgamating mental hospitals in mixed groups. The Committee was indignant and the officials were disconcerted when it emerged that the regions were not required to obey central guidelines. This issue was not pursued by the Committee, but it was periodically taken up with regional chairmen (Webster, 1988).

The Committee stumbled into another minefield on questions relating to child psychology – territory upon which Bowlby held passionate views. Dissension was stirred up within the Committee when William Rees Thomas, a senior medical figure within the Board of Control, asked for advice on the newly formed Association of Child Psychotherapists. Rees was persuaded that these lay psychotherapists might be employed within the NHS, subject to certain safeguards of the kind already developed in America. Bowlby was supportive, Lewis open to persuasion, but Curran and MacDonald were violently opposed to condescending to what they described as 'quacks'. In the absence of agreement, the issue was deferred for two years and then indefinitely.

Much greater difficulties were aroused by the Committee's seemingly innocent request in July 1949 to investigate the state of the child guidance service, as part of their general inquiry into preventive psychiatry. The Committee had the idea of inviting evidence and even attendance at meetings from other departments as well as the Ministry of Health. Bowlby and Dugmore Hunter submitted a memorandum on "Preventive Psychiatry with Special Reference to Child Guidance" as a basis for discussion, making clear their support for a unified child guidance service. At the instigation of Bowlby, the MHSAC pressed for an interdepartmental inquiry into child guidance, with terms of reference broader than the investigation into maladjustment set up by the Ministry of Education. The Board of Control quickly concluded that Bowlby was using this to advance his case for a separate government department for children's welfare. Having just emerged from delicate negotiations with the Ministry of Education over the maladjustment inquiry, the Board was opposed to reopening this issue. Barter was also concerned that Bowlby's intervention would be interpreted by other government departments as a breach of faith, after recent contentious negotiations concerning boundaries of responsibility on children's matters between the Board of Control, Ministry of Health, Ministry of Education, and Home Office. Barter was so alarmed that he sought and obtained support from the Permanent Secretary and Minister himself. The Committee was therefore deflected from conducting wide-ranging discussions, although the officials directly concerned were not satisfied that it was proper to inhibit the activities of an independent advisory body.

Preventive psychiatry and mental health education were issues upon which the MHSAC felt obliged to comment, yet its interminable deliberations generated few conclusions. The Committee's discussions were guided by reports emanating from the World Health Organization (WHO, Expert Committee on Mental Health, 1950, 1951), the Commonwealth Fund (Smith, 1949), and individuals such as Bowlby (1951) and Lemkau (1949). The WHO (1950) adopted as a major objective the "encouragement of the incorporation into public health work of the responsibility for promoting the mental as well as the physical health of the community''. The MHSAC aimed to produce a report giving substance to the WHO objectives, but, in 1950, the first effort was judged too diffuse, and eventually, in 1952, the whole enterprise was abandoned. The main aim of the Committee at this stage was to extend the mental health component in the training of public health staff, especially medical officers, and in particular the medical officers concerned with maternity and child welfare. Lewis resurrected the initiative in 1956. On this occasion, the Committee was concerned with diffusing information directly to the public by such mechanisms as films and exhibitions.

Although the above discussions were relatively innocuous, they again raised the question of the Committee's remit when questions relating to medical education arose. The Committee was permitted to comment on the Diploma of Public Health, but was warned off when it wanted to make recommendations concerning the content of undergraduate training, or when it pressed for development of academic psychiatry in the medical schools: it was then told not to trespass into the territory of the General Medical Council.

Such boundaries were difficult to draw, however. When it suited the Ministry, the Committee was encouraged to discuss training, including the development of academic psychiatry, since the shortage of well qualified applicants for training and for senior medical posts afflicted the mental hospitals from the outset. The problem was made worse in 1950, when an arbitrary freeze on medical establishments was imposed, at a time when only 480 out of the required 670 senior medical posts were filled. This occasioned one of Lewis's angry interventions, but there was very little real improvement during the early years of the NHS (Webster, 1988): the incentives were insufficient to attract candidates into training. The insufficient numbers recruited tended to drift into junior hospital medical officer posts, and many of them were eventually promoted to the senior hospital medical officer rank without experiencing academic training. This crisis dominated the work of the Committee in 1954. The geographical isolation of hospitals, the absence of adequate staff accommodation, and unattractive features of the work were blamed for the collapse of recruitment and high wastage rate among trainees. But the Committee fixed upon the ''dearth of training facilities and the lack of contact with an active medical school'' as the primary factor deterring able candidates. It was appreciated that this problem needed to be traced to its roots and that the low status of psychiatry in medical education needed to be corrected.

Pressure was therefore exerted across a broad front for the establishment of chairs and academic departments of psychiatry having parity with other specialties, for the creation of psychiatric units in teaching hospitals, and for the development of joint senior registrar posts between teaching and mental hospitals. A review undertaken in 1960 showed that the regions had developed ingenious training schemes, but most had failed to correct the sense of intellectual isolation experienced by recruits to the specialty. Only in London had joint appointments been developed on any scale.

The MHSAC intervened actively with respect to the training of hospital and public health personnel, but was much less interested in general practitioners. Co-ordination was seen as a problem for hospitals and local authorities, and to some extent, this bias is historically explained. Whereas local authorities had formerly been responsible for developing comprehensive mental health services, the NHS divided this statutory responsibility between RHBs and local health authorities. General practitioners had traditionally worked entirely outside the mental health service, and the tradition of the panel system carried over into the executive council services of the NHS; it is therefore understandable that the general practitioner presence on the MHSAC was negligible. There were further barriers to drawing general practitioners into mental health teams; in particular, the fact that since the outset of the NHS, relations between the BMA and the Ministry of Health were bad, and they were not improved until the 1970s. Consequently, general practice tended to become marginalised, and no real effort was made by the Ministry of Health to modernise primary care. Indeed, by blocking the development of health centres and penalising doctors who sought to modernise their premises and build up practice teams, the bureaucracy contributed to stifling initiative. It is therefore not surprising that a major review of services for the elderly (Boucher, 1957) ignored the contribution made by general practitioners. Despite the interest of individual doctors, little effort was made by NHS authorities to involve general practitioners in the mental health problems of the elderly (Webster, 1991).

It was not until 1956 that the subject of psychiatry and general practice was raised at the MHSAC. Watts wanted a working party to look into this subject, but, instead, the Committee delegated this responsibility to the new College of General Practitioners, whose report *Psychological Medicine in General Practice* was briefly discussed in 1958. Reflecting a growing tide of interest in psychiatry and general practice, the Ministry produced in 1960 a report on *The Part of the Family Doctor in the Mental Health Service*, which was approved by the MHSAC. However, the Committee itself was merely an onlooker in these developments.

The difficulties over recruitment of medical staff drew attention to the problem of maintaining the mental and mental handicap services at their current state, let alone at the enhanced level demanded under the NHS. A variety of solutions to the problem of medical staffing suggested themselves, but the nursing shortage was more severe and intractable. At an early meeting of the MHSAC, Lewis submitted a strongly worded memorandum describing the nursing shortage as "desperately serious", a "desperate situation". He described the situation as a downward spiral, "catastrophic and likely to become worse". His conclusion was that "something almost revolutionary is needed" (Webster, 1988).

The nursing shortage

Officials were not averse to the MHSAC drawing attention to the mental nursing shortage, which was the most serious aspect of a general nursing shortage. The Ministry had in fact evolved a scheme for solving the mental nursing problem, without consultation with the MHSAC, and up to a late point, it hoped that the Committee's involvement would be limited to supporting this plan. Using the Ministry of Labour's National Advisory Council on Recruitment and Training of Nurses, it was proposed that state-enrolled assistant nurses (SEANs) should become an established grade in mental hospitals, along the lines developed in general hospitals since the grade was established in 1943. This scheme was referred to, and was supported by, the Nursing SAC. However, the reaction of the MHSAC was altogether different. Comer, from the perspective of COHSE, was vehemently opposed and at an early stage he co-opted Lewis. This formidable partnership mounted an uncompromising assault on the Ministry's proposals. In turn, they persuaded the MHSAC, bullied the Nursing SAC into retreat, prevailed upon the Central Health Services Council to back their line, and finally fought off attempts by the Ministry to reintroduce its SEAN scheme until 1962.

The critics argued that the Ministry's proposal was founded on the false premise that mental nursing required only a low level of nursing skill, akin to that required in the care of the chronically sick in geriatric wards. Comer adopted the uncompromising line that the nursing in the mental sector should be undertaken exclusively by fully trained staff or student nurses. The primary objective should therefore be an improvement in conditions, education, and pay, which would attract recruits capable of undertaking the full course of training. This was in fact the policy traditionally adopted by the RMPA, the Mental Hospitals Association, COHSE, and the Board of Control, but in all likelihood, but for the intervention of Comer and Lewis, it would have been abandoned under the NHS. These two argued that the SEAN measure would make matters worse: on the basis of past experience, it seemed unlikely that the introduction of such a grade would attract many more recruits. Rather, it was likely to deflect students from full training, and therefore dilute standards, as well as complicating the vocational and training structure. However, as it was conceded that an entirely registered nurse workforce was not likely to be a practical proposition in the near future, it was proposed that nursing assistants, who comprised about 25% of the existing workforce, should continue to be employed, but as a fixed percentage of the nursing total, and it was agreed that elementary training should be provided for this auxiliary grade.

The Ministry was depressed by the collapse of its SEAN initiative, and an added concern was the degree to which the pay of nurses was invoked by the MHSAC as a cause for recruitment difficulties. The MHSAC was reminded that such matters fell into the remit of the Whitley Councils rather than the advisory committees, but the Committee persisted, and reference to pay was included in its final recommendations:

> "It is considered that three factors affecting recruitment of student nurses, particularly male, call for close and urgent consideration, i.e. (a) pay, (b) conditions of work, and (c) methods connected with teaching and training. It is not to be expected that there can be a satisfactory solution of the problems of nurse staffing unless these three factors are tackled realistically." (Unpublished internal memorandum of the Committee, 18 February 1954)

These conclusions provided the basis for a sustained but unsuccessful campaign by COHSE for higher remuneration for mental nurses, which in 1956 led to the first general industrial action ever taken in the NHS (Webster, 1988).

Overcrowding in hospitals

Staff shortages exacerbated an already existing problem of overcrowding. With the steady increase in demand and the threat of the system becoming swamped by long-stay elderly patients, the mental health sector faced an acute crisis in maintaining standards of treatment. In 1949, Lewis had warned that the system was on the verge of breakdown: in 1950, a level of 14% overcrowding was recorded for the mental health sector, the worst difficulties being on the female side, where there was also the most severe staff shortage. The report of the MHSAC's Sub-Committee on Coordination of the Functions of Mental Hospitals and Local Authorities, which was produced in 1956 (SAC(MH)(56)4), just after the all-time peak was reached in the mental hospital population, confirmed that without a radical change in policy, the pressures for further expansion of the institutional system were likely to continue. At this stage, regional boards had made provision for 4700 additional beds, and proposals for new mental hospitals and mental handicap institutions figured prominently in their capital spending plans. The Chief Medical Officer's report for 1954 had anticipated the provision of 9000 additional beds, while the 1956 Coordination Sub-Committee's report estimated that, to be realistic, 14 000 additional beds were required. The expansion in the number of elderly in-patients – from 16.4% in 1944 to 20.1% in 1954 – in the mental hospital sector suggested that the demand of this age group for bed space was likely to escalate. At the height of the government's campaign for retrenchment in NHS expenditure, this prospect raised the question of whether it lay within the capacity of the state to enter into such a commitment: "The burden on the State in terms of the money and absorption of manpower of provision to this extent, will be serious indeed in relation to any view of the future economy." The Coordination Sub-Committee was therefore driven to consider whether the increase in beds was the only solution, and after a critical examination of the problem, concluded that relatively simple measures might radically reduce pressure on hospital resources. Better classification might lead patients to be treated more effectively outside the mental hospital sector, while the combination of "timely medical treatment and social services" was especially hopeful. Exploitation of this alternative, education of the public, and the introduction of an active rehabilitation ethos in hospitals were thought to offer means for preventing the continuing explosion of the mental hospital population.

The combined effects of staff shortage, overcrowding, and economic pressures impelled the MHSAC to reconsider their attitudes to in-patient care in all parts of the mental health service. With respect to mental handicap patients, the Committee moved away from the policy established during the inter-war period, which favoured concentration of the handicapped in comprehensive 1000-bed institutions. They accepted proposals by Lewis which questioned the suitability of large institutions for "high grade mental defectives", who constituted more than 50% of the institutional population. Lewis proposed that such patients should be removed to small hostels, housing a maximum of 30 to 40 individuals, believing that such hostels could "bring about the restoration of a large percentage of these to an independent life in the community". An optimistic attitude was adopted towards possibilities for rehabilitation, and even 'sub-Rampton' patients were thought to be suitable, providing that appropriate industrial and agricultural schemes were devised. The Committee gained comfort from the Piercy report on rehabilitation, which gave its support for such schemes (Committee of Inquiry on the Rehabilitation and Resettlement of Disabled Persons, 1956).

The MHSAC was receptive to the extension of 'community care', and this term was part of their vocabulary from the outset. They followed with interest the expansion in occupational centres for the mentally handicapped, or plans for the wider provision of psychiatric social workers. They were sympathetic to the development of boarding-out schemes for mental patients, but little support for this idea emanated from the regions (Crutcher, 1944). Day hospitals emerged as the main hope for the extension of community care for patients in mental hospitals. The Committee's discussions of these began in November 1950, largely based on the experience of Cameron at the Allen Memorial Institute at McGill University, Montreal, where such work began in 1946. Godber visited McGill and reported on it enthusiastically in June 1951, shortly after his return from Canada. The regions were asked to give their backing to day hospitals, but there was little interest at the regional level, where it was pleaded that any experiments should be funded centrally. In most places, day hospitals were pioneered by individual enthusiasts, with little encouragement from the regional boards (Bierer, 1951).

Day hospitals emerged again in discussions of the care of the elderly (it will be recalled that this was the first problem referred to the MHSAC by the Minister). Daley led the discussion by producing a memorandum which provided an account of the LCC's experience in this field. Moreover, the Committee took its standpoint from the recent BMA report *The Care and Treatment of the Elderly and Infirm* (1947), which advocated a rehabilitation regime and less reliance on institutional accommodation. Lionel Cosin, an active member of the BMA committee, became a pioneer of the day hospital for elderly patients through his work at Cowley Road Hospital, Oxford. The MHSAC report *Care of the Aged*, produced in August 1949, followed the BMA report in proposing the establishment of geriatric departments containing psychiatric observation sections, attached to general and teaching hospitals, and also the development of long-stay annexes attached to geriatric departments or mental hospitals. It was estimated by Lewis that 18% of mental patients might be transferred to such long-stay annexes.

At the time of the MHSAC report on the elderly, a survey showed that there were in existence only six short-stay psychiatric units attached to general and teaching hospitals, three of them being associated with London teaching hospitals in the South West Metropolitan Region. Subsequent reports showed slow progress with both short-stay units and long-stay annexes. The Committee members kept up their spirits by sympathetically following imaginative schemes for reducing reliance on mental hospital facilities. As expected, their attention fixed on district psychiatric unit schemes developed in Lancashire, the best-known example being at Oldham, and also the Nottingham scheme which took Amsterdam as its model. The success of both the Oldham and Nottingham experiments depended on greater co-operation between hospital authorities and local health authorities than had proved possible in most areas, but Cuthbert, in describing his own efforts, recorded bad relations with some local health authorities. The enthusiasms of the MHSAC gradually percolated into the annual reports of the Chief Medical Officer, and the Report for 1955, produced in 1956, closely follows the thinking of the MHSAC. This report indicates a new bias of opinion within the Ministry of Health, largely anticipating the 1957 Royal Commission report: the conventional hospital building programme was played down, faith now being placed in "domiciliary care, out-patient and day hospital services, combined with proper care of the aged outside the mental hospitals". This thinking was only a short step from the dramatic formulations of Enoch Powell, which shook the mental health service to its roots in 1961 (National Association for Mental Health, 1961).

The role of the Committee

In conclusion, it cannot be pretended that the MHSAC performed the dynamic role wanted by the medical profession during the NHS negotiations. In the event, it suited both the profession and the Ministry of Health to relegate the standing advisory machinery to the sidelines, though to some extent the MHSAC resisted this diminution in its functions. However, structural factors determined that the influence of the Committee was severely limited. Sometimes, the MHSAC took up initiatives started by others in the NHS, while on other occasions, it was something of a prime mover. The Committee exercised some influence within the Ministry of Health, and its views seem particularly to have affected the annual reports of the Chief Medical Officer. This pressure radiated out in a diffuse manner in the regions, although the degree of influence attributable to the collection of central departmental agencies has yet to be determined.

The record of the MHSAC is primarily useful as an index of opinion concerning the problems of the NHS, especially among psychiatrists. Some of the major preoccupations of psychiatrists during the early years of the NHS have been discussed above. Particularly interesting is the early commitment of the MHSAC to reversing the trend towards the expansion of in-patient care, through exploitation of a variety of alternatives, mostly associated with 'community care'. Many factors drew the Committee towards this conclusion. They were aware that innovations in psychopharmacology would ease the transition to out-patient care, but this was not their primary consideration. They were perhaps especially influenced by the regime of retrenchment affecting the NHS at the time. Upon inspection, it became apparent that a significant section of the in-patient populations of mental and mental handicap hospitals was unnecessarily institutionalised. Superior non-institutional alternatives could be devised, and had been tried with some success elsewhere, but inertia and financial restraint prevented the systematic realisation of community care in Britain. Indeed, the aspirations of the MHSAC of the 1950s have hardly been realised today: the mental health services were neglected then and have remained underfunded and generally unappreciated, yet they have performed a colossal humanitarian task. A tribute paid by a senior official (Wrigley) in 1957 provides a suitable conclusion to this review, and also it is a graceful reminder of the achievements of the mental health services under the early NHS:

> "I am aware that the medical staffs of mental hospitals, no less than other members of their staffs, have carried an almost intolerable burden in recent years. To the problem of antiquated buildings has been added that of overcrowding, and greatly increased pressure on mental hospitals has coincided with a period of great advance in treatment. It is to the eternal credit of the medical staffs that in these circumstances the amount of active treatment carried out in our mental hospitals should have increased out of all measure, and the turnover of patients accelerated so greatly. The index of their success is the great number of patients now returned rapidly to their place in the community, and the increasing happiness and satisfaction of those chronic cases whose stay must, by reasons of their illness, be protracted and indeed of indefinite duration. To have achieved so much in such conditions is something which reflects the greatest credit on all members of the hospital staffs."

References

BIERER, J. (1951) *The Day Hospital. An Experiment in Social Psychotherapy*. London.

BOUCHER, C. A. (1957) *Survey of Services Available to the Chronic Sick and Elderly, 1954–1955*. London: HMSO.

BOWLBY, J. (1951) *Maternal Care and Mental Health*. Geneva: WHO.

COMMITTEE OF INQUIRY ON THE REHABILITATION AND RESETTLEMENT OF DISABLED PERSONS (1956) *Report of Committee*, cmd 9883. London: HMSO.

CRUTCHER, H. B. (1944) *Foster Home Care for Mental Patients*. New York: Commonwealth Fund.

CUTHBERT, T. M. (1967) Advisory mechanisms of the National Health Service. In *New Aspects of the Mental Health Services* (eds H. L. Freeman & J. Farndale), pp. 168–185. Oxford: Pergamon.

LEMKAU, P. V. (1949) *Mental Hygiene in Public Health*. New York: McGraw-Hill.

NATIONAL ASSOCIATION FOR MENTAL HEALTH (1961) *Everybody's Business: The 1959 Mental Health Act*. London: NAMH.

SMITH, G. (1949) *Human Relations in Public Health*. New York: Commonwealth Fund.

UNSWORTH, C. (1987) *The Politics of Mental Health Legislation*. Oxford: Clarendon.

WEBSTER, C. (1988) *Problems of Health Care. The National Health Service Before 1957*. London: HMSO.

—— (1991) The elderly and the early National Health Service. In *Life, Death and the Elderly: Historical Perspectives* (eds M. Pelling & R. Smith) (in press).

WORLD HEALTH ORGANIZATION, EXPERT COMMITTEE ON MENTAL HEALTH (1950) *Report on the First Session*, technical report no. 9. Geneva: WHO.

—— (1951) *Report on the Second Session*, technical report no. 31. Geneva: WHO.

Other sources

Internal memoranda reporting the proceedings of the MHSAC meetings, from which a number of quotations have been drawn, include DH 94101, DH 94198 and DH 94151, and the annual reports of the Chief Medical Officer have also been used. Useful collections and more recent relevant analyses of near contemporary papers include the following:

BUSFIELD, J. (1986) *Managing Madness: Changing Ideas and Practice*. London: Hutchinson.

FREEMAN, H. & FARNDALE, J. (1963) *Trends in Mental Health Services*. Oxford: Pergamon.

—— & —— (eds) (1967) *New Aspects of the Mental Health Services*. Oxford: Pergamon.

—— & BENNETT, D. H. (1990) District psychiatric services and general hospital psychiatry: origins and development. In *Community Psychiatry* (eds D. H. Bennett & H. L. Freeman). London: Churchill Livingstone.

JONES, K. (1972) *A History of the Mental Health Services*. London: Routledge.

SCULL, A. T. (1977) *Decarceration: Community Treatment and the Deviant – A Radical View*. Englewood Cliffs, NJ: Prentice-Hall.

7 The establishment of the Royal College of Psychiatrists

JOHN G. HOWELLS

Even though there is an onward surge of history, movement is irregular – sometimes halting on a plateau. Psychiatrists were on a plateau for 40 years; they should have had a College when the Royal Medico-Psychological Association (RMPA) was founded in 1926, since it then had all the attributes of one. But the strong prejudice against irrational mental patients was projected on to their helper, the psychiatrist. Ultimately, the time for change had come. This is a personal account of it, as seen by a close participant.

The change from an association to a College, like any other, has material, professional, legal, and political components, as well as a psychological one. Change is never smooth, since individuals fear the loss of their established positions, whatever those may be, and in the case of British psychiatry, those who thought they had the most to lose fought most against it. Yet it is now clear that no one had anything real to lose. Understanding this change is a lesson in applied psychology.

Historical perspective

English medicine originated in astrology, alchemy, rhetoric, and philosophy. The three early claimants in this field – surgeon (Cope, 1959), physician (Clark, 1964–72), and apothecary (Wall, 1963) – worked out their own sectors of endeavour, not without conflict. Eventually, each discipline crystallised its interests and knowledge, and founded its own corporate association, but as knowledge grew, they could not encompass the new disciplines that arose, and these too formed their own associations within the corpus of medicine. Similar historical developments took place over the years in Scotland (Comrie, 1932) and Ireland (Fleetwood, 1951).

By history and common usage, the highest professional bodies in medicine were termed 'Colleges', with special responsibilities, functions, and standards. The term originated from the European *collegium*, based on the city guilds, consisting of people with common rights and privileges. The importance of the title can be seen from the fact that the venerable Faculty of Surgeons and Physicians of Glasgow, founded in 1599, tried unsuccessfully to be called a 'College' in 1817, and only succeeded finally in 1961. Physicians formed the College of Physicians of London in 1518, but maintained from the beginning the right to represent all sections of medicine, including surgery – a claim which was only given up in the Medical Act 1956! The surgeons, frustrated on a number of occasions, achieved their Royal Charter in 1800 by an enterprising direct appeal to the King.

During the 19th century the general practitioners (GPs), some of whom belonged to the Society of Apothecaries of London, also aspired to a College. It is of interest that George Burrows, an outstanding protagonist of the Apothecaries Act 1815 that led to the accepted place of the general practitioner, was thereafter to devote his time exclusively to psychiatry. However, the GPs were to wait over 100 years before achieving their College in 1952, and a Royal College in 1967.

The physicians continued to maintain their collegiate grip on obstetrics and the surgeons on gynaecology, but the obstetricians and gynaecologists began their search for independence in the 1920s, and achieved success in 1929 with the foundation of the College of Obstetricians and Gynaecologists (Shaw, 1954; Royal College of Obstetricians and Gynaecologists 1989). The Royal College of Physicians founded a higher examination in obstetrics, in an effort to retain them within their College (Clark, 1964–72), and made similar efforts in relation to psychiatry and pathology some 30 years later. In 1937, the College of Obstetricians and Gynaecologists received a 'Royal' prefix. More recently, the pathologists became restive within the Royal College of Physicians and, faced with the alternative of a faculty within that College or a separate College, chose the latter. Their efforts, which were started in 1950, led to a College in 1963 and a Royal College in 1970 (Foster, 1981).

An unexpected but dramatic twist of fortune in the foundation of Colleges took place in 1960. Desiring an act of Parliament to move their headquarters from Trafalgar Square to Regents Park, the physicians of London found – to their chagrin and everyone's surprise – that they were not entitled to the appellation 'Royal': they had assumed it (*British Medical Journal*, 1960). The matter was put right in the College of Physicians of London Bill 1960, but opening their new building, the Queen was to gently chide them on their anticipation (*British Medical Journal*, 1964; *Lancet*, 1964*b*). Thus the physicians achieved the status of a genuine Royal College only 11 years before psychiatrists.

Psychiatrists had formed themselves into a professional body, the Association of Medical Officers of Asylums and Hospitals for the Insane, in 1841 – therefore the oldest professional body of psychiatrists in the world. In 1865, this became the Medico-Psychological Association of Great Britain and Ireland, and in 1926 it was granted the distinction of a Royal Charter, becoming the Royal Medico-Psychological Association (RMPA). However, psychiatrists were still denied a College then, and thus a place in the higher councils of medicine.

Reasons for change

The inception of the National Health Service in July 1948 brought a quiet revolution in psychiatry – quiet because psychiatrists had neither asked for it nor been in a position to influence the two fundamental changes that occurred. Firstly, the mental hospital was given the same status as the general hospital, within the same system of administration. Secondly, the most senior medical officers in mental hospitals were given the same status and conditions of service as senior clinicians in other fields; they all became consultants. Psychiatrists seemed to have parity with fellow consultants, but the control of their clinical work lay with the medical superintendent, who had powers of admission and discharge of patients.

It was the need to achieve clinical freedom which led to the formation of the Society of Clinical Psychiatrists, since the RMPA was dominated by medical superintendents. Opportunity came with the Mental Health Act 1959 when, through the Society's influence, the power of admission and discharge was given to "the responsible medical officer", that is, the consultant. The British Medical Association had set up a small group of advisers, who attended the committee stage of the bill in its passage through Parliament. When the sentence about the "responsible medical officer" was passed, Dr Sommerville Hastings, a medical Member of Parliament, waved his order paper in the air and shouted "At last we are rid of them". At last, psychiatrists had achieved clinical freedom.

The National Health Service also opened the way to redressing the balance between physical and psychological medicine, but it needed access to, and the power to influence, decision-making authorities. After a few years, psychiatrists were increasingly moving into general hospitals, and by 1961 they were the third largest group of specialists – surgeons numbering 1193, physicians 1178, psychiatrists 1063, pathologists 800, and obstetricians 590. But the protagonists of a Royal College for psychiatry were faced with a forbidding and degrading situation.

A profession's control over its own standards lies in its examinations, which monitor the national standards achieved by the training programme. However, the examination in psychiatry was not under the control of psychiatrists. The Certificate of Efficiency in Psychological Medicine was founded by the Medico-Psychological Association in 1885. This was replaced by a Diploma in Psychological Medicine in 1948 and, in 1954, leased to the Conjoint Board of the Royal Colleges of Physicians and Surgeons. There was no higher examination in psychiatry on a par with those of the Colleges. Yet most psychiatrists felt it unreasonable to have their competence in psychiatry assessed by an examination in another discipline.

Matters were no better in terms of representations to the government on matters of policy: on psychiatric matters, the government looked for this to the Royal College of Physicians. Members of the RMPA, especially Alexander Walk, spent much time and effort in preparing evidence for the Royal Commission on Mental Illness which reported in 1959. Yet its deputy chairman, Sir Cecil Oakes, told me that the Commission would be guided by the evidence coming from the Royal College of Physicians, which they regarded as being of paramount importance in psychiatric affairs.

Psychiatric presence on most influential professional committees was non-existent: specialist advisers to committees appointing consultant psychiatrists were nominated by the Royal College of Physicians, while on important professional committees, such as the Joint Consultants Committee, and on the regulatory General Medical Council, psychiatrists had no direct representation. Similarly, they had no direct representation on the National Health Services' Merit Awards Committee, and suffered thereby; only 14% of psychiatrists received a merit award in 1962, compared with over 50% of consultants in medicine and surgery.

Important *ad hoc* government committees which were set up from time to time rarely had psychiatrists among their members. Thus, there were abundant rational grounds for change, and these had been present since the foundation of the RMPA.

The quest for a College

The quest for a Royal College fell in two periods, together spanning just over ten years from 1960 to 1971. The first was concerned with inviting discussion on the issue, with psychiatrists making collective decisions, and finally resolving to ask for a Royal College. This was a phase in the open, culminating in instructions by the members to the officers to petition for a 'supplemental charter': it can be called the Years of Decision, 1960–64. The second period covered the phase of negotiation with the Privy Council, the Royal College of Physicians, and the government. All the struggle, determination, and effort that had gone on in the open before now went on in private, resulting in it being largely lost to most members, because privacy was demanded as a proper condition of negotiation. These difficult years can be termed the Years of Negotiation, 1964–71.

Although it seems obvious today that psychiatrists needed a Royal College, in 1961 few of our medical colleagues and few influential psychiatrists felt that. Even as an active supporter, I myself experienced moments of doubt in those ten years, when the thought crept in that perhaps the objectors were right in thinking that psychiatrists did not deserve the highest status.

The years of decision

The period November 1960 to July 1964 covers the events within and around the RMPA that culminated in a decision by its members to petition the Privy Council for a supplemental charter that would allow a change of name to the Royal College of Psychiatrists. The four significant steps in this phase were:

(a) the formation of a special committee to explore the desirability of a Royal College
(b) the deferred annual meeting in November 1963, which revealed overwhelming support for a Royal College
(c) the postal vote in May 1964, which confirmed the support for a Royal College
(d) the annual meeting in Basingstoke in July 1964, which instructed Council to petition.

The special committee

On a number of occasions since the formation of the RMPA in 1926, the matter of founding a Royal College had been raised in its Council meetings. In 1957, when T. P. Rees was President, a committee with N. Harris as chairman and O. W. S. Fitzgerald as secretary was appointed by Council to consider a special distinction in psychiatry – a Fellowship, to be gained by thesis and awarded by the Association. This committee reported in June 1957 (Royal Medico-Psychological Association, 1957), its rambling document expressing the fear that the Royal College of Physicians "could take offence and its MRCP be circumvented". Council took no action. In 1959, Council decided that "the time was not ripe for the establishment of a College".

It was raised yet again in 1960, probably on the initiative of T. P. Rees, who had the matter discussed in the Psychological Medicine Committee of the British Medical Association, which referred it to the RMPA Council. It was my first opportunity to speak on the issue of a College and, for my boldness, I was elected a member of the special committee set up to explore the matter. This was appointed in November 1960 and had the following members: A. Walk (Chairman and President), A. B. Monro (General Secretary), R. W. Crockett, D. Curran, M. Cuthbert, J. Howells, J. T. Hutchinson, W. M. Millar, L. Rees, W. Sargant, T. Tennent, C. Tetlow, D. H. H. Thomas, and W. Warren. It was to consider three possibilities: (a) establishing a faculty for psychiatry within the Royal College of Physicians; (b) founding a Royal College of Psychiatrists from the RMPA; (c) retaining the RMPA and improving it.

It was clear at the first meeting that the special committee, constituted as it was by Alexander Walk, would never propose a Royal College. However, each viewpoint had strong protagonists – Alexander Walk for the RMPA, Desmond Curran (with the influential support of Aubrey Lewis outside the committee) for a Faculty, and myself for a Royal College. Walk was an implacable adversary of the College. Erudite, a scholar of distinction, courteous, gentlemanly, and creative, he had served the Association loyally for many years. Denied an academic career by the need at a critical moment to support his family, his great gifts had been poured into the RMPA. He *was* the RMPA. Unhappily, he could not be brought to see that his years of toil would be rewarded by its metamorphosis into a Royal College. His formidable administrative skill was a big factor in delaying success for ten years, and his actions in this respect were at times at variance with his usual high standards.

The notion of a faculty within the Royal College of Physicians (RCP) had major drawbacks. Firstly, the RCP regarded itself as a generality that represented the whole of medicine. This claim was, of course, denied by the surgeons, obstetricians, and pathologists, who considered themselves major separate specialties; this was also true of psychiatry. Secondly, psychiatry was likely to have always a subsidiary role within the RCP, which then had 4000 members but only 900 Fellows; not many senior psychiatrists were likely to become Fellows. Only two psychiatrists, Aubrey Lewis in the recent past and Desmond Curran currently, had ever sat on its ruling body, Comitia. Thirdly, only consultants would initially become members of a faculty, so that many psychiatrists and all trainees would be left outside it. Fourthly, the RCP was the Royal College of Physicians *of London*; all Scottish and Irish psychiatrists would be lost to a faculty. Fifthly, the examination in psychiatry would not be termed 'MRCP', and might be just a diploma. In any event, the MRCP was regarded by the physicians as a mark of entry into training for physicians, whereas psychiatrists needed a higher examination that denoted the successful completion of their training. The examination would not be wholly in psychiatry, but also in general medicine. Lastly, psychoanalysts in particular were uneasy about an emphasis which the physicians might impose on the organic aspects of psychiatry.

The Comitia of the RCP probably preferred the RMPA to continue as it was but, if pressed, would found a faculty to counter a prospective Royal College of Psychiatrists. The drive for a faculty came from its Psychological Medicine Committee, chaired by Lord Brain and with Desmond Curran and Aubrey Lewis as prominent members. Though the latter two men were very different, probably the only matter they ever agreed upon was the undesirability of a Royal College of Psychiatrists, and even then they did not act together.

Aubrey (later Sir Aubrey) Lewis was brilliant, and yet cramped by nihilism; despite his exceptional gifts, his legacy of creativity was small. Trained by Adolph Meyer, he held British psychiatry in a Meyerian grip for about half a century. An elitist, he was uncomfortable with his contemporaries in the RMPA and played no part in that body's affairs. As his registrar, I had enjoyed his erudition and sense of humour, but later, matters were less cordial. He addressed an assembled company of psychiatrists at a reception at the Royal College of Physicians' beautiful building and, pointing to me, said "This man would take this away from you".

Desmond Curran was not Lewis' intellectual equal, but he had a debonair ruthlessness. Senior psychiatrist to the Navy during World War II, he was loyal to his shipmates, even after peace came. He opposed the College until its foundation, instigated the move to give the RMPA premises within the RCP, and pressed for an examination within the RCP to be announced at the time of the postal ballot of RMPA members. He wrote against the College in the *British Medical Journal* and the *Lancet*, addressed divisional meetings in the same sense, and, at meetings of the special committee, unreservedly advocated a faculty. However, when the time came, both Curran and Lewis accepted Honorary Fellowships of the new Royal College.

One meeting of the special committee took evidence from Professor W. H. McNemeney, then President of the Association of Clinical Pathologists and a friend of Curran. Opposed to the claim of pathologists for a College, since he favoured a faculty within the RCP, he yet – remarkably – thought that psychiatrists should have a College. He regarded a separate College as logical, since psychiatrists were less close to general medicine than were pathologists. In fact, the evidence from all quarters seemed to point to the need for a Royal College, yet at the first expression of the committee's opinion in March 1961, there was deadlock – approximately the same number favoured each of the three points of view. Next, a compromise took place; ten members settled for an improved RMPA, and only myself for a Royal College. Documents were then prepared to be sent to Council and afterwards to members of the Association, advocating the compromise of an improved RMPA. After advice from T. P. Rees, I asked to exercise my right to write a minority report, but despite my protests, this was never sent to Council, strongly arousing my interest in the College issue. The documents, but not the minority report, were circulated to the membership and provoked 352 letters. Of these, 183 favoured the RMPA, 105 a faculty, and only 69 (19%) a College. Though disappointing to the advocates of a College, this result was clearly understandable, in that the case for a College had not been put.

During the period 1960–63, other parallel events were taking place. The Group for the Representation of the Views of Clinical Psychiatrists changed its name in 1961 to the Society of Clinical Psychiatrists (SCP) and, thereafter, had the place in British psychiatry taken by the Group for the Advancement of Psychiatry in the United States – a goad or stimulus to the main professional body. When a questionnaire on the three points of view was addressed by the SCP to its members, 74% supported the notion of a Royal College. I prepared a memorandum for the SCP, putting and answering a dozen questions about a Royal College. When this was sent to 1000 psychiatrists in Britain, the return showed support for a Royal College from 80%.

In the meantime, there was activity within the Royal College of Physicians. At Curran's instigation, it was suggested that the RMPA should take up premises within the new RCP building. There was, however, a daunting obstacle, in that the RMPA's annual rent was then £700, but within the RCP premises, this would go up sevenfold, to £5000 per annum.

In September 1963, correspondence on the subject of the College commenced in the *British Medical Journal* and the *Lancet*, continuing to May 1964, the time of the postal ballot. Of the 67 letters that appeared, 49 were favourable to the foundation of a College and 18 were against. Each time the correspondence appeared to lapse, a provocative letter from the opposition engendered hostility, and the subject was taken up again. A new opposition group emerged in a letter representing the views of the Association of Teachers of Psychiatry in Undergraduate Medical Schools by its Chairman, William Sargant, and Secretary, Martin (later Sir Martin) Roth. This journal correspondence was necessary because the RMPA's own journal steadfastly refused to publish anything about this major issue. Alexander Walk still exercised a considerable influence over the journal and the current editor, Eliot Slater, could not or did not wish to over-rule him. In November 1961 I suggested that articles should appear on all three points of view, and these did appear, but not until January 1963, in a special supplement (*British Journal of Psychiatry*, 1963).

In October 1963, Erwin Stengel, Chairman of the Northern and Midland Division of the RMPA, suggested to me that I attend a meeting at Sheffield, when there would be an address by the President, Curran, on the notion of a Royal College (*British Journal of Psychiatry*, 1964). Curran took as his theme my letter, recently published in the *British Medical Journal*, and set about demolishing it, sentence by sentence. It was such a destructive speech that Stengel rose to his feet and suggested that as the writer of the letter was present, as a guest of the Division, he ought to be granted a right of reply. There was general agreement to this, and thus the case for a College was put, though many of the contributions which followed from the floor were against the idea. At the end of the discussion, the Chairman called for a secret ballot, after which there was lunch. When the meeting resumed, Stengel almost casually mentioned the result: there was a two-to-one majority in favour of a Royal College. This was a significant portent of events to come, and the first public breakthrough.

The deferred annual meeting, November 1963

Piqued that my minority report had not been circulated to Council and at my inability (as yet) to get the matter discussed in the *British Journal of Psychiatry*, I made a search of the RMPA by-laws, to see if there was any avenue of protest. I discovered, in fact, that any one member had the right, after giving due notice, to raise a matter at the annual meeting; this right is still preserved in the by-laws of the College. I thus wrote to the General Secretary in March 1963 with a resolution advocating a petition for a Royal College, to be moved at the annual meeting in July 1963. This action was not well received, and at the Council meeting in July, I was put under intense pressure to withdraw it. The officers claimed that the situation was inconvenient, that the issue was becoming irksome, and that it was premature. Ultimately a compromise was reached: I agreed not to upset the arrangements at the annual meeting, on condition that the business meeting was deferred to the quarterly meeting in November 1963. Being a deferred annual meeting, rather than a quarterly meeting, it was still possible for me to move my resolution. Furthermore, there was the advantage that the November meeting was being held in London.

Thus, at the November meeting, held at the Royal Society of Medicine, I was able to move my resolution and to speak in favour of the foundation of a College. It was also arranged for two additional speakers, Denis (later Sir Denis) Hill to speak on a faculty within the RCP, and Leslie Cook to speak on maintaining the status quo. That meeting was full of excitement, the ebb and flow of argument, and the decisive interventions were memorable (*British Journal of Psychiatry*, 1964*b*). William Sargant, for instance, appealed to members not to break now with the RCP. However, Henry Dicks called for a "home of our own", while T. F. Main claimed we were "a grown-up outfit", and David Stafford-Clark asserted that "we must not retreat to a corner". At the end of the discussion, Alexander Walk cleverly moved an amendment, which would have the effect of replacing my motion. This was a prescription for delay, while at the same time appealing to the members by promising a postal vote on the issue. This motion was carried, after a recount, by 70 votes to 64, but by great good fortune, Curran and Walk then made a wrong assessment: they assumed that because the amendment had been carried, the majority of those present were against a College. Responding to a member from the floor, the President called for my resolution to be put, anticipating an anti-College vote. But the resolution was carried by 85 members in favour and 26 against. Thus there was the best of all possible outcomes – the members had expressed themselves in favour of a Royal College and the officers had offered a postal vote (*British Medical Journal*, 1963). The *Lancet* (1963) commented that matters would now have to be handled "with a greater sense of urgency".

Another happy sequel occurred at the end of the meeting. W. S. Maclay, a Commissioner of the Board of Control at the Ministry of Health, approached me with the words, "I am with you now". As the incoming President of the RMPA, he would be under intense pressure from many close friends to oppose a College, but before taking up his presidency, he died from a heart attack, to the great loss of British psychiatry.

Meanwhile, in October 1963, the Psychological Medicine Committee of the Royal College of Physicians met under the President, Sir Charles Dodds. They had before them my memorandum of 12 questions which had been circulated to psychiatrists (Society for Clinical Psychiatrists, 1964). After a motion had been moved by Sir Denis Hill, a vote showed that 44 members were against the foundation of a College of Psychiatrists and five were in favour. However, only 23 were in favour of a faculty within the RCP, 21 being against. At the end of the meeting, the following motion was carried: "this meeting looks to the College [i.e. RCP] to promote the interests of psychiatry".

On 6 December, I addressed the Scottish Division of the RMPA in Glasgow. Virtually all the contributions from the floor were against the College, and I here met the most vitriolic language of the campaign. No vote was taken, but on the way out, I met an elder member of the Division who said, "Had a vote been taken, the College would have had it". This was supported by the results of the SCP questionnaire, which showed 77% support for the College in Scotland. Maurice Carstairs, the Professor of Psychiatry at Edinburgh, supported the College, but the other Scottish professors did not.

T. H. Moylett, an SPC member, had given me valuable information on the development of the Royal Colleges, so that in November 1963, I asked him if he knew whether or not it was possible to change the name of the RMPA to that of the Royal College, without an act of Parliament. He said that this was perfectly possible, and had occurred in two previous instances – for the Royal Society of Medicine by supplemental charter in 1907, and for the Royal College of Physicians of Edinburgh in 1920. Thus, at the November meeting, I was able to encourage the members that it was possible to found a Royal College now. Afterwards, I wrote to the Privy Council, asking whether it would be possible to change the name of the RMPA by supplemental charter. A reply from the Secretary of the Privy Council, Sir Geoffrey Agnew, said that this was possible. Some months later, I wrote a similar letter to the Lord Chancellor's office: Sir George Coldstream replied, agreeing that a supplemental charter alone was necessary. Moylett, a remarkably scholarly man, had pointed out that every British citizen has the right to write to both the Privy Council and to the Lord Chancellor's Office on legal matters. These letters established that the legal road to a Royal College was simplicity itself.

The postal vote, May 1964

The officers had promised members a postal vote at the annual meeting in November 1963, and this now had to be done. However, supporters of the College could see two difficulties. Firstly, it was essential that enough members of the RMPA voted on the issue; a low poll would not impress the Privy Council or the other Colleges. One year before, in May 1963, an ambiguous leaflet by the Royal Medico-Psychological Association (1963) on the future of organised psychiatry had produced two replies only! Secondly, it was essential that the ballot paper allowed for a clear result.

The special committee had the task of preparing the ballot paper. When Walk produced the first draft, it was clear that no meaningful result could arrive from this lengthy, confused questionnaire – as was intended. At the next meeting, Hutchinson, Tetlow, and myself pressed for the first question to be unambiguous. After a bitter struggle, it was agreed that one clear question for or against the three possibilities should head the ballot paper. However, in February 1964, came the news that the RMPA Council had deferred the postal ballot until May. This was because the RCP needed to prepare their offer of a higher examination in psychiatry. Additionally, it was hoped that by the time of the postal ballot, the RMPA would be physically located within the RCP.

In preparation for the ballot, the SCP had given thought to the need to encourage members to vote and, at their request, I had prepared a 'For your information' leaflet (Society of Clinical Psychiatrists, 1964/65). This behoved psychiatrists, whatever their viewpoint, to vote and to do so at once. We needed a high poll. The ballot paper arrived with members on Monday 10 May, but an account of the papers given at the November meeting did not arrive until two days later. However, by the same post as the ballot paper, came the SCP leaflet.

Thursday 13 May was an eventful day. In the *Lancet*, Curran, the President, appealed to members not to vote until they heard the particulars of the higher qualifications to be offered by the RCP, implying support for a faculty within that body. His letter had been approved by Council, and yet both he and they were meant to be impartial; it was supported by the *Lancet*, in a leader (*Lancet*, 1964*a*). On the same day came a discouraging letter from A. B. Monro, the General Secretary, to all members saying that unless the ballot was decisive no action would be taken. In the event, the members had responded to the SCP and already voted; the result was decisive. Two-thirds of members (67.8%) voted and of these, 72% were in favour of the foundation of a Royal College. Only 6% voted for a faculty within the RCP.

The RCP had in fact offered psychiatrists accommodation within their new building in Regents Park. In the spring of 1964, I was consulted by the RMPA officers on this issue: they were anxious for me to agree that there were no political implications in such a move – even with the postal ballot about to take place! I could not agree, and wrote to ten senior psychiatrists, asking for their opinion on this issue. Eight replied and all were against the move to the RCP; seven asserted that the move had "political implications". When these letters were handed to the General Secretary, it was the end of the effort to move into the RCP. Having persuaded the membership that their present accommodation was inadequate, however, the officers were now forced to move. Thus, they moved to a neutral place – the annexe of the Royal Society of Medicine.

In January 1963, the Labour Party won so overwhelmingly at the Luton by-election that it became clear the next government would be a Labour one. This carried with it the virtual certainty that the new Minister of Health would be Kenneth Robinson, which indeed proved to be the case. At the time of the College of Physicians Bill, Robinson had attempted to delay it, in order to bring to the attention of the House of Commons the damaging attitude of the physicians towards psychiatrists (*Hansard*, 1960). He said, "I think at the moment it [the RCP] is resisting, and successfully resisting, the establishment of a Royal College of Psychiatry", and "There is as yet no Royal College of Psychiatry, and I hope that there will be one before long". However, experience showed that whatever a minister's private opinions may be, in government he is bound by the advice received and is forced to compromise on many issues. Robinson's influence, though, was revealed when he talked of his partnership with Sir George Godber, the Chief Medical Officer: "We [Sir George and he] were both fairly active in getting this Royal College of Psychiatrists its Charter, to which there was quite a bit of resistance" (Freeman, 1988).

The annual meeting at Park Prewit Hospital, Basingstoke, 8 July 1964

Although a postal ballot had shown a majority of members in favour of a College, it was still necessary under RMPA by-laws to obtain the agreement of an annual meeting before there could be a petition for a supplemental charter. To make sure there was no delay, I sent a resolution to Council in May 1964, which I proposed to move at the annual meeting. This caused Council to move its own resolution.

To impress the Privy Council and the other Colleges, it was necessary to have an unequivocal vote at the annual meeting, and it was also crucial that no last-minute hitch would develop, whereby a poorly attended meeting might negate the resolution or alter it in some way. The SCP took the initiative with another information leaflet (Society of Clinical Psychiatrists, 1964/65), in which I pointed to the importance of attending the annual meeting. When the time came, the hubbub in the packed room was music to my ears; the vote in favour of petitioning for a Royal College was carried overwhelmingly by 150 votes to 9 (Freeman, 1990). This was of great significance, in that the members gave Council a clear directive to set up a petition committee to found a Royal College at the earliest possible moment. All subsequent authority sprang from this meeting.

The RCP wrote a letter of congratulation to our President which was welcoming and generous; they also, quite reasonably, asked that we refrain from using their acronym. However, the objections from the Psychological Medicine Committee within that College would continue, personified by the actions of Aubrey Lewis and Desmond Curran.

The annual meeting in 1964 saw the election of Ian Skottowe as President, replacing W. S. Maclay, who had recently died; it also saw the election of Ferguson Rodger as President-Elect, and he was on record in a letter in the *British Medical Journal* as being strongly opposed to the College. Skottowe was a man of impressive integrity; though he was unlikely to be a supporter of the Royal College, one would not detect it in his demeanour. He was the personification of impartiality. The RMPA had now reached the end of the beginning in its quest for transmutation into a Royal College.

The years of negotiation

The members of the RMPA had overwhelmingly expressed the wish for petitioning to become a Royal College, but the struggle now took on a significant difference. The events to be narrated below rarely surfaced outside the Council, the petitions committee, and the special committee on the by-laws. These were truly to be the difficult years.

Why did negotiations take such a long time – over six years – when the legal requirement was simplicity itself? During this time, the College of General Practitioners became the Royal College of General Practitioners by royal prerogative in January 1967, and the College of Pathologists became the Royal College of Pathologists in February 1970. The College of Psychiatrists of Australia and New Zealand was founded by the Companies Act 1961, incorporated in October 1963, and inaugurated in Canberra in 1964. A potent cause of delay was the lack of enthusiasm of the officers. However, insistence on a change would have had the considerable disadvantage of creating the impression of disunity; unity was preserved at the cost of delay. Only one officer's support was assured: A. B. Munro had an abiding sense of service to the membership. He strove to be fair to all members, but his resolution was sometimes sorely dented by pressure from fellow officers and senior colleagues. The negotiations involved immensely detailed secretarial duties, which he undertook with ability and despatch. Eliot Slater, the Editor-in-Chief, was an intellectual giant, kindly, a supporter of the downtrodden, but yet capable of bizarre judgement, as when he devoted the whole of the first number under his editorship of the *British Journal of Psychiatry* to his own work. Right up to the last meeting of the petitions committee, he was steadfastly opposed to the College, possibly influenced by the unrelenting opposition of his co-officer, the Librarian, Alexander Walk. The Registrar, William Sargant, was probably the best known of all the officers for his achievements in the field of physical treatment and for his publications. Erratic and tactless, he was at the same time kind and generous. Before the final petitioning, he became a wayward supporter of the College.

A particular difficulty for Monro was the fact that a new President took office every year, and it naturally took each some time to grasp the complex negotiations. After Curran, Skottowe, and Ferguson Rodger, the Presidents were Erwin Stengel (1966/67), Henry Dicks (1967/68), Francis Pilkington (1968/69), and Martin Cuthbert (1969 to foundation). After Curran, there was no complaint about lack of impartiality. In my view, the impressive Presidents were the three medical superintendents – Ian Skottowe, Francis Pilkington, and Martin Cuthbert.

The greatest cause of delay was the wrong strategy adopted in the negotiations. Because of an unfortunate misunderstanding which arose with the Privy Council, and the ensuing soured relationship, it was possible for the opposition to field the idea that the psychiatrists had "to prove that they were a College first". In this atmosphere, it was decided to petition for a Royal College and a change in the by-laws at the same time. Had the petition come first, with a few obvious changes in the by-laws, a Royal College could have been achieved quickly and the detail in the by-laws could have been changed at leisure, in further negotiations. By tying the two together, objectors guaranteed that there would be a long delay and during that time, while discussion went on over minutiae, it was always possible that some mishap could occur which would prevent the formation of a College.

The active antagonism to the foundation of a College continued as before. The only body prepared to stand up to it was the SCP, which had been founded in 1959 by Richard Crockett, and J. T. Hutchinson, supported by colleagues such as D. T. Bardon, T. H. Bewley, H. Jacobs, D. L. Leiberman, Bernard Gilsanen, Arthur Harris, Arthur Oldham, and Clifford Tetlow, with the objective of removing medical superintendents. I became its Secretary later. Though little news filtered out of the inner committees of the RMPA, the SCP had access, through some of its members, to all these. Its most powerful asset was the determination of its members to found the Royal College and to make this determination manifest. The SCP's role became crucial, and without it there could never have been a College. It had links with the Solicitor General, Sir Dingle Foot, and through him, with the Minister of Health, Kenneth Robinson. It campaigned to inform the members of the Privy Council and of Parliament and also key people in the community, such as Lord Adrian, the Chancellor of the University of Cambridge, and J. R. Rees, President of the World Federation of Mental Health, who were always responsive to a call for help. It kept psychiatrists informed of the state of negotiations, and exercised pressure to get pessimistic documents withdrawn. Its Chairman was J. T. Hutchinson, whose connections with a London teaching hospital, a mental hospital, and the British Medical Association allowed him to be remarkably well informed. At the most discouraging moments, he remained optimistic and was always ready to take new initiatives.

A chronological survey of events is now desirable. In the main, negotiations were with the Privy Council, the RCP, and the Department of Health.

1964

In July 1964, Council set up the Petition Committee consisting of Skottowe (President), Ferguson Rodger (President-Elect), Slater (Editor), Monro (General Secretary), Sargant (Registrar), Warren (Treasurer), D. H. Clark, and myself, to prepare a petition for the Privy Council. Council also set up a special committee on the by-laws and higher examination. This consisted of the President and B. Ackner, G. M. Carstairs, D. H. Clark, H. V. Dicks, J. T. Hutchinson, A. B. Monro, T. Ferguson Rodger, M. Roth, W. Sargant, A. Shapiro, E. Slater, I. Skottowe, E. Stengel, C. Tetlow, W. H. Trethowan, W. Warren, and myself again. Before the foundation of the College, this became the Special Committee, which in turn became the nucleus of the Court of Electors of the new College. In December 1965 came the first meeting between four representatives of the Petition Committee (Howells, Monro, Slater, their solicitor) and the Secretary, Sir Godfrey Agnew, of the Privy Council. It was disappointing and discouraging. We were advised that no progress could be made until we had the support of the Minister of Health, and it was especially discouraging to note that our solicitor was completely out of his depth.

Subsequently, I spoke to Sir Dingle Foot, Solicitor-General and MP for Ipswich, who advised that we should employ a Privy Council legal agent as well as counsel, and suggested for the latter Sam Silkin (later Solicitor-General and Lord Silkin). The new solicitor and Privy Council agent was Mr David Downs; throughout our quest, he was encouraging and helpful.

1965

Due to the links Sir Dingle had made with the Minister of Health, the Petition Committee was invited to meet Sir George Godber, Chief Medical Officer. Skottowe, Monro, Slater, and I were well received. In a later interview (Freeman, 1988), Sir George Godber modestly gave his role as that of "an honest broker" and was aware of where resistance lay; it was also instructive to see who had access to Sir George – mostly those unenthusiastic about a College. He promised support and advised a return to the Privy Council.

However, a week later, Monro received a personal communication from Sir George which indicated that progress could not be made, as "you are not yet a College"; we were to be on probation. He said, "You need to change your by-laws and function as a College before the Privy Council will grant a supplemental charter", though our case was that we already had all the attributes of a College. Some other influences had come to bear on the Ministry of Health and a recipe for delay had been found.

On 3 March, a second meeting took place between a delegation from the Petition Committee and the Privy Council. In our naivety, we felt that the official advice from the Chief Medical Officer was a proper opinion to stress to the Privy Council, though we also mentioned the informal advice. Only later were we to learn that, on many occasions, informal advice and overtures are of far greater importance. At first, Sir Godfrey quoted the same advice as we had recently heard, that is, that we should function as a College for a number of years, and then come back for a petition. However, when he heard of the official reaction from the Ministry of Health, his attitude changed; he became helpful and advised us just to do a brief adjustment of our by-laws, emphasising the higher examination, and to send both the petition and the by-laws in at once. He indicated that the only remaining hurdle was to get the support of the RCP. From this meeting came a sad misunderstanding. Sir Godfrey later telephoned our solicitor, Mr Downs, complaining of our lack of frankness: we should have given more weight to the informal advice from the Ministry of Health. This soured relationships with the Privy Council for some time.

In April, owing to the good offices of the Solicitor-General, a delegation from the Petition Committee met the Minister, Kenneth Robinson, and Chief Medical Officer, Sir George Godber. From this arose the suggestion that two bodies should run alongside one another with a hybrid name – the Royal Medico-Psychological Association and College of Psychiatrists. This unhappy notion, whatever the source, was a delaying tactic by the opposition, with always the possibility that the College would never happen. In June, the compromise was extended by Alexander Walk; the College part of the hybrid should be formed as a company. All this bypassed the simple and obvious device of a supplemental charter, by which the RMPA could become a College immediately.

In September, the Petition Committee met our counsel, Sam Silkin, and, because of his positive stance, it was agreed that we should continue with our petition and, at this stage, try to obtain the support of the RCP. Next month, at a special meeting of the Council, the notion of an approach to the RCP was discussed, the officers favouring an informal approach. The proponents of the College saw this as an endless source of delay: there would be no pressure on the RCP through public opinion and the matter could take decades. They proposed an open letter to the RCP; after opposition from Sargant, it was agreed to send this.

The year ended in optimism. A special annual meeting had passed the revised by-laws. Judging by Silkin's demeanour, it sounded as if Ministry support could be obtained and there was hope that the RCP would support us.

1966

On 11 February, a special meeting of Council heard that no news had been received from the RCP. There seemed to be only one way of getting a reply – by a courteous letter, stating that if we did not hear from them by April, we would assume that they could not support us. On 29 April, news was received that the Comitia had agreed to support our petition. It seems that their President, who was not unsympathetic to psychiatry, Lord (Robert) Platt, had intervened, advising his Comitia that only one reply could be given to the RMPA's letter. A generous letter was received from the RCP, and we then heard that the Privy Council was consulting them about our proposals.

Shortly afterwards, a critical meeting took place with Silkin to determine procedure for our petitioning. The ideal course was to petition for a supplemental charter at once, with a preliminary adjustment to the by-laws, as Sir Godfrey Agnew had suggested at one point. The second way was to send the petition and completely amended by-laws in together. A highly undesirable third possibility was to change the by-laws first, and only petition after they had been approved. There was strong advocacy of the last approach, and it was only after the intervention of Silkin that the second possibility was agreed. However, it was highly unsatisfactory, in that there was the chance of endless delay in the discussion of the minutiae of the by-laws with the Privy Council. And so it proved.

Silkin then advised that we write to the Privy Council, asking whether or not we should continue with our petition, but this memorandum was not sent until five months later. The year ended with no news.

1967

In May, a reply was received from the Privy Council in which they advised proceeding, agreeing to all the suggestions made by the RMPA, and adding some reasonable conditions of their own. A long wrangle ensued, in both the Petition Committee and the Council, over the acceptance of these reasonable conditions; by October, it had become possible to continue negotiations on these conditions. In December, the Privy Council expressed initial satisfaction with our amended by-laws and now asked for an immediate submission of the agreed final by-laws. This year also ended in optimism. I prepared a final draft of the by-laws and this was approved by the By-Laws Committee on 29 December.

1968

The final agreed by-laws were approved by Council and by a special annual meeting in February, and sent to the Privy Council in June. The year ended with no news from the Privy Council.

1969

In January came news that the Privy Council entirely agreed with our submission. However, Alexander Walk persisted with his notion that we should have a College and an Association. In this he was supported by Eliot Slater. This was despite the generous charter the Privy Council was prepared to give us. In February, the Privy Council received the President and General Secretary to discuss the amendment of two clauses; they were welcoming and positive. As the result of this discussion some rewording was required, but the redrafted documents were not sent in until October! Communication continued with the Privy Council over small matters of technical wording.

1970

In April, the Petition Committee considered a letter from the Privy Council indicating complete satisfaction with our proposals and advising that we should now formally petition. A remarkable intervention came from Alexander Walk, who advised the Committee to have no further truck with the Privy Council. It was as if he had succeeded in reversing the meaning of their letter. He was supported by Eliot Slater at the meeting, but this intervention was over-ruled by the rest of the Committee. The annual meeting in July approved the final submission to the Privy Council. One of the SCP members, P. L. Backus, cut through endless discussion by a positive resolution, which was carried with acclamation. The year ended with the Privy Council still calling for some small amendments.

1971

In February, the small additional amendments were agreed by Council and sent to the Privy Council. Signification of her gracious approval by Her Majesty the Queen of the Humble Petition of the Association for a Supplemental Charter occurred on 30 April, and a Royal Warrant was issued on 16 June.

Official news of a final granting of the charter came at the Edinburgh meeting of Council in May. This was the most shameful episode in the long quest for a College: goodwill disappeared, comradeship went. The lack of dignity was compounded by the facts that matters had gone on for so long in private and that the news that had filtered out was optimistic and pessimistic in turn. The scramble to climb on the bandwagon was hasty and frantic. No thanks were offered to the Petition Committee; at the next Council meeting, as one of its members, I moved a vote of thanks to it. No thanks were offered to our solicitor or counsel; I wrote to them myself.

During this long period, some parallel events were occurring. In 1967, the Joint Consultants Committee, comprising representatives of the Royal Colleges, invited the RMPA to send a representative. This was encouraging and indicative that the other Colleges were now regarding us as a College. In 1969, the RMPA gained membership of the Merit Awards Committee at the Department of Health – again, an indication of our acceptance by the other Royal Colleges. In 1968, the young members of the RMPA had also been cogitating about their place in a new College; they felt that, unlike the other Colleges, we should have emphasis on training rather than merely an examination. Opponents of the College fanned the fires, because here was a possible obstruction. In November, Council invited the young members to send representatives to meet them. An extraordinary meeting ensued: while Council sat, the young men stood before them. It was an embarrassing spectacle. They were questioned, no information was given, and after a lecture on the Council's intentions, they were dismissed. This could only breed discontent. Peace was ultimately restored by an informal meeting which brought goodwill, and by some concessions. The emphasis on training was correct and, largely owing to the young members, was acted on; but there were three powerful reasons why a higher examination had to be established. Firstly, this was the only way of guaranteeing a national standard which would be acceptable to the courts and to public opinion. Secondly, without it, trainees would be at the mercy of their local training centres. Thirdly, medical opinion expected a Royal College to have a higher qualification as a means of guaranteeing standards.

The new charter and by-laws

The main acomplishment, a supplemental charter, was simplicity itself: it granted the all-important change of name to 'Royal College of Psychiatrists'. Also, the constitution for the Royal College was a great advance on that of the RMPA. There must be a balance between leadership and democracy, and this was the case with the new constitution. The control of the College lies ultimately in the hands of the members, through its annual meeting. Between meetings, authority lies in the hands of a democratically elected Council; between annual meetings, officers and subcommittees are answerable to it. One-third of the membership of the Council are members, not fellows, thus ensuring that younger psychiatrists have a voice in the affairs of psychiatry.

The academic affairs of the College lie in the hands of the Court of Electors. They are responsible for the standards of psychiatrists, which they influence through the inspection of training centres and by the organisation of a higher qualification. The name 'Court of Electors' was suggested by Eliot Slater and accepted by the committee on the by-laws; it is linked to the notion of a College of Electors, responsible for the election of German monarchs and dissolved in 1806. The Court controls the acceptance of inceptors, elects members after they have passed its examination, and deliberates over the election of members to become fellows.

Under the new constitution, officers are elected by the whole membership through a postal ballot, while previously nominations and elections were made by the Council alone. However, it is still possible to elect a minority President. This could be overcome by the machinery of preferential voting when there are more than two candidates – a system which is now used by both the American Psychiatric Association and the British Medical Association.

Under the old arrangements, Presidents of the RMPA held office for one year; this was found to be far too short for a President to make an impression. Thus, the period was extended to three years. On the other hand, whereas in the RMPA officers tended to be in post for long periods, under the new arrangements the period is limited.

The structure of the College follows the pattern of the old guilds, with fellows (masters), members (journeymen), and inceptors (apprentices). The hard-won class of inceptor is unique to the College and is a considerable innovation. Trainees are part of the College from the commencement of training, receive its help, and are able to make full use of its resources. The term 'inceptor' was the best I could find, after a study of the *Oxford English Dictionary*. The Privy Council allowed a provisional period of ten years for the inceptor class. In the 1985 revision of the by-laws, this class became a permanent fixture of the College.

Epilogue

The Royal College has major accomplishments already and its main immediate targets have been achieved (Rollin, 1987). It fully participates in the higher committees of medicine and channels psychiatric opinion to government and other bodies. The higher examination was early established, with its rightful emphasis on standards of training. Membership, in all categories, had increased to over 7700 by 1990. Its regular meetings are well attended, its journal and publications of increasing repute; a research fund has been established, and the College's premises are in the heartland of our capital city. The acceptance of the Royal College of Psychiatrists in the British scheme of things was emphasised in 1984, when His Royal Highness The Prince of Wales graciously consented to be its first patron.

The founding of a Royal College offered an opportunity; it did not guarantee success. However, it is a strong base from which to meet the challenges of the future. No specialty had an assured place in medicine initially: each had to win its base, but we had to work rather harder for ours. This may carry the advantage of our being better equipped to handle the challenges of the future. We shall be attuned to the logic of history, we shall measure its changing currents, and we shall be ready to move forward, to the advantage of psychiatry, psychiatrists, and the psychiatric patient.

References

BRITISH JOURNAL OF PSYCHIATRY (1963) Discussion on the future of organised psychiatry. *British Journal of Psychiatry*, **109** (special supplement).

—— (1964*a*) Northern and Midland Division Autumn Meeting, 1963. *British Journal of Psychiatry*, **109** (suppl.).

—— (1964*b*) Report of the quarterly meeting, November 1963. *British Journal of Psychiatry* (special supplement).

BRITISH MEDICAL JOURNAL (1960) Title of the Royal College of Physicians of London. *British Medical Journal*, *i*, 123.

—— (1963) College of Psychiatry. *British Medical Journal*, *ii*, 1328.

—— (1964) Royal College of Physicians. Opening by the Queen. *British Medical Journal*, *ii*, 1259.

CLARK, G. N. (1964–72) *A History of the Royal College of Physicians of London*. Oxford: Clarendon Press.

COMRIE, J. D. (1932) *History of Scottish Medicine*. London: Baillière Tindall.

COPE, V. Z. (1959) *The Royal College of Surgeons of England: A History*. London: Blond.

FLEETWOOD, J. (1951) *History of Medicine in Ireland*. Dublin: Brown & Nolan.

FOSTER, W. D. (1981) *Pathology as a Profession in Great Britain and the Early History of the Royal College of Pathologists*. London: Royal College of Pathologists.

FREEMAN, H. L. (1988*a*) In conversation with Kenneth Robinson. *Psychiatric Bulletin*, **12**, 258–262.

—— (1988*b*) In conversation with Sir George Godber. *Psychiatric Bulletin*, **12**, 513–520.

—— (1990) In conversation with John Howells. *Psychiatric Bulletin*, **14**, 513–521.

HANSARD (1960) Royal College of Physicians of London Bill. *Hansard*, **623** (no. 108), 139–141.

LANCET (1963) Organisation for psychiatry. *Lancet*, *ii*, 1113.

—— (1964*a*) The London membership and psychiatrists. *Lancet*, *i*, 1085.

—— (1964*b*) Royal College of Physicians. *Lancet*, *ii*, 1006–1007.

ROLLIN, H. R. (1987) *The Royal College of Psychiatrists*. London: Gaskell.

ROYAL COLLEGE OF OBSTETRICIANS AND GYNAECOLOGISTS (1989) *The Royal College of Obstetricians & Gynaecologists 1929–89. A History*. London: Royal College of Obstetricians and Gynaecologists.

ROYAL MEDICO-PSYCHOLOGICAL ASSOCIATION (1957) *Memorandum on Fellowship in Psychiatry*. London: RMPA.

—— (1963) *The Future of Organised Psychiatry* (leaflet). London: RMPA.

SHAW, W. F. (1954) *25 Years. The Story of the Royal College of Obstetricians and Gynaecologists*. London: Churchill.

SOCIETY OF CLINICAL PSYCHIATRISTS (1964) *Forming a College of Psychiatry from the Medico-Psychological Association. A Dozen Questions Answered*. London: SCP.

SOCIETY OF CLINICAL PSYCHIATRISTS (1964/65). *For Your Information* (leaflets nos 1–3). London: SCP.

WALL, C. (1963) *A History of the Worshipful Society of Apothecaries of London, vol. 1: 1617–1815*. London: Wellcome Historical Medical Museum.

II. Ideas

8 Legal frameworks for psychiatry

ROGER SMITH

Psychiatry has not been a realm of autonomous endeavour forced into shape by negative legal constraints. From its modern beginnings in the late 18th century, it has been an activity with legally defined boundaries, constituted in and through the way the legal system mediates political society and regulates individual conduct. The law exists as a framework for the practice of the whole of modern psychiatry: statute law and the criminal and civil common law structure the professional occupation.

> "Law actually constitutes the mental health system, in the sense that it authoritatively constructs, empowers, and regulates the relationships between the agents who perform mental health functions." (Unsworth, 1987, p. 5)

This is not the way many psychiatrists, particularly those who have identified their occupation with a progressive humanitarian impulse, view the matter. They have sometimes hotly contested the legal mediation of the 'obviously' desirable goal of mental health, claiming that this goal could be achieved only by the unfettered advance of medical science and expertise. Legal conservatism has thus appeared as a negative force:

> "For with such direct antagonism to medical doctrines and practice on the side of the law, the existing prejudices in the mind of the public . . . will be more deeply rooted; so that we shall have greater difficulties to encounter in treating the insane, in bearing witness to their infirmities in courts of law, and in enlightening the public on a subject which most deeply concerns it." (Laycock, 1862, p. 1132)

From this perspective, the history of modern psychiatry has appeared as a struggle to convince society, and its system of ordering affairs as embodied in law, of the "plain, unvarnished facts as they occurred in nature" (Ray, 1962, p. 192) about mental disorder and its therapeutic needs.

Kathleen Jones (1960) used the term 'legalism' to describe this understanding of the law as a negative power. Describing the Lunacy Act 1890, she wrote:

> "Every safeguard which could possibly be devised against illegal confinement is there . . . . The result, from the legal point of view, was very nearly perfect. From the medical and social view-point, it was to hamper the progress of the mental health movement for nearly seventy years." (Jones, 1960, p. 40)

In the 20th century, then, the history of the mental health area appears as a political struggle to assert the dominance of either legal criteria regulating the relations between the rights and duties of doctors and citizens, or medical criteria freeing psychiatrists to act in what they judge to be the best interests of their patients (an opposition analysed and criticised by Rose (1986*b*)). Thus, the 1890 Act reinforced legal controls over the grounds and procedures of certification, while the Mental Treatment Act 1930 gave medical criteria a more extensive sphere of application by establishing the category of voluntary in-patients.

A parallel analysis applies to the criminal law: the 1843 McNaughton rules articulated a lawyer's conception of the test of non-responsibility (lack of knowledge of a certain kind), while the Homicide Act 1957, by introducing the plea of diminished responsibility into the English jurisdiction, seemed to acknowledge a medical conception of degrees of irresponsibility. The criminal law's commitment to finding an unambiguous verdict of guilty or not guilty had always clashed forcibly with a medical sense of gradation in mental pathology. (In Scottish law, however, there had been a *legal* conception of degrees of responsibility for killing for many years (Walker, 1968).)

The two positions – that the law has created the framework within which psychiatry exists as an occupation, and that legal thought and psychiatry have been conflicting agencies – are not necessarily incompatible. The former develops a political sociology of psychiatry, integrating it with broad social changes that are associated with modernity and bureaucratic welfarist tendencies in 20th-century society (Rose, 1986*a*). More especially, it locates psychiatry in relation to the diversification and particularisation of modes of social ordering – of education, poverty, crime, as well as illness – in industrial society. Nevertheless, the achievement of social order is endlessly varied in detail, and at this level of analysis, a conflict between legalistic and psychiatric values has frequently been real enough. Specific historical settings often reveal a *local* conflict between legal and psychiatric ends.

As a social phenomenon, modern psychiatry has been constructed and reconstructed through statute, through court practice, and through administration, which itself operates "in the shadow of the law" (Smith & Wynne, 1989). Such a claim does not exclude or denigrate the activities of medical men though: it was not the law which created the idea of the asylum, nor did the law dictate that asylums should have medical directors. Nevertheless, by the mid-19th century, legal structures did form an inescapable framework for psychiatric activity.

A chapter on "Insanity and the law" must therefore choose from many possible themes, without claiming exclusive rights or even some kind of historical priority for any one. There is something to be said for highlighting a theme that has carried great symbolic weight, very visibly representing psychiatry's position in society at large. In the late 1850s or mid-1870s, this might have been the question of the wrongful confinement of 'alleged' lunatics; in the late 1960s and early 1970s, it might have been the claims and counterclaims of antipsychiatry. But many of the most tightly focused and theatrical moments have been in response to the plea of insanity (or, latterly, in English law, the plea of diminished responsibility) in criminal cases. The names of James Hadfield (1800), Daniel McNaughton (1843), Ronald True (1922), John Straffen (1952), and Peter Sutcliffe (1981) remain familiar. Their cases were contentious when they were first heard and they have continued to feature in the literature on law and psychiatry. Clearly, something more than the outcome of individual trials has been at issue, and it may be possible to interpret this phenomenon as an index of the political resolution, mediated by law, of the place of psychiatry in human affairs.

Such an approach must be clearly distinguished from a historical search for the causal roots of psychiatry's changing position, since, as Nigel Walker (1968, p. 243) observed, there "has been the almost complete absence of any connection between the changes in the courts' behaviour, as reflected in statistics, and the cases which have made legal history". We need to bear in mind that while the spectacular individual case has historical meaning, meaning is not the same as causal significance. The history of the insanity defence in particular cases provides important evidence about psychiatry's position in society, the relation between medical and legal occupations, the expression of social values, etc., but does not itself explain change. We would need to integrate medicolegal experience with a wider history before undertaking such an explanation.

Medical expertise and the law: the 1840s

The founders of the Association of Medical Officers of Asylums and Hospitals for the Insane in 1841 gave concrete expression to the arrival of a new kind of occupational expertise. The medical officers claimed a novel combination of medical and administrative expertise: medical skill in identifying, classifying, and treating insanity, and administrative skill in fulfilling legal obligations regarding the insane, administrating the isolation of lunatics in specialist institutions (public or private), and managing these asylums. The felt need for a new medical society reflected the peculiar way in which medicine and law together had created a new occupation. Further, once the asylums had such a definite legal existence, this created special conditions in which to experience insanity in all its variety. There were new, rich possibilities for medical experts to exploit.

Early Victorian alienists felt, with good reason, that the question of their expertise was an important public matter. The decade of the 1840s opened with the trial of Edward Oxford, the first of many mentally disordered people to attack Queen Victoria (Walker, 1968), and it closed in 1849 with the humiliation of medical opinion and of the Commissioners in Lunacy by the court finding for the plaintiff in a case of false confinement (*Nottidge* v. *Ripley and another*). In between lay: the consolidation of Home Office administrative regulations about insane criminals, the Insane Prisoners Act 1840; the founding of the Association in 1841; the trial of Daniel McNaughton for shooting the private secretary of Sir Robert Peel and its aftermath, the McNaughton rules, in 1843; Lord Ashley's national survey, the *Report of the Metropolitan Commissioners in Lunacy* (1844); the opening of the Irish criminal lunatic asylum at Dublin in 1845 (Finnane, 1981); and finally the passing of two acts in 1845 in which Parliament created a nationwide legal framework for psychiatry, the Lunatics Care and Treatment Act and the Lunatic Asylums Act (Fry, 1854; Phillips, 1858; Scull, 1979; Mellett, 1982).

The 1840s was therefore a key decade in the history of British psychiatry, though all the events had their origins in the preceding half century. Yet if we look more closely at how statute and common law construed medical expertise on the subject of insanity, the decade's achievement, from the point of view of psychiatry, begins to look much more problematic. Indeed, we might conclude that this decade left a legacy in regard to the social standing of psychiatric expertise which the passage of time has modified but not discarded.

Looking first briefly at the subject of certification, we find that the Lunatics Care and Treatment Act imposed legal decision-making not just as a supplement to but as the framework for the medical diagnosis of certifiable lunacy, and for paupers it set this firmly within the context of Poor Law administration. Further, it gave no acknowledgement of any kind to the idea that there might be a *specialised* medical expertise involved: it gave powers to medical men in relation to their occupation (thus, for example, it involved Poor Law officers), and not because they possessed special expertise or training in relation to insanity. (Indeed, the question as to how to define a 'medical man' had no definitive statutory answer until 1858, and there was certainly no special training for psychiatrists until much later.) This was of very real concern to alienists, who had to contend with scepticism about their expertise as much from general medical colleagues as from the wider public. The presence of two quite separate certification procedures, for pauper and for private lunatics respectively, was again a legal and administrative requirement, indicating that the categorisation of patients was a social and financial transaction before it was a medical one. In these circumstances, psychiatric expertise could appear in practice to mean expertise in applying the procedures which Parliament had laid down.

This picture of a legally constituted reality appears even stronger in the light of the annual reports of the Commissioners in Lunacy – the body established in 1845 as a full-time central administration (Mellett, 1981; Hervey, 1985). The Commissioners regulated asylum construction, management, and finance, oversaw proper record keeping and certification, and pursued questions concerning domestic arrangements, staffing, and sometimes of violence to patients; but they had little to say in relation to diagnosis or treatment in terms other than those represented by these administrative and institutional matters.

Just how exposed the specific medical claim to possess expertise might be became clear in *Nottidge* v. *Ripley*, when the court found in favour of an eccentric spinster claiming wrongful confinement, and against the doctors who had certified her. More significantly, it was in this case that Lord Chief Baron Pollock laid down the legal dictum, "that you ought to liberate every person who is not dangerous to himself or others", which called forth an impassioned rejoinder from John Conolly and which haunts psychiatry as a denial of medical criteria of judgement (quoted by Scull, 1984, p. 795).

Cases of false confinement coming to court were in fact rare (McCandless, 1981; Hervey, 1986); nevertheless, this is an issue which has kept a hold on the public's conscience from the earliest years of lunacy reform into the present. It has taken only the occasional but much publicised case to reawaken scepticism as to the validity of psychiatric judgement in such matters. In 1861, Victorians read in their newspapers about the succession of medical expert witnesses, on both sides, who followed each other into the witness box during the lunacy inquiry into W. F. Windham (initiated by the family trying to protect the estate from an eccentric and profligate heir). The Lord Chancellor himself denigrated the contradictory but well paid psychiatric evidence – "between these learned doctors, who is to determine?'' (*Hansard*, 1862) – prompting some embarrassed reflection on their role by medical psychologists (Laycock, 1862; Pitt-Lewis *et al*, 1895; Jones, 1971). It was, as it has remained, extremely uncomfortable for medical men, whose sense of professional identity was bound up with a claimed objectivity, to find themselves subservient to the legal adversarial system. Since people could buy expertise about madness, for example in assessing testamentary capacity, the relevant experts could not escape the accusation that they were part of the embattled world of the market and of politics.

The Lunacy Act 1890 rewrote previous amended legislation and retained legal controls over certification and asylum administration (Pitt-Lewis *et al*, 1895; Unsworth, 1987). The act was the result of a protracted struggle (going back at least to a select committee in 1877) to achieve a compromise between public and legal fears of psychiatric misrule on the one hand and the alienists' fear that a clinical judgement supporting certification might conclude with a civil suit and that legal controls inhibited patients from receiving treatment on the other. The act imposed legal constraints, though conceding protection from suit (doctors could stay the proceedings unless there was a *prima facie* case for malpractice), in response to medical threats not to co-operate with certification. Although the concession was not wholly effective from the medical point of view, one has the impression that specialists in mental diseases lived in a world of legal formality rather than legal constraint, following the 1890 Act (Chapter 5).

It is perhaps not stretching comparison too far to discern a similar compromise in the 1983 legislation, though of course there is much difference in detail, especially to accommodate the major 20th-century developments of the informal admission of psychiatric patients and the formal removal of the social distinction between 'pauper' and 'private'. (The category of 'voluntary' patient existed in legislation between 1930 and 1959; the merely temporary existence of such legal categories itself illustrates the recurrent difficulty.) The structural problem remains – that of finding a legally workable third way, avoiding both what those concerned with liberties fear may become coercion and what psychiatrists fear may become interference with clinical judgement. The history of this problem, from the Victorian period to the present, is not a history of law versus medicine but a political history of the social institutions, whether legal, medical, or administrative, through which a practical ordering of affairs is achieved (Rose, 1986*a*; Unsworth, 1987).

The expert witness and the defence of insanity

If we return to the experience of the Victorian medical psychologists, we must accept that they often feared the law as an antagonistic power. This confrontational experience was at its sharpest in the area of the criminal law. Medical men had appeared in the courts for centuries but, before the late 18th century, it was unusual for them to give evidence that differed qualitatively from that of other relatively educated witnesses. Indeed, the English legal concept of the 'expert witness' emerged only slowly, and much later than in certain Continental jurisdictions. Between 1780 and 1830 matters began to change in that coroners', criminal, and civil courts all started to regard the medical witness as a special or expert contributor to the decision-making process (Forbes, 1978;

Crawford, 1987). It was no coincidence that medical jurisprudence appeared as a separate specialist area, first in Scotland and then in England and Wales at the end of this period, again much later than its counterparts in German, French, or Italian jurisdictions. The protagonists of the new specialties assumed that it would include witnessing as to lunacy, especially in the context of the criminal court (Guy, 1844; Taylor, 1844). It was only very gradually, during the course of the 19th century, that what we would now perceive as the separate occupations of forensic medicine and forensic psychiatry began to diverge.

Expert witnessing on questions of lunacy and the increasing utilisation of the insanity plea emerged in tandem (Eigen, 1985). It appears that the courts themselves were the main motor for change, with barristers newly developing adversarial practice and this practice then gradually establishing habits and expectations in relation to experts. In the background lay the national agitation over the lunacy question, the general air of reform in social administration over such areas as poverty and criminal sentencing, and of course the lunacy specialists' own claims to be reconstructing knowledge of madness, especially by introducing new disease categories, such as partial insanity or moral insanity, which had legal implications (Prichard, 1842; Bucknill, 1857; Ray, 1962). The more regular appearance of medical witnesses in court, carrying some status as experts which differentiated them from ordinary witnesses, thus occurred primarily for legal reasons, though these experts perceived in it an opportunity for professional advancement (Scull, 1979).

That perception, initially uninformed by experience of the realities of entrenched legal power, did generate conflict between law and medicine. This conflict was most emotional when medical experts, and this was especially characteristic of insanity specialists, attributed their new role to the growth of knowledge. The general atmosphere of reform in the early Victorian period encouraged alienists to evaluate their expertise as nothing less than the advance of science and to equate science with progress (Smith, 1988). It thus appeared to the most enthusiastic among them, such as Forbes Winslow, that the legal acceptance of the authority of the psychiatric expert was an index of something much grander – the progress of humanity itself. As Winslow wrote (1855, p. 3), following the unsuccessful insanity defence of Luigi Buranelli in 1855: "The execution of Buranelli will, we fear, be a foul stain and a 'damned spot' upon the humanity and intelligence of the nineteenth century." More mundanely, if the public was to admit alienism to the standing of a profession, this appeared to require an acknowledged standing for the expert in mental pathology in the public forum of the court-room.

It is possible to trace the varied fortunes of psychiatric evidence in the court-room in some well-known cases. In 1800, at the treason trial of James Hadfield for shooting at George III, it was not 'expert' medical evidence that played a role in securing his acquittal on the ground of insanity, since he had a head wound from soldiering which the jurymen could see for themselves (*State Trials*, 1820; Walker, 1968). Subsequent cases showed that Hadfield's acquittal, in fact, had no 'liberalising' consequences and that it was not an important step in the history of psychiatric evidence. However, by the time of Oxford's trial in 1840, also for treason (this time pistols had been fired at the young Victoria and her consort), the jury did hear 'expert' argument, as witnesses linked Oxford's delusions about a secret society to a morbid inheritance (*State Trials*, 1892; Walker, 1968). They also heard the judge, Lord Denman, say that "if some controlling disease was, in truth, the acting power within him which he could not resist, then he will not be responsible" (*English Reports*, 1900–32, vol. 173, p. 950). Critics regretted that the jury found Oxford insane: by detaching the judge's statement from its context, it could appear that an expert view of madness, as a disease whose consequences could not be controlled and which could not therefore entail responsibility, had determined the outcome.

There was a similar appearance about McNaughton's trial. The defence called four medical witnesses, who all agreed in describing McNaughton as suffering from a delusion which left him without self-control; two of these doctors based their expert opinion merely on having heard the evidence in court. Lord Chief Justice Tindal himself then decided enough was enough, and in his summing up did not even recapitulate the medical evidence (which the prosecution had not attempted to rebut). His action, followed by the acquittal, embarrassed the law officers and the government at a time of considerable political fears about Chartism (with which McNaughton was associated). The turmoil was dampened down in the House of Lords by the device of putting questions to the judges collectively, the answers to which are known as the McNaughton rules (*State Trials*, 1892; Walker, 1968; Moran, 1981). In retrospect, the trials of Oxford and McNaughton do appear as something of a high point in relation to judicial sympathy with medical evidence.

Two possibilities exercised medicine's critics: firstly, that the grounds for the exculpation of extremely serious crimes had expanded, permitting non-resistance to deluded motives itself to entail a lack of responsibility; secondly, that self-styled experts – whose expertise might be questioned – had somehow usurped the system of judge and jury. The McNaughton rules answered the first criticism directly, since they stated clearly that a jury, in order to acquit on the ground of insanity, had to be persuaded that there had been a lack of knowledge of the kind necessary for criminal intent, not that disease had created an impulsion (*English Reports*, 1900–32, vol. 8). The rules also answered the second criticism, though not so much through what they actually said as through the manner in which they were arrived at, which presupposed a legal framing of the issues. It occurred neither to the House of Lords nor to the judges to consult medical opinion, let alone to formulate propositions with *legal* standing that incorporated a *medical* way of framing the issues.

Formulating the rules was emblematic of society's exclusion of reformist ideals and claims to expert status associated with psychological medicine. It is therefore understandable that subsequent generations of psychiatrists have treated the rules as a reference point for objecting to society's devaluation of what psychiatric expertise has to offer. Throughout the second half of the 19th century, insanity specialists commented with some acerbity on the unscientific and backward-looking nature of the rules: "as there is a true and a false religion, so there is a medical psychology and a legal psychology" (Davey, 1858, p. 89).

It is quite another matter to assume that the rules determined decisions in the courts in any straightforward sense. In fact they did not, and the outcome of individual cases was highly dependent on local variables. A variety of decisions, some of which came remarkably close to admitting the legal *bête noire* of irresistible impulse, occurred in the 19th century (Smith, 1981, 1983; White, 1985). This becomes most evident when one turns away from the famous cases to those which aroused less interest, for example, cases of infanticide. The outcome of particular cases was dependent on a huge range of variables, most notably perhaps the accused's relationship to the victim in crimes of personal injury, any of which might prove decisive. The wording of the McNaughton rules proved to be sufficiently open-ended – most often as interpreted by jurors, but sometimes also in judicial summings up – to permit a finding of insanity, although some findings provoked adverse legal, public, and even medical comment. Sometimes expert evidence regarding insanity appears to have played an important role in a case, sometimes expert language appears merely to have reinforced a lay or common-sense perception of insanity, and sometimes expertise was openly scorned. It is thus a very questionable business for the historian to generalise about the standing of psychiatry purely on the basis of knowledge of the outcome of individual trials, including McNaughton's.

Criminal insanity and social administration

It is therefore necessary to turn from the drama of the court-room to the administrative routines of government. I suggest that psychiatric expertise has acquired its modern position through interaction with the machinery of government, within a framework of law but not directly in the legal setting. Clearly, there have also been changes in the position of psychiatrists in summary hearings or in criminal trials, but it may be legitimate to understand them as indirectly reflecting administrative changes. It has been administration, and to some extent penology, rather than the court-room, that has proved to be permeable to psychiatric ways of thought, and even to be a source of novel psychiatric practice.

It was in this area that Hadfield's trial was significant, since it led to the Criminal Lunatics Act 1800, which provided powers to hold those found not guilty on the ground of insanity 'at His Majesty's pleasure', and it was followed by state funding of criminal lunatic accommodation at Bethlem. The state entrenched its role by negotiating in 1814 for special male and female criminal lunatic wings at Bethlem's new site at Southwark. This was an early example of central regulation of social administration. The state also continued to support many criminal lunatics in a variety of establishments across England and Wales, including private asylums and even workhouses (Saunders, 1988*a*, *b*). After considerable discussion about the issue and prevarication about the cost, Parliament passed the Criminal Lunatics Asylum Act 1860, which led to Broadmoor and ultimately to the modern system of special hospitals (Walker & McCabe, 1973; Allderidge, 1974).

These acts provided central funds for special institutions and legitimacy for special categories of the mentally disordered; beyond this, they both reflected and reinforced new occupational activities centring on new thoughts about the criminal and, more widely, on constructing a body of knowledge about disorder and pathology in society at large. The category of the criminal lunatic, combining even in its name reference to both legal sanctions and medical treatment, stood at the threshold of a new social policy. The vicissitudes of this category followed the general ambivalence about the appropriateness of either punishment or treatment as a response to social disorder generally.

But the centralisation of control was a distinct indication of the long-term trend of administration.

The doctors who directed the new institutions, such as Charles Hood at Bethlem or much later W. C. Sullivan at Broadmoor, encouraged a commitment to psychiatric expertise within the Home Office (Hood, 1860; Sullivan, 1924). In conjunction with the Commissioners in Lunacy (after 1913, the Board of Control), they formed an arm of medicine that was integrated with the machinery of everyday administration. The law and psychiatry were not here in conflict, since they combined in a procedure for managing dangerous individuals, and constructed a unified occupation in the light of this common social purpose.

The situation was even more propitious for the expansion of psychiatric influences. Acts in 1816, 1840, and 1853 enlarged the category of 'criminal lunatic' to include both convicted and remand prisoners who were certified as insane, and required the Home Secretary to act accordingly (Walker & McCabe, 1973). This established a process akin to civil certification as a standard procedure for drawing distinctions among criminals in the light of medical information. This obviated the role of judge and jury. From a wider perspective, it was a small aspect of the way that the prison administration acquired grounds of action independent of the judiciary in the 19th century. Thus, psychiatry became occupationally associated more with the new specialty of penology than with the legal profession, and practitioners in penology and psychiatry, unlike many lawyers, shared a utilitarian rather than retributive attitude towards offenders. The growing independence of psychiatry from legal direction was bound up with the growing separation of penal sanctions from judicial control.

By the mid-19th century, therefore, alternative but parallel routes were in existence for classifying a criminal as insane: the judicial route, in which the courts retained power and imposed punitive sanctions, sometimes mitigated by humanitarian and medical considerations; and the administrative route, in which experts acquired new powers, a new sphere of operation, and even a new branch of knowledge, building medical thought (and perhaps humanitarian values) into the ordering of society. In order to contrast these two routes and the wider ambivalences which they represent, it is instructive to compare the cases of George Victor Townley (1863) and Peter Sutcliffe (1981). There is an element of anachronism in any comparison of events separated by more than a century, but the comparison does illustrate a continuity of attitudes.

It took the jury at Derby assizes only five minutes to find Townley guilty of murdering the girl who had been his fiancée; it clearly gave scant credence to the expert medical witness for the defence, Forbes Winslow, and voiced the popular desire for retribution. Mr Baron Martin, a little more circumspectly, wrote to the Home Secretary (as judges were required to do in all capital cases) and noted the medical view that at the time of the trial Townley was insane. Townley's solicitor meanwhile had his client certified, requiring the Home Secretary, Sir George Grey, to class him as a criminal lunatic; public opinion was shocked that this procedure appeared to enable Townley to 'escape'. Assessed differently by the two routes, Townley precipitated a conflict of policy. Feeling for a way in which to reconcile these confusions, the Home Secretary received reports from two separate commissions into Townley's insanity, one finding him insane and the other sane, but both agreeing that he had been rightly convicted. The Home Secretary reached the pragmatic compromise of classifying Townley as a criminal, mollifying public opinion, but commuting the capital sentence, thus precluding medical and humanitarian criticism for hanging a possible lunatic. Townley then committed suicide (Maudsley & Robertson, 1864; Smith, 1981).

One hundred and twenty years later, psychiatrists following standard pre-trial assessment procedures diagnosed Peter Sutcliffe as suffering from paranoid schizophrenia. The prosecution legal officers, following what was by then common practice where psychiatric opinions were unanimous, agreed to accept this diagnosis, creating the expectation that the court would not hear the case but would agree to Sutcliffe being held in a special hospital. This expectation realistically reflected the standing of psychiatry within the ordinary procedures of criminal administration. At the last moment, however, the trial judge ruled that the court would not accept the 'administrative route', and determined that the matter of Sutcliffe's insanity should go before a jury. Quite why Mr Justice Boreham took this 'judicial route' is a matter for speculation, but there can be no doubt that it opened space for the re-entry of the public's concern with retribution.

Sutcliffe pleaded diminished responsibility to a specimen murder charge, but the jury rejected defence medical opinion (and what, before the trial, had been the prosecution's opinion) and found him guilty of murder (*The Times*, 5–23 May 1981; Prins, 1983). Nevertheless – and this is very significant for the point being emphasised here – the administrative route, which is dependent on the specialist judgement of psychiatric personnel, reasserted itself subsequently. After a time, which allowed public emotion to cool, the Home Office agreed with the psychiatric view, and Sutcliffe was transferred from prison to a special hospital. Thus, on this very disturbing occasion – given the devastating effect which Sutcliffe had had on the community – one route, rejecting psychiatric expertise, performed a cathartic public ritual, while the other route, deploying psychiatric expertise, achieved a medical ordering.

The broad framework of issues exhibits a significant degree of continuity from the Victorian period to the present. In the very exceptional way in which expert opinion did not decide the outcome in the pre-trial procedure, however, the Sutcliffe case cast in relief the major change since the Victorian period, that is, the consolidation of psychiatry in administrative decision-making. What in effect has happened is that civil certification has provided a model for the administration of the criminal area, and the growth of centralised government has given it a power base that is regulated only indirectly by law. Nevertheless, as Sutcliffe's case showed, considerable legal powers may still be exercised in certain cases; and indeed they may operate on a regular basis, for example, in a magistrates' court sceptical of a psychiatric view of minor offenders.

Forensic psychiatry and the prisons

In the 19th century, the medical men involved with the area of criminal lunacy, whether as expert witnesses, asylum superintendents, commissioners, or specialists in medical jurisprudence, formed a diverse group. Probably only since the 1950s is it really legitimate to refer to forensic psychiatry as a distinct and coherent occupation with its own training and institutional base (at the Institute of Psychiatry, at the Maudsley Hospital, and at regional, hospital-based centres).

However, in the late 19th and early 20th centuries, individual self-styled experts, like Charles Mercier, as well as superintendents of Broadmoor (and, in the 1920s, Rampton) had a significant influence on the character of practice.

The prison medical officers also deserve comment for the special part which they have played in giving content to psychiatry's relation to the criminal law. The development of medicine's presence within the prisons suggests that the history of law and insanity cannot simply refer to the growth of psychiatry influencing the administration of crime. Rather, the medical presence has generated new forms of understanding, neither straightforwardly medical nor straightforwardly judicial, making possible both criminology and forensic psychiatry as novel specialties (Garland, 1985, 1988; Watson, 1988).

Early in the 19th century, the Old Bailey sessions papers record that the earliest regular medical witness to the prisoner's state of mind was the Newgate surgeon, Gilbert McMurdo (Eigen & Andoll, 1986). The holding of prisoners on remand created conditions in which they could be observed over a period of time by someone with medical experience. It remained common through the mid-19th century for gaol surgeons to be called as witnesses, not infrequently by the prosecution to rebut 'specialist' psychiatric evidence with 'common-sense' medical experience. Thus, one surgeon responded to defence counsel scepticism about his expertise by observing that "when you converse with a man I do not think much professional skill is required. In the course of a long conversation you might arrive at the truth" (*Journal of Mental Science*, 1863, p. 133). The role of the prison surgeon was perhaps especially important where there was a question of the prisoner's fitness to plead, since it had long been established that the courts would not try those whose mental state precluded their comprehension of the proceedings, and it was often the surgeon who was in the position best able to notice this (Walker, 1968).

It was therefore of the greatest importance to the relations between medicine and the law when the Prison Act 1865 regularised the presence and routine of the prison medical officers within a progressively uniform and centralised prison system. Before this date, the prison chaplain as well as its surgeon was likely to draw the authority's attention to mental disorder. After this date, a clearly defined group of medical men had as an occupation the observation of mental disorder in offenders, whether to assist a court's deliberations or to decide fitness for punishment (both special punishment such as flogging and the general penal sentence).

The occupation thus created had special duties to observe weak-minded or otherwise 'inadequate' prisoners. The prison doctors also had medical responsibility for those on remand, and the courts' desire to take advantage of this situation evolved into the system of medical reports on remand prisoners which, in the 20th century, became a major part of some prison medical officers' activity and income. A few individuals, notably Norwood East, acquired through this route considerable standing as specialist experts on the whole question of relations between crime and mental abnormality, which is a central focus of modern forensic psychiatry (Walker & McCabe, 1973; Gunn *et al*, 1978).

The prison medical officers' preoccupation with mental disorder also led to new forms of knowledge, notably the category of 'moral imbecility', which was incorporated into the Mental Deficiency Act 1913. This category was neither 'medical' nor 'legal' in origin; rather, it originated in prison record-keeping, which led to a knowledge of habitual criminality, combined with the interest of the prison medical officers in a class of weak-minded prisoners who were unaffected by punishment (Watson, 1988). As it turned out, few diagnoses of moral imbecility were made, but the existence of this category in the statute books was an index of the government's slow acceptance of the social sciences, in this context subsuming psychiatry and a protocriminology, as the proper basis for a collective response to social problems. This policy – if a development so gradual and piecemeal can be so dignified – goes far beyond the relations between law and psychiatry, but it has formed the political setting in which those relations have developed since the inter-war period.

Political ambivalence about the proper allocation of punishment and therapy remains, of course. It is this which gives such intensity and confusion to debates about 'psychopathy', a category in mental health legislation defined explicitly by criteria of social performance (for a critical review of interpretations, see Holmes (1988)). With justice, some commentators regard this category as a weak point in the modern system of dealing with mentally abnormal offenders: if such offenders are a medical problem, then it cannot be right to admit a category defined by conduct and not symptoms; if such offenders are a criminal problem, then it cannot be right to admit the category into mental health legislation. Yet others believe that the category has pragmatic value, and this suggests yet again that in the present century, law and psychiatry should be analysed together – not as opposed institutions, but as alternative routes within a wider framework of achieving social order.

Psychiatry and social policy

It is therefore necessary to have a perspective on wider social policy and the political process in order to understand the relations of law and psychiatry. Although day-to-day decision-making about mental disorder has become the province of experts in the last 150 years, and although the law itself sometimes appears to constrain medical action, it is ultimately political questions of social policy which set the parameters of the psychiatric occupation. This is a multidirectional process. Thus, at times, the conduct of psychiatry under law has created practices or ways of thought that have proved significant in reconstituting policy. Alternatively, society's failure to achieve a consistent policy has sometimes imposed on psychiatry a highly questionable role in the legal system. Only the briefest illustration of these two points can be offered in conclusion.

Nineteenth-century prison medical officers and superintendents of asylums formed occupational groups whose daily practice led to a special interest in the relation between the criminal and the mentally disordered person. This occupational activity joined together with aspects of late-19th-century thought to create a climate of opinion in which the mentally abnormal offender appeared as a symbol of social degeneration. In the light of deterministic theories of disease and heredity, coupled to an evolutionary approach that linked together biological and social change (Maudsley, 1879, 1883; Jones, 1980), the apparent growth of the numbers of mentally inadequate criminals excited attention as a threat to social progress and imperial ambition.

For a time, it was common to think about social problems in terms of a medical model which suggested that policy should become a matter of developing an appropriate body of scientific expertise, diagnosing pathology in the form of degenerate individuals, and then intervening to isolate the diseased types. Fear of the poor prospects for a curative response, whether for pauperism, criminality or insanity, turned attention towards projects of mental or social hygiene, eugenics, and 'social defence' generally. Psychiatrists and others involved with the administration of mental and criminal disorder played a prominent part in these movements, thus projecting outward their daily activity as a model for wider political action (Searle, 1976; Rose, 1985; Jones, 1986).

There was in fact little direct legislative consequence; even the Mental Deficiency Act 1913, which set out the framework for a national system of institutions to isolate mental defectives, owed more to the problems of prisons and workhouses than to eugenic ideals (Watson, 1988). Nor is there any sign that the criminal courts became more sympathetic to the insanity defence. What did occur, however, was the expansion of public support, particularly where it mattered in politics and administration, in favour of a scientific and expert orientation towards social questions. In the inter-war period, and especially after 1945, this helped create the conditions for approval of the modern system of professional decision-making in dealing with mental illness, criminality, and social inadequacy in all its forms (Unsworth, 1987).

Psychiatrists active in criminal law have nevertheless inherited a set of contradictions going back to the earliest years of this activity, in the 19th century. Whereas the most enthusiastic among them initially hoped that enlightened scientific progress would lead the law to defer to expertise, most quickly realised that the law would do no such thing and that consequently, the advancement of psychiatric status and influence lay with the integration of medical activity with criminal law and social administration. This has occurred, especially in the 20th century, as part of a wider politics which has built expert practices into the administrative fabric of society. All the same, the continuation of legal decision-making, retaining powers to subordinate medical opinion entirely, sometimes leaves psychiatrists in a position of very ambivalent authority. The continuation of this position, in its turn, reflects the way in which psychiatry as an occupation is involved in areas where there are deeply contentious and inconsistent social values.

There is one special question that seems now to encapsulate the historically derived dilemmas of forensic psychiatry. Forensic psychiatrists sometimes give evidence to the effect that a person's mind was disordered when killing or being the accomplice to the death of an ill or aged relative. They may do this in the court's and their own clear but unspoken knowledge that they are creating a medical fiction in order to permit a verdict in which the judge has discretion in sentencing (i.e. a verdict of manslaughter and not murder), since euthanasia is no defence in English law. The psychiatrist's activity, in a strict sense, is neither legal nor medical; yet many would argue that, in the circumstances, it is both ethical and socially valuable (Stone, 1984). The psychiatrist professionally occupied by the relation of law and insanity manages a social problem about which political society is divided and inconsistent. This chapter has sought to show that this has been a general feature of the psychiatric occupation over the last century and a half.

Acknowledgements

I gratefully acknowledge help and comments in preparing this chapter from Sonja Bradshaw, Michael Clark, Clive Unsworth, and Stephen Watson.

References

ALLDERIDGE, P. H. (1974) Criminal insanity: from Bethlem to Broadmoor. *Proceedings of the Royal Society of Medicine*, **67**, 897–904.

BUCKNILL, J. C. (1857) *Unsoundness of Mind in Relation to Criminal Acts* (2nd edn). London: Longman, Brown, Green, Longmans and Roberts.

CRAWFORD, C. (1987) The emergence of English forensic medicine: medical evidence in common-law courts, 1730–1830. Unpublished DPhil thesis, University of Oxford.

DAVEY, J. G. (1858) On the relations of insanity and crime. *Journal of Mental Science*, **5**, 82–94.

EIGEN, J. P. (1985) Intentionality and insanity: what the eighteenth-century juror heard. In *The Anatomy of Madness: Essays in the History of Psychiatry, vol. 2* (eds W. F. Bynum, R. Porter & M. Shepherd). London: Tavistock.

—— & ANDOLL, G. (1986) From mad-doctor to forensic witness: the evolution of early English court psychiatry. *International Journal of Law and Psychiatry*, **9**, 159–169.

ENGLISH REPORTS (1900–32) *English Reports*. Edinburgh: W. Green & Son.

FINNANE, M. (1981) *Insanity and the Insane in Post-famine Ireland*. London: Croom Helm.

FORBES, T. R. (1978) Crowner's quest. *Transactions of the American Philosophical Society*, **68**, part 1.

FRY, D. P. (1854) *The Lunacy Acts*. London: Charles Knight.

GARLAND, D. (1985) *Punishment and Welfare: A History of Penal Strategies*. Aldershot: Gower.

—— (1988) British criminology before 1935. *British Journal of Criminology*, **28**, 131–147.

GUNN, J., ROBERTSON, G., DELL, S., *et al* (1978) *Psychiatric Aspects of Imprisonment*. London: Academic Press.

GUY, W. A. (1844) *Principles of Forensic Medicine*. London: Henry Renshaw.

HANSARD (1862) House of Lords. *Hansard*, **165**, col. 782.

HERVEY, N. (1985) A slavish bowing down: the Lunacy Commission and the psychiatric profession. In *The Anatomy of Madness: Essays in the History of Psychiatry, vol. 2* (eds W. F. Bynum, R. Porter & M. Shepherd). London: Tavistock.

—— (1986) Advocacy or folly: The Alleged Lunatics' Friend Society, 1845–63. *Medical History*, **30**, 245–275.

HOLMES, C. (1988) The concept of psychopathy: an historical review and reformulation, with a consideration of implications for moral responsibility. Unpublished MPhil Thesis, University of Lancaster.

HOOD, W. C. (1860) *Criminal Lunatics. A Letter to the Chairman of the Commissioners in Lunacy*. London: John Churchill.

JONES, G. (1980) *Social Darwinism and English Thought: The Interaction Between Biological and Social Theory*. Brighton: Harvester Press.

—— (1986) *Social Hygiene in Twentieth Century Britain*. London: Croom Helm.

JONES, K. (1960) *Mental Health and Social Policy 1845–1959*. London: Routledge & Kegan Paul.

JONES, K. (1971) The Windham case: the enquiry held in London in 1861 into the state of mind of William Frederick Windham, heir to the Felbrigg Estate. *British Journal of Psychiatry*, **119**, 425–433.

JOURNAL OF MENTAL SCIENCE (1863) Regina v. Fooks. Dorset Spring Assizes, 1863. *Journal of Mental Science*, **9**, 125–137.

LAYCOCK, T. (1862) On law and medicine in insanity. An introductory lecture. *Edinburgh Medical Journal*, **7**, 1132–1146.

MCCANDLESS, P. (1981) Liberty and lunacy: the Victorians and wrongful confinement. In *Madhouses, Mad-doctors, and Madmen: The Social History of Psychiatry in the Victorian Era* (ed. A. Scull). Philadelphia: University of Pennsylvania Press.

MAUDSLEY, H. (1879) *The Pathology of Mind*. London: Macmillan.

—— (1883) *Body and Will*. London: Kegan Paul, Trench.

—— & ROBERTSON, C. L. (1864) *Insanity and Crime: A Medico-legal Commentary on the Case of George Victor Townley*. London: John Churchill.

MELLETT, D. J. (1981) Bureaucracy and mental illness: the Commissioners in Lunacy, 1845–90. *Medical History*, **25**, 221–250.

—— (1982) *The Prerogative of Asylumdom: Social, Cultural, and Administrative Aspects of the Institutional Treatment of the Insane in Nineteenth-Century Britain*. New York: Garland.

MORAN, R. (1981) *Knowing Right from Wrong: The Insanity Defense of Daniel McNaughtan* New York: Free Press.

PHILLIPS, C. P. (1858) *The Law Concerning Lunatics, Idiots, & Persons of Unsound Mind*. London: Butterworths.

PITT-LEWIS, G., SMITH, R. P. & HAWKE, J. A. (1895) *The Insane and the Law*. London: J. & A. Churchill.

PRICHARD, J. C. (1842) *On the Different Forms of Insanity, in Relation to Jurisprudence*. London: H. Baillière.

PRINS, H. (1983) Diminished responsibility and the Sutcliffe case: legal, psychiatric and social aspects (a 'layman's' view). *Medicine, Science and the Law*, **23**, 17–24.

RAY, I. (1962) *A Treatise on the Medical Jurisprudence of Insanity* (reprint). Cambridge, MA: Belknap Press of Harvard University Press.

ROSE, N. (1985) *The Psychological Complex: Social Regulation and the Psychology of the Individual*. London: Routledge & Kegan Paul.

—— (1986*a*) Psychiatry: the discipline of mental health. In *The Power of Psychiatry* (eds P. Miller & N. Rose). Oxford: Polity Press, Blackwell.

—— (1986*b*) Law, rights and psychiatry. In *The Power of Psychiatry* (eds P. Miller & N. Rose). Oxford: Polity Press, Blackwell.

SAUNDERS, J. (1988*a*) Criminal insanity in 19th-century asylums. *Journal of the Royal Society of Medicine*, **81**, 73–75.

—— (1988*b*) Quarantining the weak-minded: psychiatric definitions of degeneracy and the late-Victorian asylum. In *The Anatomy of Madness: Essays in the History of Psychiatry, vol. 3* (eds W. F. Bynum, R. Porter & M. Shepherd). London: Routledge.

SCULL, A. T. (1979) *Museums of Madness: The Social Organization of Insanity in Nineteenth-Century England*. London: Allen Lane.

—— (1984) The theory and practice of civil commitment. *Michigan Law Review*, **82**, 793–809.

SEARLE, G. R. (1976) *Eugenics and Politics in Britain 1900–1914*. Leyden: Nordhoff International.

SMITH, R. (1981) *Trial by Medicine: Insanity and Responsibility in Victorian Trials*. Edinburgh: Edinburgh University Press.

—— (1983) Defining murder and madness: an introduction to medicolegal belief in the case of Mary Ann Brough, 1854. In *Knowledge and Society: Studies in the Sociology of Culture Past and Present. A Research Annual, vol. 4* (eds R. A. Jones & H. Kuklick). Greenwich, CT: JAI Press.

—— (1988) The Victorian controversy about the insanity defence. *Journal of the Royal Society of Medicine*, **81**, 70–73.

—— & WYNNE, B. (eds) (1989) *Expert Evidence: Interpreting Science in the Law*. London: Routledge.

STATE TRIALS (1820) *State Trials, vol. 27* (ed. T. B. Howell) London: Longman, Hurst, Rees, Orme, and Brown.

—— (1892) *State Trials, vol. 4* (new series) (ed. J. E. P. Wallis). London: HMSO.

STONE, A. (1984) *Law, Psychiatry and Morality: Essays and Analysis*. Washington, DC: American Psychiatric Press.

SULLIVAN, W. C. (1924) *Crime and Insanity*. London: Edward Arnold.

TAYLOR, A. S. (1844) *A Manual of Medical Jurisprudence*. London: John Churchill.

UNSWORTH, C. (1987) *The Politics of Mental Health Legislation*. Oxford: Clarendon Press.

WALKER, N. (1968) *Crime and Insanity in England. Vol. 1. The Historical Perspective*, pp. 138–146. Edinburgh: Edinburgh University Press.

—— & MCCABE, S. (1973) *Crime and Insanity in England. Vol. 2. New Perspectives and New Problems*. Edinburgh: Edinburgh University Press.

WATSON, S. (1988) The moral imbecile: a study of the relations between penal practice and psychiatric knowledge of the habitual offender. Unpublished PhD thesis, University of Lancaster.

WHITE, S. (1985) The insanity defense in England and Wales since 1843. In *The Insanity Defense* (ed. R. Moran). *Annals of the American Academy of Political and Social Science*, **477**, 43–57.

WINSLOW, F. (1855) *The Case of Luigi Buranelli Medico-legally Considered. Journal of Psychological Medicine*, (suppl.).

9 Colonial psychiatry: the European insane in British India, 1800–58

WALTRAUD ERNST

"We have our jails, our schools, and our dispensaries in almost every Zillah, and why should we not have our Asylums too?" This view, expressed here in the *Calcutta Review* in 1856, characterised the European community's prevailing attitude towards the institutionalisation of the mentally ill in British India (Macpherson, 1856). What is more, by the middle of the 19th century, existing provision was considered adequate neither in scope nor in quality. The East India Company had by then established a dozen or so 'lunatic asylums' for Indians or 'natives' in the various provinces under its administration, and three more institutions were available in the main centres of Calcutta, Bombay, and Madras, that specialised in the treatment of Europeans (Ernst, 1987). The European lunatic asylums in particular had for several decades drawn adverse public attention for their notorious overcrowding, facilities which had deteriorated since their inception in the early decades of the 19th century, and buildings which were in general considered to have fallen behind the standards of asylum architecture established by reformers such as Conolly and the Commissioners in Lunacy in England.

In 1828, in contrast, the distinguished asylum reformer Sir Andrew Halliday had considered the scope, administration and general control of asylums in India as "much further advanced than England" (Halliday, 1828). He consequently bestowed "the highest praise" on the East India Company's court of directors "for their attention to the subject". On the basis of their records, drawn up not very long after the asylums' establishment, in 1819, he was convinced that the European asylum at Madras, for example, "surpasses many of the European establishments that have long been considered as the most perfect of their kind". Similarly, the small institution in Bombay was regarded as having "every comfort and convenience that such an asylum ought to possess".

The question then arises as to what extent judgements as diverse as these adequately reflected the state of asylum provision in British India in the first half of the 19th century. Of course, both Halliday and John Macpherson (on whose report on insanity among Europeans in Bengal the article in the *Calcutta Review* has been based) had their personal interests. Like so many other social reformers during the early decades of the 19th century, Halliday was trying to induce the British Parliament to amend existing legal provision, and therefore tended to compare the "present state of lunatics, and lunatic asylums" in Great Britain somewhat less favourably with measures taken in "some other kingdoms".

Macpherson, in contrast, had been in medical charge of the European asylum in Calcutta and had carried out his own private investigations into the prevalence of insanity among army personnel in Bengal. His interest therefore focused on the situation of the mentally ill in the colony, and on their treatment in the Company's asylums, which he considered at the time to be "doubtless much below par".

In fact, in the light of both institutional and government records, neither Halliday's nor Macpherson's judgements were particularly revealing of the state of asylum provision in British India during the first half of the century. From the beginning of the century the East India Company had had problems in enforcing regulations and curbing corrupt practices in its asylums. Public control of institutions and regular inspection of premises were by no means imposed as stringently in practice as was suggested in those reports which Halliday had taken at their face value. Nor was the situation of asylum inmates during the 1850s as uniformly below the standard of institutions in Britain as asserted by Macpherson. Despite a general tendency towards common regulations, asylums in Britain – as much as in British India – came in all shapes and sizes.

Administration

What then were the main features of the development of emergent 'colonial psychiatry'? The earliest traceable official accounts of institutions specialising in the confinement of 'lunaticks' date from the late 1780s and 1790s. In Bengal, for example, the surgeon W. Dick kept a lunatic asylum for the Company some time before 1788, into which both "Insane Officers and private men" and civilians of various stations in life were received (Bengal Hospital Board, 1788). Dick's establishment was small and although a surgeon had to supervise it medically, there were no explicit regulations laid down as to his exact responsibilities. The usual practice seems to have been that military lunatics were transferred and paid for by the military authorities, while the justices of the peace or the officers of police were empowered to send civilians to Dick's establishment. For the East India Company, the Bengal Hospital Board had merely to examine and pass bills for "Cott beds and the bed cloathing", and a sergeant and three soldiers, all invalids, were employed to attend to the insane. The staff were paid a monthly allowance of ten rupees in order to "encourage [them] to do their duty with diligence and humanity", and for each patient the surgeon in medical charge of the asylum was allowed to "draw for one Cooly for attending him at four Rupees per Mensem" (Bengal Hospital Board, 1788).

Dick's establishment, like the other two lunatic asylums for Europeans, in Bombay and Madras, was run as a private enterprise. The authorities in India had approved of these establishments because they expected them to be "extremely beneficial . . . to the Community at large by affording Security against the perpetration of those Acts of Violence which had been so frequently committed by unrestrained lunatics" (Madras Military Letter, 1794). Yet it soon emerged not only that the madhouse proprietors tended to overcharge government exorbitantly for the maintenance of its patients, but also that premises were not kept in an acceptable state of repair.

In an attempt to check these abuses, the Bombay government, for example, sanctioned in 1820 the establishment of a new government lunatic asylum on the grounds that the "defective state" of the private madhouse had effected the "agonizing suffering of some of the patients" (Bombay Medical Board, 1820). The new building was designed to receive 100 insane persons, "including Europeans of all ranks and descriptions as well as Natives both male and female" (Bombay Medical Board, 1820). Similarly, the Bengal government founded a 'Government Insane Asylum' in 1802. Although formally a public institution, the new arrangement still enabled the medical superintendent to derive considerable private profit from its operation, as he was solely responsible for board and lodging, clothes, and contingency supplies as well as medical attendance (Bengal Military Dispatch, 1816).

The Company's authorities in London became aware of the full extent of the problem in 1816. Around that time, the tide of public and Parliamentary concern in England for lunatics had peaked with a Parliamentary select committee on the regulation of madhouses. A copy of the committee's report was sent to Bengal by the Company's court of directors, with a note that "some suggestions . . . may be generally applicable to Institutions for the Custody and management of Lunatics", and the comment that "the system in use at your Presidency will admit and indeed calls for much and important alterations". There was indeed ample scope for change. One important suggestion for reform implied that the medical officer in charge of the asylum be no longer permitted to act as a member of the very board which was supposed to oversee the institution's management. Further, the Company's authorities decreed that the surgeon "be required to abstain from all private practice or other pursuits which can interfere in the most remote degree with the care and proper conduct of the establishment" (Bengal Public Letter, 1817).

Faced with the new regulations, the medical officer in charge of the asylum in Calcutta, the surgeon R. Leny, for example, chose to quit his appointment as superintendent and instead kept his influential position as member of the medical board, which allowed him to continue to pursue various other profitable interests. The Company found that it had to sanction a sixfold increase in the superintendent's salary in order to encourage surgeons to forgo the income engendered by private practice and involvement in trade and land speculation. (The Bengal Medical Board, however, had stressed that only such an increase would be "an adequate compensation for the trouble and responsibility attending the discharge of the duties of one of the most difficult situations in the medical Branch . . . proportionate to the arduous nature of the duties to be performed" (Bengal Public Letter, 1817).)

The situation in Madras was no less characterised by a conflict between the Company's authorities (determined to economise on asylum expenditure) and the medical officers (eager to maximise their own personal fortune). There, the surgeon V. Conolly, who had owned the province's European lunatic asylum since 1793, returned to England, having accumulated great wealth, as well as the reputation of being a formerly poorish Englishman who had turned *navab* after a few decades of service in the employ of the East India Company (Lee & Stephen, 1887). On Conolly's departure the value of the "trade in lunacy" was revealed when the asylum was sold at nearly three times the building's estimated value (Madras Military Letter, 1794). It took, however, a further decade for the authorities there to realise the disadvantage that this constituted for the treasury. It was not until 1815 that the government of Madras objected to the repeated transfer of the asylum's lease, when the then owner, the surgeon J. Dalton, considered selling the place for a highly inflated price. It was held that "the principle of selling not merely the building, but the charge of the Patients contained in it, to any Individual however qualified, or personally unobjectionable" could not be sanctioned by government (Madras Military Dispatch, 1823). Surgeon Dalton was consequently not only stuck with the asylum, but on his retirement to Europe, had also to hand over the medical charge of the institution to a surgeon who was henceforth appointed by government, on recommendation from the Medical Board.

Although the Madras government did not totally do away with its medical officers' involvement in the 'madbusiness' until 1823, it had, as early as 1808, at least taken steps towards clarifying authority structures. It had empowered the Medical Board with sole authority to admit patients and to recommend their proper classification, as well as their treatment. Further, in an attempt to restrict at least somewhat the misappropriation of public funds, the superintendent of the asylum no longer received comprehensive class-specific rates for patients, but had instead to draw a fixed monthly allowance, with expenses for the care and treatment of particular patients being henceforth met only against detailed bills. These administrative measures turned out to be relatively effective not only in saving the Madras government expense, but also in avoiding in the long run the asylum superintendent's bitter resistance to the lowering of rates.

In Bengal, in contrast, disputes between asylum proprietor, medical superintendent, medical board and government were to be the order of the day for many decades to come. Only in 1856 did the government authorities curb petty corruption there also, by means of increased public control and clarified authority structures.

Apart from the interval between 1802 and 1821, when the Calcutta asylum had formally been a government institution, European lunatics were until 1856 confined in a privately owned and managed house. The proprietors, Mr I. Beardsmore (a former soldier and, according to the Bengal Medical Board (1836), an "industrious but uneducated man" who "pretended to no medical knowledge") and his wife, were on many occasions the objects of the Medical Board's and the medical superintendent's censure, yet they always managed to escape any restrictions or reprimands by the local government. Carried along on a wave of *laissez-faire*, governors-general such as Lord Auckland were disposed to reduce rather than widen the Medical Board's authority. In 1836, for example, when Beardsmore again approached government as the final arbiter in his struggle with the Medical Board (which in 1836 had questioned the classification and rates charged for several patients and criticised a perceived "paucity of European attendants"), Auckland submitted that the Board "should refrain, as far as possible, from Exercising any more minute interference in regard to the details of [Beardsmore's] management than has heretofore been the practice" (Bengal Government, 1836).

Auckland's advocacy of non-interference in the asylum's internal management was at the time justified by the belief that considerable pecuniary advantage was occasioned by the contract with Beardsmore (India Public Dispatch, 1839). Reflecting this 'hands-off' attitude favoured by government, the 'medical code' of 1838 contained no rules for the inspection of lunatic asylums (in contrast to the relatively detailed statements in the 1819 code which Halliday had praised so highly). The Medical Board henceforth restricted its control of the private institution to vaguely formulated tasks such as "inspecting the accommodation of the patients and assuring themselves in the performance of their duty as visitors that their cleanliness and comfort were duly cared for" (Bengal Medical Board, 1847).

Consequently, in the late 1840s when the tide of *laissez-faire* had turned, the Board was described by government officials as having failed to "exercise the powers vested in them . . . sufficiently at the onset", and thus to have engendered a "lax system, which then they were unable to improve" (Undersecretary to the Bengal Government, 1849). In justice to the Medical Board, however, it ought to be noted that it was the local government which seemed unwilling to enforce orders effectively and to pursue a consistent lunacy policy. Indeed, it seemed not to be sure to what extent it wanted to endow the Medical Board with discretionary authority. The inability to define the Board's authority and enforce efficient control and supervision, without interfering with professional medical judgement, was equally characteristic of the medical officers, the local government, and the Company's court of directors in London. Such diffusion of control and lack of direction could, of course, easily be exploited by owners of private madhouses, such as Mr and Mrs Beardsmore. However, whether or not this dilution of supervision changed the condition of asylum inmates for better or worse cannot be ascertained.

Expansion

Notwithstanding the obvious lack of uniformity in the three local governments' policies towards European lunatics and a certain indecisiveness on the part of the Company's London authorities as to the extent to which government interference and control was desirable and called for, some features characteristic of the administration of colonial psychiatry in British India did emerge towards the middle of the century in all three provinces. By 1856, the transformation of privately owned small asylums into large public institutions was complete. Bureaucratic procedures concerning the admission and discharge of patients were systematically applied, and the authority to supervise the treatment of the mentally ill had been solely vested with medical experts. The policy of sending European lunatics back to England if they did not recover within a year, first introduced in Bengal in 1819, was implemented as a matter of routine and had become a decisive factor in keeping down the number of European asylum inmates in India, despite a rise in the average number of Europeans admitted to the asylums in all three provinces. The number of Eurasian and Indian inmates admitted to, and kept in, the asylum for extended periods, also increased (Ernst, 1991). This was partly due to the passing of the Criminal Lunatics Act 1851, which provided the legal basis for the confinement of violent and allegedly socially harmful lunatics.

The British in India developed, with the consolidation of the *Pax Britannica*, a sense for civil order and well regulated community life, and as a consequence became ever more sensitive to the public nuisance constituted by beggars, vagrants, and lunatics (Arnold, 1979). Although the lunatic asylum was, on account of the high costs involved, not a particularly convenient place for locking up *any* disturbing deviant, it had (together with prisons, workhouses, sailors' homes, and orphanages) become an essential part of British attempts to guarantee the European community's peace and order. Asylum premises consequently became hopelessly crowded, so that, by the 1840s, asylum superintendents like W. Arbuckle in Bombay, for example, pleaded with government that the police authorities should be made to refrain from sending any more "alleged lunatics" or those among the mentally ill who were merely a nuisance but not violent, to the asylum (Bombay Asylum Report, 1849).

European inmates were but slightly affected by the increase in the number of Indian and Eurasian patients, since inside the asylums, a system of classification and segregation was applied that emphasised the separation of patients on the basis of their race, social class, and gender. In Calcutta, Indian lunatics were debarred from reception into the better-serviced European lunatic asylum, as the "propriety of mixing Europeans labouring under mental derangement with natives in the same unfortunate condition" had been judged by the Bengal Medical Board (1821) to be neither "practical or expedient". Asiatics were consequently sent to a separate 'native lunatic asylum'. Yet even at the institutions in Bombay and Madras, where a less fierce racial climate prevailed, a system of what has aptly been labelled "segregative control" (Scull, 1967) was at work, that not only aimed at keeping the Indian and Eurasian lunatic apart from the European, and the females away from the males, but also entitled first-class patients to treatment in highly superior apartments (Ernst, 1991). The rise in the asylums' overall population did, however, put ever more pressure on medical officers, who found it difficult under crowded conditions to guarantee race- and class-specific confinement and to practise the regime of moral management then so popular in England. In Bombay, according to the superintendent, the situation had reached the point where 80% of the patients were confined in half the building (Bombay Asylum Report, 1852). In the face of similar space constraints and the "highly dangerous state" of the premises in Madras from the 1840s, higher-class Europeans there would only rarely be admitted to the asylum at all (Superintending Surgeon, 1846).

The nature of policy in India

Most of the features that came to be characteristic of lunatic asylums in British India were present in asylums in England too. The private 'madbusiness' was being gradually curbed, and a consolidated lunacy policy being introduced; even the number of asylum inmates grew as relentlessly in England as in British India, and neither in the East nor in the colonial motherland was an egalitarian system of classification of patients applied. What, then, if anything, was different about British India?

The feature that seems to stand out most is that British India experienced its first period of state interference in the lunacy sector during the 1810s and 1820s – several decades before anything comparable occurred in England and Wales. Contingent factors were certainly at play here. The dispatch of European lunatics to small institutions in the main cities, which had been practised on a sporadic basis from the late 18th century, had gradually become routine. Once the precedent was set and the ponderous bureaucratic machine had been started, the civil and military authorities made increasing use of asylums for the disposal of unproductive employees and others.

There were other factors involved, too – factors that were strongly linked with the peculiar nature of colonial rule during the early part of the 19th century. The first two decades of the century in particular constituted the period when the East India Company succeeded in establishing military supremacy in strategically important areas in India, and when "British rule grew from mere collection of *loot* . . . into an orderly, if still burdensome, administration" (Kiernan, 1969). Lunacy policy was admittedly an area of public administration that assumed but minor relevance, but the emergent colonial state would still flex its muscles and assert its authority even in such a marginal sphere.

As in many other areas of colonial administration, the main impetus for policy consolidation and reforms came from the Company's authorities in London. As has already been noted, the court of directors became determined to modify the practice of confining European lunatics in small private asylums when it was, in 1816, alerted to the high maintenance costs and the potential for mismanagement and abuse. The suggestions of select committees for the more efficient and humane organisation of lunacy provisions, in particular through state intervention and control, in England, apparently met sympathy with the Company. They not only fitted in well with the Company's general endeavour to strengthen its colonial administrators' firm grip on public affairs, but also facilitated increased control over maintenance costs. Furthermore, the implementation of a reform policy could be held out as attesting to the Company's concern with enlightened government and humanitarian practices. This latter aspect had become increasingly important, ever since the Company had been made accountable to the British Parliament: a 'board of control' supervised its affairs, and every 20 years, the charter under which it operated was renewed only after detailed investigation into Indian administration.

The early reform and general consolidation of European lunacy policy in British India during the first two decades of the 19th century therefore owed much to the endeavour to impress humanitarian campaigners and Parliament at home, as well as reflecting the emergent colonial state's emphasis on financial economy, state control, and humanitarian mission. Despite fluctuations in the implementation and success of such policies, towards the end of the Company's administration, a uniform lunacy policy, backed up by comprehensive legal enactments, was enforced in all areas under British rule.

Another main feature of European lunacy policy in India was that it was mainly based on an institutional and administrative response, rather than on informal family or community networks. Again, reasons to do with the colonial order of things can be offered to account for this. To begin with, the majority of Europeans belonged to the military, and would usually not have any relatives in the East. Furthermore, there were comparatively few European women in British India, who could have taken on the traditional role of wives as carers (Royal Commission on the Sanitary State of the Army in India, 1863). Finally, the small communities of European civilians that were scattered over the various provinces had as yet no traditional parochial relief networks in case of hardship or disease.

Moreover, during the course of the 19th century, the significance of institutions went far beyond their functional and practical role as substitutes for communal care and personal initiative. They had become important means of signalling a nation's social, spiritual, and technical progress. The lunatic asylum in particular "took on for a time a status as panacea equivalent to the steam engine, the rights of man, or the spread of universal knowledge" (Bynum *et al*, 1988, p. 3). This was true for Britain, and even more so for British India. In the East, the very existence of European institutions, such as prisons, hospitals, orphanages, workhouses, and asylums, became a marker of colonial rule, aimed at impressing indigenous subject peoples and at justifying the imposition of colonial rule by virtue of the alleged good which institutions *per se* were seen to endow.

During the early 19th century, asylum architecture had not yet assumed the same degree of bricks-and-mortar power display as had been typical of other public buildings such as hospitals and prisons in major Indian towns. The Calcutta General Hospital, for example, had been built on a grandiose and impressive scale that did much justice to the place's reputation as the 'city of palaces'. The European lunatic asylum, in contrast, having been built by a private entrepreneur rather than government, was much less ostentatious than such "magnificent buildings, and so large an establishment" as the metropolis' European hospital (M'Cosh, 1841). Despite their more humble external appearance, on a symbolic and ideological level, asylums were nevertheless considered one of those eminent features of colonial rule that were used as an example whenever the continued British presence in India had to be justified. This is captured in a little episode related by Aberigh-Mackay (1902, pp. 184–185): the Liberal Member of Parliament who (to the consternation of the European community in India) visited British India in order to convince himself of the propriety of continued British rule in the East, will "ask you to take him, as a preliminary canter, to the gaol and lunatic asylum; and he will make many interesting suggestions to the civil surgeon as to the management of these institutions, comparing them unfavourably with those he has visited in other stations". Afterwards, it was held, he "will probably write his article for the *Twentieth Century*, entitled 'Is India worth keeping?' ".

Psychiatric institutions, *qua* institutions, were one of colonialism's ideological pillars, but the politico-ideological functionality of colonial psychiatry, or of the 'management of the insane', as it was then called, was not restricted merely to confinement inside institutions. One of the main attractions of lunatic asylums to the local communities was certainly that they would be instrumental in keeping those Europeans out of sight who were seen to be out of their minds. Yet the permanent seclusion of the European mentally ill behind asylum walls appears not to have been regarded as a completely adequate means of concealment.

The repatriation of the European insane

From 1820 onwards, repatriation of those among the mentally ill whose state of mind did not improve within a year came to be routinely enforced (Madras military dispatch, 1820). This measure had originally been introduced by the

Company in order to economise on the high maintenance rates that prevailed in European asylums in India, but it had also been highly functional in another light. Not only did race- and class-conscious and socially pretentious expatriates loathe having to put up with vagrants and lunatics amid their own communities; they were also keen to preserve their image as representatives of an allegedly perfect and formidable ruling class, as well as of a spiritually and morally enlightened people.

As early as 1793, Henry Dundas, President of the Company's Board of Control, expressed another aspect of this endeavour when he argued in the Commons that "indiscriminate and unrestrained colonization" would destroy that "respect, or rather eradicate that feeling, which is so general among the Native, of the superiority of the English character . . . . It is a fact, that upon this feeling of the superiority of the Europeans, the preservation of our empire depends." On a more evangelical note, Charles Grant, former Company servant and a founder member of the Clapham Sect, proclaimed that a liberal immigration policy might allow "low and licentious" Europeans to "vex, harass and perplex the weak natives" instead of adhering to "prudent, kind and attractive communication of our light and knowledge" (Embree, 1962).

There certainly existed no better means of maintaining the prestige which was presumed than that of making invisible those among one's own kind whose presence was considered undesirable. The most permanent and ultimate way of achieving this end was certainly by providing people of 'bad character' and lunatics with a passage back to England.

The institutionalisation of European lunatics in British India and their deportation back to Britain can be described as attempts to control deviant and socially harmful strata of society, and to 'subjugate unreason'. Moreover, these two measures assumed an important ideological dimension, in that they were geared to ensuring the continued preservation of the white rulers' image. Seen as such, colonial psychiatry gains importance for an adequate understanding of alien rule. It is also within this context that the emergence of 'colonial psychiatry' as a special medical discipline toward the second half of the 19th century has to be set.

The asylum superintendents

The question then arises as to what was the specific sociopolitical role of those who were expected to execute the Company's lunacy policy in British India's European lunatic asylums. First, it is important to note that from the asylums' inception, superintendents had as a rule to be endowed with some sort of formal medical qualification – however dubious. By the 19th century, the days when a butcher could allegedly get a surgeon's certificate were gone (Beatson, 1902), as was the discretion of Company directors to sponsor their favourite candidates for the medical service in India. From 1822, applicants had to produce a diploma from one of the Royal Colleges of Surgeons (London, Dublin, or Edinburgh), or the College and University or the Faculty of Physicians and Surgeons of Glasgow. With the introduction of competitive examinations in 1855, the process of turning medical service in the East (with its promise of wealth through speculation and trade) into a professional career in its own right was completed.

Although it was more or less guaranteed by the middle of the century that asylum superintendents would possess a genuine medical qualification, it was not yet required that they be specialised in the treatment of the insane. Previous experience in the management of the mentally ill was (of course) considered a desirable additional attribute, but not a prerequisite. Vacancies were still filled on the basis of seniority, and in practice no acknowledged formalised professional specialists had as yet emerged. ''In India, no distinction is made between the practice of medicine and surgery'', remarked M'Cosh (former graduate of the Royal College of Surgeons, Edinburgh, and lecturer in clinical medicine at the New Medical College, Calcutta) in his *Medical Advice to the Indian Stranger*. Every officer therefore had to ''act in either capacity, as circumstances demand'' and had to be willing to ''exercise his profession in the most comprehensive sense of the word''. This rule applied to the superintendent in charge of either one of the 'native' or European lunatic asylums as much as to the regimental surgeon.

Gradual professional specialisation was, however, discernible towards the middle of the century. Superintendents such as W. Campbell in Bombay, for example, were then left in charge of the insane for a couple of decades, rather than merely for a few years. In Bengal, T. Cantor had been made superintendent of the two asylums in the Calcutta area on the basis of his previous experience in the lunatic asylum in Penang, and was expected to reform thoroughly the formerly privately owned European establishment.

It was also towards the 1850s that more and more medical officers became aware of the formidable role that medicine in general was seen to play in the colonial context, although in fact medicine had always been intrinsically linked to colonial expansion. The majority of medical officers in the Company's employ worked in the military sphere, and all of them had to relinquish any civil duties in case of extraordinary military demand. Moreover, it was the regimental surgeons who were expected to reduce mortality rates in the barracks, and to sift those who were malingering from the really ill.

What is more, along with the upsurge of the ideological role of medical institutions, as part of what came to be labelled 'cultural imperialism', went the elevation of the medical officer as an agent of the colonial effort. Together with the schoolmaster, who, according to Macaulay's dictum, had been expected from the 1830s to be instrumental in raising up an Anglicised middle class ''who may be interpreters between [the British] and the millions whom [they] govern – a class of persons Indian in colour and blood, but English in tastes, in opinions, in morals, and in intellect'', the medical practitioner was to become a major pillar of the ideological if not the moral justification of colonial endeavours (Macaulay, 1835). What Macpherson, in his demand for ''a lunatic asylum in every Zillah'', and many of his colleagues in the Indian medical service came to aspire to was not only acknowledgement as experts in the practice of professional specialties, but also respect as protagonists of an assumed noble mission.

McDonald (1950) pointed this out when he quoted Hubert Lyautey's epigram that ''[l]a seule excuse de la colonisation c'est le médecin'' as a *leitmotiv* to his book on the history of the Indian medical service. The work of the Company surgeons (and with them the asylum superintendents) as medical practitioners and their rise to professional expert status came to be ever more closely linked with the ideological justification of colonial rule in British India.

References

ABERIGH-MACKAY, G. (1902) *Twenty-One Days in India. Being the Tour of Sir Ali Baba, K.C.B.* Calcutta: Thacker & Co.

ARNOLD, D. (1979) European orphans and vagrants in India in the nineteenth century. *Journal of Imperial and Commonwealth History*, **7**, 106–114.

BEATSON, W. B. (1902) The IMS. Past and present. *Asiatic Quarterly Review*. Reviewed in *British Medical Journal*, *ii*, 1182.

BYNUM, W. F., PORTER, R. & SHEPHERD, M. (eds) (1988) *The Anatomy of Madness, Essays in the History of Psychiatry. Vol. 3 The Asylum and its Psychiatry*. London: Routledge.

DUNDAS, H. (1793) Parliamentary debates, House of Commons. *Hansard*, **30**, 676.

EMBREE, A. T. (1962) *Charles Grant and British Rule in India*. London: Allen & Unwin.

ERNST, W. (1987) The establishment of 'Native Lunatic Asylums' in early nineteenth-century British India. In *Studies on Indian Medical History* (eds G. J. Meulenbeld & D. Wujastyk), pp. 169–204. Groningen: Egbert Forsten.

—— (1991) *Mad Tales from the Raj: The European Insane in British India, 1800–1858*. London: Routledge.

HALLIDAY, A. (1828) *A General View of the Present State of Lunatics, and Lunatic Asylums, in Great Britain and Ireland, and in some other Kingdoms*. London: Thomas & George Underwood.

KIERNAN, V. G. (1969) *The Lords of Human Kind. European Attitudes to the Outside World in the Imperial Age*. London: Weidenfeld and Nicolson.

LEE, S. & STEPHEN, L. (eds) (1887) *The Dictionary of National Biography*. Vol. 12. London: Oxford University Press.

MACAULAY, Z. (1835) Minute on education. In *Selections from Educational Records* (compiler H. Sharp (1920)). Calcutta: Superintendent of Government Printing.

MACPHERSON, J. (1856) Lunatic asylums in Bengal (review). *Calcutta Review*, **26**, 594.

M'COSH, J. (1841) *Medical Advice to the Indian Stranger*. London: W. H. Allen.

MCDONALD, D. (1950) *Surgeons Twoe and a Barber. Being Some Account of the Life and Work of the IMS (1600–1947)*. London: Heinemann.

SCULL, A. T. (1967) Madness and segregative control: the rise of the insane asylum. *Social Problems*, **24**, 337–351.

Other sources

Sources cited but not listed above are available at the India Office Library and Records, London: the Court of Directors of the East India Company's Despatches; Letters/Despatches of the Governor-(General) in Council of the various Presidencies to the Court of Directors of the East India Company; Consultations/Proceedings of the Governor-(General) in Council of the various Presidencies, Board's Collections.

10 Tuke's *Dictionary* and psychiatry at the turn of the century

WILLIAM F. BYNUM

There can be little doubt that the most ambitious British psychiatric work of the 19th century was *A Dictionary of Psychological Medicine*, published in 1892 by J. & A. Churchill (Tuke, 1892). Its two stout volumes contain 1477 double-columned pages, written by an international cast of 128 authors and edited by one of the major figures of the discipline during the last half of the century, Daniel Hack Tuke (1827–95). While no single work could completely reflect the complex social, cognitive, and professional dimensions of psychiatry, the *Dictionary*, by its very attempt to be comprehensive, offers a unique window into the late-Victorian profession. I use it here as the primary basis of a description of the profession in the 1890s, but intersperse my examination of Tuke's *Dictionary* with a few reflections on the major changes within psychiatry between then and the outbreak of World War I.

The editor

Daniel Hack Tuke's life and work are described elsewhere in this volume (Chapter 3), so that there is no need to do more here than mention a few aspects of his career which were relevant in making the *Dictionary* the kind of book it was.

Tuke bore one of the most famous names in 19th-century psychiatric circles, as the great-grandson of the founder of the York Retreat, and the son of Samuel Tuke (1784–1857), the man whose *Description of the Retreat* (1813) did so much to put that Quaker institution and its programme of moral therapy on the map (Digby, 1985). It is perhaps symptomatic of the changing status of medicine and of the shifting values within the Tuke family that Samuel had not been permitted to enter the medical profession, and that the Quakerism within which Daniel was raised was replaced in his adult life by a more general set of philosophical and religious beliefs. He retained a reverence for spiritual values, but became less interested in the specific doctrines of formal religion. Two psychiatric colleagues of Daniel Tuke – Harrington Tuke and J. Batty Tuke – shared the same surname, but were not actually related to him. (Harrington Tuke insisted gratefully that Daniel Hack Tuke's books and reputation had brought him (Harrington Tuke) a lot of patients (Ireland, 1895), but the fact that Harrington Tuke was John Connolly's son-in-law would not have hurt his practice.)

Tuke seemed to have been especially attracted to psychiatry. He once remarked that "actual residence in an asylum is almost essential to a thorough understanding of the life, nightly as well as daily, of the inmates" (Ireland, 1895). It is hard to imagine a better description of what Karl Jaspers was much later to call "asylum psychiatry" (Jaspers, 1972), but the truth of the matter is that Tuke had no vast experience of asylum life. He spent a formative couple of years at the York Retreat, before deciding to pursue a medical career, during which time he was influenced by the Retreat's medical superintendent, John Thurnam. After studying at St Bartholomew's Hospital Medical School, and obtaining an MD from Heidelberg, he returned to York, where he became visiting physician to the Retreat and contemplated opening a private asylum. However, the appearance of symptoms which were feared might be tubercular cut short his career in York and forced him to seek the milder climate of Falmouth, where he stayed for 15 years.

After his health improved, Tuke gravitated to London, the scene of the last two decades of his career. He became a governor of Bethlem Hospital where, according to his obituarist, he made frequent use of the wards and morgue to improve his knowledge of his specialty. He lectured on mental diseases at Charing Cross Medical School, and became – at the end of his life – the examiner in 'mental physiology' for the University of London. He was also a consultant physician to the private asylum, Featherstone Hall, at Southall. He played a leading role in the Medico-Psychological Association (MPA), editing (with George Savage) the *Journal of Mental Science* from 1880, and serving as the Association's President in 1881 (Ireland, 1895).

These were the trappings of a highly successful career. Nevertheless, there was a certain bookishness about Tuke's writings, which were as likely to be concerned with historical or administrative matters as clinical ones. It was Tuke above all who moulded Victorian perceptions of psychiatry's past, with his evocations of hysterics being burned as witches, the brutality of unreformed Bedlam, and the humaneness of moral therapy. He was a good 'party' man, devoted to improving the status of his profession in Britain, but from his early days, he was also outward looking. His honeymoon was largely devoted to a tour of Continental asylums, and he continued to take a keen interest in Continental and North American psychiatric matters. He admired Charcot and followed with interest the French neurologist's explorations of hysteria and hypnotism, at a much earlier period than many of his British colleagues. It was a tribute to both Tuke and his friend and collaborator John Charles Bucknill that their friendship and fruitful collaboration survived disagreement about Charcot's later work, among other issues.

Tuke was the ideal man to put together the *Dictionary*, and despite the big textbook he wrote with Bucknill, which dominated psychiatry for three decades, or the other dozen or so books and scores of articles, the *Dictionary* remains his *magnum opus*. Its encyclopaedic scope reflected his own catholic interests, and its internationalism was possible because of the vast network of correspondents and colleagues that he had built up over the years, as traveller, editor, and leading light in the MPA. The volumes took two years to complete, and their publication – just after the MPA had celebrated its 50th anniversary – coincided with the centennial of the founding of the York Retreat. In July 1892, the MPA met at the Retreat, where Tuke was able to present the first copy of the *Dictionary* to Robert Baker, Superintendent of the Retreat and President of the Association. Whatever the hostility that great-grandfather William had had for the medical profession, or the explicit antiprofessionalism of early moral therapy (Bynum, 1974), it can be said that with this presentation of his *Dictionary*, Tuke firmly cemented the relationship between his family, their hospital, and the psychiatric profession.

The authors

Besides Tuke, who himself wrote more major articles than anyone else, the list of contributors included 80 British and 47 foreign authors. Unsurprisingly, they were all male, although Tuke's preface thanked one woman, Mrs Stanley Boyd, MD, for help with the revision of proofs. She had survived having the maiden name of Florence Nightingale Toms, had qualified as a Licentiate at the Irish College of Physicians, and in 1888 had received (*avec grande distinction*) a Brussels MD. She practised in Harley Street as an obstetrician and gynaecologist, and would already have been known personally to Tuke. Her husband, the surgeon Stanley Boyd, was a close friend of one of the *Dictionary*'s contributors, Harrington Sainsbury, who was Tuke's son-in-law. The only other individual who had not written any articles but was singled out by Tuke's preface was his colleague at Charing Cross Hospital Medical School, Ernest Fricke, a demonstrator in physiology. A native German, Fricke translated most of the articles from foreign contributors.

The occupations of the contributors are shown in Table 10.1. Some of the occupational categories are not without ambiguity, of course. I have included John Langdon Down (1828–96) as a psychiatrist, for example, because he devoted a good deal of his professional life to studying and caring for the mentally deficient (Zihni, 1989). However, he also lectured on 'materia medica' and medicine at the London Hospital. James Anderson (1853–93) is counted as a physician, despite the fact that he was a physician to the National Hospital, Queen Square; he might well have become a specialist in neurology, but for his premature death. Victor Horsley (1857–1916) could justifiably be included with either the surgeons or the scientists; I have chosen the former. Likewise, Sydney Ringer (1835–1910) and Thomas Lauder Brunton (1844–1916) count as physicians rather than scientists. The pathologist Sims Woodhead (1855–1921) is classified as a scientist, although he had a good deal more clinical orientation than the physiologist

TABLE 10.1
Occupations of the contributors to the Dictionary

Profession	*British*	*Foreign*
Psychiatrists	42	31
Neurologists	3	5
Physicians	18	5
Surgeons	4	1
Obstetricians	2	0
Scientists	5	1
Psychologists	2	3
Miscellaneous	5	1
Total	81	47

Augustus Waller (1856–1922), who, like most physiologists of his day, was medically qualified. Among British contributors, the only ones who were not medically qualified were W. C. Coupland (an essayist, philosopher, and translator), J. Elmer (former clerk to the Masters in Insanity), Henry Hawkins (chaplain at the Colney Hatch Asylum), A. Wood Renton (a barrister), and the evolutionary biologist George John Romanes.

The foreign contributors present rather fewer ambiguities. J. M. Charcot and Pierre Marie are easy enough to categorise as neurologists, but Charcot's other pupil, Gilles de la Tourette, could have been counted as a psychiatrist rather than (as I have done) a neurologist. Because he was listed as 'Formerly Assistant Professor of Physiology in Harvard University, USA', J. Stickney Lombard, MD (the name was not invented by Charles Dickens), has been elevated to the position of sole foreign scientist.

While these and other problems with rigorous occupational categories make Table 10.1 only a general guide to what the contributors did professionally, it nevertheless highlights a number of significant points about the late-Victorian profession. In the first place, the internationalism of the contributors is significant, if hardly surprising, given Tuke's own interests in Continental and, to a lesser extent, American issues. Internationalism was a prominent feature of 19th-century science and medicine, with international congresses mounted for many themes and disciplines (Garrison, 1929, p. 789). The Seventh International Medical Congress, held in London in 1881, attracted some 3000 delegates, and though this one was exceptionally large, any medic or scientist would have had little difficulty finding a regular stream of international meetings to attend in almost any area of interest, even if they might have had to pay their expenses themselves.

Despite the regular appearance of abstracts of foreign books and articles in the *Journal of Mental Science*, it would be easy to exaggerate the impact of internationalism on British psychiatry during the mid-Victorian period, even if, by the last decades of the century, this was beginning to change, partly through Tuke's own efforts. Psychiatry as a whole was rather late in coming to the international-congress bandwagon. There were periodical congresses of 'mental medicine' after the one held in Paris in 1878, but they do not seem to have attracted much British following, with the important exception of Tuke himself. The first international congress of psychology was held in Paris two years before the appearance of the *Dictionary*, and was followed by one on alcoholism in Brussels in 1894. The first congress on the 'care of the insane' was not organised until 1902, in Antwerp, and it could be argued that it was only with the deliberate internationalism of the 'mental hygiene' movement, associated with Clifford W. Beers and Adolf Meyer, that the international theme achieved real prominence in psychiatry (Dain, 1980). Debates from the 1860s between British and American psychiatrists on such topics as the non-restraint system or the compulsory institutional treatment of alcoholics suggest that fairly strong native traditions militated against the casual adoption of overseas ideas or practices (Tomes, 1988). The ranks of foreign contributors to the *Dictionary* were swelled to the extent of about one-third by Tuke's decision to include articles on provision for the insane in the main outposts of the British Empire and in most European countries. The authors of these were naturally derived from the relevant country, although I examine below a number of instances where Tuke chose foreign contributors to deal with specific conceptual or diagnostic issues.

Despite the fact that psychology had already been a theme for an international congress, there was relatively slight input into the *Dictionary* from the few individuals who can be identified as psychologists. W. C. Coupland provided a general philosophical overview, Havelock Ellis wrote (unsurprisingly) the entries on "Sex, Influence of, and Insanity", as well as the plethysmograph and (interestingly) "Urinary bladder, influence of the mind on". Although Ellis had recently qualified medically, he chose not to list his single qualification (LSA) after his name. Some Wundtian themes (e.g. "Psycho-physical methods") were covered by Henry Donaldson, but of the five contributors I have classified as psychologists, only Donaldson and his fellow American Joseph Jastrow had formal institutional appointments. Both were operating within the Wundtian tradition, which so strongly influenced late-19th-century American academic psychology (Boring, 1950). For the most part, however, the coverage of experimental psychology in the *Dictionary* does not suggest that psychology and psychiatry were particularly well integrated, although some of the entries by the psychiatrist W. Bevan-Lewis (as well as Bevan-Lewis's textbook) suggest that he at least was receptive to the psychiatric possibilities of a laboratory-based psychology.

Given the institutional history of psychology in Britain, the relatively slight coverage of the subject in the *Dictionary* is hardly surprising (Hearnshaw, 1964). That so few British neurologists contributed is unexpected, however, given the visibility which men such as W. R. Gowers, John Hughlings Jackson, and David Ferrier had given the subject (Spillane, 1981). 'Neurology' did not even rate a definition, much less a full-length article, and none of those three leading neurologists contributed, even if aspects of their work were discussed in articles such as "Aphasia", "Epilepsies and insanities", and "Brain, Physiology of". In general, however, mainline neurology was absent. Of the British contributors, only Charles Beevor was especially distinguished in neurology, and among the Continental contributors, Charcot and Marie wrote on "Hysteria, mainly Hystero-Epilepsy" (H. B. Donkin provided a separate English perspective on hysteria), rather than more neurological topics. A neurological disorder such as Parkinson's disease was considered only under "Paralysis Agitans, insanity associated with", and a reader wishing to find out about diseases of the spinal cord would discover only the entry entitled "Spinal Cord, changes of, in the insane", written by George Savage.

This does not mean that the psychiatry of the *Dictionary* had lost the somatic orientation characteristic of so much earlier work in the field (Clark, 1981). However, it was general physicians rather than neurologists who supplied much of the 'medicine' of the book's full title. A distinguished group of physicians and surgeons such as T. Clifford Allbutt, J. S. Bristowe, Thomas Lauder Brunton, Humphry Rolleston, Victor Horsley, and Sydney Ringer contributed pieces on diagnostic, pharmacological, and pathological topics. These were supplemented by articles on topics such as "Pulse in insanity", "Urine", "Phthisical insanity", and "Cardiac disease in the insane", written by psychiatrists. The generous representation of entries on the relationship between psychiatric and general medical or physiological issues underscores the extent to which psychiatrists believed that the diagnostic and therapeutic methods of late-19th-century medicine and surgery provided the firmest scientific foundations for psychiatry.

It is significant that, on balance, the physicians and surgeons who contributed to the *Dictionary* had secured wider scientific recognition than their psychiatric colleagues. Ten Fellows of the Royal Society contributed: two of them were 'scientists' (Romanes, Waller), one (Horsley) was a surgeon, and seven were consultant physicians. The only psychiatric Fellow of the Royal Society who figured in the *Dictionary* was Tuke's old friend J. C. Bucknill, to whom the volumes were dedicated. By the 1890s, it was becoming much more difficult for medical men to be elected to the Royal Society simply on grounds of clinical (or social) eminence, and it is hard to believe that Bucknill himself would have been elected in a later generation. Nevertheless, the absence of psychiatrists from the Royal Society is symptomatic of the failure of the discipline to exploit fully the scientifically based medicine of the late 19th century. Only one psychiatrist – F. W. Mott – was elected FRS between 1890 and 1914.

Although the MPA had instituted the Certificate of Efficiency in Psychological Medicine in 1885, this can hardly be described as an overwhelming success (see below), so that in 1892 and for many years afterwards, psychiatrists had to look elsewhere for more general ratification of professional competence. For many of the psychiatric élite, this could be only in medicine itself, through the Royal College of Physicians of London. Of the 42 British psychiatrists who contributed to the *Dictionary*, nine, including Tuke, were Fellows of the London College, to which can be added two who had obtained the London Membership (one of whom, Joseph Wigglesworth, subsequently was elected to Fellowship), two (T. S. Clouston and J. Batty Tuke) who were Fellows of the Royal College of Physicians of Edinburgh, and one (Charles Mercier) who was a Fellow of the Royal College of Surgeons. Mercier subsequently achieved Fellowship in the Royal College of Physicians. Others possessed qualifications from some of the other medical corporations in Britain and Ireland.

There are some other significant features in the educational backgrounds of this (admittedly élite) group. All but four of them had university degrees (MB or MD). Bevan-Lewis had only the London Conjoint qualifications (LRCP, MRCS) (although Leeds later awarded him an honorary MSc), Hayes Newington was only a member of the Edinburgh College of Physicians, S. W. North gave his qualifications as MRCS, FGS (Fellow of the Geological Society), and Conolly Norman was MRCPI and FRCSI. Of those with university degrees, four (W. C. S. Clapham, William Orange, G. E. Shuttleworth, and Tuke himself) had foreign MDs, and three possessed MDs from Aberdeen or St Andrews, at a time when it was possible to obtain them rather easily, after establishing oneself in practice. Of the rest, London and Edinburgh MDs predominate, with a reasonable number of graduates from Glasgow and Oxford. There was a good sprinkling of Cambridge graduates among the physicians and surgeons, but none among the psychiatrists.

Our knowledge of the history of psychiatric education in Britain is still fragmentary, but the group of individuals whom Tuke recruited to write for the *Dictionary* suggest that the situation was beginning to change during the later decades of the century. Anecdotal evidence from the mid-century indicates that medical men went into psychiatry for a variety of personal or idiosyncratic reasons, and that knowledge of the subject was routinely acquired in the county asylums. The basic pattern still undoubtedly obtained for much of the period, but an increasing number of recruits would at least have had an opportunity to acquire a smattering of psychiatric knowledge as medical students, and psychiatry became a compulsory part of undergraduate medical education in 1893. No fewer than 14 of the 42 psychiatrists who wrote for the *Dictionary* held, or had held, lectureships in psychological medicine in the medical schools or medical corporations of Britain. Exactly half of these were in the London schools, three in Scotland (including Batty Tuke, who lectured on mental diseases at the Royal College of Surgeons of Edinburgh), and four in provincial England (Leeds, Durham, twice, and Liverpool).

Nor was there any shortage of general surveys and textbooks on the subject. Bucknill and Tuke's *Manual of Psychological Medicine* dominated the field through the period of its currency (first edition 1858, fourth edition 1879), but a number of shorter books, aimed primarily at students and young practitioners, began to appear from the 1870s, including works by G. F. Blandford, Thomas Clouston, Bevan-Lewis, Charles Mercier, and George Savage. Several of them went through more than one edition, and a medical student interested in psychiatry in 1892 could have chosen from a number of indigenous synthetic accounts, including Mercier's *The Nervous System and the Mind: A Treatise on the Dynamics of the Human Organism* (1888), the third edition of Savage's *Insanity and Allied Neuroses, Practical and Clinical* (1891), Bevan-Lewis's *A Textbook of Mental Diseases, with Special Reference to the Pathological Aspects of Insanity* (1889), James Shaw's *Epitome of Mental Diseases* (1892), the third edition of Clouston's *Clinical Lectures on Mental Diseases* (1892), or the fourth edition of Blandford's *Insanity and its Treatment* (1892). There were also translations of foreign textbooks, as well as American ones available. These bald facts need to be put into an educational context, but they at least highlight the extent to which a kind of academic core and related textbooks were in existence by the last decade of the century.

One further characteristic of the 42 British psychiatric contributors to the *Dictionary* is worth mentioning: their hospital connections. It is well known that the Victorian psychiatric profession developed within the context of the large county asylums that were mandated by the 1845 Act. Reformers like Lord Shaftesbury, who was chairman of the Commissioners of Lunacy, campaigned for stricter control – and possibly even total abolition – of the private madhouses (Hervey, 1985; Finlayson, 1981). This was as much a reflection of the Victorian horror of insanity and the accompanying sentiment that no one should make a profit from this most terrible of human afflictions, as it was from any bad publicity that shady private madhouse keepers had acquired. In any case, except for single boarders, there was a set of regulations protecting psychiatric patients from collusion between relatives and unscrupulous doctors. For a variety of reasons, however, the relative importance of the private and public sectors shifted markedly during the century and, by 1890, pauper lunatics accounted for 91% of the total number of psychiatric patients known to the Commissioners (Scull, 1979, p. 244).

Given this situation, it is worth noting that Tuke's contributors included a significant number who were active within the private sector. Virtually all of them list current or former hospital or asylum affiliations; 12 may be identified with private madhouses, and since there were three associated with Bethlem (a licensed hospital) and one with the York Retreat, the continuing attraction for leading psychiatrists of private hospitals and consultancy work is clear. This should be no surprise, but it does suggest that the career structure of élite psychiatrists was rather more like that of their colleagues in medicine or surgery, although several of them had spent some time earlier in their careers in one of the county asylums.

One final point can be made about the group who wrote for Tuke's *Dictionary*: there was a distinct bureaucratic presence. Psychiatry had been subject to more Parliamentary legislation than any other medical specialty, and part of the book's subtitle makes it clear that "the law of lunacy in Great Britain and Ireland" was considered by Tuke to be part of his brief. Two barristers, the former Chief Clerk to the Masters in Lunacy, the Deputy Commissioner in Lunacy for Scotland, the Inspector of Asylums, New South Wales, and the former Inspector for the Massachusetts State Board of Health, Lunacy and Charity were among the contributors. Entries on the provision for the insane in different countries devote a good deal of space to administrative issues such as the certification process, the number and type of hospital and asylum beds, the insanity defence, and the law surrounding the practice of psychiatry. For no other branch of medicine – except for public health – would a comparable work require so much social and legal placement. Symptomatic is the table (pp. 1411–1412), listing more than 200 legal cases cited in the *Dictionary*.

The contents

The *Dictionary* was simultaneously a dictionary proper, giving brief unsigned definitions of psychiatric words, and an encyclopaedia which offered summaries – often substantial – of more important issues and concepts. Tuke obviously took the former function of the book seriously, invoking Dr Johnson and his own great *Dictionary* in the preface.

The short definitions were supplied primarily by two young medical graduates, James Pietersen (MB, London, 1882) and William G. Willoughby (MD, London, 1889). Pietersen covered the letters A–M and his was the easier task, since the first volume, covering those letters, of *The New Sydenham Society's Lexicon of Medicine and the Allied Sciences*, edited by Henry Power and Leonard Sedgwick, had just been completed and Pietersen was able (with permission) to avail himself of this work. However, there was a vigorous tradition in Britain of medical lexicography, dating back to John Quincy (who died in 1722), which Willoughby could also rely on.

A few key words will highlight some of the differences between contemporary psychiatry and that of a century ago. 'Psychiatry' itself was missing, though the German '*Psychiatrie*' was there. 'Psychopathy' was defined simply as "mental disease", and there was no place for 'dementia praecox', although 'hebephrenia' rated a definition. 'Egoism' but not 'ego' was included, there was no 'malingering', and 'katatonia' was not yet Anglicised to begin with a 'c'. There was no 'unconscious', though 'unconsciousness' was "the antithesis of consciousness", and 'unconscious cerebration' and 'unconscious kinaesthetic impressions' rated slightly longer entries. 'Compulsion' and 'repression' were missing, but Tuke himself wrote the entry on 'Dreaming'.

Psychoanalytically related and biochemical words apart, however, it is perhaps surprising what a generous portion of contemporary psychiatric words were already in existence, especially those describing mental states. A random check of 20 words in Tuke's *Dictionary* with the fourth edition of Hinsie & Campbell's *Psychiatric Dictionary* (1970) reveals that 17 were in both dictionaries, although the meanings of three of them had changed significantly, and a further word from Tuke was given as 'obsolete' in Hinsie & Campbell. It is a sign of our times that 'Cynicism, morbid' was considered by Tuke to be worth including, but no form of 'cynicism' was elevated to disease status in Hinsie & Campbell. A random check between Hinsie & Campbell and Tuke reveals only 6 out of 20 words are contained in both. There was no 'insight' in Tuke, nor 'initiation', 'intersex', or 'linonophobia'. Tuke would, however, have understood 'linonophobia' ('fear of string') and, since he was Latinate, he would have understood 'lapsus calami', even if slips of the pen were neither defined nor discussed in his *Dictionary*.

It is, however, through the more substantial, signed articles, ranging from a couple of paragraphs to more than 30 pages, that the best portrait of late-Victorian psychiatry can be gleaned. I here comment on only three themes: (a) psychiatric nosology; (b) therapeutics; and (c) Continental themes.

(a) Psychiatric nosology

The *Dictionary* contained major pieces on each of the principal psychiatric disorders identified by Victorian medical men. Conolly Norman contributed six pages on 'mania' and Benjamin Ward Richardson almost as many on 'Manias, fasting' ('anorexia nervosa' was briefly described under 'anorexia hysterica' and in passing under 'Neuroses, functional'). There were in addition long entries on 'dementia' (T. Claye Shaw), 'delirium' (Samuel Wilks), 'general paralysis of the insane' (Julius Mickle), 'melancholia' (Charles Mercier), 'neurasthenia' (Rudolf Arndt), 'idiots and imbeciles' (G. E. Shuttleworth), 'idiocy, forms of' (J. Langdon Down), 'phthisical insanity' (T. S. Clouston), and 'puerperal insanity' (George Savage).

These and a large number of shorter articles allow us to piece together a picture of the major diagnostic categories used by Victorian psychiatrists, which the summary article 'Insanity' clarifies. Tuke himself was keenly interested in psychiatric nosology, having contributed the section on 'classification' to Bucknill & Tuke's *Manual*, and he played a major role in standardizing diagnostic categories in the admission forms used in the county asylums. These formed the basis of the statistics compiled by the Commissioners in Lunacy. He was thus the natural author for the entry on 'classification' in the *Dictionary*. In it, he surveyed the various approaches to the topic adopted by selected British and Continental authors.

Several historians have analysed more general aspects of 19th-century approaches to the problems of disease classification, especially the alternatives between what have been called 'pathological' and 'physiological' orientations, and the impact that germ theory had on aetiological thinking (Faber, 1930; King, 1982). Early in the century, the French clinicopathological school had replaced 18th-century nosologies based largely on symptoms such as pain or fever, with one in which the pathological changes revealed at autopsy were given greater prominence. This lesion-orientated approach dominated medical thinking for much of the 19th-century, but from the 1850s or so, experimentalists such as Claude Bernard argued that the pathological lesion discoverable at post-mortem examination was the result of dynamic, pathophysiological processes, and that the physiological understanding of disease offered much more in the way of therapeutic possibilities (Canguilhem, 1978). At about the same time, germ theory offered a new model of disease which reinforced notions of the specificity of diseases and made aetiological considerations seem more important in their classification.

Psychiatric nosology was not unaffected by these developments, and Tuke's article dealt with pathological, physiological, and symptomatological approaches to classifying mental disorder. There is, however, little evidence in the *Dictionary* that germ theory had made much impact on psychiatric thinking. Even Clouston's article on 'phthisical insanity' could have been written before Robert Koch's discovery of the tubercle bacillus a decade previously, and syphilis was only one of a number of factors mentioned in the causative background of general paralysis of the insane (GPI). Neither Koch nor Pasteur is to be found in the index of the *Dictionary*; psychiatric preoccupation with germs and their breakdown products was to be coincident with the association established between syphilis and GPI early in the present century. It was to be the more elastic notion of bacteriological breakdown products – toxins, ptomaines, etc. – that was to provide men like Henry Cotton with the main theoretical foundations of their concepts (Scull, 1987), but it could be argued that the 'poison' model of insanity had its origins in speculations which preceded and were independent of germ theory.

Tuke located the origin of pathologically orientated nosological schemes in Gall's phrenological propositions that the different portions of the brain subserve different functions. Tuke himself had been attracted to phrenology in his youth, but in 1892 he believed that pathological classifications in psychiatry were inadequate: "Our knowledge is too limited to allow of this principle being adopted". Theodor Meynert's was the "latest attempt of importance in this direction", but Meynert's scheme found little favour with Tuke or his colleagues.

Physiological schemes were somewhat more promising. Within this tradition, Tuke placed Thomas Laycock and David Ferrier, and James Anderson's article on 'Epilepsies and insanities' contains an evocative exposition of the leading ideas of the man who provided the most suggestive framework for a physiological understanding of insanity: John Hughlings Jackson. Dewhurst (1982) has examined his 'psychiatry' historically, but despite the richness of Jackson's evolutionary model of psychophysiological functioning, there is little evidence that psychiatrists of his day found it of much use in classifying the patients with which they were confronted. Accordingly, Tuke devoted about three-quarters of his article to symptomatological classifications.

Within this tradition, he placed *inter alia* the broad and relatively simple scheme proposed by Pinel, Esquirol's modification of it, and the more recent classifications of B. A. Morel, David Skae, and T. S. Clouston. Skae and Clouston had attempted *aetiological* classifications, based largely on the life stages of events (lactational, climacteric, senile insanity) or on associated disorders (syphilitic, alcoholic, phthisical insanity). Clouston also provided a symptomatological classification, based primarily on mental states (depression, exaltation, alternating, fixed and limited delusion, enfeeblement, stupor, defective inhibition, and the 'insane diathesis'). Each of these main categories had various subdivisions. For instance, states of mental depression were divided into nine forms of melancholia, while those of 'defective inhibition' included Prichard's concept of moral insanity along with various manias or impulses (pyromania, kleptomania, suicidal impulse).

The main desideratum of the late-19th-century psychiatric community, however, was a simple system which would be agreed internationally and could serve as the basis for the uniform statistics collected by medical superintendents. At the 1885 international congress in Antwerp, a commission was appointed to draw up an international scheme, and although one was agreed at the 1889 congress, Tuke commented that "the prospect of union cannot be said to be hopeful". This scheme consisted of 11 main diagnostic categories, of which the grouping of epilepsy with hysteria and hypochondriasis as one of the 'insane neuroses' was perhaps the most noteworthy. It is not immediately clear what "progressive systematical insanity" meant (Tuke, 1892, pp. 229 ff.).

Tuke's doubts about the widespread acceptance of the international classification were well founded, although the nosology adopted by the MPA (through its Statistical Committee), and in use in the 1890s by the asylum medical superintendents, bore some resemblance to the international one. It recognised eight broad groups: (1) congenital or infantile mental deficiency, (i) with epilepsy, (ii) without epilepsy; (2) epilepsy (acquired); (3) general paralysis of the insane; (4) mania – recent, chronic, recurrent, *a potu*, puerperal, senile; (5) melancholia – recent, chronic, recurrent, puerperal, senile; (6) dementia – primary, secondary, senile, organic; (7) delusional insanity; (8) moral insanity. American asylum superintendents adopted a similar one, with the omission of moral insanity and the adoption of a diagnostic category of toxic insanity, partially to take account of the fact that cases of acute and chronic alcoholism were commonly treated in American asylums, although the label also embraced other 'toxic' states.

The most striking characteristic of the MPA classification was its thoroughly traditional nature. The first six categories can be found in the Hippocratic writings, and the last two were initially included as optional diagnoses, being retained only because superintendents employed them so frequently. The entry on 'Delusion' by Charles Mercier makes it clear that 'delusional insanity' was the diagnostic category favoured by British alienists for a variety of conditions which on the Continent were being denominated by such labels as 'paranoia', 'persecution mania', 'hebephrenia', or 'dementia praecox'. In fact, the *Dictionary* can be viewed as the culmination of Victorian psychiatric nosology, when in Britain Richard von Krafft-Ebing rather than Emil Kraepelin was the more influential German-speaking psychiatrist and the influential work of Bleuler was still in the future.

(b) Therapeutics

As one of the principal psychiatric historians of his generation, Tuke had been instrumental in the historical depiction of moral therapy as one of the great psychiatric triumphs, as a crucial step in the creation of the humane psychiatry of his day. Since, as we have seen, 'morbid cynicism' is no longer considered a disease, it comes as no surprise that modern historians have examined moral therapy, and the rise of psychiatric professionalism, in a rather different light (Foucault, 1971; Scull, 1979; Doerner, 1981).

Despite Tuke's unsurprising insistence that the foundation of the York Retreat was a milestone in the history of the care of the insane (Tuke, 1882), the reader of the *Dictionary* interested in the late-19th-century resonances of 'moral therapy' would be disappointed. The 18th-century term 'management' was not even included, and under 'Moral treatment of the insane', Tuke himself wrote the entry of just over five pages, in which he dealt with a large number of issues, including bed rest, occupational therapy, exercise, education, the problem of mechanical restraint and seclusion, and whether appeals to reason can be effective in treating the insane. Tuke could refer to recent literature on several of the topics, but it was hardly a central article: even the non-restraint debate (which occupied almost half of Tuke's entry) had lost most of its bite, as Tuke simply dismissed radical adherence to a policy of non-restraint ("the triumph of Conollyism") as impractical (Tomes, 1988).

Tuke also supplied the general article on 'Therapeutics', where pharmacological and physical remedies were discussed. The use of baths, electricity, diet, massage, and sedatives also merited separate entries. Electricity was a relatively new therapeutic modality in psychiatry (Beveridge & Renvoize, 1988), but much of the rest, including leeching and counter-irritation, would not have surprised a clinician a century earlier. There were, to be sure, some new drugs (chloral, paraldehyde, bromides), and Tuke referred readers to articles on individual disorders for particular therapeutic discussion, but it is striking how traditional the therapeutic sections were. One exception – though not actually cross-referenced to any of the more general therapeutic entries – was the cluster of articles dealing with hypnotism. Although Tuke did not write any of them, their inclusion reflected his own interest of more than three decades in the subject (Tuke, 1884). The British surgeon James Braid had coined the word 'hypnotism', but the *Dictionary* articles on the subject have a Continental flavour, and are appropriately considered as one of the areas where European psychiatry was beginning to influence British conceptions and practice.

(c) Continental themes

It has already been noted that internationalism was prominent in Tuke's professional life, and therefore not surprising that the *Dictionary* reflected this: no fewer than 30 Continental psychiatrists or neurologists contributed articles on specific topics, as opposed to the survey pieces on the provision for the insane in various countries. A systematic examination of this is beyond the scope of this chapter, but many of these articles cluster into three broad headings which are worth brief consideration.

The first group, mentioned above, relates to hypnotism. While the article on the history of hypnotism (the only entry actually arranged historically) was contributed by an English physician, Arthur Myers (brother of Frederic Myers, one of the founders of the Society for Psychical Research) (Oppenheim, 1985), Tuke persuaded Charcot to co-author two articles, one on 'Hypnotism in the hysterical', with Gilles de la Tourette, and one on 'Hysteria mainly hystero-epilepsy' with Pierre Marie. Since Charcot died in 1893, these represent significant summary statements on subjects which had preoccupied him during the last two decades of his life (Goldstein, 1987; Harris, 1989; Micale, 1989). The debates between Charcot in Paris and Hippolyte Bernheim in Nancy are well known, and need not be rehearsed here (Harris, 1985) , but in the interests of fairness, Tuke made certain that both sides were represented in the *Dictionary*:

in addition to Charcot's articles, Bernheim contributed an entry on 'Suggestion and hypnotism'. By contrast, the *Dictionary* contained no article on 'psychotherapy' itself, and it was through concern with hypnotism, suggestion, and related phenomena that newer psychological techniques were to be integrated into British psychiatry in the Edwardian period and after.

The second group of foreign articles are those clustering around the concept of hereditary degeneration. Henry Maudsley is generally seen as the principal British exponent of degenerationist ideas (Turner, 1988), but Maudsley was a curiously shadowy figure in the *Dictionary*. He wrote nothing for it and has only 10 citations in its index, in contrast to Lombroso and Magnan, who each received 12, Krafft-Ebing with 18, or Griesinger with 22. Although Charles Mercier wrote a rather bland, general article on 'Heredity', Havelock Ellis wrote on 'Criminal anthropology', and Tuke himself contributed 'Degeneration' (with six of seven references to French literature). Foreign authors wrote most of the entries on related topics; thus, Moritz Benedikt wrote on 'Craniometry' and 'Criminals, Brains of', Paul-Maria Legrain furnished 'Poisons of the mind' and the numerous entries on alcoholism and related phenomena, Dr Bouchereau contributed 'Erotic insanity', 'Nymphomania' and 'Satyriasis', Collin and Garnier wrote 'Homicidal monomania', Régis provided 'Regicides', and Erlenmeyer wrote 'Cocomania' (addiction to cocaine, not hot chocolate), 'Morphinomania', and on the effects of tobacco on the nervous system. Oddly, the word 'addiction' did not even rate a definition. While there was no shortage of British interest in these issues, the extent to which Tuke turned to Continental colleagues to summarise current opinion emphasises the fact that the intellectual structure and much of the detail of degenerationism derived from French and German thinkers (Bynum, 1987).

The third major area of Continental authorship consisted of diagnostic categories and descriptive psychopathology not commonly employed in Britain. Entries on '*Cérébraux* (a kind of traumatic insanity first described by Lesègue), '*Katatonia*', 'Mania of persecution', 'Obsession and impulse', 'Verbigeration', 'Circular insanity', and 'Transitory mania' were all contributed by Europeans, and to this list must be added several that Tuke himself summarised largely from Continental authorities: 'Paranoia', '*Verrücktheit*', '*Verwirrtheit*', and 'Imperative ideas'. It is hard to read the *Dictionary* without Kraepelinian spectacles, and not to conclude that if Jaspers were right to insist that Kraepelin and Wernicke between them changed the face of psychiatry, the *Dictionary* represents the culmination of the tradition that was to be utterly transformed. There are only three minor references to Kraepelin in Tuke's book, and one to Wernicke.

Psychiatric education

The relative insularity of British psychiatry in the late Victorian period should not surprise us, given the fact that education for the specialty was still largely the practical matter of on-site training as a resident medical officer in one of the large county lunatic asylums. That this was so was as much a reflection of the resistance of the British medical establishment to specialisation and postgraduate medical qualifications as it was of the marginal status of psychiatry as a discipline. Between the establishment of the General Medical Council (GMC) under the Medical Act 1858 and the end of the century, only one specialist group had managed to secure legal recognition of their position. These were the Medical Officers of Health (MOH), who, through their association, succeeded in 1894 in making the postgraduate Diploma in Public Health (DPH) mandatory for employment as an MOH in populous districts (Watkins, 1984; Fee & Acheson, 1991). Many other groups (e.g. obstetricians, neurologists, laryngologists) started specialist societies and journals, but they had no legal recognition (Stevens, 1966).

This does not mean that psychiatric issues were completely neglected at the undergraduate level. As we have seen, a generous proportion of the contributors to the *Dictionary* held (or had held) academic posts. In 1888, the GMC had recommended that the study of psychiatry was "desirable" for all medical students; T. S. Clouston had urged the Scottish Universities' Commission to go even further in 1890, and in 1893, the GMC acceded to suggestions from various quarters and made psychiatric instruction (but not examination) compulsory for all medical students (Clouston, 1911). In Clouston's words, this "was the charter of our real and full incorporation into general medicine" (p. 210).

On the other hand, the MPA had less success in achieving recognition for its prime educational initiative during the period: the inauguration, in 1885, of a Certificate of Efficiency in Psychological Medicine (MPC). A benefaction the following year from the sister of Samuel Gaskell (1807–86), a former Commissioner in Lunacy, enabled the Association to award the Gaskell Prize to those who, having passed the MPC, performed to a high standard at an honours examination which included brain histology and psychology among its subjects.

In 1911, Clouston could report that "some 328 men" (in fact some women had taken the examination) had taken the MPC since it had first been offered in 1886. But he could not disguise the fact that, for unexplained reasons, the experiment had been less than outstandingly successful. The numbers presenting themselves had decreased after a few years – curiously, at just about the time when psychiatry had become a compulsory subject at the undergraduate level. The examination itself – the questions were generally published in the *Journal of Mental Science* – tended to be rather broad and general: "Describe Alcoholic Insanity, and mention how it resembles and differs from General Paralysis" was one of six questions in the 1895 paper. As Clouston summarised it, the Certificate "was not registrable, and it was not academic" (Clouston, 1911, p. 213). Symptomatic of the failure of the Certificate to catch on was the fact that, after the first few years, MPA members who held the Certificate stopped putting 'MPC' along with their other qualifications in the Association's membership lists.

Examinations never offer more than an imperfect mirror of what was taught to or known by the candidates, nor do the papers themselves give much clue to the quality of answer that would be deemed of a pass standard. Clouston obviously felt that educational and research initiatives had been more significant than the Certificate examination. Among these, he noted the establishment of pathological laboratories attached to asylums: the one at Morningside in Edinburgh, that at the West Rising Asylum in Wakefield; and the London County Council's decision to equip one at Claybury, where F. W. Mott was appointed (Chapter 4). As for teaching itself, he placed his own University of Edinburgh at the forefront, with its continuous modern tradition dating to Thomas Laycock's appointment as Professor of Medicine in 1857 and culminating in the approval, in 1911, by Edinburgh's University Court, of a diploma in psychiatry. The inattentive reader of Clouston's paean of praise to his Alma Mater ("the greatest of all the schools of medicine in Great Britain") might have failed to notice that Manchester and Durham had also initiated diplomas, but Clouston would at least have made him aware that the MPA itself was by 1911 actively involved in the status of psychiatric training within the context of the GMC and of the examining bodies in the UK. Unlike the Certificate, the diploma was not based simply on an examination, but required a prior course of postgraduate study in the relevant university, as well as being registrable with the GMC. Although Clouston was nearing the end of his life in 1911, and the diploma in psychiatry was still untested, his advice may not have been unjust: "If I were now an assistant medical officer I should without hesitation at once set myself to obtain the diploma." The role of the diploma in psychiatry, however, lay in the future.

Conclusion

It would be hazardous to base general conclusions about the late-19th-century psychiatric profession on a single book, even a multi-authored reference work such as Tuke's *Dictionary*. Nevertheless, two brief points may be made.

Firstly, the role of medicine within psychiatry ('psychological medicine') was important. This can be seen in the number of entries written by consultant physicians as well as in the frequency of psychiatrists themselves achieving Membership or Fellowship in either the London or Edinburgh College of Physicians. Contributors to the *Dictionary* form an élite sample, but my preliminary work with the membership lists of the MPA as a whole suggests a positive correlation between advanced medical qualifications and eminence within the Association. This is not to deny the powerful geographical and intellectual isolation created by the discipline's principal institution, the asylum; rather, it is to suggest that psychiatry's links with medicine as a whole continued to play a crucial role within the discipline. We need to know much more about the practice of psychiatry outside the asylum.

Secondly, there were small but genuine gains in psychiatric education, with hints of a new academic core within the profession, lectureships in most of the medical schools and the modestly successful Certificate of Efficiency in Psychological Medicine. On the other hand, these developments should not mask the fact that the MPC was an examination without a curriculum or legal standing. Few people doubted the necessity of the discipline, and with an overcrowded medical profession as a whole, psychiatric recruitment seems to have presented few difficulties. But it is hard to escape the conclusion that the promise of the mid-century foundations remained unfulfilled.

References

Beveridge, A. W. & Renvoize, E. B. (1988) Electricity: a history of its use in the treatment of mental illness in Britain during the second half of the 19th century. *British Journal of Psychiatry*, **153**, 157–162.

Boring, E. G. (1950) *A History of Experimental Psychology*. New York: Appleton-Century-Crofts.

BYNUM, W. F. (1974) Rationales for therapy in British psychiatry, 1780–1835. *Medical History*, **18**, 317–334.

—— (1987) Alcoholism and degeneration in 19th century European medicine and psychiatry. *British Journal of Addiction*, **79**, 59–70.

CANGUILHEM, G. (1978) *On the Normal and the Pathological*. Dordrecht: D. Reidel.

CLARK, M. J. (1981) The rejection of psychological approaches to mental disorder in late nineteenth-century British psychiatry. In *Madhouses, Mad-doctors and Madmen* (ed. A. Scull). London: Athlone Press.

CLOUSTON, T. S. (1911) The Diploma in Psychiatry. *Journal of Mental Science*, **57**, 208–218.

DAIN, N. (1980) *Clifford W. Beers: Advocate for the Insane*. Pittsburgh: Pittsburgh University Press.

DEWHURST, K. (1982) *Hughlings Jackson on Psychiatry*. Oxford: Sandford.

DIGBY, A. (1985) *Madness, Morality and Medicine: A Study of the York Retreat 1796–1914*. Cambridge: Cambridge University Press.

DOERNER, K. (1981) *Madmen and the Bourgeoisie: A Social History of Insanity and Psychiatry*. Oxford: Basil Blackwell.

FABER, K. (1930) *Nosography: The Evolution of Clinical Medicine in Modern Times*. New York: Paul B. Hoeber.

FEE, E. & ACHESON, R. (1991) *'To Mock Doctors' Rules': A History of Education in Public Health*. Oxford: Oxford University Press.

FINLAYSON, G. B. A. M. (1981) *The Seventh Earl of Shaftesbury 1801–1885*. London: Eyre Methuen.

FOUCAULT, M. (1971) *Madness and Civilization: A History of Insanity in the Age of Reason*. London: Tavistock.

GARRISON, F. H. (1929) *An Introduction to the History of Medicine*. Philadelphia: W. B. Saunders.

GOLDSTEIN, J. (1987) *Console and Classify: The French Psychiatric Profession in the Nineteenth Century*. Cambridge: Cambridge University Press.

HARRIS, R. (1985) Murder under hypnosis in the case of Gabrielle Bompart: psychiatry in the courtroom in belle époque Paris. In *The Anatomy of Madness Vol. 2, Institutions and Society* (eds W. F. Bynum, R. Porter & M. Shepherd). London: Tavistock.

HARRIS, R. (1989) *Murders and Madness. Medicine, Law and Society in the Fin de Siècle*. Oxford: Oxford University Press.

HEARNSHAW, L. S. (1964) *A Short History of British Psychology, 1840–1940*. London: Methuen.

HERVEY, N. (1985) A slavish bowing down: the Lunacy Commission and the psychiatric profession 1845–1860. In *The Anatomy of Madness, Vol. 2, Institutions and Society* (eds W. F. Bynum, R. Porter & M. Shepherd). London: Tavistock.

HINSIE, L. E. & CAMPBELL, R. J. (eds) (1970) *Psychiatric Dictionary*. New York: Oxford University Press.

IRELAND, W. W. (1895) Daniel Hack Tuke M.R.C.S., M.D., LL.D. *Journal of Mental Science*, **41**, 377–386.

JASPERS, K. (1972) *General Psychopathology* (trans. J. Hoenig & M. W. Hamilton) (4th impression). Manchester: Manchester University Press. Chicago: The University of Chicago Press.

KING, L. S. (1982) *Medical Thinking: A Historical Preface*. Princeton, NJ: Princeton University Press.

MICALE, M. (1989) Hysteria and its historiography: a review of past and present writings, Parts I and II. *History of Science*, **27**, 223–261, 319–351.

OPPENHEIM, J. (1985) *The Other World: Spiritualism and Psychical Research in England, 1850–1914*. Cambridge: Cambridge University Press.

SCULL, A. (1979) *Museums of Madness. The Social Organization of Insanity in Nineteenth-Century England*. London: Allen Lane.

—— (1987) Desperate remedies: a Gothic tale of madness and modern medicine. *Psychological Medicine*, **17**, 516–577.

SPILLANE, J. D. (1981) *The Doctrine of the Nerves: Chapters in the History of Neurology*. Oxford: Oxford University Press.

STEVENS, R. (1966) *Medical Practice in Modern England: The Impact of Specialization and State Medicine*. New Haven, CT: Yale University Press.

TOMES, N. (1988) The great restraint controversy: a comparative perspective in Anglo-American psychiatry in the nineteenth century. In *The Anatomy of Madness, Vol. 3, The Asylum and its Psychiatry* (eds W. F. Bynum, R. Porter & M. Shepherd). London: Routledge.

TUKE, D. H. (1882) *Chapters in the History of the Insane in the British Isles*. London: Kegan Paul, Trench.

—— (1884) *Sleep-walking and Hypnotism*. London: J. & A. Churchill.

—— (ed.) (1892) *A Dictionary of Psychological Medicine*, 2 vols. London: J. & A. Churchill.

TURNER, T. (1988) Henry Maudsley: psychiatrist, philosopher and entrepreneur. In *The Anatomy of Madness, Vol. 3, The Asylum and its Psychiatry* (eds W. F. Bynum, R. Porter & M. Shepherd). London: Routledge.

WATKINS, D. E. (1984) "The English revolution in social medicine, 1889–1911". Unpublished PhD thesis, University of London.

ZIHNI, L. S. (1989) "The relationship between the theory and treatment of Down's syndrome in Britain and America from 1866 to 1967". Unpublished PhD thesis, University of London.

11 Psychosurgery in Britain and elsewhere: a conceptual history

GERMAN E. BERRIOS

The history of psychosurgery can be written in a number of ways: for example, around the biography of a particular individual, or through some guiding idea, such as the curiosity that through the ages seems to have driven men to explore the contents of the skull. The former approach is limited; the latter, also called the 'chain of being' technique, is prone to identify unreal connections between activities remote from one another, such as trephining among the Incas or during the Renaissance, together with the later work of Shaw, Burckhardt, or Moniz. The problem with this historical approach is that in order to sustain a speculative link, it must detach these surgical events from their historical context. In this chapter, two periods of psychosurgical activity (as determined by a definitional criterion) are compared in terms of their historical context and conceptual and technical underpinnings. It is hoped that this method will illustrate both the internal and external factors involved in these perilous therapeutic activities.

The search for the absolute 'origins' of any medical procedure often leads to anachronisms, since the current 'definition' of the object is bound to cause unwarranted strictures on the breadth of the search. The current definition of psychosurgery is based on four criteria: direct interference with brain tissue, irreversibility of the procedure, normality of the affected tissues, and alleviation of psychiatric illness. But how are these to be interpreted? In addition to resection, should the criterion of interference with brain tissue also include relief of excessive pressure of cerebrospinal fluid or electrical stimulation by implanted devices? The determination of irreversibility and of the 'normality' of the tissues is clearly dependent on scientific advance. What counts as psychiatric disorder is dependent on the descriptive and prescriptive mores of a culture. Does this mean, then, that the history of psychosurgery will need to be periodically rewritten, with many historical events being included or excluded, according to the latest interpretation of the criteria?

Definitions cannot be absolute (nor take their cues only from the present), but must be qualified in terms of the historical context, intentions of the participants, and their ideological assumptions. Thus, surgery for brain injuries, space-occupying lesions, and epilepsy has been excluded, even if such interventions are known on occasion to affect behaviour. On the other hand, operations to alleviate general paralysis of the insane (GPI), because they targeted mental symptoms, and because during the period in question GPI was considered as a form of insanity, are included. In other words, psychosurgical operations are defined as procedures which have as their primary objective the alleviation of psychopathology; they thus include trephining of the skull and direct or indirect interference with brain tissue.

It is further assumed that the history of knowledge of the brain is constituted by a series of research programmes, paradigms, and themes which change periodically (Clarke & Jacyna, 1987). For example, the current 'episteme' (i.e. set of views about psychiatric illness) started sometime during the 19th century, and since then, in spite of major technological advances, no real conceptual break has taken place. If so, it can be assumed that the conceptual factors that generated the British and Swiss psychosurgical attempts of the 1890s were no different from those that, 40 years later, led Moniz to start his work. Within the ongoing paradigm, though, hypotheses are changing all the time: for instance, views on the function of the frontal lobes, on neuronal theory, on synapses, and on cell assemblies have changed, as well as the neurosurgical techniques that are used. But the principles have remained the same. It is not surprising, therefore, that the arguments used in 1890 against psychosurgery were the same in Great Britain and Continental Europe, and indeed, the same as those levelled later against Moniz and his followers.

Pre-19th-century psychosurgery

Before the 19th century, historical and cultural domains can be identified which favoured the view that trephining of the skull may result in behavioural change: sometimes this occurred in practice, but it would not fit into recent (narrow) definitions of psychosurgery, as defined above. The reason for this lack of fit is that up to the time of Moniz, most aetiological accounts of insanity (i.e. of the psychoses) assumed that related brain tissues were abnormal.

Trephining among the Incas (Broca, 1867, 1874) to release the evil spirits that caused madness has occasionally been included as an early example of psychosurgery (O'Callaghan & Carroll, 1982). No written document corroborating these claims is available (since the Incas had no writing) and little that is useful can therefore be said about them. A second historical stop, however, is provided by the fascinating visual world of Hieronymus Bosch (Jowell, 1965; Hemphill, 1965; Lucas, 1968) and other Dutch and Flemish painters, who repeatedly depicted operations for *cephalic calculi*, or stones (Brabant, 1976; Quetel & Morel, 1979). One of the earliest medical analyses of these grotesque paintings from the High Renaissance was by Meige (1895, 1898, 1899, 1900) and his group in Paris (Chipault & Daleine, 1893; Gaudier, 1900). Their work, though, has not thrown light on whether these paintings chronicled actual operations, reflected ongoing linguistic or artistic symbolisms (probably inspired in mystery plays and pageants), were metaphorical extrapolations from other surgical interventions (e.g. for bladderstones or gallstones), or had cultural meanings which have since been lost, or were combinations of any of these.

The next documented period in the history of psychosurgery is the work during the late 19th century of G. Burckhardt, described (Müller, 1960) as the pioneer who set the stage for Moniz, the real prince of the story. It is interesting that both defenders and denigrators of psychosurgery agree with the conventional view that before attending the 1935 London Neurology Meeting, Moniz had no idea of the operation: the hypothesis that it was Fulton's views on the functions of the frontal lobe that influenced Moniz has been subject to historical analysis (Pressman, 1988).

It seems as if the conventional view needed to have a clear starting point, and that the choice of Moniz to play this role perhaps reflected the way in which psychosurgery was to develop after him (Willett, 1960; Rylander, 1973; O'Callaghan & Carroll, 1982). However, the popularity criterion is often a bad indicator of novelty. Indeed, Moniz's work reflects beliefs on the aetiology of mental disorder, the organisation of the brain, the usefulness of certain surgical techniques, and the ethics of brain interventions which were already present during the late 19th century (Willett, 1960; O'Callaghan & Carroll, 1982). In a conceptual sense, little was new in this work. In this account, the historical information is grouped in two sections: firstly, the psychosurgical developments that occurred in the 1890s, including the work of Shaw in Great Britain and of Burckhardt in Switzerland; and secondly, Moniz's own contribution. Nothing is said on Freeman, Watts, and the many others who came later, since their work can rather be considered as historic variations upon well known themes.

The 1890s: Claye Shaw and the British debate

Late in 1889, Claye Shaw (1889) (see Biographical note 1, at the end of this chapter) reported the case of a male patient suffering from GPI; on 15 August, he had been operated on in London by Mr Harrison Cripps, who had removed a piece of his temporoparietal skull, sectioned the dura, and drained much yellow fluid. By 16 November, his insanity having remitted, the subject was discharged. Shaw intimated that David Ferrier (see Biographical note 2) had been consulted on "performing an operation which might or might not be creditable to brain surgery" (p. 1091). He also reported that before discharge, the patient had been assessed by Clifford Allbutt (see note 3), who felt that he was no longer insane. Shaw's report suggested that one of the reasons for improvement might have been that the operation released mechanical pressure which was compressing the brain.

Soon after, the correspondence column of the *British Medical Journal* (*BMJ*) was set alight by a debate uncannily similar to the one that surrounded the leucotomy question in the 1950s. Two weeks after Shaw's article, the first two letters appeared: one by J. Adams (1889) suggested that spontaneous remissions occurred in GPI; the other, by G. Revington (1889) from the Prestwich asylum in Manchester, included a major theoretical attack. He stated three conditions for any operation of this nature: clear knowledge of the pathogenesis of the disease, availability of technical and operatory means, and a method to show that the improvement was due to the procedure. Revington claimed that Shaw had not met any of these. Furthermore, he called the hypothesis of increased fluid pressure "mechanical non-sense" and suggested that if fluid was to be important, it would be only in the formation of oedema, so that only slicing of the cortex (which Shaw and Cripps had not done) might help. He concluded that the improvement had resulted from spontaneous remission.

In a most measured letter, Cripps (1889) replied that he was "interested to learn" that the patient had got better, and declared that his hypothesis concerning the effect of increased pressure leading to atrophy of the brain had been conceived as an extrapolation from the mechanism of glaucoma (p. 1215). Next appeared a long paper by Batty Tuke (1890) (see note 4) from Edinburgh, reporting a second case, operated on by J. Duncan, who did not coauthor the article; the patient had also improved. Tuke suggested that he (and not Cripps) was the initiator of the hypothesis of the increased pressure of cerebrospinal fluid (CSF). The same issue of the *BMJ* carried an article by Percy Smith, then medical superintendent of the Bethlem Royal Hospital, who reported four cases of GPI which had exhibited spontaneous remission, and suggested that Shaw's case belonged to this category. He also criticised Revington for having used the phrase "mechanical non-sense" (Smith, 1890). Revington (1890) replied, this time attacking Batty Tuke for not dealing with the issue of spontaneous remission. Once again, he criticised the increased-pressure hypothesis and quoted Clouston and Bevan Lewis in support of the view that mental symptoms resulted not from increased pressure, but from degeneration of nervous tissue.

Then, Shaw & Cripps (1890) reported another case, this time of a 29-year-old man who had been trephined on the left parietal eminence, with both bone and dura removed. They said that the subject's mental state (but not his motor symptoms) had improved dramatically, and he had consequently been discharged. They also reported that their first patient, after seven months of improvement, had developed epilepsy and died, early in February the same year. However, they again defended the pressure hypothesis, stating that the target of the operation had been the mental and not the motor symptoms. Earlier in the same year, the first American case was reported, of a 32-year-old black patient (Wagner, 1890).

The year 1891 saw a great deal of activity, and at a meeting of the British Medical Association (BMA) on 31 July held at Bournemouth, a debate took place on the surgical treatment of GPI. Shaw (1891) delivered a long paper on the "propriety" of the operation and on its theoretical bases, which he divided into two: general, relating to the release-of-pressure hypothesis; and special, suggesting that the operation afforded a new nutritional and drainage system for the brain by encouraging reactive vascularisation and the formation of new lymphatic vessels. He also discussed criteria for deciding on the side of the operation and on the possible mechanisms involved in the increased CSF pressure, as well as reporting a case operated on by Barton and Gayton at the Brookwood asylum.

Victor Horsley (see note 5) congratulated Shaw on the favourable results, but claimed no personal experience in this area. Charles Mercier (see note 6) stated that on account of its seriousness, the operation should not be done lightly, and that if relieving pressure was the only reason, why not bore a smaller hole? He saw no reason for the grandiose delusions of GPI to improve after surgery, since this would be tantamount to saying that a "church ritual could be improved by taking a few slates off the roof of the building!" The spontaneous-remission hypothesis was defended with some force by Macpherson, Herbert, and Snow, while Needham suggested that the patients might have been simulators who used the opportunity of the operation to abandon their symptoms. D. H. Tuke defended Shaw's view, and Moritz Benedikt (1835–1920), attending the meeting as a foreign guest, said that more practical results were needed before conducting a theoretical debate.

In another major paper, Shaw (1892) set out his views on what he called a "general conceptual analysis" of insanity, concluding that the only way to test the increased-pressure hypothesis was to operate on an ordinary patient, whose insanity was not due to this mechanism. He went on to reveal that such a control operation had in fact been carried out in a 28-year-old, impulsive, and deluded subject who was refusing food and in danger of dying. Since in this case the symptoms did not favour a particular surgical site, Cripps trephined on the middle line. After some initial improvement and relapse, the subject had had a good remission. Shaw concluded, rather pessimistically: "that the operation will ever become more than an occasional one is doubtful; it takes much time, it requires special surgical skill, and the idea of it is formidable. At best it seems only palliative, at any rate in its present development" (p. 68). He was not to carry out, or at least report, another operation.

More operations, however, were to be undertaken elsewhere. Macpherson & Wallace (1892), from the Stirling asylum, reported five cases, with short-term remission of mental symptoms in three; two patients were followed up to post-mortem and since no new lymphatic vessels were found, the authors concluded that Cripps' hypothesis was probably wrong. They also concluded that, in their hands, the operation had been successful from the surgical, but not from the psychiatric point of view. They speculated that perhaps this was due to the advanced state of the cases, and suggested earlier interventions but concluded that, at that time, the operation was "of no material benefit whatsoever" (p. 170).

From the USA, Alder Blumer (1892) reported ten cases; of these, two had dementia and melancholia, and their symptoms had partially remitted; the operations were of the 'release of pressure' type. He acknowledged the contributions of Shaw and Cripps, but concluded that the latter's lymphatic hypothesis was wrong (p. 231). He also referred to Wagner's negro case, who had in fact died two months after operation; post-mortem had showed that the dura opening had closed.

Sporadic cases continued to be reported, both in Britain and elsewhere, but it is difficult to estimate how many operations were actually carried out, as many are likely to have remained unreported. For example, Goodall (1893) published the case of a woman from the Wakefield asylum who sustained cortical damage during the operation, which led to focalised convulsions and bilateral musical hallucinations, although her mental state improved. Rey (1891) also reported an operation carried out in February of 1891 in Marseilles on a 40-year-old man with GPI, depression, and psychotic symptoms; the latter improved, but his motor symptoms remained unaltered.

The final analysis of the effectiveness of the operation was made at the 1894 meeting of the Edinburgh Medico-Chirurgical Society. Batty Tuke claimed that most specialists had accepted his "encephalic pressure hypothesis", and reported that another seven patients had been operated on by J. Duncan, in four of whom good results had been obtained. However, other speakers at this meeting did not agree: William Ireland stated that he did not believe that GPI could be treated by trephining. Thomas Clouston (see note 7) took a middle course and, referring to the English cases, stated that he did not believe that they were really cured, although in hopeless cases the operation should still be tried. He wondered whether, in the instances where improvement had occurred, the diagnosis of GPI had in fact been right, and also questioned the increased-pressure hypothesis.

The operation and subsequent debate were widely quoted abroad. As mentioned above, Americans had carried out a number of operations, and at least one had been performed in France. Guiseppe Seppilli (1891), summarising the British evidence, felt that the number of reported cases was too small and that the increased-pressure hypothesis was unlikely to be correct. He concluded that further knowledge of the mechanisms involved in the production of symptoms was needed before more should be undertaken.

Four years later, Semelaigne (1895) (see note 8) published his masterly review on the uses of brain surgery in insanity. Reflecting the pre-1900 view that all forms of insanity were organic in nature, he grouped them all under the same rubric, irrespective of whether they resulted from trauma, epilepsy, or general paralysis. He concluded that because the results were so varied, this type of treatment should not be granted right of abode in the therapeutic armamentarium of psychiatry until more information became available. By then, however, no more cases were being reported.

The 1890s: Burckhardt's work

Parallel to the British work, Gottlieb Burckhardt, a Swiss psychiatrist, carried out his solitary work at the asylum of Préfargier; always mentioned *in passim*, there is surprisingly little detail on his achievement. From the historical point of view, the fact that his operation was not widely adopted is less important than that in his thought, the historian finds the same concepts as those inspiring the British experience, which were to be rehearsed again during the mid-1930s.

Burckhardt (see note 9), like Shaw, was intellectually a child of the second half of the 19th century, and three conceptual trends supported his outlook. Firstly, there was the view that all mental disorders had a physical basis, that is, they reflected particular brain states. Secondly, associationism and connectionism were still the predominant models of nervous functioning – the nervous system was conceived of as including three systems: an input or afferent or sensory system; a linking or connecting system, where information processing took place; and an efferent, motor, or output system. Thirdly, each mental module (or faculty) was considered to be related to a brain site. This same model was, for example, behind Wernicke's wiring diagram for language, which not only could be superimposed on what was known of the anatomy of the left hemisphere, but also could explain symptom clusters in relation to lesions in specific sites. Charcot and Pitrés had done similar work for the motor areas, and others were to do the same for vision and the higher cortical functions.

It was according to this model that Burckhardt (1891) predicted that lesions in certain association areas might change behaviour in particular ways. He wrote:

> "if excitation and impulsive behaviour are due to the fact that from the sensory surfaces excitations abnormal in quality, quantity and intensity do arise, and do act on the motor surfaces, then an improvement could be obtained by creating an obstacle between the two surfaces. The extirpation of the motor or the sensory zone would expose us to the risk of grave functional disturbances and to technical difficulties. It would be more advantageous to practice the excision of a strip of cortex behind and on both sides of the motor zone creating thus a kind of ditch in the temporal lobe." (p. 478)

TABLE 11.1
Details of Burckhardt's six cases (1891)

Case No.	*Sex*	*Age: years*	*Target symptoms*	*Side*	*Site*	*No. of operations*	*Complications*	*Outcome*
1	F	54	Aggression	R	Parietotemporal	4	Motor	No change
2	M	31	Excitement	L	Frontal	1	Epilepsy	Quieter
3	M	35	Violence	L	Temporal	1	–	Quieter
4	F	37	Paranoid	L	Temporal	1	Word deaf	No change
5	M	26	Paranoid	L	Temperofrontal	1	–	Improvement
6	M	33	Violence	L	Temporal	1	Epilepsy	Death

A retrospective diagnosis of schizophrenia, although anachronistic, is warranted in all six cases by the completeness of the case reports.

Starting in December 1888, Burckhardt seems to have operated on at least six patients – two women and four men – and on one of the women at least four times. Analysis of his case reports suggests that all were suffering from schizophrenia, and that the target symptoms were aggression, excitement, and paranoid violence (Table 11.1). He had little surgical experience and the operations seem to have been carried out in a small room in the grounds of the Préfargier clinic; since his instruments and technique were primitive, the patients, not surprisingly, exhibited a number of adverse effects. One subject died in status epilepticus, and on post-mortem the destructive effects of the 'topectomy' were clearly visible. In three subjects, though, symptoms seem to have partially improved.

Burckhardt presented his findings to the Berlin Medical Congress of 1890, which was also attended by Horsley, Erb, Schultze, Mendel, Magnan, Dagonet, and Kraepelin (see note 10). Reports on this meeting were published in a number of countries. For example, Worcester (1891) presented a summary to his American colleagues, emphasising the adverse effects and short follow-up. Kraepelin (1983) referred to Burckhardt's intervention with disrespect: "He suggested that restless patients could be pacified by scratching away the cerebral cortex" (p. 64). Reporting Burckhardt's paper to an Italian audience, Seppelli (1891) stated that the latter's modular view did not "fit with the view held by most that the psychoses reflect a diffuse pathology of the cerebral cortex and with the view of essential unity of the psyche" (p. 371). He concluded that because of the weakness of the theoretical basis on which the operations had been performed it was unlikely that anyone would follow Burckhardt's example. Semelaigne (1895) also reported Burckhardt's paper at length, and, after attacking his theory and results, concluded that "an absence of treatment is better than a bad treatment" (p. 402).

After the Berlin meeting, Burckhardt (1891) went on to publish his cases in a masterly paper, often quoted but rarely read, in the *Zeitschrift für Psychiatrie*. It is 88 pages long and includes all six case histories, repeated mental state assessments, a complete review of the clinical and experimental literature on brain localisation, and a tight theoretical argument. The paper was quoted at length abroad, but he never wrote on the subject again. In Britain, William Ireland dedicated six pages to it, wondering whether any English physician would have "the hardihood to imitate" Burckhardt (p. 614). Ireland (1891, pp. 617–618), however, summarised his views well:

> "Dr Burckhardt has a firm faith in the view that the mind is made up of a number of faculties, holding their seats in distinct portions of the brain. Where excess or irregularity of function occurs he seeks to check it by ablation of a portion of the irritated centres. He defends himself from the criticisms which are sure to be directed against his bold treatment by showing the desperate character of the prognosis of the patients upon whom the operations were performed."

Five years after Burckhardt's death, a harsher criticism was to appear in a paper by Bechterew & Poussépe (1912), probably the last important work on surgical approaches to insanity to be published before World War I. After summarising the cases, the authors said: "We have quoted this data to show not only how groundless but also how dangerous these operations were. We are unable to explain how their author, holder of a degree in medicine, could bring himself to carry them out" (p. 85). Many years later, Poussépe (1937), then a senior surgeon, returned to the point in a talk given to the Medical Academy of Turin. After attacking Burckhardt, he went on to confess that in 1910 he had, in fact, carried out three unsuccessful operations in subjects with manic–depressive psychosis and "epileptic-equivalents", whose "association fibres" he had removed in the frontal and parietal lobes.

Apart from Poussépe, however, no one seems to have repeated Burckhardt's operation. The early 20th century was a different world: together with the growth of psychoanalysis, other major changes were taking place in the concept of mental disorder. Holistic views on the functioning of the brain, resulting from the work of Head, Monakow, Mourgue, Lashley, and others, held temporary sway (Hecaen & Lanteri-Laura, 1977), but, by the early 1930s, the modular view was once again in the ascendant. The organic view of mental illness had also been revitalised by the observation of a variety of tardive mental disorders caused by encephalitis lethargica (Von Economo, 1931). It was on this fertile ground that Moniz brought about the second period in the development of psychosurgery.

Moniz

From a conceptual point of view, there is little that was new in Moniz's views (see note 11). The old arguments were all present, as indeed was the 19th-century neuropsychological model of the relationship between brain and mental function. Even the therapeutic objective of targeting symptoms rather than diseases was the same. There is, however, an important difference, which relates to the brain site most commonly chosen for the operation, the frontal lobes. This choice needs explanation. Piecing together the historical events that led to the 1935 operations by Moniz and Almeida Lima has proved surprisingly difficult, owing to the discrepancies between the various extant accounts, including those by Moniz himself. For example, his fresh description in the 1936 book (clearly written in a hurry) differs from his much elaborated one of 1948. These two, in turn, differ from the official view.

Moniz's accounts versus the conventional view

The official view states that Moniz heard a presentation by Fulton & Jacobsen (1935) at the London Neurological Meeting on the tranquillising effects of frontal lobectomies in primates suffering from behavioural disorders caused by experimental neurosis procedures. His opportunist mind seized on the possibility of carrying this out in people who were suffering from agitated mental illness. He approached Fulton, who was rather "startled" by the idea (Fulton, 1949, p. 64). Nonetheless, Moniz returned to Lisbon and went ahead, operating on about 20 subjects in a period of three months.

Moniz's two accounts, however, differ from the official one, and his 1936 version does not bear out the 'knife-happy' image that some have tried to create. He starts by saying that his ideas on the theoretical basis for the operation are presented with reservations, and that research into this area is "very difficult because it may jeopardise patients' lives, which have for us, physicians, the highest value" (p. 5). Concerning the origin of his ideas on the operation, Moniz says: "We had already told confidentially Dr Almeida Lima of our idea more than two and a half years before" (p. 6). This certainly dates his intentions to a period far earlier than the London meeting, and dispels the view that he was simply an opportunist. With respect to targeting the frontal lobes, it is interesting that in his book Moniz mentions as his sources Kleist, Claude, Choroscko, and others, including Brickner's detailed report of a subject with amputated frontal lobes, but does not refer to Fulton & Jacobsen's experiments in any detail. He refers to them, however, as "extremely valuable" (p. 582) in his 1948 account.

In this connection, it is of interest that in his Birmingham lectures of 1948 Fulton wrote in an almost exculpatory tone:

> "In the thoughtful prefatory chapters of Egas Moniz's monograph on lobotomy he indicates that for some years prior to 1935 he had entertained the thought of interrupting frontal lobe projections as a possible therapeutic weapon for dealing with some of the more severe psychoses. He cites the work of Henri Claude on the functions of the frontal lobe and also the observations of the late Clovis Vincent. He was likewise familiar with Richard Brickner's well-known case of a bilateral frontal lobe removal in man. Finally he directs attention to the report which I made with Jacobsen on the behavioural changes observed in chimpanzees following bilateral removal of the frontal areas. Although Moniz later stated that the results reported for the chimpanzee convinced him that the operation would be useful in man, *one should not forget that he had considered surgical interference long before hearing of our experimental results.*" (Fulton, 1949, p. 62 – my italics)

In 1936, Moniz identified two bases for his operation: the 'substitution' principle (which he said he had taught for years), according to which the brain could functionally adapt by replacing damaged areas (p. 42), and the 'fixed connections' principle, according to which certain circuits, created by aberrant learning, were responsible for mental symptoms, so that their partial destruction might lead to improvement (p. 46). This rationale was different from that suggested by Fulton to explain the reduction in affective responses ("frustrational behaviour") shown by Becky the chimpanzee after bilateral excision of the frontal lobes. According to Fulton, hyporeactivity resulted from damage to the anterior cingulate gyrus (area 24) leading to a loss of the animal's "social conscience"; that is, "monkeys lose some of the social fear and anxiety which normally governs their activity and thus lose the ability to accurately forecast the social repercussions of their own actions" (p. 67). This is indeed different from Moniz's view, which

Table 11.2

Details of Moniz's first 20 cases (November 1935–January 1936)

Case no.	*Sex*	*Age: years*	*Family history*	*Duration*	*Main diagnosis*	*Other diagnoses*	*Main symptoms*	*Technique*	*Complications*	*Follow-up weeks*	*Outcome*
1	F	60	–	22 years	Manic-depression	Alcoholism	Agitation	Alcohol	Fever	10	Improved
2	F	62	Positive	8 years	Depression	–	Anxiety	Alcohol	Fever	10	Improved
3	M	36	–	12 years	Schizophrenia	Brain injury	Paranoia	Alcohol	Fever	9	No change
4	M	46	?	6 years	Schizophrenia	–	Paranoia	Alcohol	Fever	8	No change
5	M	37	Manic–depression	4 years	Catatonia	Alcoholism	Excitability	Alcohol	Fever	8	Improved
6	M	41	–	4 years	Schizophrenia	–	Paranoia	Alcohol	Incontinence	4	No change
7	F	47	–	9 years	Panic disorder	–	Anxiety	Alcohol	Fever	3	Improved
8	F	47	Depression	2 years	Depression	–	Anxiety	Leucotomy	–	3	No change
9	F	59	Depression	20 years	Depression	–	Anxiety	Leucotomy	Fever	2	Discharged
10	F	31	Depression	1 year	Depression	–	Anxiety	Alcohol	Fever	2	Improved
11	M	27	–	4 weeks	Schizophrenia	–	Agitation	Alcohol	–	5	No change
12	F	43	Anxiety	20 years	Panic disorder	–	Anxiety	Alcohol	Hypothermia	4	Improved
13	F	61	–	31 years	Depression	–	Agitation	Leucotomy	–	6	No change
14	M	64	Depression	19 years	Depression	Alcoholism	Agitation	Leucotomy	Confusion	4	Improved
15	F	44	–	8 weeks	Depression	–	Agitation	Leucotomy	Fever	7	Improved
16	F	44	Depression	17 years	Schizophrenia	–	Agitation	Leucotomy	Fever	2	No change
17	M	51	Depression	24 weeks	Depression	Syphilis	Agitation	Leucotomy	–	2	Improved
18	M	29	–	1.5 years	Schizophrenia	Alcoholism	Agitation	Leucotomy	Fever	1	No change
19	F	52	–	16 weeks	Depression	–	Agitation	Leucotomy	Fever	1	Improved
20	F	29	–	1 year	Mania	Epilepsy?	Agitation	Leucotomy	Confusion	2	No change

postulated the existence of aberrant pathways that were responsible for mental symptoms, and suggested that they must be destroyed before the subject could be free of symptoms. Whatever the early role played by Fulton in Moniz's decision to go ahead with the operations, it is clear that, after some hesitation, Fulton was happy to act as a 'patron' to subsequent American psychosurgeons, particularly Watts (Pressman, 1988).

So far as technique is concerned, it must be remembered that Moniz started by injecting alcohol into the white matter, and not by excising tissue as Fulton & Jacobsen had done. The alcohol idea was apparently taken from the well known operation of injecting the Gasserian ganglion for trigeminal neuralgia. Moniz's (1948) account in "Mein Weg zur Leukotomie" (far more elaborate than that included in his 1936 book) starts by mentioning Ramón y Cajal, Held, and a long list of other authors. However, he reiterated his view about aberrant and fixed synaptic circuits:

> "sufferers from melancholia, for instance, are distressed by fixed and obsessive ideas . . . and live in a permanent state of anxiety caused by a fixed idea which predominates over all their lives . . . in difference to automatic actions, these morbid ideas are deeply rooted in the synaptic complex which regulates the functioning of consciousness, stimulating it and keeping it in constant activity . . . all these considerations led me to the following conclusion: it is necessary to alter these synaptic adjustments and change the paths chosen by the impulses in their constant passage so as to modify the corresponding ideas and force thoughts along different paths." (p. 583)

Moniz's cases

The 1936 book (which includes verbatim the papers published the same year in *L'Encéphale* and in *Lisboa Medica* (Moniz & Lima, 1936)) reports the first 20 cases (Table 11.2). Moniz concluded that 35% of cases had shown great improvement, 35% mild improvement, and 30% no change. He attempted to analyse his cases by symptoms and diagnoses, but his subgroups were too small, and no statistics

TABLE 11.3
Moniz's first 20 cases (1936): comparison of outcome groups

	Improvers (n = *11*)	*Non-improvers* (n = *9*)	
Age: years	50 (8.7)	40 (8.6)	$P^1 < 0.1$
Sex			
male	10	3	$P^2 < 0.5$
female	2	5	
Diagnosis			
affective	10	2	$P^2 < 0.1$
non-affective	1	7	
Technique			
alcohol	6	4	NS
leucotomy	5	5	
Target symptom			
agitation	6	4	NS
anxiety	5	1	

1. Mann–Whitney *U* test.
2. Fisher's exact test.

were then available to cope with this. Table 11.3 shows, however, a statistical comparison of his improvers versus non-improvers on a number of variables. Surprisingly clear results are obtained: older male subjects responded significantly better, as did those with affective disorder, whereas the surgical technique and target symptom made no difference.

Discussion

The work of Freeman and Watts in the USA, and that of others in Europe and elsewhere, led to the temporary acceptance of surgical operations for the alleviation of some symptoms of mental disorder, and, as a result, thousands of patients were operated on. Analysis of the reasons for this acceptance and for the debates that the operations were to generate is beyond the scope of this chapter, however.

Three conceptual changes made psychosurgery possible. The first was a convenient working model of the brain and its relationship to mental symptoms. Such a relationship had oscillated during the 19th century (and indeed has continued doing so during the 20th) between periods of predominant localisation, when it has been claimed that mental faculties are as specifically localised as the motor and sensory functions, and periods of holism, when the brain has been conceived of as an equipotential, diffuse organ. Periods of predominant localisation have coincided with the view that the mental functions themselves can be neatly separated into modules or faculties (Fodor, 1983; Shallice, 1988). It is not surprising that psychosurgical operations, at least the three episodes of them dealt with in this paper, occurred during periods when localisation theory was predominant.

However, a second assumption was also needed – that causing a lesion of a particular site can abolish a particular form of behaviour, without releasing others which would be equally or even more maladaptive. This assumption could not be made by the various hierarchical models that, after Reynolds, have been propounded by Jackson, Monakow, Ey, and others (Monakow & Mourgue, 1928; Ey, 1975; Berrios, 1985). It was made, however, by Ody (1938), who (independently of, and in theoretical opposition to, Moniz) resected the entire right frontal lobe of a young man to alleviate stereotyped behaviour and violence.

Yet a third assumption was required. In order for psychosurgery to work, two notions must be true about psychiatric illness: that it has an organic substratum, and that this is not unitary – that symptoms result from multiple lesions (whether anatomical or physiological). In this way, the surgeon can target individual symptoms, as Shaw, Burckhardt, and Moniz did, and not worry about trying to cure the entire disease.

In one way or another, these three assumptions can be found underlying the working models of all three men. They shared a similar, albeit simple, model of the way in which brain and mental disease related. Whatever differences there were between them, they can be traced to their auxiliary hypotheses, and hence the original tenets were not invalidated. For example, Shaw and Cripps believed that increased CSF pressure caused a generalised effect which was responsible for the mental symptoms; they believed, for instance, that the motor symptoms of GPI were the result of brain degeneration. They also believed that the operation itself improved nutrition and drainage.

Burckhardt, in turn, believed that severing connections at the second (association) stage of brain transmission would prevent symptoms without hampering input or output routes. He also believed that the operation would prevent not only the expression of the symptoms, but also their actual experience by the subjects. For his part, Moniz believed in the existence of aberrant, perseverative, facilitated circuits, held to be responsible for mental (emotional) symptoms, and that these were sited in the prefrontal cortex. Consequently, he was led to deduce that their partial lesioning would abolish the related symptoms. Current practitioners of psychosurgery have their own beliefs. They postulate that the limited and controlled lesions delivered during cingulectomy, for example, affect specific mesocortical (mostly dopamine) pathways, thereby leading to a reduction in the expression and (it is hoped) the experiencing of certain symptoms (Kelly, 1980). But none of these differences can be said to invalidate their general model.

Historical analysis also shows that Shaw, Burckhardt, and Moniz were aware of the seriousness of their procedures, and that they sought to found them on ethical principles. They even risked ostracism by going against the beliefs of the medical community. This certainly happened to Burckhardt. After the original debate, Shaw and Cripps quietly decided to drop their operation. Moniz's work was soon taken over by larger forces in the United States; when the great reaction took place, he was no longer part of the scene.

This differential response suggests that major social forces contributed to the growth of psychosurgery. Why it spread in the 1930s and not in the 1890s is a legitimate question for sociologists to ask. One 'internal' answer is that the attempts of Shaw or Burckhardt did not have sufficient scientific definition, and their technique had not yet developed clear algorithms. Both factors were operational in the work of Moniz. The 'external' answer, however, is far more complex and probably more interesting, for it would include a serious analysis of the views that alienists were to acquire in the *inter-bellum* period of their therapeutic rights (i.e. how far could they go in their pursuit of effective treatments), and also of the view that society at large developed on the needs and rights of the mentally ill. To answer these questions properly would demand more than historical information. It would, for instance, require primary data sources on historical ethics, which are not yet available. The formulation and legitimisation of such evidence are beyond the scope of this paper.

Biographical notes

(1) Thomas Claye Shaw was born in Stockport in 1841 and died in Cheltenham in 1927. He trained in medicine at King's College, London, where he was a gold medallist, and in psychiatry at the Colney Hatch Asylum. He became physician superintendent of Leavesden, a metropolitan asylum, and then of the Middlesex County Asylum at Banstead. He was Lecturer in Psychological Medicine at St Bartholomew's hospital, and soon acquired a reputation as a clear and outspoken teacher. His interests included the development of psychiatric units in general hospitals, after-care, and alcoholism (Brown, 1955; *Lancet*, 1927). At St Bartholomew's, he supported the *Reports* (the house journal), and was elected President of the Abernethian Society. Very late (1904), he became a member of the Medico-Psychological Society and in the same year published *Ex-Cathedra Essays on Insanity*, which collected his main lectures and papers. He was a member of

the Garrick Club, was a keen actor, and held quaint views on women. In a notorious lecture, he warned a woman that "her new activities in sport and independence in life would mar the beauty of her face, change her nature, and alienate male sympathy" (*British Medical Journal*, 1927, p. 169).

(2) Sir David Ferrier (1843–1928) was a Scottish disciple of Alexander Bain, another great Aberdonian. One of the great defenders of localisationism, he was a founder of the Physiological Society and of the journal *Brain*. In 1889, he acceded to the chair of Neuropathology at King's College, London. Ferrier would not have been averse to the rationale behind Claye Shaw's operation.

(3) Sir Thomas Clifford Allbutt (1836–1925), educated at Cambridge and St George's, spent a period in France with Trousseau and Duchenne. On his return he was, successively, a consulting physician at Leeds, a Commissioner in Lunacy, and, after 1892, Regius Professor of Physic at Cambridge. He worked at Addenbrooke's Hospital from 1900 until his death. He contributed to neurology, endocrinology, and psychiatry.

(4) Sir John Batty Tuke (1835–1913) was born in Surrey and died in Edinburgh. He took his degree at the University of Edinburgh and, after serving as an assistant physician at the Royal Edinburgh Asylum under Skae, became Medical Superintendent of the Fife and Kinross Asylum. He did neurobiological research under Rutherford, Goodsir, and Stirling, was twice Morrison Lecturer to the Royal College of Physicians of Edinburgh, and became its President in 1895. He was also President of the British Neurological Society. His main contribution to histopathology was the redescription of 'miliary sclerosis'. He wrote often and well, and published both in learned journals and in popular works such as the *Encyclopaedia Britannica*.

(5) Sir Victor Horsley (1857–1916) was at the time the major figure of neurosurgery in Britain. Trained under Bastian, Schäffer, and Beevor, he received a good grounding in the neurosciences. At 29, Horsley became surgeon to the National Hospital, Queen Square, and soon after, at the request of Gowers, carried out a pioneering operation for a tumour of the spinal cord. At the Berlin Congress (where Burckhardt also presented his results), Horsley gave a paper reporting his first 44 neurosurgical operations, in only ten of which patients had died. A crusader for medical and educational reform, and an apostle of temperance, Horsley saw active duty during World War I and died in Mesopotamia of heatstroke. His views on Claye Shaw's operation remained positive. In a later review of the uses of trephining for insanity, commissioned by D. H. Tuke, Horsley (1892) accepted the need for the operation, although he called into question the lymphatic vessels hypothesis.

(6) Charles Arthur Mercier (1852–1919) was of Huguenot descent, and trained as a physician and surgeon at the London Hospital. He was superintendent of the Bethel Hospital in Norwich, before becoming assistant medical officer at the Leavensden asylum. He lectured on nervous diseases at the Westminster Hospital and later at the Charing Cross, being a prolific writer on insanity, including its psychological and forensic aspects.

(7) Sir Thomas Smith Clouston (1840–1915) was born in Orkney and trained at Aberdeen and Edinburgh. At the latter university, he came under the influence of Thomas Laycock, which marked his views on neurosciences for life. He worked at the Royal Edinburgh Asylum, first as an assistant to David Skae and then as its superintendent. His views on the taxonomy and clinical analysis of mental disease are contained in his famous *Clinical Lectures*, which went through many editions.

(8) René Semelaigne (1855–1934) was, up to 1921, director of the Saint-James hospital at Neuilly. He was first a corresponding member of the Royal Medical-Psychological Association and from 1911 an honorary member. Semelaigne did not do a great deal of primary research, but was a magnificent reviewer and compiler. His work on the history of French psychiatry remains essential reading to this day.

(9) Gottlieb Burckhardt was born in 1836 in Basle, the son of a physician and into a famous family. He studed at Basle, Göttingen, and Berlin, and practised for a while as a general practitioner in his home town, after graduating with a thesis on the epithelium of the urinary tract. In 1873, he became physician to the Waldau Psychiatric University Clinic of Berne (Bach, 1907; Hagenbach, 1907). Soon after, he published his book on the

physiological diagnosis of nervous diseases. In Waldau, he worked under Schärer, became a regular reviewer for the *Korrespondenzblatt für Schweizer Ärtze*, and undertook research into the possible relationship between brain temperature and mental illness. In 1881, Eugen Bleuler became his assistant. He left the next year for Préfargier, a psychiatric clinic near Lake Neuchâtel, where he remained until 1896. It was in this clinic that, in 1888, he carried out his first topectomies. After losing his wife and one of his sons in 1896, he left his post and retired to Basle, where for a while he directed the Sonnhalde Clinic. He died of pneumonia in 1907. Burckhardt remained a psychiatric outsider. He is not often mentioned as attending international meetings and after his paper of 1891, where he reported his operations, he never wrote a major piece again. Forel (1937), another great Swiss psychiatrist, described him in his memoirs as a "thoroughly sincere man . . . the customary courtesies were distasteful to him" (p. 207).

(10) The greatest alienists of the time congregated in Berlin for the 1889 meeting. Towering among them was Valentin Magnan (1835–1916), who, although he had lost to Benjamin Ball the first chair of mental diseases in France in 1877, was a great classifier and clinician, and a tenacious sponsor of the degeneration theory. Emil Kraepelin (1856–1926), the great German psychiatrist, was also present at the meeting (on his way home, after visiting Chester and north Wales). Years later, Kraepelin lamented that although he had been introduced to Magnan on that occasion, they had only had time to exchange few words.

(11) Antonio Caetano de Abreu Freire (the real name of Egas Moniz) was born in Avanca, northern Portugal, on 27 November 1874 (Barahona Fernandez, 1956; Walker, 1970). The name 'Egas Moniz' belonged to an 11th-century Portuguese hero of the resistance against the Moors, and it is unclear who gave him the name. Some have claimed that it was his godfather at the christening; others that it was Moniz himself, who adopted it as a pen name during his political struggle against the monarchy. He graduated from the University of Coimbra in 1899, and obtained his MD in 1902. The same year, he left for France, where he trained as a neurologist under Pitrés and Régis in Bordeaux, and under Raymond, Pierre Marie, Babinski, and Dejerine. He seems to have felt particularly close to Marie, Pitrés, and Babinski, whose pictures he kept until his death (Anonymous, 1979).

He returned to the University of Lisbon in 1911 (the date of the initiation of the Republic) as a lecturer. He founded the Neurological Clinic of Santa Marta and was later to serve as Foreign Minister, Ambassador to Spain, and was the Portuguese signatory of the Treaty of Versailles. His political fortunes changed after 1920, and this led him back to his early interest in the neurosciences. His research on angiographic techniques followed, culminating in 1927 in the publication of his famous paper on carotid angiograms which used sodium iodide as the contrast medium. His book on the same topic, with an introduction by Babinski, followed in 1934.

Moniz turned to brain surgery for some symptoms of insanity in 1935. Between the end of that year and the early part of 1936, he had 20 patients operated on by Dr Almeida Lima, a neurosurgeon. The patients were from the Bombarda asylum and selected by Professor Sobral Cid, director of this institution. Some of the assessments and follow-ups were carried out by Dr H. J. Barahona Fernandez, who was to become a distinguished psychiatrist in his own right and who at the time was still training under Kleist in Germany. In 1936, Moniz published a major book on the subject, and a number of papers followed where the official account of the development of the operation crystallised. He retired in 1944, and in 1949 was awarded the Nobel Prize for medicine and physiology, the citation referring to his "invention of a surgical treatment for mental illness and to his elaboration of the psycho-physiological concepts that made it possible". At the age of 65, he was shot and wounded by a patient suffering from schizophrenia. He recovered, and died on 18 December 1955.

References

ADAMS, J. (1889) Is general paralysis of the insane a curable disease? *British Medical Journal*, *ii*, 1187.

ANONYMOUS (1979) *Catalogue: 'Exposição sobre a vida e obra de Egas Moniz'*. Porto: Faculdade de Medicine do Porto, Bial.

BACH, C. (1907) Nekrolog Dr G Burckhardt. *Allgemeine Zeitschrift für Psychiatrie*, **64**, 529–534.

BARAHONA FERNANDEZ, H. J. de (1956) Egas Moniz. In *Grosse Nervenärzte. Vol. 1* (ed. K. Kolle), pp. 187–188. Stuttgart: Thieme.

BECHTEREW, W. & POUSSÉPE, M. (1912) La chirurgie des Aliénés. *Archives de Neurologie*, **34**, 1–17, 69–89.

BERRIOS, G. E. (1985) Positive and negative symptoms and Jackson. A conceptual history. *Archives of General Psychiatry*, **42**, 95–97.

BLUMER, A. (1892) The surgical treatment of insanity. *American Journal of Insanity*, **49**, 222.

BRABANT, H. (1976) Les traitements burlesques de la folie aux XVIe et XVIIe siècles. In *Folie et Déraison à la Renaissance*, pp. 75–98. Brussels: Éditions de l'Université de Bruxelles.

BRITISH MEDICAL JOURNAL (1891) Surgical treatment of general paralysis of the insane. *British Medical Journal*, *ii*, 596.

——— (1927) Thomas Claye Shaw (obituary). *British Medical Journal*, *i*, 169.

BROCA, P. (1867) Trépanation chez les Incas. *Bulletin de l'Academie de Médicine, Paris*, **32**, 866–871.

——— (1874) Sur les trépanations préhistoriques. *Bulletin et Mém Société d'Anthropologie de Paris*, **9**, 542–557.

BROWN, G. H. (1955) *Munk's Roll: Lives of the Fellows of the Royal College of Physicians of London 1826–1925*, Vol. IV. London: RCP.

BURCKHARDT, G. (1891) Ueber Rindenexcisionen, als Beitrag zur operativen Therapie der Psychosen. *Allgemeine Zeitschrift für Psychiatrie*, **47**, 463–548.

CHIPAULT, A. & DALEINE, E. (1893) Notes iconographiques sur l'histoire de la trépanation. *Nouvelle Iconographie de la Salpêtrière*, **6**, 292–304.

CLARKE, E. & JACYNA, L. S. (1987) *Nineteenth Century Origins of Neuroscientific Concepts*. Berkeley, CA: University of California Press.

CRIPPS, H. (1889) The surgical treatment of general paralysis. *British Medical Journal*, *ii*, 1215–1216.

EY, H. (1975) *Des idées de Jackson à un modèle organo-dynamique en psychiatrie*. Paris: Privat.

FODOR, J. A. (1983) *The Modularity of the Mind*. Cambridge, MA: MIT Press.

FOREL, A. (1937) *Out of My Life and Work* (trans. B. Miall). London: George Allen & Unwin.

FULTON, J. F. (1949) *Functional Localization in the Frontal Lobes and Cerebellum*. Oxford: Clarendon Press.

——— (1951) *Frontal Lobotomy and Affective Behavior. A Neurophysiological Analysis*. New York: W. W. Norton.

——— & JACOBSEN, C. F. (1935) The Functions of the Frontal Lobes: A Comparative Study in Monkeys, Chimpanzees and Man. In *Proceedings of 2nd International Congress, Neurology, Abstracts*. (No publisher.).

GAUDIER, H. (1900) À propos d'un tableau du musée de St-Omer représentant les 'arracheurs de pierres de tête'. *Nouvelle Iconographie de la Salpêtrière*, **13**, 205–209.

GOODALL, E. (1893) Transient motor and sensory disturbance following upon trephining in a case of General Paralysis of the Insane. *British Medical Journal*, *ii*, 117.

HAGENBACH, N. (1907) Dr Gottlieb Burckhardt. *Korrespondenzblatt für Schweizer Ärzte*, **37**, 257–260.

HECAEN, H. & LANTERI-LAURA, G. (1977) *Évolution des connaissances et des doctrines sur les localizations cérébrales*. Paris: Desclée de Brouwer.

HEMPHILL, R. E. (1965) The personality and problem of Hieronymus Bosch. *Proceedings of the Royal Society of Medicine*, **58**, 137–144.

HORSLEY, V. (1892) Trephining. In *A Dictionary of Psychological Medicine, Vol. 2* (ed. D. H. Tuke), pp. 1324–1327. London: Churchill.

IRELAND, W. W. (1891) Operative treatment of insanity. *Journal of Mental Science*, **37**, 613–618.

JOWELL, F. (1965) The paintings of Hieronymus Bosch. *Proceedings of the Royal Society of Medicine*, **65**, 131–136.

KELLY, D. (1980) *Anxiety and Emotions*. Illinois: Charles Thomas.

KRAEPELIN, E. (1983) *Lebenserinnerungen*. Berlin: Springer.

LANCET (1894) Edinburgh Medico-Chirurgical Society. Discussion on intracranial surgery. *Lancet*, *i*, 607–609.

——— (1927) Thomas Claye Shaw (obituary). *Lancet*, *i*, 260.

LUCAS, A. R. (1968) The imagery of Hieronymus Bosch. *American Journal of Psychiatry*, **124**, 1515–1525.

MACPHERSON, J. & WALLACE, D. (1892) The surgical treatment of general paralysis of the insane. *British Medical Journal*, *ii*, 167–170.

MEIGE, H. (1895) Les peintres de la médecine (Écoles flamande et hollandaise). Les opérations sur la tête. *Nouvelle Iconographie de la Salpêtrière*, **8**, 228–264, 291–323.

—— (1898) Les peintres de la médecine (Écoles flamande et hollandaise). Documents nouveaux sur les opérations sur la tête. *Nouvelle Iconographie de la Salpêtrière*, **9**, 199–212, 321.

—— (1899) Un nouveau tableau représentant les arracheurs de 'pierres de tête'. *Nouvelle Iconographie de la Salpêtrière*, **12**, 170–176.

—— (1900) Les peintres de la médecine (Écoles flamande et hollandaise). 'Pierres de tête' et 'Pierres de ventre'. *Nouvelle Iconographie de la Salpêtrière*, **13**, 76–99.

MONAKOW, C. & MOURGUE, R. (1928) *Introduction biologique à l'étude de la neurologie et de la psychopathologie*. Paris: Alcan.

MONIZ, E. (1936) *Tentatives opératoires dans le traitement de certaines psychoses*. Paris: Masson.

—— (1948) Mein Weg zur Leukotomie. *Deutsche Medizinische Wochenschrift*, **73**, 581–583.

—— & LIMA, A. (1936) Premiers essais de psycho-chirurgie. Technique et résultats. *Lisboa Medica*, **13**, 152–161.

MÜLLER, CH. R. (1960) Gottlieb Burckhardt: Le Père de la Topectomie. *Revue Médicale de la Suisse Romande*, **28**, 726–730.

O'CALLAGHAN, M. A. J. & CARROLL, D. (1982) *Psychosurgery. A Scientific Analysis*. Lancaster: MTP Press.

ODY, F. (1938) Le traitement de la démence précoce par résection du lobe préfrontal. *Archivio Italiano di Chirurgia*, **53**, 321–330.

POUSSÉPE, L. (1937) Alcune considerazioni sugli interventi chirurgici nelle malattie mentali. *Giornále Accadémia Médica Torino*, **100**, 3–16.

PRESSMAN, J. D. (1988) Sufficient promise: John F. Fulton and the origins of psychosurgery. *Bulletin of the History of Medicine*, **62**, 1–29.

QUETEL, C. & MOREL, P. (1979) *Les fous et leurs médecines de la Renaissance au XXe siècle*. Paris: Hachette.

REVINGTON, G. (1889) Is general paralysis of the insane a curable disease? *British Medical Journal*, *ii*, 1187.

—— (1890) The surgical treatment of general paralysis of the insane. *British Medical Journal*, *i*, 749.

REY, M. (1891) Trépan dans un cas de paralysie générale. *Archives Neurologie*, **22**, 260.

RYLANDER, G. (1973) The renaissance of psychosurgery. In *Surgical Approaches in Psychiatry* (eds L. V. Laitinen & K. E. Livingston), pp. 3–12. Letchworth: MTP Press.

SEMELAIGNE, R. (1895) Sur la chirurgie cérébrale dans les aliénations mentales. *Annales Médico-Psychologiques*, **1**, 394–420.

SEPPILLI, G. (1891) La cura chirurgica delle malattie mentali. *Rivista Sperimentale di Freniatria e di Medicina Legale*, **27**, 369–374.

SHALLICE, T. (1988) *From Neuropsychology to Mental Structure*. Cambridge: Cambridge University Press.

SHAW, T. C. (1889) The surgical treatment of insanity. *British Medical Journal*, *ii*, 1090–1091.

—— (1891) Surgical treatment of general paralysis of the insane. *British Medical Journal*, *ii*, 581–583.

—— (1892) Surgery and insanity. *Saint Bartholomew's Hospital Reports*, **28**, 55–68.

—— & CRIPPS, H. (1890) On the surgical treatment of general paralysis. *British Medical Journal*, *i*, 1364.

SMITH, P. (1890) The surgical treatment of general paralysis. *British Medical Journal*, *i*, 11–12.

TUKE, J. B. (1890) The surgical treatment of intracranial fluid pressure. *British Medical Journal*, *i*, 8–11.

—— (1891) A plea for the scientific study of insanity. *British Medical Journal*, *i*, 1161–1166.

VON ECONOMO, C. (1931) *Encephalitis Lethargica. Its Sequelae and Treatment* (trans. and adapted K. O. Newman). London: Oxford University Press.

WAGNER, C. G. (1890) A case of trephining for general paralysis. *American Journal of Insanity*, **47**, 59–66.

WALKER, A. E. (1970) Egas Moniz. In *The Founders of Neurology* (2nd edn) (eds W. Haymaker & F. Schiller), pp. 489–492. Illinois: Thomas.

WILLETT, R. A. (1960) The effects of psychosurgical procedures on behaviour. In *Handbook of Abnormal Psychology* (ed. H. J. Eysenck), pp. 566–610. London: Pitman Medical.

WORCESTER, W. L. (1891) Surgery of the central nervous system (account of the Berlin meeting). *American Journal of Insanity*, **47**, 410–413.

12 Psychodynamic psychiatry before World War I

R. D. HINSHELWOOD

A materialist and increasingly physiological approach to psychiatry has contested with a psychodynamic, often idealist, approach for two centuries. Only the arguments and the relative dominance of one or the other have changed somewhat from time to time. From the 1890s to World War I, psychodynamic ideas began to gain an ascendancy within the 'new psychiatry', which survived until after the end of World War II.

The main factors influencing this development are to be found in 19th-century culture and in psychiatric practice and thinking. Firstly, technological progress and social changes conveyed the idea that progress and change could apply to the lives of the mentally ill, as well as to other individuals.

Secondly, the experimental emphasis in contemporary psychology moved it increasingly towards a natural-science approach to the mind (Bain, 1855, 1859; Spencer, 1855), and the increasing trajectory towards experimental physiology progressively limited interest in the nature of mind.

Young (1970) has traced the way that the mind/body debate was transformed into various answers to the question: how far up the central nervous system did the sensory-motor (reflex arc) activity extend, before it became intelligence and mind? In the end, this became a debate over the demonstrable sensory and motor activity of the cerebral cortex and the search for localisation on it. This was a profoundly important scientific endeavour and spawned impressively intricate methods, but, at the same time, it became an increasingly poverty-stricken psychology.

Thirdly, in the late 19th century, another kind of scientific psychology had begun to develop, especially in the universities (Hearnshaw, 1964); it involved methods for quantifying mental functions, instead of brain pathology. This return to mental functioning came into conflict with physiological psychology and with psychiatry (Maudsley, 1900; Rivers, 1900).

Fourthly, Darwinian evolution loosened religion's grip on the minds of even the humbler man in the street, and yet mortality still threatened. The Victorians suffered nothing short of a crisis over death: if religious 'belief' in the afterlife was no longer convincing, scientific proof of it became essential (Oppenheim, 1985). A galaxy of intellectuals, drawn together by Henry Sidgwick, one of the leading philosophers at Cambridge, and Frederic Myers, a brilliant maverick, founded the influential Society for Psychical Research.

Psychiatry was then a marginalised activity, given low social status, and with the medical profession in general occupied with upgrading its status, psychiatry lagged behind. Its location, out of the way in the asylums, no doubt contributed to this inferiority. Its espousal of phrenology (Conolly, 1856), and then of physiological psychology (Maudsley, 1867), both of which flourished in the asylums, was an accommodation to developments elsewhere in society. Later, however, the shunning of hypnosis, disappearance of moral treatment (Scull, 1981), and discrediting of phrenology (Cooter, 1982) had all been setbacks to the mid-Victorian mental approach, leaving the way open, by the end of the century, for a fully fledged materialist view of psychiatry. Indeed, prioritising the processes of either the body or the brain was important in the struggle to make psychiatry a medical and professional endeavour (Clark, 1981). The narrowness of orthodox physiological psychology, however, offered very few specific treatment methods. It led to a particular view of insanity that was wholly based on the asylums: admission to the asylum *was* the treatment, and this subsided into a therapeutic pessimism. Maudsley and others began to campaign to move out of the asylums and, with difficulty, to develop early treatment (Walk 1976; Boyle, 1905).

This medical approach to the physical body resulted in a view of insanity that rested upon the material conditions of the brain; for example: *The mind operates independently of the brain so long as brain function is normal. Mental symptoms therefore are simply an epiphenomenon demonstrating a progressive leakage across the divide from brain to mind, with dementia the inevitable end-result.* Therefore, there was little interest in mind – only in its loss (Clark, 1981; Bynum, 1982); mental symptoms were regarded as a distraction from the underlying physical degeneration (Dewhurst, 1982).

Continental influences

Although James Braid (1795–1860) put hypnosis on a more scientific footing (Braid, 1843), it was persistently discredited because it undermined the fragile medical status of psychiatry in that it was often practised by non-medical people – in other words, quacks. However, Continental neurologists, notably Paul Broca (1824–80) and Jean-Martin Charcot (1825–93), first began its official rehabilitation. Charcot thought the capacity to be hypnotised was an abnormality, a part of the degenerative process towards dementia; since it resembled the symptoms of hysteria, he thought it was, in fact, one of them. Hypnosis was therefore a disease, not a treatment (Charcot, 1887). In contrast, Hippolyte-Marie Bernheim (1837–1919) in Nancy found that more or less anyone can be hypnotised, that symptoms could be removed by suggestion under hypnosis, and that even suggestion in the waking state could be effective (Bernheim, 1884). The Nancy school used post-hypnotic suggestion as a therapeutic method, while Paul Dubois and Joseph-Jules Dejerine (1849–1917) developed suggestive methods in the waking state.

Sigmund Freud (1856–1939) visited both Paris (1885–86) and Nancy (1889) and was aware of Janet's developments (see below). He adopted Josef Breuer's use of hypnosis, which was different from the French methods in that he did not use suggestion. Under hypnosis, a particular hysterical patient (described as Anna O) was invited to talk about her symptom, and this became reduced in severity; in the course of talking in this way, the patient retrieved memories of early traumatic incidents in her life. Thus, instead of suggestion under hypnosis, Freud and Breuer induced the patient to reminisce. The idea of memories that were not available consciously was clearly close to Janet's views. Later, however, Freud dropped hypnosis, substituting free association in the waking state.

Pierre Janet (1859–1947) hypnotised a psychic medium called Leonie, though he later became interested in the medical implications rather than the spiritual, and developed a 'deep theory' of hysteria (Janet, 1892). Post-hypnotic suggestion pointed to a 'region' of the mind which Janet called the subconscious; he thought that under psychological tension in hysteria, some aspect of the conscious mind separates off, forming another consciousness. Janet's model was profound and influential, being later developed by Bleuler as a theory of schizophrenia.

The fundamental common ground between Freud and Janet was their interest in deeper, explanatory theories of hysteria and of the nature of mind. However, they differed significantly, firstly in their methods – eliciting unconscious reminiscences (Freud), as opposed to suggestion or persuasion (Janet) – and secondly in the origin of the unconscious (Freud) or the subconscious (Janet) – Janet thought that, under stress, parts of the conscious mind became severed from the rest of consciousness (dissociation), while Freud described an active process of repression of certain contents of the mind, due to traumatic experiences in the past (Janet, 1899; Breuer & Freud, 1895).

Thus, by the turn of the century there were, on the Continent, two psychodynamic methods. They became and remained rivalrous.

Psychodynamic methods in Britain

Around 1890, hypnosis was being dabbled in at the National Hospital for Nervous Diseases by several people including Hughlings Jackson (Hunter & Hurwitz, 1961), and a watchful interest was being kept in Britain on the Continental developments. Reports and reviews appeared in the *Journal of Mental Science* (Pierre Janet's *États mental des hystériques* (1892) was reviewed in 1893) and in *Brain*. During this period and until well after 1900, the main topics of interest to psychiatrists were hysteria, epilepsy, and general paralysis; relatively little was written about therapeutics, and hypnosis, as it came in, appeared to be an exotic oddity.

Lloyd Tuckey's *Psycho-Therapeutics or Treatment by Hypnotism and Suggestion* was published in 1888 and rapidly went to a third edition, when it was reviewed in the *Journal of Mental Science* in 1891. Bernheim's major work was translated in 1890, and Tuckey wrote a critical digest of recent literature on hypnosis and suggestion, mostly French work, for *Brain* in 1898.

Percy Smith and Alfred Myers, in the *Journal of Mental Science*, called for serious attention to be given to hypnosis in psychiatry, and recommended more research (Smith & Myers, 1890). Myers also wrote the section on hypnosis in Hack Tuke's standard work, *A Dictionary of Psychological Medicine* (Tuke, 1892). George Robertson, of the Royal Edinburgh Asylum, made a serious study tour of the French centres of the new psychodynamic methods in 1892, and this was given generous space in the *Journal of Mental Science*; in the following year, he surveyed the use of hypnosis in psychiatry, showing caution but some optimism (Robertson, 1892, 1893). Janet's major report of his work was reviewed in the *Journal of Mental Science* in 1893, and Janet reviewed Hack Tuke's book in *Brain* in the same year. J. M. Clarke's (1892) review dealt with no fewer than 12 books on hysteria, published mostly in France between 1887 and 1891.

In 1894, Clarke again reviewed the subject of "Hysteria and neurasthenia" in *Brain* when he summarised for the first time in a medical journal the preliminary communication of Breuer & Freud in the previous year, noting that, unlike other forms of treatment which rely on suggestion, theirs consisted of enabling patients to give expression to their ideas. Later, he reviewed Breuer & Freud's *Studien über Hysterie* (Clarke, 1896), noting the problem that the suggestibility of hypnotised patients may cloud the expression of reminiscences. J. Bresler (1895) reported for the *Journal of Mental Science* on the current state of psychiatry in Germany, making brief but significant reference to Breuer and Freud.

Hypnotism continued to be of some interest until 1900; J. Milne Bramwell wrote on James Braid in 1896 (Bramwell, 1896), while Braid's original work of 1843 was offered in a new edition in 1899, and reviewed by Bramwell, in *Brain*. A large survey of 184 patients treated with hypnosis (Woods, 1897) was particularly notable: the sample included carefully diagnosed patients suffering from a variety of psychiatric and neurological conditions, with a general tendency for those we would now regard as 'psychogenic' to do better than those with clear neurological disorders. Although later papers tended to be more optimistic, interest in hypnosis was waning by 1900.

Psychodynamics in the United States

However, interest in the subject was taken up more on the other side of the Atlantic, particularly by the neurologists Smith Ely Jeliffe, Stanley Hall, and Morton Prince. Prince (1854–1929) published an account of a psychic medium who exhibited various personalities (Prince, 1906), somewhat replicating Janet's study of Léonie, and clearly using Janet's concept of dissociation. However, like Janet, Prince was less interested in the content of the dissociated personalities of these subjects than the structure (Porter, 1987); this was in marked contrast to psychoanalysis, where the content was everything. Prince and Hall were both members of the Society for Psychical Research, and actively supported suggestive therapies and hypnosis through their journals. The *Journal of Abnormal Psychology*, founded in 1906 by Prince, was the first to publish a paper by Jung in English (Jung, 1907); and Stanley Hall, editor of the *American Journal of Psychology*, was responsible for the invitation to Freud and Jung to speak at Clark University in 1909, and published their papers (Freud, 1909*a*; Jung, 1909). Janet had previously been invited to Harvard University and gave a series of 15 lectures in 1906 (Janet, 1907).

Smith Ely Jeliffe (with William A. White) translated the work of both Dubois and Déjerine (Dubois, 1906; Déjerine & Gauckler, 1913). Jeliffe was editor (as well as founder and publisher) of the *Journal of Nervous and Mental Diseases*, and he was the first to publish Freud's work in English – Brill's translation of Freud's work on hysteria (Freud, 1909*b*).

The mind/body problem

The relevance of and interest in hypnosis, psychical phenomena, and hysteria varied according to different views on the relationship between mind and brain: this unsolved Cartesian problem is central in the metaphysical or philosophical approach to the mind. In 1887, however, in the interests of scientific investigation, Hughlings Jackson laid down his "doctrine of concomitance" (see Jackson, 1931): in investigating nervous diseases, one could simply ignore the mind and its connections with the brain. It was a practical way of taking the metaphysical problem out of scientific work, but it was not a philosophical view. Not everybody, though, was in agreement on these issues.

The aim of the Society for Psychical Research was to examine psychic phenomena rigorously for scientific evidence of the spirit world and of communication with it. It stood for a different position on the mind/body problem – an interactionist one in which the mind and the brain mutually interact and influence each other. It was more influential among psychiatrists in America than in England, and Janet was involved in setting up a branch of the Society in France; this no doubt reflected a greater interest in hypnosis in these countries before World War I.

But, in Britain, an interactionist view developed separately from psychiatry, within an élite sector of intellectual and cultural life that centred particularly on Cambridge and the Society for Psychical Research. Frederic Myers (1843–1901) noted similarities between 'psychic' phenomena and hysteria; he was aware of the developments in France and of the similarities between hysteria and hypnosis. He is known to have gone to witness Janet's experiments in Le Havre in 1886, travelling with his younger brother Arthur (1851–94), an even more brilliant scholar, and a doctor interested in hypnosis (Taylor & Marsh, 1980). Correlating the changed states of consciousness in psychical phenomena, hysteria, and hypnosis, Frederic Myers developed his own theory of the mind, in which he postulated a number of subliminal 'consciousnesses', with the waking conscious having no necessary priority over others (Myers, 1891/92, 1893/94; Williams, 1985). Myers' psychodynamic theory was strongly supported by William James (James, 1903).

Myers' work was important because it was a point of access into Britain for Continental psychodynamic ideas, and he was in fact the first person in Britain to note Breuer and Freud in 1893, regarding their clinical work as a fortunate support for his own interactionist views on hysteria. The influence of interactionist ideas emanating from the Society for Psychical Research prepared the ground, within the Cambridge circle, for psychodynamic concepts, particularly psychoanalysis, which influenced the development there of experimental psychology (McDougall, 1923), progressive education (Isaacs, 1930; Lampe, 1959), literature (Woolf, 1914), philosophy (Russell, 1921, 1922; Stephen, 1933), and psychotherapy (Rivers, 1920; Strachey & Strachey, 1986).

Freud in fact was not an interactionist, and tended to adopt Hughlings Jackson's notion of concomitance: Jackson left the mind aside, while he concentrated on the brain; Freud, although wishing to do the same, found himself increasingly investigating the mind, while leaving aside the mechanisms of the brain. At this time, however, Freud was still hovering between the two positions, and this may have made his views appear to offer a mediation of the metaphysical problem.

Clark (1983) has described how British psychiatrists persisted in worrying away at the metaphysical problem of mind/body relations, and for reasons of professional independence and status, saw their science, however much it was looked down upon, as peculiarly original in its 'dual aspect', focusing on both mind and brain. In spite of Hughlings Jackson's influence, his doctrine of concomitance was taken as a philosophical position on the mind/body problem (Mercier, 1890), not as a scientific device for getting around it. In trying to mediate the problem, though, British psychiatry was distorting Hughlings Jackson. At the same time, the contrasting point of view, the interactionist one, also rejected Jackson's 'doctrine of concomitance', again on mistaken grounds – that it was metaphysically materialist – one instance being Morton Prince's (1891) attack.

Freud's position represented a third approach to the problem at this time. Although he initially embraced Jackson's scientific agnosticism on the mind/brain problem, this empirical materialism met, in Freud, a cultured European mind that thought as much in the mode of the German idealist *Naturphilosophie* as in the scientific mode. Curiously, the Continental idealism stemmed from English mental philosophy, Locke, and associationist psychology, via Condillac and the French *Idéologues*. At the same time, these contrasting aspects of Freud, giving a spurious sense of mediating the metaphysical problem, were initially more favourable to British psychiatrists than the idealist or mentalist suggestive therapies, though the sexual side of this bodily approach became a hindrance later on.

Psychodynamics in the 'new psychiatry'

Despite the lull in interest in hypnosis, by 1906 there were sufficient people (assisted by American translations) to found an organisation in Britain known as the Medical Society for the Study of Suggestive Therapies (later called the Psycho-Medical Society). However, at this time, a more prominent interest in psychoanalysis developed. This came about from Freud's prolific writing – *The Interpretation of Dreams* (Ellis (1901) reviewed Freud's shortened version, *Über den Traum*, partly because Freud had referred to him, and they had started a correspondence (Grosskurth, 1981)), *The Psychopathology of Everyday Life* (reviewed fairly widely), and the Dora case (Freud, 1905), which excited Wilfred Trotter and Ernest Jones in 1906. Jones first met Jung in 1907 and Freud in 1908 (Brome, 1982), when their writings were beginning to appear in English; thereafter, he sought and attained a pre-eminent position as activist within the international psychoanalytic movement (Paskauskas, 1988).

In 1908, Bernard Hart (1880–1960) began to write serious critiques and appreciations of Freud's work in the journals (Hart, 1908, 1910, 1911). Later, his *Psychology of Insanity* (1912) became the most influential book in the new psychiatry; it was a largely psychoanalytic account of mental illness. Stoddart's *Mind and its Disorders* (1908) was an early Kraepelinian work, but its subsequent editions introduced psychodynamic and Freudian ideas. Hart and Stoddart were the two most prominent figures in what came to be known as the 'new psychiatry', and both later joined the British Psycho-Analytical Society (Chapter 13). From about 1905, British psychiatry developed a blend of several strands – physiology, Kraepelinian observation and diagnosis, academic and psychometric psychology, early or out-patient treatment – which seemed to resurrect the old moral treatment methods as well as the new psychodynamic ones (Boyle, 1905), and above all in Britain, psychodynamic psychology (especially Freudian).

In 1913, the Medico-Psychological Clinic (known as the Brunswick Square Clinic) was established by Jessie Murray, a doctor and a suffragette, who had studied in Paris with Janet, and psychology at University College, where Hart was already teaching psychodynamic psychiatry (Boll, 1962). It employed various methods, including psychodynamic ones, but the increasingly orthodox psychoanalytic method steadily gained ground, resulting in the clinic being disbanded in 1924, to be partly absorbed into the British Psycho-Analytical Society.

The psychodynamic therapies met considerable opposition, both for not being materialist enough (Mercier, 1902) and for their sexual biology being too much so! For instance, the *British Medical Journal*'s blistering leader, in January 1907, slashed at this aspect of the psychoanalytic method – "[It] usurps the confessional . . . [and is] in most cases incorrect, in many hazardous, and in all dispensible." What was eventually decisive, however, in establishing psychodynamics – especially psychoanalysis – was the effect of World War I. War neurosis was an unstoppable psychological haemorrhage from the armies on both sides, and psychoanalysis was the only psychiatric approach which came up with both an explanation and an effective treatment for some cases. This so convinced the military mind that the influence of psychoanalysis (and therefore of the 'new psychiatry') was enormously enhanced in the immediate aftermath of the war.

Acknowledgement

I am grateful to Robert M. Young for commenting on this paper and particularly for elucidating the cultural 'loop' linking *Naturphilosophie*, associationist psychology, and the French *Idéologues*.

References

BAIN, A. (1855) *The Senses and the Intellect*. London: Parker.

——— (1859) *The Emotions and the Will*. London: Parker.

BERNHEIM, H.-M. (1884) *De la suggestion et des applications à la thérapeutique*. Paris: Doin (1900, *Suggestive Therapies*. London: Pentland.)

BOLL, T. (1962) May Sinclair and the Medico-Psychological Clinic of London. *Proceedings of the American Philosophical Society*, **106**, 310–326.

BOYLE, H. A. (1905) Some points in the early treatment of nervous and mental cases. *Journal of Mental Science*, **51**, 676–681.

BRAID, J. (1843) *Neurypnology, or the Rationale of Nervous Sleep Considered in Relation to Animal Magnetism or Mesmerism* (reprinted 1899). London: George Redway.

BRAMWELL, J. M. (1896) James Braid, surgeon and hypnotist. *Brain*, **19**, 90–116.

BRESLER, J. (1895) Progress of psychiatry in 1895 – Germany. *Journal of Mental Science*, **42**, 438–444.

BREUER, J. & FREUD, S. (1893) Über den psychischen Mechanismus hysterischer Phänomene (Vorläufige Mitteilung). (The psychical mechanism of hysterical phenomena (Preliminary communication). *Neurologisches Zentralblatt*, **12**, 4–10, 43–47

——— & ——— (1895) *Studien über Hysterie*. Vienna: Deuticke.

BRITISH MEDICAL JOURNAL (1907) Freud and hysteria (Leader). *British Medical Journal*, *i*, 103–104.

BROME, V. (1982) *Ernest Jones: Freud's Alter Ego*. London: Caliban.

BYNUM, W. F. (1982) Theory and practice in British psychiatry from J. C. Prichard to Henry Maudsley. In *History of Psychiatry* (ed. Ogawa). Tokyo: Saikon.

CHARCOT, J.-M. (1887) *Leçons sur les maladies du système nerveux*. Paris. (1889, *Lectures on Diseases of the Nervous System*. London: The Sydenham Society.)

CLARK, M. (1981) The rejection of psychological approaches to mental disorder in late nineteenth century British psychiatry. In *Madhouses, Mad-Doctors and Madmen* (ed. A. Scull). London: Athlone Press.

—— (1983) A plastic power ministering to organisation: interpretations of the mind–body relation in late nineteenth century British psychiatry. *Psychological Medicine*, **13**, 187–197.

CLARKE, J. M. (1892) On hysteria. *Brain*, **15**, 522–612.

—— (1894) Hysteria and neurasthenia. *Brain*, **17**, 261–321.

—— (1896) Review of Breuer and Freud, Studien über Hysterie. *Brain*, **19**, 401–414.

CONOLLY, J. (1856) *The Treatment of the Insane without Mechanical Constraints*. London: Smith, Elder.

COOTER, R. (1981) Phrenology and British alienists. In *Madhouses, Mad-Doctors and Madmen* (ed. A. Scull). London: Athlone Press.

DEJERINE, J.-J. & GAUCKLER, E. (1913) *The Psychoneuroses and their Treatment by Psychotherapy* (trans. S. E. Jeliffe). Philadelphia: Lippincott.

DEWHURST, K. (1982) *Hughlings Jackson on Psychiatry*. Oxford: Sandford.

DUBOIS, P. (1906) *The Psychic Treatment of Nervous Diseases* (trans. S. E. Jeliffe & W. A. White). New York: Funk & Wagnalls.

ELLIS, H. (1901) Review of Freud's Über den Traum. *Journal of Mental Science*, **47**, 370–371.

FREUD, S. (1905) Fragment of the analysis of a case of hysteria. *Monatsshrift für Psychiatrie und Neurologie*, **18**, 285–310, 408–467.

—— (1909*a*) The origin and development of psycho-analysis. *American Journal of Psychology*, **21**, 181–218.

—— (1909*b*) *Selected Papers on Hysteria. Journal of Nervous and Mental Diseases, monograph 4.*

GROSSKURTH, P. (1981) *Havelock Ellis: A Biography*. London: Allen Lane.

HART, B. (1908) A philosophy of psychiatry. *Journal of Mental Science*, **54**, 473–490.

—— (1910) The psychology of Freud and his school. *Journal of Mental Science*, **56**, 431–452.

—— (1911) Freud's concept of hysteria. *Brain*, **33**, 339–386.

—— (1912) *The Psychology of Insanity*. Cambridge: Cambridge University Press.

HEARNSHAW, L. W. (1964) *A Short History of British Psychology*. London: Methuen.

HUNTER, R. & HURWITZ, L. J. (1961) The case notes of the National Hospital for the Paralysed and Epileptic, Queens Square, London before 1900. *Journal of Neurology, Neurosurgery and Neuropsychiatry*, **24**, 167–194.

ISAACS, S. (1930) *Intellectual Growth in Young Children*. London: Routledge & Kegan Paul.

JACKSON, J. H. (1931) *Selected Writings of John Hughlings Jackson*. London: Hodder & Stoughton.

JAMES, W. (1903) Frederic Myers' service to psychology. *Proceedings of the Society for Psychical Research*, **17**, 13–32.

JANET, P. (1892) *États mental des hystériques*. Paris: J. Rueff.

—— (1899) *Traité de thérapeutique appliqué*. Paris: J. Rueff.

—— (1907) *The Major Symptoms of Hysteria*. New York: Hafner.

JUNG, C. (1907) On the psychophysical relation of the association experiment. *Journal of Abnormal Psychology*, **1**, 247–255.

—— (1909) The association method. *Journal of Abnormal Psychology*, **21**, 219–269.

LAMPE, D. (1959) *Pyke: The Unknown Genius*. London: Evans Bros.

MAUDSLEY, H. (1867) *The Physiology and Pathology of Mind*. London: Macmillan.

—— (1900) The new psychology. *Journal of Mental Science*, **46**, 411–424.

MCDOUGALL, W. (1923) *An Introduction to Social Psychology*. London: Methuen.

MERCIER, C. (1890) *Sanity and Insanity*. London: Walter Scott.

—— (1902) *Textbook of Insanity*. London: Swan.

MYERS, F. (1891/92) The subliminal consciousness. Chapter I: General characteristics of subliminal messages. *Proceedings of the Society for Psychical Research*, **7**, 298–355.

—— (1893/94) The subliminal consciousness. Chapter IV: The mechanism of hysteria. *Proceedings of the Society for Psychical Research*, **9**, 3–128.

OPPENHEIM, J. (1985) *The Other World: Spiritualism and Psychical Research in England, 1850–1914*. Cambridge: Cambridge University Press.

PASKAUSKAS, R. A. (1988) The Jones–Freud era, 1909–1939. In *Freud in Exile* (eds E. Timms & N. Segal). New Haven: Yale University Press.

PORTER, R. (1987) *A Social History of Madness: Stories of the Insane*. London: Weidenfeld & Nicolson.

PRINCE, M. (1891) Hughlings Jackson on the connection between the mind and the brain. *Brain*, **14**, 250–269.

—— (1906) *The Dissociation of a Personality*. New York: Longmans.
RIVERS, W. H. R. (1900) Discussion of Maudsley's 'The new psychology'. *Journal of Mental Science*, **46**, 424.
—— (1920) *Instincts and the Unconscious*. Cambridge: Cambridge University Press.
ROBERTSON, G. M. (1892) Hypnotism at Paris and Nancy: notes of a visit. *Journal of Mental Science*, **38**, 494–531.
—— (1893) The use of hypnotism among the insane. *Journal of Mental Science*, **39**, 1–12.
RUSSELL, B. (1921) *The Analysis of Mind*. London: Allen & Unwin.
—— (1922) Review of Rivers' 'Instincts and the Unconscious'. *The New Leader*, **1**, 12.
SCULL, A. (1981) Moral treatment reconsidered: some sociological comments on an episode in the history of British psychiatry. In *Madhouses, Mad-Doctors and Madmen* (ed. A. Scull). London: Athlone Press.
SMITH, R. P. & MYERS, A. T. (1890) On the treatment of insanity by hypnosis. *Journal of Mental Science*, **36**, 191–213.
SPENCER, H. (1855) *The Principles of Psychology*. London: Williams & Norgate.
STEPHEN, K. (1933) *Philosophy and Medicine: A Study of the Wish to Fall Ill*. Cambridge: Cambridge University Press.
STODDART, W. H. B. (1908) *Mind and its Disorders*. London: H. K. Lewis.
STRACHEY, J. & STRACHEY, A. (1986) *Bloomsbury/Freud*. London: Chatto & Windus.
TAYLOR, D. & MARSH, S. (1980) Hughlings Jackson's Dr. Z.: the paradigm of temporal lobe epilepsy revealed. *Journal of Neurology, Neurosurgery and Neuropsychiatry*, **43**, 758–767.
TUCKEY, L. (1888) *Psycho-Therapeutics or Treatment by Hypnosis and Suggestion*. London: Baillière, Tindall & Cox (3rd edn, 1891).
—— (1898) Critical digest. *Brain*, **14**, 538–556.
TUKE, D. H. (1892) *Dictionary of Psychological Medicine*. London: J. & A. Churchill.
WALK, A. (1976) Medico-psychologists, Maudsley and the Maudsley. *British Journal of Psychiatry*, **128**, 19–30.
WILLIAMS, J. P. (1985) Psychical research and psychiatry in late Victorian Britain: trance as ecstacy or trance as insanity. In *The Anatomy of Madness: Essays in the History of Psychiatry* (eds W. F. Bynum, R. Porter & M. Shepherd). London: Tavistock.
WOODS, J. F. (1897) The treatment by suggestion with and without hypnosis. *Journal of Mental Science*, **43**, 248–326.
WOOLF, L. (1914) (Unattributed) Everyday life. *New Weekly*, 13 June, 412.
YOUNG, R. M. (1970) *Mind, Brain and Adaptation*. Oxford: Clarendon Press.

13 The development of the psychodynamic movement

MALCOLM PINES

I attempt in this chapter to show what the climate of philosophical and psychological ideas in Britain was in the years preceding World War II, as this is relevant to the acceptance of psychodynamic ideas. An immense impetus was given to psychotherapy by World War I, through the new understanding of the psychogenesis of the shell-shock syndrome and the effectiveness of psychotherapy in its treatment (Chapter 15). After 1918, it was found necessary to continue the out-patient treatment of war neuroses, and opinion began to favour the early treatment of psychiatric disorders in such clinics. The Tavistock Clinic and the Cassel Hospital were both founded in the immediate post-war years, representing a recognition of the need for better research and treatment methods in the neuroses.

The development of the psychodynamic movement was closely intertwined with the history of psychoanalysis in Britain, but was not identical with it, and some little-known contributions to psychotherapy are mentioned here.

> ''At different epochs, different schemes of ideas have determined the mental perspective in England. There are persistent bodies of belief that govern an epoch, guiding enquiry in many fields, directing intellectual interest, and shaping the methods of reflection. These enduring intellectual traditions are forms of intelligibility. They are expectations or demands that the world should be understood according to certain co-ordinated sets of principles intimately related to the prevailing moral and religious inclinations of the age, to the kind of hopes and dreads with which its experience is coloured.'' (Carre, 1949, p. 12).

These remarks on English patterns of belief by a philosopher exemplify many features of the reception of psychodynamic thought. In his autobiography, Ernest Jones (1959, p. 23) described the different climates of opinion towards psychiatry in England and North America respectively in those pre-war years. He had been Professor of Psychiatry in Toronto from 1908 to 1913, and had been partly responsible for founding both the first Psycho-analytical Society in North America and the American Psychopathological Association. Before he left London, he had been a hard-working physician whose aim was to establish himself as a consultant in neurology at a London teaching hospital, but who began to explore psychiatry when he realised that his career as a neurologist was likely to be blocked. In 1902, he began to visit Bernard Hart and W. H. Stoddart at the mental hospitals where they worked, as well as reading widely in the current psychiatric literature. He had also made study tours on the Continent – to Kraepelin in Munich, and to Bleuler and Jung in Zurich – and had a good working knowledge of European psychiatry. He described a very highly developed neurological science in England, but psychiatry as almost non-existent – much below the level recorded even in France and Italy; it was thus entirely subordinate to neurology and took its cue from the latter. However, in America the reverse held: "neurology did not have the prestige that it had in England and psychiatrists such as Adolf Meyer and August Hoch, were free to take an independent line, which they did." Jones clearly overstates his case about British psychiatry and was certainly unacquainted with the state of Scottish psychiatry (Henderson, 1964), which seems from the evidence of Isabel Hutton (1960) to have been well advanced in its management of asylum patients.

Continental medicine, especially in Germany, contained a significant element of the school of Romantic medicine, which had strongly combated the materialism and rationalism of the 19th century. The development of psychoanalysis in Germany and Austria can be seen as a confluence of the streams of scientific rationalism and Romanticism, but the same cannot be said of psychiatry in England, where the predominant 19th-century philosophy of positivism was strongly based on a foundation of Newtonian physics and evolutionary theory. Massive philosophical systems, the most significant being that of Spencer, attempted to give a totally encompassing and coherent scheme of human knowledge, based on these foundations. Agnosticism and empiricism were greatly strengthened by the scientific advances of the century, which included rapidly expanding knowledge of the nervous system. More and more, the brain was being seen as the organ of the mind, and in this the work of Hughlings Jackson was pre-eminent. He wrote that "Psychical Symptoms are to medical men only signs of what is wrong in a material system" (Clarke, 1981, p. 283). Thus, all mental symptoms were seen as the result of either deficiency or defective inhibitory control of lower by higher functional systems of the central nervous system, arising from deficiency or defect in that system. Henry Maudsley, the most significant late-19th-century psychiatrist in England, wrote:

> "It is not our business, it is not in our power to explain *psychologically* the origin and nature of any of the depraved instincts manifested in typical cases of insanity. It is sufficient to establish their existence as facts of observation, and to set forth the pathological conditions under which they are produced; they will be observed and classified like other phenomena of disease . . . . The explanation, when it comes, will not come from a mental, but from a physical side – from the study of the *neurosis* not from the analysis of the *psychosis*."

By 'neurosis' he meant a physical disturbance of the central nervous system, not a psychological disorder, as we now assume.

Thus, under the dead hand of materialistic medicine, British psychiatry was confined to the establishment of diagnosis and the containment of illness within institutions. Psychiatrists were aware of the importance of their relationship with patients, but this was seen in a one-sided manner. The doctor had a moral/pastoral responsibility for the mentally disordered patient, this being authoritarian and patriarchal, as was well exemplified in the treatment of

Virginia Woolf (Trombley, 1981). The mentally disturbed patient had been physiologically deprived of the use of his/her psychological faculties, and the doctor had to take responsibility for the patient's life, until such time as these faculties became normal again, through the remission of the physiological cause. Indeed, as psychiatrists had so little in the way of effective treatment available to them, their authority and status were based more on the exercise of the moral/pastoral function than on any other, and any question of examining the nature of that relationship was clearly a serious threat to professional identity.

This must account for some of the opposition to psychodynamic ideas, which in fact involved such an examination. Some of the most prominent opponents of psychoanalysis, Mercier and Donkin among them, emphasised the doctor's need to project an authoritative image and to be able to outplay the hysteric in the psychological game of chess that the patient attempts. "The emphasis was on the dramaturgic enactment of a necessary relationship between the physician's insight and authority and the patient's submission and compliance, rather than on any real attempt to come to terms with the patient's individual psychological problems as such" (Clarke, 1981, p. 297). Thus, the new methods of psychological analysis were perceived as being incompatible with the traditional professional conception of the doctor's moral/pastoral responsibilities. However, there were significant precedents to psychodynamic psychiatry that had begun to prepare for the cultivation of new understandings. Some of these came from the unlikely direction of research into spiritualism and psychic phenomena (see Chapter 13, and Gould, 1986).

A significant figure of this period was Havelock Ellis, who did much to make it possible to write about sexuality, its development, and both its normal and abnormal manifestations. Ellis had a great deal of prestige, and both Ernest Jones and Freud were glad to have his support in the early days of psychoanalysis in England, though later they both turned against him. Indeed, it was Ellis who made one of the first references to Freud in the psychological literature, as well as showing good knowledge of, and a critical approach to, Freudian theory in his later writings (Brome, 1979).

However, Ernest Jones' account (1959) does not mention some significant ventures to establish early out-patient treatment of psychoneurosis. Dr Helen Boyle conceived of the idea of a hospital where patients suffering from 'nervous breakdown' could be treated when practising in the East End of London at the end of the last century. She had worked for two years at Claybury asylum, visited Continental clinics, and in 1905 founded the Lady Chichester Hospital at Hove. She had already established a small out-patient dispensary there, and now added ten beds for the treatment of in-patients. In 1911 these were increased to 38, and she described her ideas in a paper "The ideal clinic for the treatment of nervous and borderline cases" (Boyle, 1922).

In her autobiography, Isabel Hutton (1960) described her work from 1925 at the British Hospital for Functional Nervous Disorders. This had been founded in 1890 by Dr Forbes Winslow, and was the only clinic at which cases of mental disorder were treated as out-patients. Little, however, is known of the functioning of this hospital until Dr Hutton, together with Dr Marjorie Franklin and Dr Hilda Weber, joined it in 1925. Later renamed the Camden Hospital, it has continued to flourish as the Paddington Centre for Psychotherapy, where psychoanalytic psychotherapy is available under the National Health Service.

Hutton's career is of considerable interest in representing that of a pioneer, both as a woman psychiatrist and a psychotherapist. She was an Edinburgh graduate, and worked at Morningside Hospital (later the Royal Edinburgh) under George Robertson, the first Professor of Psychiatry there. Her description makes clear that a humane, considerate form of custodial psychiatry was practised under him, but that in 1914, when Dr William Stoddart gave three lectures to the Scottish branch of the Royal Medico-Psychological Association on the 'new psychiatry', this had a great impact in Scotland – both positive and negative.

> ''Many of the senior psychiatrists heard about Freud's researches for the first time and could hardly believe their ears. One learned doctor stumped out during the first lecture and many were heard to bark 'utter rubbish', 'preposterous', 'filthy', 'vile', 'nothing but sex', which greatly amused us and exposed their ignorance of contemporary medical literature. Our chief was greatly interested and began to pick our brains in the light of this 'new psychiatry of Freud and Jung' and immediately introduced it into his lectures. He was delighted to be instructed, but he soon outstripped us in the practical application of his new knowledge.'' (Hutton, 1960, p. 128)

Indeed, both Stoddart and Robertson were very significant proponents of psychoanalysis in the pre-war years. Robertson's obituary in the *Journal of Mental Science* (1932) stated that:

> ''when several years later Freud produced a theory and method of psychoanalysis, Robertson became a devout disciple. These earlier converts from orthodox psychiatry to Freudism stood with a foot in each camp; their voice was the voice of Jacob, but their hands were the hands of Esau. Robertson, however, was entirely sincere in his convictions; and he had no doubts as to the philosophical or the biological soundness of the Freudian theory.''

Robertson was President of the Royal Medico-Psychological Association in 1922 and then of the Royal College of Physicians of Edinburgh. His position undoubtedly contributed to the relatively positive attitude to psychoanalysis in Scottish psychiatry that was described by Sir David Henderson in his *History of Scottish Psychiatry* (Henderson, 1964).

The second proponent in these early days was ''the Pupil of Hughlings Jackson, the Lecturer in the Faculty of Medicine, London University, Professor of Psychological Medicine to the Royal Army College, a vast, portly figure who conducted his ward rounds in morning coat and top hat''. This was William Henry Butter Stoddart. Rickman (1950*a*,*b*) says that he was a man of courage, of good nature, of great clinical gifts, and of utter common sense. In many respects, he was not the kind of person to associate with a pioneering spirit: placid, apparently lazy, fat, affable, always well dressed, he enjoyed good food, good wine (or rather champagne), and idle days on the river. His cigar case, matchbox, cigar clipper, all of gold, even his diamond ring, were part of an easy existence and were engulfed in the portly urbanity that was the essential Stoddart. However, this intriguing mixture of a man was a former Superintendent of Bethlem and Lecturer in Psychiatry at St Thomas's, as well as author of a highly regarded textbook of psychiatry, *Mind and its Disorders*, that was very well received in its first two editions. In the third edition, he declared his adherence to psychoanalysis and, from then onwards, threw his not inconsiderable weight into the battle to establish psychoanalytical psychiatry, although in many quarters his change of view was not welcomed. A review of this edition in the *Edinburgh Medical Journal* of 1920 states that "the extreme Freudian view is presented in a manner which suggests that no one has any scruples or doubts about its full acceptance; there is not a hint from first to last that any controversy exists on the subject." It attacked the book for various forms of confusion, such as between materialism and the new interest in the psyche, concluding with regret that "it must be said that this book is one which will do much to retard the psychological methods in the treatment of disease". Stoddart assumed that attacks would come, and he assumed that they would cease in time. Meanwhile, life was pleasant, and his attackers were, after all, good fellows, but mistaken. He did not want to reform the world, but if he thought a thing true he said it as clearly, as tactfully as possible, and left it at that. It was almost impossible to keep on being an enemy of Stoddart, and at a time when psychoanalysis was ill-received such a personality was, to say the least, useful to its establishment among the institutions in this country (Rickman, 1950*a*,*b*).

Two further significant figures in pre-World War I psychiatry were Bernard Hart and Hugh Crichton-Miller. Hart became Consultant in Psychological Medicine at University College Hospital (UCH) in 1913 and his book *The Psychology of Insanity* was probably the most widely read and influential work on a psychoanalytic approach to psychiatry for more than two decades. His career spanned much of the development of modern psychiatry, as he was appointed to UCH in 1913 and died at the age of 86, in 1966. Aubrey Lewis wrote that "Bernard Hart blended to an uncommon degree shrewd practical judgement with a philosophical approach to the problems of psychological medicine". As a young man he recognised the powerful implications of Freud's ideas, and his article on the unconscious was described by Freud in a letter to Ernest Jones in 1910 as the "first clever word on the matter" and "the best paper on the damned topic of the unconscious I have read in the last years". Indeed, Hart's (1910) article on the unconscious in *Subconscious Phenomena* is an elegant and clear presentation of the subject. Referring to Karl Pearson and his *Grammar of Science*, he distinguished between phenomena and concepts, regarding Freud's as the first consistent attempt to construct a conceptual psychology, which he compared with Janet's 'phenomenal subconscious'. Freud's work was said to be on a deeper plane, his aim being not a description of the facts but the conceptual explanation of the facts, which is the progression by which the method of science is invariably characterised. Undoubtedly, Hart's elegant but critical descriptions of Freud's work greatly helped to establish the serious nature of analytic theory in the minds of British psychiatrists.

In his later book *Psychopathology*, Hart (1927) reviewed the current status of psychotherapy and psychopathology. Although he continued to consider suggestion and persuasion of clinical value and recognised the importance of Janet's ideas in explaining the symptoms of hysteria, he confirmed his support of the dynamic point of view, which he compared with Kepler's work and Newton's formulation of the law of gravity. The dynamic point of view was seen as a concept that added greatly to the understanding of the observed sequence of phenomena, and Freud's was the chief impetus in dynamic psychopathology.

Hart praised Freud's empirical approach, which slowly and tentatively built up his theoretical concepts.

The life of Crichton-Miller is intimately bound up with the foundation of the Tavistock Clinic after World War I and is discussed here in that connection, but even before 1914, he began to practise as a psychotherapist. He had been a fashionable general practitioner, both at San Remo in Italy where he was born, and in Scotland at Aviemore. In 1911, he moved to Harrow-on-the-Hill and opened Bowden House as a nursing home for functional nervous disorders. In 1913, he was joined by Maurice Nicoll, a determined psychotherapist who rather quickly moved from Freud's psychoanalysis to Jung's analytical psychology, but in 1924 ceased to practise as a psychotherapist and became a principal English advocate of the systems of Ouspensky and Gurdjieff.

Maurice Nicoll was the son of Sir William Robertson Nicoll, a great figure in the world of literature, the founder and editor of the *British Weekly* and *The Bookman* (Pogson, 1961). Maurice Nicoll himself wrote both novels and articles; he graduated in 1910 from St Bartholomew's and spent a year studying the new forms of psychology in Paris, Berlin, Vienna, and Zurich. There, Jung made a great impact on him, and in 1914 he returned to Zurich for further work with him; their friendship remained throughout their lives.

The final pioneer from pre-war days was the remarkable David Eder (1866–1936), who came from a middle-class Jewish family and was first cousin to the novelist Israel Zangwill. He was a man of many parts: an early socialist who took part in the Bloody Sunday riot in Trafalgar Square of 1887, leaving him with a scar on his head; he took a BSc in psychology in 1891. He graduated from St Bartholomew's in 1895 and began his career as a general practitioner in Johannesburg. A great traveller, he then worked as a doctor in Colombia and made three journeys into the Andes. He was caught up in South American revolutions, was a surgeon in the field, and in one dramatic episode fell ill among cannibals! In 1908, he took part in the expedition to Brazil to investigate the possibility that it might become a land for Jewish immigrants.

Between 1908 and 1914, he was active in medicine for poor people and was a founder of the London Labour Party; he was medical officer to the pioneering Margaret MacMillan Clinic for children, Director of the Deptford Clinic, a promoter of school hygiene, and he edited the journal of that name until 1921 (Steedman, 1990). In 1911, he presented a paper to the Neurological Section of the British Medical Association on a case of hysteria and obsessional neurosis treated by Freud's psychoanalytic method: "When Dr. Eder had finished speaking the Chairman and the entire audience, numbering about 9 rose and stalked out without a word" (Hobman, 1945). He started in private practice in Welbeck Street in 1912, and in 1913 went to Vienna for analysis with Freud, who, however, referred him to Victor Tausk, with whom he had a brief analysis, later followed by another with Ernest Jones in 1914. Significantly, Jones does not mention this in his own autobiography, in which he is somewhat disparaging about Eder, as he also is about Stoddart. Eder served in the Royal Army Medical Corps in Malta, and wrote a significant book entitled *War Shock*; he opposed the use of the term 'shell-shock' because of its pseudo-organic connotation. After the war, he worked in the Ministry of Pensions and neurological clinics, which continued the psychotherapy of cases of war neurosis. His energies were diverted for four years between 1918 and 1922, when he became political officer to the Zionist

Commission in Palestine, during which time he reorganised the orphanages of Jerusalem.

Eder's original allegiance to Freud switched to Jung, much to Ernest Jones' displeasure. However, in 1923, he went to Budapest for eight months' analysis with Ferenczi, in which he "found the solution of his main problem" (Hobman, 1945, p. 100). He continued to have a very active involvement with psychoanalysis and in 1932 took part in the development of the Institute for the Scientific Treatment of Delinquency, as a member of its council and scientific committee and as physician to its clinic. Eder was greatly admired by such persons as D. H. Lawrence, the future President of Israel Chaim Weizmann, and Wyndham Deedes, whom he had worked for in Palestine. It was the influence and example of men such as Eder, Stoddart, and Robertson that spread the knowledge of psychoanalysis in those early days and ensured that it had some acceptance.

One further significant contribution that is yet little known was the Medico-Psychological Clinic of London, which was founded in 1913 by Dr Jessie Murray, a graduate of the Royal Free Hospital (Boll, 1962). She had attended Janet's lectures in Paris and conceived of a clinic to treat functional nervous disorders with new therapeutic methods. She was joined by Julia Turner, who was not medically qualified, and in 1913 they opened their clinic at 14 Endsley Street, Bloomsbury. Later, this moved to 30 Brunswick Square and became known as the Brunswick Square Clinic. Among its directors and founder members were Dr Hector Munroe, Professor Charles Spearman, and Dr J. H. Spencer. The fee for a consultation or treatment was 2*s*. 6*d*., and it was open from 2 to 4 p.m., four days per week. Five hundred pounds was given for the support of the clinic by May Sinclair (1863–1946), a novelist, philosopher, critic, and poet, who used psychoanalytical ideas to describe the struggle of the individual to create a coherent human identity.

In 1915, this clinic recognised the need to train psychotherapists, and the Society for the Study of Orthopsychics was founded, its first President being Professor Percy Nunn and its second the sociologist Professor L. T. Hobhouse. The Society offered a three-year course, which included personal psychoanalysis under the direction of Dr Jessie Murray, and the syllabus embraced science, biology, physiology, psychology, philosophy, anthropology, comparative religion, and mythology! Between 1916 and 1917, they leased additional premises to be able to treat war-shocked patients. In 1918, James Glover, one of the most significant of the early psychoanalysts, who had had analysis with Julia Turner, joined them; he became director of the clinic and the honorary secretary of the Society. Dr Murray had to retire in 1919 because of cancer, and James Glover and Julia Turner then became co-directors. In 1919, Dr Sylvia Payne, later a prominent English woman analyst and President of the Psychoanalytical Society, came to Glover for analysis, influenced by her experience of the treatment of war neurosis at a hospital in Torquay. In 1920, Glover went to the Psychoanalytical Congress at The Hague, where he met Karl Abraham and arranged to have analysis with him in Berlin. The consequence of this experience was that Glover became a convert to a more disciplined form of psychoanalysis, and therefore opposed the eclectic therapy that was practised at the clinic; he suggested an affiliation with the British Psychoanalytical Society, and met Ernest Jones to discuss this. Glover joined the Psychoanalytical Society in 1921 and, by this time, his brother Edward was also active in the work of the Society.

Another future prominent psychoanalyst, Ella Sharpe, was working with the Glovers, and was persuaded to train with Hans Sachs in Berlin.

In 1911, there was a split between the clinic and Society, and the Society was eventually liquidated. The larger share of its endowment in its experience and training was bequeathed to two institutions – the Tavistock Square Clinic for functional nervous disorders and the British Psychoanalytic Society. The majority of the students and staff also moved to the Psychoanalytical Society. Among the students of the Brunswick Square Clinic and the Society had been such future well known psychoanalysts as Mary Chadwick, Ella Sharpe, Nina Searle, Susan Isaacs, Iseult Grant-Duff, Marjorie Brierley, and the Jungian Constance Long.

The impact of World War I

> "The war crumbled the cement of Victorian standards into disused rubble and opened up unmendable fissures in the gilded Edwardian way of life. The political emancipation of women, the equalising tax structure, the consolidation of the working class, the rise of collectivism and state control, the growth of the Labour Party, the changes in dress, manners and public attitudes to questions of morality, all helped to reform the fabric of class and relation." (Holroyd, 1968).

An article in the *Lancet*, September 1917, stated:

> "One of the results of war on the colossal scale of today has been the appearance of military and civilian hospitals and analogous institutions of mental and nervous cases by literally thousands. The welcome sequel has been a quickening of interest from the part of the medical profession as a whole in these types of cases, of which in many instances the medical practitioner was little qualified either by education or by previous experience to take cognizance. The Medical profession, including many of its younger members, has been brought into contact with phases of mental or nervous disturbance to a degree hitherto impossible; has realised its lack of learning, its unfamiliarity with the subject, due in part at least to seriously inadequate teaching; and as a result has determined to acquire information while the occasion continues. An outcome of this revised interest is undoubtedly the expression of dissatisfaction with these risks existing in methods of handling such cases in civilian life. We do not misrepresent the situation when we state that the average neurologist has, as a rule, been preoccupied with the organic nervous disease to the exclusion of functional disease; while the psychiatrist, attached to an institution, has little or no chance of studying, and no incitement to study, mental disease in its early manifestation. In our columns we have repeatedly drawn attention to the inferior position we occupy among the nations in our attitude to psychiatry. But the war is changing things. The problems of 'shell shock' and other new more mysterious illnesses, they are of the every day problems of 'nervous breakdowns'."

The article concluded by discussing a small book, *Shell Shock and its Lessons* by Professor G. Elliot Smith, an anatomist, and T. H. Pear, a psychologist. This was said to show that "mediaeval traditions are still encumbering English psychiatry: indifference, inertia, a lack of knowledge are still all too apparent."

The great inertia of British psychiatry did not survive World War I, though certainly there was conflict between psychiatry and neurology, with neurologists trying to maintain the organic nature of the hysterical disorders in the military population. There had been strenuous opposition to the concept of male hysteria, since hysteria was regarded as 'the female malady' (Showalter, 1987). Extraordinarily violent and sadistic methods for its treatment were used by some neurologists and psychiatrists, but a great number were converted to the use of psychotherapeutic methods and, with admirable efficiency, the army responded to the new situation by creating hospitals for the treatment of these patients and the training of professionals to deal with them.

Maurice Nicoll (Dodgson, 1961, p. 58) wrote in 1917:

> "Our lot is composed of Dr. Morris Craig, Henry Head, Farquhar Buzzard, McDougall, Fernside, Professor Elliot Smith, Bramwell, MacNamara, Millard, Riddoch, and myself and they are, thank the Lord, all as keen as mustard, now this has come to a tussel. But what this really means in the spiritual sense is that the orthodox medical reactionaries have been smashed and psychology has been born. The door is wide open for ever, so I feel that all my talks and dinners and harangues and explanations of the last 8 months have not been in vain. For it was I who got Buzzard to move, and he is the pillar, being a square man."

Indeed, the door was then pushed open, and psychotherapists took their place in the hierarchy of military psychiatrists; the lesson was learnt, though soon forgotten. The official War Office Committee of Inquiry into Shell Shock (1922) recommended that "special instruction should be given to Royal Army Medical Corps Officers in psychoneurosis and psychosis as they occur in war, and selected officers should be encouraged to specialise in these disorders". However, the official history of neurasthenia and war neurosis stated that:

> "special medical officers for the various army centres and neurological centres at the base should be appointed, and the whole scheme for dealing with the subject of psychoneurosis should be co-ordinated by a *consultant neurologist*, who should lay down the lines of treatment and define the scope of the work to be attempted in the forward areas and at the base."

The conflict between neurology and psychology is strongly brought out by the psychologist C. S. Myers, who finally published *Shell Shock in France 1914–1918* in 1940. He did this because he feared the lessons of World War I would be lost and that neurology might again defeat psychology. Myers did magnificent work in recognising the psychological nature of the physical presentation of war stress and was responsible almost single-handedly for setting up a modern system of diagnosis and treatment. He implies, but does not clearly state, that he resigned from his duties in France and returned to England because the neurologists were interfering with his work.

The *Official History* of World War I (Macpherson, 1923) estimates that there was a total of 80 000 psychiatric casualties, of whom 30 000 were received in England, 12 500 of them at the Maudsley. After the war, the Ministry of Pensions had to set up psychiatric clinics to deal with the 65 000 persons who were receiving pensions in 1921, reducing to 50 000 in 1922. This *History* states that simple forms of psychotherapy were the treatment of choice for battle hysteria and neurasthenia, and that only the more severe cases would be returned to Britain. There, many hospitals developed special services, but the most severe cases, which did not then respond quickly to treatment, were referred to Maghull or Springfield Hospitals.

The full history of Maghull Hospital, near Liverpool, where training for the treatment of the psychoneuroses was given between 1917 and 1919 to 67 RAMC, Canadian, and US officers, has not yet been written, though Bernard Hart, Millais Culpin, T. H. Pear, Elliot Smith, and W. H. R. Rivers were trained or worked there under the direction of R. G. Rows. A glimpse of the atmosphere at Maghull is given by Rivers (see Slobodin, 1978, p. 55), who describes it as "a society in which the interpretation of dreams and the discussion of mental conflicts formed the staple subject of conversation". Of the patients, Rivers wrote that "these are men whose minds the Dead have ravished". He is probably the best known of these wartime psychiatrists, through his treatment of Siegfried Sassoon at Craiglockhart, Edinburgh. Sassoon was brought there by his friend, the poet Robert Graves, who had persuaded him to accept treatment instead of having to face a court martial for his refusal to continue to carry out military duties after he had publicly protested by flinging his Military Cross into the River Mersey. Sassoon, who gave the name "Dottyville" to Craiglockhart, wrote that, "my definite approach to mental maturity began with my contact with the mind of Rivers" (Hynes, 1990). Rivers later went on to become the first psychologist to the Royal Flying Corps, where he did highly original research into the stress of flying and, in doing so, took part himself in aerobatic manoeuvres (see below).

Other psychiatrists who contributed to the psychodynamic approach in wartime included William McDougall, David Eder, David Forsyth, Frederick Dillon, C. S. Read (at Netley Hospital), and J. A. Hadfield, who did important work in the use of hypnosis. The physicians and neurologists who supported this new approach included such distinguished names as Henry Head, Farquhar Buzzard, and Aldren Turner.

The post-war period

The immediate post-war years saw the establishment of Ministry of Pensions psychiatric clinics, for which David Forsyth, a psychoanalyst, was a senior psychiatrist. The widespread recognition of the need for out-patient clinics led directly to the founding of the Tavistock Clinic and Cassel Hospital, supported by public figures such as Lord Haig and Lord Dawson of Penn. Farquhar Buzzard and Langdon Brown, future Regius Professors of medicine at Oxford and Cambridge respectively, were members of the management committee of the Cassel; when Buzzard resigned, his place was taken by his brother, General George Buzzard, who took a particular interest in the pig herd! Wartime experiences had edged themselves deeply into the minds of these senior men, who recognised the intolerable strain to which their colleagues and friends had been exposed, and were determined that they should receive both respect and treatment.

Some of these wartime psychiatrists espoused psychoanalysis. The British Psychoanalytical Society was formed soon after the war, replacing the London Psychoanalytical Society, which Jones had wound up because of his conflicts with those members who were attracted to Jung. Jones himself had not been accepted on to the staff of Palace Green Hospital – a wartime temporary psychiatric unit in London – and attributed this to a personal hostility towards him by an influential member of its management committee, based on pre-war rumours about his personal life, which had blocked his appointment to a teaching hospital. Jones was out to re-establish his supremacy in the new society, and clearly drew lines between those whom he was prepared to recognise as psychoanalysts and those whom he was not. Among the latter were Rivers, Hadfield, and William Brown. Yet such men contributed greatly to the acceptance of psychoanalysis, teaching dynamic psychotherapy and influencing the climate of opinion within psychiatry. Bernard Hart did in fact become an Associate Member of the Psychoanalytical Society, but does not seem to have been active in it and always maintained an attitude of objectivity and detachment to psychoanalysis.

The most interesting and significant of this group was W. H. R. Rivers (Slobodin, 1978). His death in 1922 from a strangulated hernia, which occurred over a Bank Holiday weekend, when he was in his rooms at St John's College, Cambridge, and therefore not found for nine hours, was indeed a tragic loss. Rivers made three distinguished careers – in experimental psychology, anthropology, and psychotherapy. Born in 1864, he took his medical degree at St Bartholomew's, showed an early interest in psychiatry, and in 1891 was appointed house physician to the National Hospital, Queen Square. There, he met Henry Head, whose intimate he became, and together they later carried out classic work on the physiology of sensation. He soon became an authority on the physiology of vision, on fatigue, and on the influence of drugs on the capacity for both muscular and mental work. After study under Kraepelin, his work was carried out in the first laboratory for experimental psychology in England, at Cambridge; at one time, he was director both of this laboratory and of the one at University College, London. The classic Head/Rivers experiment – on the effect of severing a peripheral nerve and then minutely studying the return of sensation – led to the important theory of epicritic–protopathic sensation, which still attracts the interest of research workers.

Rivers' second career – as an anthropologist – began in 1898, when he joined the Cambridge Anthropological Expedition to the Torres Straits. This remarkable expedition, which represented the founding of the British School of Anthropology, included three doctors – Rivers, McDougal, and Myers. Rivers himself carried out work on colour vision, and he became aware of how strongly physiological responses were influenced by cultural forces. This led to his wholesale immersion in anthropological research, which made him probably the most distinguished anthropologist in Britain in the early years of the 20th century. He was made an FRS in 1907, and among his students were Radcliffe-Brown, William McDougall, C. S. Myers, Frederick Bartlett, R. G. Thouless, and the Jungian anthropologist-psychotherapist, John Layard. Rivers' wartime experience led him to support much of Freud's theories, though he differed in not attributing such great dynamic force to the sexual instinct. His books, *Instinct and the Unconscious* and *Conflict and Dream*, made clear his independent views on the dynamic functioning of the mind, the nature of the unconscious, and unconscious defence mechanisms. Unfortunately, his work was critically seized upon both by psychoanalysts and their opponents, and it is in retrospect that we can see how Rivers' anthropological experience gave him a perspective on psychodynamics which was lacking in Freud and Jones. It was Jones in particular who attacked Rivers in critical reviews, perhaps motivated by feelings of jealousy and competitiveness, since Rivers was an FRS – a distinction that Jones longed for, but never achieved – had a tremendous reputation as an academic, and occupied an important position at Cambridge. He was the establishment figure that Jones longed to be, but never became, other than in the restricted world of psychoanalysis. Yet it was Rivers who, probably more than anyone else, made psychoanalytic thinking acceptable to a wide circle of influential persons – psychiatrists, psychologists, and anthropologists.

William McDougall, who went on to achieve great fame both in England and America, where he became Professor of Psychology at Harvard, had also been active in wartime psychiatry. He had a good working knowledge of psychoanalysis, but again differed from Freud in his own theory of instincts. For him, these were purposive, 'Hormic', goal-directed behaviour – the energies of man. In some way, contemporary psychoanalysis had moved from wholesale support of Freud's version of instinct theory to seeking a much wider basis for motivation as the driving force for human development and behaviour (Klein, 1976).

J. A. Hadfield and William Brown both had distinguished careers in psychology and psychotherapy; both were prolific authors and influential teachers. After his wartime service, Hadfield was appointed in 1920 as Lecturer and University Psychotherapist at the University of Birmingham. A year or two later, he moved to London and joined the staff of the Tavistock Clinic, as well as lecturing at Bethlem on psychopathology. In 1931, he became Lecturer in Psychopathology and Mental Hygiene at the University of London, holding this appointment until his retirement in 1958. At the Tavistock Clinic, he was Director of Studies for many years, and as part of his programme, brought Jung and McDougall to give lectures. Many psychiatrists went to Hadfield for training analysis, including W. R. Bion, who later wrote scathingly about this experience. The son of a missionary, Hadfield was born in the Loyalty Isles, South Pacific. He was a religious man and tried to combine psychodynamics with an exploration and understanding of spiritual values, which caused him to be regarded by psychoanalysts as a less effectual psychotherapist. However, J. R. Rees (1967), then Director of the Tavistock, wrote that "Hadfield was a leader in every way. Not only . . . one of the great pioneers of analytic psychotherapy [but] also one of its outstanding practitioners" (Rees, 1967).

William Brown was educated at Oxford and did postgraduate work in Germany, studying mathematics, classics, physiology, and philosophy. He was a pioneer in experimental psychology, working with McDougal, Cyril Burt, Flugel, and Spearman in the assessment of intelligence. He became head of the Psychological Department at King's College, London in 1908, and was appointed Reader in Psychology in 1914. During the war, he worked both at Maghull and at Craiglockhart. He succeeded McDougall as Wilde Reader in Mental Philosophy at Oxford and founded the Institute of Experimental Psychology there. The person who had endowed the Wilde Readership specified that the holder should not engage in experimental psychology, but Brown brushed that opposition aside and established the beginnings of the subject at Oxford. "Brown was at all times an enthusiast and so tended to move away now and again from the trends supported by his contemporaries; for example for some time he placed more reliance on the use of suggestion than on the psychoanalytical approach and diagnosis, and after a staunch support of Freudian principles revolted against their over-emphasis on materialism'' (*Munk's Roll*, 1968). His early writings, however, represent clear support of psychoanalysis, at a time when support of persons like himself in distinguished academic positions was sorely needed. However, Brown too suffered at the hands of psychoanalysts, who reviewed his books in very scathing terms.

While McDougall and Brown established psychodynamic psychology at Oxford, John MacCurdy did so at Cambridge. An American, MacCurdy had been with the American armed forces in World War I and trained at Maghull. He wrote an important book, *The War Neurosis* (1918), which showed how officers and other ranks were exposed to different types of stresses and had different expectations of themselves as to how they should behave under stress; these factors affected the form of breakdown that they respectively incurred. MacCurdy had worked with Hoch in New York and was an avid student of psychoanalysis before the war; he came to England in 1922, having already been President of the American Psychopathological Association. In 1926, he became a Fellow of Corpus Christi College and University Reader in Psychopathology. His books *The Psychology of Emotion* and *Problems in Dynamic Psychiatry* also received savage criticism from psychoanalysts, not least because he was impressed by Trigant Burrow, whose views on Narcissism and the primary mother–child relationship anticipated much later work in psychoanalysis and have never been fully acknowledged. MacCurdy had an important influence on the study of psychology at Cambridge, and through Sir Samuel Hoare was appointed Psychological Consultant to the Royal Air Force; he was active in World War II in the field of psychological warfare.

Conflict in the 1920s

The aftermath of the war saw much suffering, many brave men broken down by the stress of warfare, and many left cruelly and stupidly treated by neurologists, who saw it as their task to force distressed soldiers, by whatever means they chose to apply, to give up their symptoms. Psychoanalysis had some strong and influential opponents, including Charles Mercier, a colleague of Hughlings Jackson, who wrote:

> ''It is true that psychoanalysis is past its perihelion, and is rapidly retreating in to the dark and silent depths from which it emerged. It is well that it should be systematically described before it goes to join pounded toads and sour milk in the limbo of discarded remedies.'' (Mercier, 1916)

He warned that the purpose of psychoanalysts was to get hold of children and undermine the foundations of their morality; it was the latest manifestation of ''the rottenness of German teaching in mental disease''. He proclaimed himself the lonely prophet in the wilderness, who had been crying out to oppose the credulity with which German psychiatry was gulped down, but he was now justified. To combat the prejudice that it was a German-inspired method, Stoddart (1915) pointed out that Freud was a ''Pure Jew''.

J. Shaw Bolton, was the first Professor of Psychiatry to be appointed in Britain: he held the chair at Leeds and was Director of the West Riding Mental Hospital, Wakefield. In 1926, he published "The myth of the unconscious mind" in the *Journal of Mental Science*. Bolton used the writing of Freud, Jones, Stoddart, and Wittels to make his case against the "seething mass of foulness published by the greater Freudians". He lampooned methods of dream interpretation and concluded:

> "I have now completed a task which, in spite of its repugnant nature, I have felt it my duty to perform . . . this insidious poison which is being instilled into the minds of the young by countless psychoanalysts, is doing untold harm."

Two fellows of the Royal College of Physicians, Sir Bryan Donkin, a prison psychiatrist, and Sir Robert Armstrong Jones, a former Superintendent at Claybury and later Lord Chancellor's Visitor in Lunacy, also strongly opposed psychoanalysis. They gave evidence at the Committee on Psychoanalysis of the British Medical Association (BMA), while the *History of the Royal College of Physicians of London* (Cook, 1972) records questions as to why certain Fellows were making attacks against other Fellows – presumably Stoddart in particular. This is the only time psychoanalysis was referred to by the College. Another distinguished Lord Chancellor's Visitor in Lunacy was Sir James Crichton-Browne, a close friend of Hughlings Jackson. In his "Notes on psychoanalysis and psychotherapy" in the *Lancet* of 1920, he issued a milder, but still firm reproof, and echoing Mercier's outspoken views:

> "I would acknowledge first our debt to psychoanalysis for having used us to take a more psychical and a less material view of insanity, and for having instituted on the importance of tracing back to its early manifestations. However, notwithstanding the diligent efforts made to acclimatise it, [Freudianism] will, I feel sure, never take root in this country."

Psychoanalysis, though, did not lack its own knighted supporters. Farquhar Buzzard, Langdon-Brown, and Henry Head supported it, all having been converted from an organic viewpoint by the experience of the war. Head wrote sympathetically about the diagnosis of hysteria and the need to understand the underlying dynamic and mental mechanisms that gave rise to the symptoms, while Buzzard was a great supporter of the Cassel Hospital. In his 1920 presidential address to the Section of Psychiatry of the Royal Society of Medicine, Buzzard described psychoanalysis as being "as necessary for the study of psychiatry as accurate and patient history-taking is necessary for the elucidation of medical problems of organic origin". However, his approach was really to equate it with psychotherapy in general, and it is doubtful how well acquainted he was with current developments in psychoanalysis itself. Walter Langdon-Brown, a physician at St Bartholomew's, was a greatly respected teacher of medicine. His essays *Thus We are Men* (Langdon-Brown, 1938) are impressive in their depth of understanding of human nature and their erudition; they reveal a man of outstanding intellectual and moral calibre.

Within the field of psychology, Cyril Burt, the first Professor of Psychology in the University of London, was a pioneer in the acceptance of psychoanalytic theory, and encouraged its teaching. In his department, this was carried out principally by J. C. Flugel, a lifelong friend of Burt since they had been students together in Germany. Flugel had a very distinguished career, both in academic psychology and in psychoanalysis, and Burt himself pioneered a dynamic approach to the treatment of juvenile delinquents. The controversies that have later clouded Burt's reputation should not diminish such great achievements.

Hearnshaw (1979), in describing the influences shaping Burt's psychology, points to the work of James Ward and of G. F. Stout. Regarding Stout, Hearnshaw states: "Mind, in other words, was active not passively receptive, as it had been conceived in the older associationism." It was this doctrine, set out in Stout's *Analytical Psychology* (1896) and *Manual of Psychology* (1898) and widely accepted in Britain, that was largely responsible for the cool reception by British psychologists of Pavlovian and behaviouristic ideas before World War II, and on the other hand for their receptiveness to both Gestalt psychology and psychoanalysis.

The BMA Psychoanalysis Committee

In 1926, at the Annual Representative Meeting of the Association, it was agreed "That the Council be instructed to investigate the subject of psychoanalysis and report on the same". Isabel Hutton, who represented the Medical Women's Federation, was a member of that Committee and described how, at that time, the medical profession was hardly less ignorant than the public. However, as there was an increasing interest in psychoanalysis, and since medical opinions on it were so conflicting, anxious relatives and patients sought in vain for information about this new method of treatment. *The Times* (8 January 1926) and other newspapers were clamouring for a medical investigation of psychoanalysis, since both the Royal College of Physicians and the Commissioners in Lunacy had discussed the matter, but had decided to do nothing about it. The International Council of Mental Hygiene had appointed a committee, but nothing came of that either, so that no authoritative statement could be given to the public.

The significant members of this Committee were Ernest Jones and H. Godwin Baynes, who represented the Jungians, J. R. Rees for the Tavistock, and T. A. Ross for the Cassel. William Brown and R. G. Gordon, both psychotherapists but not psychoanalysts, were also members, and Gordon became the Honorary Secretary. The Chairman was Dr R. Langdon-Down, a specialist in mental deficiency. Isabel Hutton devised a questionnaire which was sent to 157 practitioners, and 78 replies were received. Strong opposition to psychoanalysis came from Dr Peter McBride, who compared psychoanalysis to Christian Science, and Dr A. Wohlgemuth, who had published a book on the subject and purported to show that psychoanalysis had no scientific merit. Isabel Hutton wrote:

> "It was clear that the temper of the Committee had changed throughout the years for, begun in an atmosphere of fierce opposition, it ended in something like complete conversion to Freud's theories. This metamorphosis was entirely due to Dr Ernest Jones and the manner in which he conducted what might well be called a one-man defence of Freudian psychoanalysis.

> It was impressive to watch his masterly exposition of Freud's theories as, without persuasion, suggestion or charm, he proceeded to prove his belief in their truth. He spoke throughout with a clarity I have never heard surpassed, with authority and obvious sincerity. A spare upright figure, his brooding, ivory mask pierced by glowing eyes, he never missed a point or lost his calm, and respect for him grew as time went on." (Hutton, 1960)

When published, the report seemed to end medical criticism, and both the public and press gradually lost interest in the subject. The Committee acknowledged that psychoanalysis was an authentic form of treatment and that the term should not be used for any other technique or theory, apart from those described by Freud. This result was very welcome to the British Psychoanalytic Society.

The *Journal of Mental Science* (1929, vol. 75, pp. 131–132) refers to a Psychotherapy and Psychopathology Sub-Committee of the Royal Medico-Psychological Association:

> "the ultimate objective of which is the dissemination of knowledge of psychopathology and psychotherapy . . . [it] promotes the foundation of Study Groups and puts individual workers in touch with each other; initiates and administers schemes of research; cites and classifies current knowledge and teaching, and makes reports thereon, and does all in its power to stimulate interest in these subjects."

Its Honorary Secretary was Dr J. Ernest Nicole, and the local London group met under the leadership of Dr Margery Franklin, a pioneer psychoanalyst. However, this subcommittee does not seem to have made much impact. Nicole was the author of a significant textbook of psychopathology, which went through many editions; he had a good theoretical grasp both of psychoanalysis and of the other competing schools of psychopathology. From 1937 to 1953, he was Superintendent of Winwick Hospital in Lancashire, and received the OBE for his organisation of rehabilitation programmes during World War II. He lectured in psychopathology at Liverpool University (*British Medical Journal*, 1963).

The Tavistock Clinic

Hugh Crichton-Miller founded the Tavistock Clinic in 1920 and remained its director until 1934 (Anonymous, 1961). Born in 1887 in Genoa, where his father was a Protestant minister, and living there until he was 12, he was brought up in a cosmopolitan society, without the insularity of the ordinary Briton. His schooling and medical training took place in Edinburgh and he was fluent in both French and Italian. During World War I, he was officer-in-charge of functional nervous cases at the 21st General Hospital, Alexandria, and in 1917 was appointed consultant in shell-shock to the Fourth London General Hospital. Impressed by these experiences, he decided to found a clinic for the treatment of functional nervous disorders, and soon attracted to it a number of like-minded persons. Crichton-Miller was always an eclectic, both a supporter of psychoanalysis and an advocate of holistic medicine. He insisted that the patient should have a full physical examination, and for a while was an enthusiast for the theories of 'focal sepsis' and of endocrine disorders in neurosis. However,

Crichton-Miller's eventual resignation as medical director and his replacement by J. R. Rees seems to have been related to demands by the staff that a less eclectic approach be adopted, and possibly also to rivalry with Hadfield, who was director of studies and who took many staff members and other psychiatrists into didactic short-term analysis. Bion (1985) refers to Hadfield as "Dr. Feel it in the Past" (p. 34).

The history of the Tavistock Clinic has been described by Henry Dicks (1970), but a more sociological view was presented by Miller & Rose (1988) and Rose (1985). They placed the Tavistock in the setting of the mental hygiene movement that followed World War I, where the 'new psychology' began to present normality and pathology in terms of 'adjustment' and 'maladjustment' – a new development that moved away from constitutional and reductive schemes. The Tavistock approach was more important not only in the treatment of adults but in making the general public more aware of the significance of childhood and of the influence of the family on the developing mind. It was very significant in the development of the child guidance movement – a crucial element in the network of the mental hygiene movement, through which the emotional lives of citizens were to become matters of public concern, expert knowledge, and professional guidance. The family was to be maintained, not as a legal duty, nor as a moral imperative, but as a means of personal contentment and fulfilment.

Despite the recognition which the Tavistock achieved as a focus of progressive mental hygiene and as the main centre of psychodynamic psychotherapy in Britain, it never received academic recognition: there was no affiliation to the University of London as a specialised postgraduate institute, which was in no small part due to the opposition of Edward Mapother, Professor of Psychiatry at the Maudsley Hospital. He irrationally opposed recognition of the Tavistock, as if he feared that it might in some way compete with the Maudsley (Dicks, 1970).

The Maudsley itself opened a psychotherapy unit, and this was welcomed by J. R. Rees, who wrote that "no rivalries, save those that are friendly, would ever be allowed to spoil work that is so much needed. Co-operation might, in any case, almost be said to be 'the watchword' of psychology." Rees maintained friendly relationships with Mapother, despite the latter's energetic rejection of psychodynamic psychology – an attitude which contributed to the unfortunate division between the organic psychiatry of psychosis and the psychotherapeutic approach to neurosis. In his last illness, "as a good Catholic", Mapother apologised to Rees for his opposition to the Tavistock, and expressed his regret. It may be that Mapother was envious of the number of postgraduates and overseas visitors that came to the Tavistock, rather than to the Maudsley; he seems to have needed to have people under his control, and, as he could not establish this over the Tavistock, opened his own psychotherapy unit.

After succeeding Crichton-Miller, in 1933, Rees threw himself with great energy into developing the Tavistock and making links with other disciplines. He was active in the National Council for Mental Hygiene, and in World War II was appointed Director of Army Psychiatry. Together with Ronald Hargreaves as Assistant Director, he was responsible for fashioning a dynamic approach to the psychological problems of wartime. The achievements of the Tavistock staff in setting up schemes for officer selection, for the rehabilitation of battle casualties and of returned prisoners of war, and for studies on morale were very significant (Trist & Murray, 1990).

A great deal of the post-war reputation of the Tavistock Clinic rests on John Bowlby's achievements. His work on maternal deprivation, with a later extension of psychodynamic development psychology through the combination of ethology and psychodynamics, has received worldwide recognition. He has also been seen as a representative of 'object relations theory' – a particularly British development with psychoanalysis. Through this, developmental psychoanalytic psychology takes far more account of the experience of the infant in relation to its caregivers in its earliest years of life and has moved away from the instinctual-drive theory of classic psychoanalysis. The internalisation of aspects of the relationship between the infant and the caregivers, the process of projection of affects onto adults, and the re-internalisation of these experiences, all build up the infant's internal representational world. Within this internal world, there are representations both of the self and of others, which are necessarily primitive to start with – split between good and bad images. Over time, these separate representations come together and form the beginning of a more integrated world. Although much of this theory is connected with the work of Melanie Klein and undoubtedly is greatly influenced by her, this separate development characterised British psychoanalysis during the 1920s and '30s, and might well have taken place without her presence.

A contributor to this line of thinking, who influenced Bowlby considerably, was Ian Suttie. He was a leading member of the Tavistock staff and attempted to make a synthesis of anthropology, biology, and psychology in *The Origins of Love and Hate* (1988). Suttie opposed a good deal of the then contemporary psychoanalytic psychology, but, in contrast, emphasised the importance of both the relationship between the infant and mother and of that between children and their peers. His wider-ranging psychology made a bridge between social and individual psychology, played down the primacy of the instinctual drives, and strongly opposed the concept of the death instinct. Suttie seems to have been regarded as the most original of the Tavistock staff, and his untimely death in 1936 contributed to the subsequent neglect of his work; he saw neurosis as being very much based on separation anxiety.

Separation anxiety is closely related to grief, and the 1920s and '30s was a time in which grief began to be studied deeply. In the aftermath of the war, almost every family in the country was touched by grief from the loss of a member. The country as a whole was deeply aware both of the loss of so many outstanding members of its youthful generation and – unconsciously – of that of the structure of pre-war society. The foundations of emotional security in religion, social and class structure, and developing economic prosperity were lost. Enormous social changes took place in the 1920s, which was a time of economic distress and social unrest; family structure had to cope with the new aspirations of women, who wished to continue the great emancipation from household drudgery they had experienced through the full employment of the war years. Thus, the country was ready for the psychological issues of separation and mourning (Newcombe & Lerner, 1982).

In Austria, Freud was exploring mourning and melancholia, while Melanie Klein, who came to England in 1926, and other child analysts were making new discoveries about early psychic life, which included separation anxiety. Klein soon established a strong following in the Psychoanalytical Society, where she had been sponsored by the Stracheys and by Ernest Jones, who asked her to analyse his own children. It has been said of Klein that she did for pathological mourning what Freud did for other neurotic illnesses: pathological adult grief could now be linked with childhood. In the 1930s, the eclectic school, partly represented by the Tavistock Clinic, and psychoanalysts within the Psychoanalytic Society both emphasised object relationships. This British school followed a largely separate developmental line from that of the Viennese. However, there was a definite cleavage between the Tavistock and the Psychoanalytical Society, which seems to have been largely the work of Ernest Jones. He felt the need to maintain strict control of psychoanalysis, and therefore forbade members of the Psychoanalytical Society to work at the Tavistock – a ban only removed after World War II. Jones would most certainly not have attended the series of lectures that were given by Jung at the Tavistock in 1936. Wilfred Bion, who was then a relatively obscure member of the Tavistock staff, attended these lectures together with his own analytical patient, Samuel Beckett (Anzieu, 1989).

Among the pioneering work carried out at the Tavistock were the explorations into psychosomatic medicine by Eric Wittkower and A. T. M. Wilson. Wittkower worked in dermatology at St Bartholomew's, Wilson on peptic ulcer at the Royal Free Hospital. Research in the children's department in 1939 by Dr Alan Maberley on the results of child guidance showed that 70% of children followed up had significantly improved and had maintained that improvement (Maberley & Sturge, 1939).

The post-war history of the Tavistock represents the end of the period of eclectic psychotherapy and the full dominance of psychoanalysis. The 'invisible college' of Tavistock staff who had been active and successful in wartime psychiatry came together in 1945 and, under the chairmanship of Bion, made a successful take-over bid. Long-standing members of the pre-war Tavistock staff eventually resigned, and the new clinic began to take shape. There was a tremendous enthusiasm for a psychodynamic form of social psychiatry which would make the most of the valuable lessons learned during wartime. With a great emphasis on group psychotherapy, under the leadership of Bion, Sutherland, and Ezriel, such interest in social psychology was continued after the creation of the National Health Service (NHS) in 1948 by the establishment of the separate Tavistock Institute of Human Relations. This body, which remained outside the NHS, continued to explore issues in social psychology and became a research institute, working in industry and financing itself.

The Maudsley

The story of the foundation of the Maudsley Hospital is described in Chapter 4, but a great deal of its early history is connected with the personality and work of Edward Mapother. Born in Ireland in 1881, he joined the staff of Long Grove Hospital at the age of 27 in 1908. At the time, this was a very progressive hospital, where there was much interest in Janet and Freud, and one of his colleagues was Bernard Hart; a critical climate of care included an interest in the neuroses. In 1917 Mapother came to Maghull Hospital for training in the treatment of war neurosis; in 1919, after demobilisation, he returned to the Maudsley Hospital, which was still under the control of the Ministry of Pensions.

Mapother had shown an interest in psychoanalysis, and some of his early papers were influenced by it. In his first annual report, he wrote that the

Maudsley "encourages unprejudiced trial of every form of treatment", and in the section for 1923 headed "Psychotherapy", stated that:

> "all forms of this have been practised here. Ordinary suggestion, persuasion and re-education, superficial analysis, exploration under light hypnosis and complete psychoanalysis. Though I find myself incapable of excepting all the alleged facts of any school of psychoanalysis, or all the concepts proposed by them, yet there is no doubt of the great advance which the intensive methods introduced by these schools have made in their understanding of cases, nor is there any doubt that in certain cases results are achieved by psychoanalysis which cannot be otherwise obtained, whatever the exact explanation may be." (Unpublished annual report, 1923)

In the report for 1927–31, Mapother said that:

> "little of mental illness can be dealt with by drugs. Most of out patient treatment resolves itself into direct psychotherapy and attempts to modify the psychological environment . . . Recent increases of staff here have provided more adequately for such treatment. Four of the junior members of the staff at present are adherents of the psychoanalytic school undergoing the recognised training. Whatever difference there may be about underlying theory, probably all would agree about the rarity with which psychoanalysis in the strict sense can be carried out with hospital cases . . . in the course of training for such intensive study probably much is learnt that proves of the practical value in connection with simpler methods. Personally I feel that if psychopathology is to rise like other branches of biology from the anecdotal to the scientific level, and if psychotherapy is to become rational and define its limitations then uncontrolled clinical findings must clearly be supplemented by observations as to the effect of standard experiences under experimental conditions capable of repetition."

Mapother published a paper "The early treatment of the psychosis and psychoneurosis" in the *British Medical Journal* in 1928, but there is no further mention of his attitudes to psychotherapy in the annual reports. However, Aubrey Lewis (1969) quotes him as writing "the time is past for crying that Freud's findings as to the content of the neurosis and psychosis are horrid . . . and for substituting witticism for criticism". Nevertheless, he allowed himself in subsequent years to combine the two on occasion. In 1936, he made proposals for reorganisation that eventually were accepted: six of the 20 senior doctors were to be part-time psychotherapists.

Mapother made an appreciation of Freud's work for the memorial meeting of the Royal Society of Medicine held shortly after Freud's death. In it, he acclaimed Freud's genius for "fertility and hypothesis and the penetration with which he discerned analogies and connotation where they had never before been explicitly noted . . . he brought to psychology and psychiatry more of the imagination of the great artist than of the solid objectivity and rigid logic of the scientist". Lewis says that Mapother had a generally friendly attitude towards the Tavistock, but that at the same time, he did not see any reason for encouraging the London County Council to give the Tavistock Clinic financial support.

Significant studies of psychotherapy at the Maudsley were published by W. Lindesay Neustatter in 1935 and 1936; he became psychotherapist at the

Maudsley in 1931, and in 1938 was appointed physician in psychological medicine at Queen Mary's Hospital for the East End as well as to a similar post at the Royal Northern Hospital in 1948. Neustatter stated (1935) that "while psychotherapeutic methods are so time consuming, they seem to me to be the only system which is ultimately fair to the very considerable bulk of patients who do need intensive treatment"; the maximum number of interviews was three per week, each of three-quarters of an hour.

C. P. Blacker was a consultant at the Maudsley with a reputation for military discipline and a strong opinion on eugenics, but the preface to his book *Human Values in Psychological Medicine* (1933) states:

> "It will be difficult to exaggerate the influence which, in the last 30 years, has been exerted upon psychological medicine by the writings of Freud. Every practitioner in this specialty who is under 35 years of age would probably acknowledge that his outlook on psychopathology had been deeply influenced by the writer, and many under 55 would have meant that their views had been radically changed by him."

He said that he could not consider himself a psychoanalyst, as he had not had analysis, "But my debt to the genius Freud is no less great for this". He concluded the preface with:

> "My intellectual debt to the genius of Freud is immense. In fact to him is largely attributable the responsibility to my having taken up medicine at all. My views on psychology and in fact my whole outlook on life have been much influenced by his writings."

Under Aubrey Lewis in post-war years, the unit that eventually became a psychotherapy department expanded considerably. S. H. Foulkes taught out-patient group analytic psychotherapy to generations of trainees; W. Hoffer tried to inspire registrars with psychoanalytic thinking; Henri Rey contributed a unique combination of Piaget, psychoanalysis, endocrinology, and neurophysiology, while Heinz Wolff and Murray Jackson were important teachers for generations of Maudsley trainees. Analytical psychology was represented by E. A. Bennet and Robert Hobson.

Psychoanalysis and the Bloomsbury Group

The brilliant group of mainly Cambridge intellectuals, many of them members of the Apostles – that exclusive group of 'brothers' who regarded themselves as the elite of Cambridge intellectual life – had many connections with what later became the Bloomsbury Group. Their intellectual mentor was the philosopher G. E. Moore, whose *Principia Ethica* was their bible, though it was the personality of Moore and his direct influence that was as or more influential than his writings.

Moore dominated the Apostles in the years between the end of the century and World War I. Bertrand Russell, Maynard Keynes, Lytton Strachey, and James Strachey were among those who acknowledged his leadership, though Russell and Moore had an uneasy and basically hostile personal relationship. Moore's intellectual and emotional honesty was outstanding and it was this, together with his writings, that set the tone for his followers. This resulted in the practice of a fierce form of introspection regarding their emotions, especially in their relationships with one another. This replacement of the religious 'conscience' – the doctrine that the aim of self-examination is to establish the relationship between the individual and his maker – by 'consciousness', which for this group was the privilege and duty of the individual fully to be aware of his reasons for acting, was a significant part of their revolt against their Victorian forebears. Moore proposed that personal affection and aesthetic enjoyment were the only true goods in human experience and the only genuine justification of the performance of duty. This represented a direct challenge to the Victorian parents of his own Edwardian group, who saw evidence of emotional impoverishment and lack of personal intimacy in their patients.

Moore's form of introspection did not extend beyond the conscious and pre-conscious aspects of mind, and there is no evidence that he was interested in or influenced by the psychoanalytic model of the mind. He had faith that human rationality could endow affective life with rational traits, and that emotion could be controlled and educated. He himself was of a shy nature and his emotional life remained under strict control, until his eventual happy marriage at the age of 43 in 1916. He had had the courage to present a paper to the Apostles in 1894 entitled, "Shall we take delight in crushing our roses?", in which he discussed his own sexual experience, gently alluding to masturbation and his own virginity (Levy, 1979). Moore came from a Quaker and evangelical background, as did many of his fellow Apostles, and retained much of the morality of his ancestry. He was well aware and apparently tolerant of the 'higher sodomy' that became a leading characteristic of the Apostles in the years leading up to World War I. This note had been largely introduced by Lytton Strachey who, with Maynard Keynes, were the leaders of this group, which included the future psychoanalyst and translator of Freud, James Strachey. James Strachey was deeply in love with Rupert Brooke, who was not a member of the Apostles. However, Brooke was a central figure of a rival, more heterosexual group, the Neo-Pagans, who pursued a more athletic and tough-minded style of life than the Apostles; H. Godwin Baynes, the most distinguished of early Jungian analysts, was one of them.

The influence of psychoanalysis on the intellectual life of Bloomsbury was not deep. Keynes described them as "intellectually pre-Freudian", breathing a purer air than that of Freud and Marx. They knew of Freud's work through Leonard Woolf, who had reviewed *The Psychopathology of Everyday Life* in 1914 and who, impressed by this, went on to read *The Interpretation of Dreams*. Lytton Strachey's *Elizabeth and Essex*, dedicated to James and Alix Strachey, was considerably influenced by psychoanalytic ideas transmitted to him by James, and Freud wrote to praise Lytton Strachey for this aspect of his work.

James and Alix Strachey became psychoanalysts in the early 1920s, followed later by Virginia Woolf's younger brother Adrian and his wife Karen, who had been a philosopher in the Bergson tradition. Bloomsbury had to know about psychoanalysis because it was in intellectual vogue, but they rejected the deterministic and reductionistic views that they both thought and felt it represented, especially regarding art and aesthetics. Roger Fry and Clive Bell, the group's most influential writers on art, publicly opposed psychoanalytic doctrines. Virginia Woolf herself, the most central Bloomsbury figure, the elder sister of Adrian, never sought psychoanalytic help for her severe manic-depressive illness, which Leonard was largely responsible for managing. This is remarkable, for the Hogarth Press, founded by Leonard in order to provide Virginia with occupation while recovering from psychotic episodes, became the official publishers of psychoanalysis in English. Virginia Woolf, however, avoided reading Freud for many years. Her early attitude to psychoanalysis was that it represented an unbearable intrusion into personal privacy, for even the private realm of illness should remain veiled. The psychiatrist Charlotte Wolff recounts a visit to Virginia Woolf in 1935 in which, after tea, Virginia suggested that they talk while sitting back to back, as it was easier for her to relax that way. Charlotte Wolff was asked what she thought of Freudian psychoanalysis, and she spoke of the help that she had received from Jungian analysis. Virginia Woolf's response was, "I have misgivings about psychiatry" (Wolff, 1980, p. 147). Eventually in 1939, in *The Leaning Tower*, she effected a reconciliation with Freud: the Tower is the place of the writer in society, the writer's position in the world. In the 20th century, this had become a leaning tower, for writers were no longer firmly and unconsciously rooted in a stable society and had therefore begun to write about themselves, showing what she called "great egotism", telling unpleasant truths about themselves "with the help of Dr. Freud".

Virginia Woolf's treatment at the hands of Sir George Savage, and later of Sir Maurice Craig, had consisted of the very undynamic Weir–Mitchell regime of heavy feeding, removal from stress, and enforced rest. The only one of her medical attendants who was influenced by psychoanalysis was Sir Henry Head, who, however, was only consulted once about her. He had been recommended by Roger Fry, as both Fry and Head came from a Quaker background (Trombley, 1981). Head was a close friend of W. H. R. Rivers, and in his writings showed a sympathetic grasp of Freud's work on the unconscious and the concept of repression. Head, who became a Fellow of the Royal Society, was one of the most distinguished leaders of British neurology; his contact with psychotherapy came as a result of his experience in World War I in the treatment of shell-shock.

The connection between the Hogarth Press and psychoanalysis was through Ernest Jones and James Strachey. The International Psychoanalytic Press, founded to publish works in English, had collapsed and the Hogarth Press was henceforth to publish the "International Psychoanalytic Library", which led eventually to the monumental Standard Edition of Freud's work, occupying James and Alix Strachey for over 25 years in the task of translation and editing. James Strachey, the analyst of Donald Winnicott, wrote a classic paper on the theory of interpretation. His correspondence with Alix, who was living in Berlin while undergoing analysis with Karl Abraham, includes a lively portrait of Melanie Klein as a passionate dancer in the nightclubs of Berlin, once dressed as Cleopatra with a deep cleavage (Meisel & Kendrick, 1986). Adrian Stephen became Scientific Secretary of the Psycho-Analytic Society, while his wife Karen gave the first lectures to Cambridge medical students on psychoanalysis, published in book form as *The Wish to Fall Ill.*

Leonard Woolf himself, despite his claim to a deep knowledge of Freud, did not display either in his life or his writings on politics or communal psychology that this was the case. However, he remained a strong supporter of the psychoanalytic publishing enterprise.

An interesting vignette on the place of psychoanalysis in British intellectual life is provided by the distinguished analyst Roger Money-Kyrle. In his autobiographical note (1978), he describes how he first made contact with psychoanalysis through an analysis with Ernest Jones in about 1920. After a while, he moved to Vienna for academic work and continued his analysis with Freud. In Vienna, he met Frank Ramsay the mathematician, an important member of the Apostles group, Lionel Penrose, later Professor of Genetics in London University, who became a Fellow of the Royal Society and a member of the Psycho-Analytical Society, and the future Professor Sir Lewis Namier, all being secretly analysed! Another prominent intellectual who became closely connected with psychoanalysis was A. G. Tansley, Professor of Botany at Cambridge, who wrote an influential book, *The New Psychology*, which was an exposition of Freud's work. Tansley also became a Fellow of the Royal Society.

Psychoanalysis and the NHS

There was a considerable expansion in psychodynamic resources following the creation of the NHS. Since then, psychoanalysts and analytical psychologists have joined with psychiatric colleagues in the committees of the Royal College of Psychiatrists and in the Psychotherapy Sub-Committee of the Joint Committee on Higher Psychiatric Training to supervise psychodynamic training in all regions. Consultant psychotherapists and consultants with special interest in psychotherapy now train senior registrars and organise psychotherapy services throughout Britain. Thus, the development of psychodynamic psychotherapy is no longer solely dependent on the training institutions (Institute of Psychoanalysis, Society of Analytical Psychology, the British Association of Psychotherapists, the London Centre for Psychotherapy, and the Institute of Group Analysis) outside the NHS, which itself cannot possibly replace the training these institutions provide. The Association of Psychoanalytic Psychotherapists now provides a forum for psychotherapists working in the NHS, and is emerging as a powerful force in foreseeing the needs for psychotherapy and in planning for the future. The growth of the psychodynamic movement is shown by the foundation of two journals in recent years, *Psychoanalytic Psychotherapy* and the *British Journal of Psychotherapy*. The psychotherapy training institutions have made considerable progress towards establishing agreed standards of training and practice, under the aegis of the Standing Conference on Psychotherapy. However, while the psychodynamic movement is firmly established in British psychiatry, it has not yet received academic recognition or been granted an adequate share of research facilities. Few senior academic posts exist, though the recent establishment of a Chair in Psychotherapy at the University of Warwick and a full-time Chair of Psychoanalysis at University College, London may presage further developments.

This contribution to the place of the psychodynamic movement in British psychiatry is an outline of future work, which may well be amplified by others.

References

ANONYMOUS (1961) *Hugh Crichton-Miller 1877–1959. A Personal Memoir by his Friends and Family.* Dorchester: Longmans, Friary Press.

ANZIEU, D. (1989) Beckett. *International Review of Psychoanalysis*, **16**, 163–169.
BION, W. R. (1985) *All My Sins Remembered. Another Part of a Life*. Abingdon: Fleetwood Press.
BLACKER, C. P. (1933) *Human Values in Psychological Medicine*. Oxford: Oxford University Press.
BOLL, T. E. (1962) May Sinclair and the Medico-Psychology Clinic of London. *Proceedings of the American Philosophical Society*, **106**, 310–326.
BOLTON, J. S. (1926) The myth of the unconscious mind. *Journal of Mental Science*, **72**, 25–38.
BOYLE, H. A. (1922) The ideal clinic for the treatment of nervous and borderline cases. *Proceedings of the Royal Society of Medicine*, **15**, 39–48.
BRITISH MEDICAL JOURNAL (1963) J. E. Nicole (obituary). *British Medical Journal*, *i*.
BROME, V. (1979) *Havelock Ellis Philosopher of Sex*. Manchester: Carcanet.
CARRE, M. (1949) *Phases of Thought in England*. Oxford: Oxford University Press.
CLARKE, M. J. (1981) The rejection of psychological approaches to mental disorders in late nineteenth century British psychiatry. In *Madhouses, Mad-Doctors and Madmen* (ed. A. Scull). London: Athlone Press.
CRICHTON-BROWNE, J. (1920) Notes on psychoanalysis and psychotherapy. *Lancet*, *i*, 1218–1229.
DICKS, H. V. (1970) *50 Years of the Tavistock Clinic*. London: Routledge & Kegan Paul.
GOULD, A. (1986) *The Founders of Psychic Research*. London: Routledge & Kegan Paul.
HART, B. (1910) In *Subconscious Phenomena* (ed. H. Munsterberg). Boston: R. G. Badger.
—— (1927) *Psychopathology*. Cambridge: Cambridge University Press.
HEARNSHAW, L. S. (1979) *Cyril Burt Psychiatrist*. London: Hodder & Stoughton.
HENDERSON, D. K. (1964) *The Evolution of Psychiatry in Scotland*. Edinburgh: E. & S. Livingstone.
HOBMAN, J. B. (1945) *David Eder, Memoirs of a Modern Pioneer*. London: Gollancz.
HOLROYD, M. (1968) *Lytton Strachey. The Years of Achievement 1910–1932*. London: Heinemann.
HUTTON, I. (1960) *Memories of a Doctor in War and Peace*. London: Heinemann.
JONES, E. (1959) *Free Associations*. London: Hogarth Press.
JOURNAL OF MENTAL SCIENCE (1932) George Robertson (obituary). *Journal of Mental Science*, **78**, 447–451
KING, P. & STEINER, R. (eds) (1990) *The Freud-Klein Controversies 1941–45*. New Library of Psychoanalysis 11. London: Tavistock/Routledge.
KLEIN, G. (1976) *Psychoanalytic Theory*. New York: International Universities Press.
LANGDON-BROWN, W. (1938) *Thus We are Men*. London: Kegan Paul, Trench, Trubner.
LEVY, P. (1979) *G. E. Moore and the Cambridge Apostles*. London: Weidenfeld & Nicolson.
LEWIS, A. J. (1966) Obituary of Bernard Hart. *British Medical Journal*, *ii*, 806.
—— (1969) Edward Mapother and the Makings of the Maudsley Hospital. *British Journal of Psychiatry*, **115**, 1344–1366.
LINE, W. (1934–35) Some impressions of British Psychiatry. *American Journal of Psychiatry*, **91**, 1059–1077.
MABERLEY, A. & STURGE, B. (1939) After-results of child guidance: a follow-up of 500 children treated at the Tavistock Clinic, 1921–34. *British Medical Journal*, *i*, 1130–1134.
MACCURDY, J. (1923) *Problems in Dynamic Psychiatry*. Cambridge: Cambridge University Press.
—— (1925) *The Psychology of Emotion*. London: Kegan Paul, Trench, Trubner.
MACPHERSON, W. G. (1923) Neurasthenia and war neuroses. In *History of the Great War Based on Official Documents. Diseases of War, vol. 2*, pp. 1–67. London: HMSO.
MAPOTHER, E. (1928) The early treatment of the psychosis and psychoneurosis. *British Medical Journal*, *ii*, 304–306.
MEISEL, P. & KENDRICK, W. (eds) (1986) *Bloomsbury/Freud. The Letters of James and Alix Strachey 1924–1925*. London: Chatto & Windus.
MERCIER, C. A. (1916) Psychoanalysis. *British Medical Journal*, *ii*, 897–900.
MYERS, C. S. (1940) *Shell Shock in France 1914–1918*. Cambridge: Cambridge University Press.
MILLER, P. & ROSE, N. (1988) The Tavistock programme: the government of subjectivity and social life. *Sociology*, **22**, 171–192.
MONEY-KYRLE, R. (1978) *Collected Papers* (ed. D. Meltzer & E. O'Shaughnessy). Perthshire: Clunie Press.
MUNK'S ROLL (1968) William Brown (obituary). *Munk's Roll*, **5**, 56–57.
NEUSTATTER, W. L. (1935) The result of fifty cases treated by psychotherapy. *Lancet*, *i*, 47–62.
—— (1936) Some methods and problems of psychotherapy. *Journal of Mental Science*, **82**, 47–62.
NEWCOMBE, N. & LERNER, J. C. (1982) Britain between the wars: the historical context of Bowlby's theory of attachment. *Psychiatry*, **45**, 1–12.
NICOLE, J. E. (1930) *Psychopathology*. London: Baillière.
POGSON, B. (1961) *Maurice Nicoll. A Portrait*. London: Vincent Stuart.
REES, J. R. (1967) Obituary of J. A. Hadfield. *Lancet*, *ii*, 742.
RICKMAN, J. (1950*a*) Obituary of W. H. B. Stoddart. *International Journal of Psychoanalysis*, **31**, 286–287.

—— (1950*b*) Obituary of W. H. B. Stoddart. *Lancet*, *i*, 4.

ROSE, N. (1985) *The Psychological Complex*. London: Routledge & Kegan Paul.

SHOWALTER, E. (1987) *The Female Malady. Women, Madness and English Culture 1830–1980*. London: Virago Press.

SLOBODIN, R. (1978) *W. H. R. Rivers*. New York: Columbia University Press.

STEEDMAN, C. (1990) *Childhood, Culture and Class in Britain. Margaret McMillan, 1830–1931*. London: Virago Press.

STODDART, W. H. B. (1915) The new psychiatry. *Lancet*, *i*, 583.

SUTTIE, I. (1988) *The Origins of Love and Hate*. London: Free Association Books.

TAYLOR, F. K. (1958) A history of group and administrative therapy in Great Britain. *British Journal of Medical Psychology*, **31**, 153–173.

TRIST, G. & MURRAY, H. (1990) *The Social Engagement, Social Science. A Tavistock Anthology*. Philadelphia: University of Pennsylvania Press.

TROMBLEY, S. (1981) *"All That Summer She Was Mad": Virginia Woolf and Her Doctors*. London: Junction Books.

WAR OFFICE COMMITTEE OF INQUIRY INTO SHELL SHOCK (1922) *Report of the Committee*. London: HMSO.

WOLFF, C. (1980) *Hindsight. An Autobiography*. London: Quartet Books.

14 British psychopathology since the early 20th century

GERMAN E. BERRIOS

To trace the roots of psychopathology in Great Britain, the historian must distinguish the history of the word from that of related concepts and assumptions, and of its referents, that is, the experiences and behaviour which word and concepts were meant to capture (Berrios, 1984). Thus, since the 1850s the English term 'psychopathology' has changed meaning at least three times, and each has been associated with both a different conceptual framework and a set of anomalous forms of behaviour. Because the history of current British psychopathology only started at the beginning of the 20th century, this chapter concentrates on that period.

The word 'psychopathology' started life in the English language in 1847, when H. E. Lloyd and B. G. Babington used it as a transliteration of the German term *Psychopathologie*, as used by the great Austrian physician Baron Ernest von Feuchtersleben (1806–49) (Feuchtersleben, 1845). The context indicates that this early usage was explicative rather than descriptive: "Psychopathology has not yet acquired sufficient light respecting these critical processes" (Feuchtersleben, 1847, p. 70) (the 'processes' referred to here are the ways in which mind and body may interact to generate mental disease). This usage did not catch on in England; for example, Forbes Winslow (1848) disregarded it in his mammoth review of the book. However, the term 'psychopathology' re-emerged at the very end of the century, carrying a specific forensic meaning, for example, "the science which treats of the legal aspects of insanity; i.e. of the rights and responsibilities of lunatics" (Tuke, 1892, p. 1014). This meaning was echoed in the most popular British general medical dictionary of the period (Quain, 1894).

A reason for the lack of success of the term might have been that during the second half of the 19th century, rival terms such as 'psychological medicine', 'mental science', 'mental pathology', and 'mental physiology' were available in British psychiatry. At the beginning of the 20th century, however, the term began to gather momentum: the forensic meaning was dropped, and new referents were added which were to last well into the 1950s. The reasons for this are not clear, but the pace of change is likely to have been quickened by foreign (mainly French and German) influences as well as internal conceptual and social needs. For example, Pierre Janet (1859–1947) and Georges Dumas (1866–1946) founded in 1903 the *Journal de Psychologie Normale et Pathologique*, and the latter published in 1908 his classic manifesto *Qu'est-ce que la psychologie pathologique?*, in which he made the strongest case yet in France for psychological pathology being a branch of normal psychology (Dumas, 1908). Indeed, Binet had drawn attention to this fact as early as 1889: "with few exceptions, the psychologists of my country have left psychophysical research to the Germans, comparative psychology to the English, to dedicate themselves completely to pathological psychology" (Beauchesne, 1986, p. 67). This view was part of a wider disagreement as to the nature of mental 'symptoms' and their relationship to normal behaviour.

Two views vied for supremacy during this period (Lanteri-Laura, 1968, 1983). The 'pathological psychology' view – favourite among psychologists, and sponsored by Ribot, Binet, and Dumas – defined psychopathology as a branch of psychology dealing with experiential and behavioural phenomena which resulted from the disturbed expression of 'normal' mental functions. The 'psychological pathology' approach, on the other hand, considered psychopathology to be an independent science dealing with mental phenomena that appeared *de novo* in the evolution of a mental illness, and hence were unrelated to 'normal' mental functions. Popular among alienists, this view had as its sponsor Philippe Chaslin (1857–1923), one of the greatest exponents of French descriptive psychopathology and author of a book on this subject that was published a year before Jaspers' *General Psychopathology* (Chaslin, 1912). These two views have been called the 'continuity' and 'discontinuity' views, respectively (Berrios, 1984).

At the beginning of the 20th century, a similar debate developed in Britain, and a term was needed to name the branch of psychology dedicated to offering psychological (rather than somatic) explanations for mental dysfunction. 'Mental science', 'psychiatry', and 'psychological medicine' were not considered by psychologists and alienists of psychodynamic persuasion (see below) to be acceptable terms, since all were tainted by an organicist, medical approach. With Jastrow (1902), the term 'psychopathology' acquired its widest definition in the English language: "the general study of diseased mental conditions; a synonym of psychiatry and abnormal psychology, but rather more comprehensive than either, because it emphasizes the general scientific study of all forms of mental aberration" (p. 391). This definition was to remain popular, particularly in the USA, where the term 'psychopathology' has for long been used almost as a synonym of psychiatry (Henry, 1935; Page, 1966; Hinsie & Campbell, 1970; Maser & Seligman, 1979; Eisdorfer & Kleinman, 1981).

Bernard Hart and the psychodynamic movement

By the time of the onset of World War I, the meaning of psychopathology had become stable in Britain. Thus, in the 1926 Goulstonian Lectures, Hart (1879–1966), one of the best-known and most respected British alienists of the early 20th century, stated: "Psychopathology connotes not a mere description of mental symptoms, but an endeavour to explain disorder or certain disorders in terms of psychological processes" (Hart, 1927, p. 2). He differentiated this type of explanation from those used by 'psychiatry', which were somatic in nature. In this lecture, in fact, Hart repeated a concept that he himself had first put forward in 1912, in a little book entitled *The Psychology of Insanity*, which went through many editions and was obligatory reading among psychiatric trainees up to the 1930s (Hart, 1916). For example, it was listed in the reading list for the Cambridge Diploma in Psychological Medicine (awarded between 1912–37), one of the earliest qualifications in the subject offered in the UK. Hart's work illustrates well the manner in which psychoanalysis became assimilated into the epistemology of British alienism (Chapter 13). While using a number of classic Freudian categories, Hart constantly felt the need to appear to be practising a 'scientific' and 'empiricist' approach (in the British sense of these terms). This need is almost painfully expressed in the way in which he clung to the definition of science that had been put forward by Pearson in his *The Grammar of Science* (Pearson, 1892).

Myers, Rivers and MacCurdy

Hart was not alone in this endeavour. C. S. Myers (1873–1946) and W. H. R. Rivers (1864–1922) in Cambridge had also been influenced by psychoanalytic concepts, and had tried to develop a "science of psychopathology" (Crampton, 1978). This took clear expression in their (successful) efforts to create a lectureship in psychopathology in the University. The General Board approved their request and advertised the post in January 1923 (Cambridge University Press, 1923). At the end of March the same year, the appointment of Dr J. T. MacCurdy, a psychiatrist and psychologist from Canada, was confirmed by the Special Board of Medicine (to which the lectureship was attached). MacCurdy (1886–1947) was at one with Rivers and Myers in regarding psychopathology as both the description and explanation of mental symptoms, whose main limitation was not to make use of somatic hypotheses (Banister & Zangwill, 1949).

This view was influential among British psychiatrists in a number of ways. A vivid illustration is provided by the way in which the concepts of 'reactive' and 'neurotic' depression emerged, of which R. D. Gillespie (1897–1945) was the protagonist (Berrios, 1991). In 1926, at the British Medical Association meeting in Nottingham, Gillespie accused no less a person than Edward Mapother, then superintendent of the Maudsley Hospital, of having perpetrated the "psychiatrist's fallacy", that is, of having suggested a somatic explanation for manic-depressive illness (*British Medical Journal*, 1926). The strength with which Gillespie defended a psychological view of psychopathology has been conventionally explained by the fact that, at the time, he was working at the Cassel Hospital (Kendell, 1968), a famous psychotherapeutic centre, under T. A. Ross, who had recently published his popular book on the psychotherapy of the common neuroses (Ross, 1923). Lewis (1934) has also suggested that Gillespie might simply have repeated Lange's (1926) classification of depression. Analysis of the psychodynamic model entertained by Gillespie at the time, however, shows that neither explanation is correct. On the one hand, Ross's ideas (which were just an English version of Dejerine's (Dejerine & Glaucker, 1911)) are not what Gillespie was defending in 1926; on the other, Gillespie (1929, p. 310) specifically criticised Lange's criteria for differentiating true from "psychically produced melancholia" as being "very indefinite". In fact, Gillespie had already read MacCurdy's book on the psychology of emotion (MacCurdy, 1925), and, only a year later, was successfully to apply for the Pinsent–Darwin Scholarship at Cambridge, to work with MacCurdy. This award had been recently created to commemorate the death of David Pinsent, the closest Cambridge friend of Ludwig Wittgenstein (McGuiness, 1988), and Gillespie was its first holder. MacCurdy's influence shows clearly in Gillespie's famous paper on 'reactive' depression (Gillespie, 1929). Indeed, from then on, his general views on psychopathology were those sponsored by the Cambridge school. The concept of reactive depression was to reign supreme in Britain until the statistical debates of the 1960s.

McDougall

William McDougall (1871–1938) carried out most of his important psychopathological work either in Cambridge, where he trained, or in Oxford, where he occupied a number of positions including that of Wilde Reader in Mental Philosophy (McDougall, 1930; Oldfield, 1950). He started with a wide view of 'clinical psychology' (including the study of mental disorder), which he persuasively presented in his presidential address before the Medico-Psychological Association of Great Britain and Ireland (McDougall, 1919). In his *Outline of Abnormal Psychology* (first edition, 1926), McDougall used the term 'abnormal psychology' to refer to psychopathology. He quoted with approval Eugen Bleuler's well-known statement that "one of the most important, if not the most important, of all paths to a knowledge of the human soul is by way of psychopathology" (p. vii, McDougall, 1926). The variegated views on which McDougall based his ideas are not relevant here; suffice it to say that he developed an idiosyncratic model in which the central role was played by the *horme*, an energising principle which had a great deal to do with Freud's *libido*, Bergson's *élan vital*, and Oskar Vogt's *neurokyme*. In his autobiography, he wrote: "I built up my abnormal psychology incorporating what seemed most sound in the teachings of Freud, and Jung and Morton Prince, especially the principles of conflict, repression and dissociation, and the subconsciously working complex" (pp. 215–216, McDougall, 1930). However, the influence of McDougall on British psychopathology has been limited: Gillespie (1929, p. 878), for example, called it "academic psychology" (p. 878, *British Medical Journal*, 1926), and considered it an unsafe basis on which to build the concept of manic–depressive psychosis (*British Medical Journal*, 1926).

The German émigrés

From what has been said so far, it is clear that by 1930, there had developed in Britain a more or less stable view of psychopathology. This will help to make clear why the ideas brought by the German-speaking *émigrés* took some time to germinate. Willy Mayer-Gross, Eric Guttmann, Alfred Meyer, Stephen Krauss, and Erwin Stengel imported with them an entirely new view of psychopathology. That brought by Mayer-Gross in particular was based on the views of Karl Jaspers (with whom he had worked), and, more loosely, on the phenomenological tradition which was still taking shape on the European continent (Lewis, 1970).

Until this period, British thinking had been closed to phenomenological ideas. In 1922, E. Husserl (1859–1938) (by common agreement the founder of the philosophical school known as 'phenomenology' – Farber (1943)) delivered four lectures on the 'phenomenological method' at the University of London, but these had little impact (Spiegelberg, 1982). Gilbert Ryle, during the early stages of his career, flirted with phenomenology and learned German to read Husserl's *Logische Untersuchungen*; he even reviewed Heidegger's *Sein und Zeit* (Ryle, 1929). In his autobiography, he vividly describes the lack of interest in this type of philosophy in the Oxford of the 1920s. Concerning his own position, he stated: "it is sometimes suggested that in my well or ill spent youth I had been for a while a disciple of Husserl's phenomenology. There is not much truth in this" (Ryle, 1970, p. 9).

The approach to psychopathology brought by the German-speaking *émigrés* was meant to encourage the construction of neutral or atheoretical descriptions of mental symptoms (Berrios, 1989). Indeed, some believed that this was what Jaspersian phenomenology was all about. For example, Kräupl Taylor (1966) reassuringly wrote that "phenomenology provides us with information but not with explanations" (p. 767).

The view that 'theory-free description' is possible, however, is mistaken. All descriptive activity, whether in ordinary language or psychopathology, is subject to two levels of theoretical control. An overt, first-order theory governs the understanding of the information captured by descriptive categories (e.g. their experiential content). A covert, second-order theory, ordinarily beyond the conscious purview of the psychiatrist, controls their application to the continuous reality of abnormal behaviour (e.g. the way in which it is to be parsed out or what scientific narrative is to be used).

First-order theories can be 'bracketed out' with great facility, and Jaspers and the 'bracketing' tradition in phenomenology were happy to discard them. Second-order theories, however, are resistant to this treatment, which is to be expected, since it is impossible to use descriptive categories without having rules for their application. This becomes even more obvious in clinical practice, when subjective events are described. For example, a visual hallucination may be described as a 'coloured patch', with the assertion that in doing so no assumptions had been made in regard to its origin, cause, or meaning (what Kräupl Taylor called 'explanations'). This is acceptable in terms of first-order theory, but it does not follow that what has been captured is a 'pure-fact' (Parain-Vial, 1966; Fleck, 1979). Meta-theories still remain active, determining the way in which the 'coloured patch' is to be segregated from the larger patch of reality. This truth does not seem to have been yet fully accepted in British descriptive psychopathology.

Nicole and Malamud

In spite of the apparent influence of the German *émigrés*, no clear signs of the Jaspersian influence can be found in British psychopathology until the 1950s, when the Manchester group, under the leadership of the Professor, E. W. Anderson, began their programme of translations of German classics, culminating with that of Jaspers' *Allgemeine Psychopathologie*, which appeared for the first time in English in 1963 (Jaspers, 1963). To illustrate the limited influence of phenomenological ideas before this period, two books will be contrasted. One – *Psychopathology* – by Ernest Nicole, honorary secretary of the Psychopathology Sub-committee of the Royal Medico-Psychological Association, appeared in 1930 and went through six editions, becoming the most popular book in this field. Indeed, its fourth edition, published in 1946, contained about 1400 references, by far the longest list ever included in a book on psychopathology. No reference, however, is made in it to Jaspers or to Mayer-Gross (Nicole, 1946). Throughout the various editions of his book, Nicole's conception of psychopathology remained pre-1930 in spirit, and amounts to a list of explanations for all mental disorders, including some somatic theories.

Another book of the same period, by William Malamud – *Outlines of General Psychopathology* – was published in 1935 and was also popular in Britain. In this, psychopathology was defined as "a science that deals with the recognition, description, classification, and understanding of phenomena of abnormal mental activity" (Malamud, 1935, p. 10), and its outline included chapters on the psychopathology of the various mental functions. It had a much shorter list of references, but this included Jaspers' third German edition of *General Psychopathology*, published in 1923. Malamud was even influenced by the structure of Jaspers' book (see, for example, p. 44) and even attempted to include a phenomenological analysis of symptoms and of their determinants and relationships, as well as a final synthesis. Malamud was Professor of Psychiatry at the University of Iowa, and his book was simultaneously published in the USA and Britain. G. Thompson, who defended a strong 'relational' view, stated that in psychopathology, it was never possible to "give a satisfactory account of a disorder without reference to any person other than the patient" (Thompson, 1949, p. 30); this suggests that Malamud's view had only limited influence on British views of psychopathology.

Jaspers' influence

As mentioned above, Jaspers' *General Psychopathology* appeared in English in 1963. In a penetrating aside in the Foreword, Anderson stated:

> "that this school [phenomenology] should have been insufficiently recognized in England is perhaps hardly surprising. Many reasons can be adduced for this, first and foremost of which is the linguistic barrier. Secondly, even for those familiar with the German language, Jaspers's thought and style are difficult, due no doubt to his training as a philosopher, and his consequent use at times of terms specially devised to express some nuance of meaning not easily, if at all, to be translated intelligibly. To the English with their ingrained empiricism such an approach might well repel . . . yet this is a superficial evaluation."

And referring to the type of psychopathology which was popular in Britain Anderson stated:

> "By a remarkable paradox, however, our supposedly empirical countrymen have accepted readily enough, and on the whole with an astonishing lack of criticism, the unproven and unprovable assertions of the so-called psychodynamic schools." (Anderson, 1963, pp. v–vi)

There is little doubt that Anderson was thinking here of the work of Hart and Nicole. The Jaspersian influence in Britain, therefore, is not as old as has sometimes been suggested. However, once Jaspers' ideas were accepted, they became subject to uncritical adulation, and somewhat superficial accounts of what 'phenomenological psychopathology' was supposed to mean have appeared

(Taylor, 1967; Shepherd, 1982). On the other hand, some foreign observers have published extremely perceptive accounts of the real impact of Jaspersian ideas in Britain (Berner & Küfferle, 1982). At the present time, though, some reassessment of the conceptual, historical, and clinical aspects of Jaspers' work is proceeding in Britain (Jenner *et al*, 1986; Ebmeier, 1987; Grounds, 1987; Walker, 1988; Berrios, 1989).

Taylor and Fish

In 1966, in the first edition of his *Psychopathology*, Taylor stated (p. ix):

> "Psychopathology is a word of many meanings. It has a chequered career in the history of modern psychiatric thought, acquiring new meanings and connotations with the advent of every new theory of mental illness."

In spite of his overt support for phenomenology, Taylor still conceived of psychopathology as a form of physiology of the mind (p. 10) and, well within the old Nicole tradition, talked of neurones, genetics, etc. Taylorian psychopathology is therefore both descriptive and explanatory, as was that presented by D. R. Davies (1972), the successor of MacCurdy as Cambridge Lecturer in Psychopathology.

Also in 1966, Frank Fish was invited by Professor Sisler to give a series of seminars on the phenomenology of mental illness at the University of Manitoba, Canada. Fish published these lectures in 1967 under the title *Clinical Psychopathology* (1967). Although his emphasis was then descriptive, he felt forced to state:

> "this book has been written from the descriptive stand-point and hence over-emphasizes certain aspects of psychiatry. This does not imply that the author believes that interpretative psychology, such as Freudian psychopathology, and experimental psychology have nothing to contribute to our understanding of psychiatric signs and symptoms."

In 1974, the book was updated by Max Hamilton, who wrote that "anyone who is acquainted with Anglo-American psychiatric literature will know that the careful description of psychiatric symptoms in English is conspicuous for its absence" (Hamilton, 1974, p. 1) and, referring to Jaspers' *General Psychopathology*, stated: "It is unfortunate that this should be the only account of German views on symptomatology in English, because the book is overloaded with philosophy, is somewhat out of date, and does not do justice to the views which Jaspers does not accept" (Hamilton, 1974, p. 1); a fairer and more succinct judgement would be difficult to make.

Eysenck and Shapiro

In 1960, Hans Eysenck edited an important book which he called *Handbook of Abnormal Psychology* and dedicated to Kraepelin. This book was to be influential among psychologists and, in fact, included chapters by the best research psychologists of the late 1950s. Eysenck attempted an "integration through theory, an attempt to see abnormal psychology as a part of general, experimental psychology" (Eysenck, 1960, p. xiii). His view of symptoms was dimensional and continuous, and he saw psychopathology (which he considered a synonym of abnormal psychology, like McDougall) as having the task of working out or deducing "the details of abnormal behaviour from general laws". He quoted Jaspers extensively to support this view.

A second edition of Eysenck's book, carrying the same introduction but a different panel of experts, was produced (Eysenck, 1973). This time, it included a separate section on "Experimental studies of abnormal behaviour". Neither edition, however, dealt in any depth with the kind of (molar) symptoms that psychiatrists observe in their clinical practice. Hallucinations, delusions, depersonalisation, obsessions, etc., were mentioned *in passim*; instead, the volumes include excellent reviews of psychophysics and physiological psychology as applied to the 'molecular' disorders of behaviour, that is, to changes which cannot be observed by the naked eye and require specialised instruments for their assessment. This had not been the intention of Kraepelin, whose main interest was the understanding of molar symptoms by means of experimental psychology techniques (Kraepelin, 1896).

Perhaps the most original British writer on descriptive psychopathology in recent years has been M. B. Shapiro, whose paper of 1975 has unfortunately been neglected. Shapiro developed a 'continuity view', according to which psychopathology should be both inductive and catholic in its theoretical approach. It should resist closure and operational definitions and "not make use of arbitrary definitions which are not immediately testable" (Shapiro, 1975, p. 150). It should also be less concerned with the frequency of psychological dysfunction in the general population, and with diagnostic groupings and nosology. Finally and most importantly, psychopathology "does not have to assume that every symptom must be the expression of an underlying disorder" (p. 150). This view allows for the possibility that certain molar 'symptoms' (e.g. 'manipulation') may not need to be mapped onto 'hardware' deficits, but only be explained in 'software' terms. A very similar approach has recently been suggested in the USA, although Shapiro is not mentioned (Persons, 1986).

Discussion

Since the 1960s, there has been little or no redefinition of the term 'descriptive psychopathology' in Britain. Psychologists and psychiatrists have continued along the furrows ploughed by Eysenck and Jaspers, respectively. The continuity and discontinuity views run parallel, and this two-tier system is readily seen in current textbooks. For example, *Adult Abnormal Psychology* (Miller & Cooper, 1988) follows Eysenck in "classifying material in terms of essentially psychological rather than psychiatric concepts" (p. 2). Shepherd & Zangwill (1983) included in a book entitled *General Psychopathology* chapters on diseases, clinical phenomena, and classificatory questions. Earlier, Shepherd had also endorsed the English translation of Scharfetter's *General Psychopathology* (1980) which, although sailing under the usual Jaspersian flag of convenience, offered a combination of descriptions, psychodynamics, and Gestaltism. This book has had little influence on British psychiatry, however.

The most recent addition to the literature in this area is *Symptoms in the Mind*, an excellent book by Professor Andrew Sims (1988) who, from within the tradition of Hart and Nicole, has defined psychopathology as: "the systematic study of abnormal experience, cognition and behaviour" (p. 1). This book has the great quality of interpreting 'systematic study' as verbal and numerical description, and hence avoids incursions into causal explanations. From this point of view, it manages to follow those injunctions that have been conventionally attributed to Jaspers.

But how does the average British psychiatrist understand psychopathology and practise it in everyday clinical work? It is now customary to teach that 'descriptive' psychopathology studies the 'form', and 'psychodynamic' psychopathology the 'content', of the symptoms. The former, in turn, is divided into 'phenomenological' (verbal) and 'experimental' psychopathology. No set of rules or dictionary, however, has ever been created to cross-refer from one to the other, and hence the classification is likely to be only a compromise between parallel psychopathological approaches. As described above, the first psychopathological tradition to become established in Britain was a variant of the psychodynamic approach. Its exponents strove for the development of a science of the abnormal mind, of a set of descriptions and explanations of mental symptoms which were not couched in somatic language. This tradition was predominant up to the 1930s, when the German-speaking *émigrés* brought with them a view that combined Jaspersian descriptive psychopathology and the search for the organic causes of mental disease. Although superficially Jaspersian in inspiration, their view of the limits of psychopathology went well beyond the experiential analysis suggested by Jaspers. It also included signs of mental disease which were not necessarily present at any time in the patient's consciousness. For example, Mayer-Gross & Guttmann (1937) undertook a number of projects on apraxia and other manifestations of organic brain disease. In this work, as in that by their successors, the historian can identify the mixed or combined approach that was to become the hallmark of British psychopathology. While purporting to follow an atheoretical, purely descriptive view of psychopathology, British psychiatrists have searched for nosological rules and for aetiological mechanisms, most of which were not 'psychological' in the sense that the traditional British model enjoined psychiatrists to practise.

Most British psychiatric researchers have, however, succumbed to understandable methodological pressures, and have made 'reliability' in the capture of data the main objective of their research. This has led to the acceptance of closed psychopathological glossaries, the use of structured instruments, and the neglect of open, less reliable psychopathological techniques, which perhaps are the only ones that may lead to the identification and accruing of new signs and symptoms of mental disease. Signs of this can be clearly seen in British psychiatric publications, which now contain comparatively little research focusing on the actual sensitivity and specificity of symptoms, on their validity, or on their capacity to capture information. These features of the conventional symptoms are taken for granted, and descriptive psychopathology has become 'user transparent', that is, considered as 'given', or as an instrument which, in itself, is no longer problematic. The old Psychopathology Sub-committee of the Royal Medico-Psychological Association has no counterpart in the present Royal College of Psychiatrists.

The reasons for this neglect of descriptive psychopathology are many. One is, perhaps, the traditional British empirical approach, particularly as it manifests itself in the clinical and applied sciences. Another is a widespread and genuine belief that descriptive psychopathology is theoretically neutral, or that if it is not, the theory it embodies is tame - can be fully specified and controlled - and that whatever mild biases it might introduce can be corrected by good empirical method. Yet another is represented by the training requirements of the Royal College of Psychiatrists, which, although impeccable in terms of clinical practice, encourage little questioning or intellectual irreverence. Teaching models are based on a 'progressionist', positivist view of the clinical sciences, and hence there is a belief that what is known today must be better than that which was practised yesterday. While this view is highly defensible in areas such as therapy and clinical practice, it may be less so in the field of descriptive psychopathology, where decision rules to choose between rival descriptive psychopathological approaches have not yet been developed.

It must not be forgotten that psychopathology, whatever approach is taken, has a history of no more than 150 years, and indeed since its beginnings has not spawned more than two or three different approaches. These, although superficially different, share the same ontological and logical assumptions in regard to abnormal behaviour. In fact, no effective rival system (to the European one) has yet developed to the point of gaining full credibility. A sort of mortal embrace has been established between the psychopathology of closed systems and current clinical and neurobiological knowledge, in that the latter is dependent upon the way in which abnormal behaviour is being dismembered by the available descriptive psychopathology.

British psychopathologists have also been resistant to the adoption of new instruments, as shown by the muted response to the *Manual for the Assessment and Documentation of Psychopathology* (Guy & Ban, 1982; Bobon *et al*, 1983; Bobon & Woggon, 1986), whose psychopathology symptoms scale (no. 4) is an excellent semi-open glossary for the rating of psychiatric symptoms.

It is difficult to envisage a model which can break up this tautological state of affairs, other than an open descriptive system, running parallel to current 'closed' symptom lists or glossaries such as DSM-III-R (American Psychiatric Association, 1987) or the Present State Examination (PSE; Wing *et al*, 1974). Open systems (Shapiro, 1975; Guy & Ban, 1982) may have lower reliability coefficients, but are likely to facilitate the identification of new symptoms which, once added to those already known, will increase the validity of the diagnostic categories.

From the evidence above, a number of conclusions would seem to be warranted. In the first place, there was little during the 19th century in the way of a native British psychopathology. Secondly, a psychopathology began to develop during the years before World War I and consolidated in the 1920s. This approach was eclectic, moderately psychodynamic, and strove for the identification of descriptions and psychological explanations of abnormal mental states. It tended to assume that the latter were continuous with some forms of normal behaviour. Thirdly, the 1930s saw the arrival in Britain of first-class, German-speaking *émigrés*. They brought with them Jaspersian ideas which, although taking at least 20 years to germinate, began to be accepted as the conventional guiding lines, and remain to this day as the foundations of British psychopathology. These ideas, however, have been superficially understood by most, and are not usually discussed in any depth. Fourthly, descriptive psychopathology has become 'user transparent' – most users believe that the terms used to describe symptoms are satisfactory, and most research is directed at the clinical and neurobiological characteristics of the behaviour mapped by these terms. Little research is directed at evaluating the capacity of the symptoms themselves to capture information.

Finally, there is little evidence that this is going to change. British psychiatrists' attitudes to psychopathology are determined not only by vague factors such as national personality and the traditional empirical approach, but also by the tenets of psychiatric education. While it would be churlish to criticise this teaching system, considered by many to be one of the best in the world, such a system is unlikely to generate enough new psychiatrists who may want to challenge the categories of descriptive psychopathology.

References

AMERICAN PSYCHIATRIC ASSOCIATION (1987) *Diagnostic and Statistical Manual of Mental Disorders* (3rd edn, revised) (DSM-III-R). Washington, DC: APA.

ANDERSON, E. W. (1963) Foreword. In *General Psychopathology*, by K. Jaspers (trans. J. Hoenig & M. Hamilton), Manchester: Manchester University Press.

GUY, W. & BAN, T. A. (eds) (1982) *Manual for the Assessment and Documentation of Psychopathology*. Berlin: Springer.

BANISTER, H. & ZANGWILL, O. L. (1949) John Thomson MacCurdy, 1886–1947. *British Journal of Psychology*, **40**, 1–4.

BEAUCHESNE, H. (1986) *Histoire de la psychopathologie*. Paris: Presses Universitaires de France.

BERNER, P. & KÜFFERLE, B. (1982) British phenomenological concepts: a comparative review. *British Journal of Psychiatry*, **140**, 558–565.

BERRIOS, G. E. (1984) Descriptive psychopathology: conceptual and historical aspects. *Psychological Medicine*, **14**, 303–313.

—— (1989) What is phenomenology? A review. *Journal of the Royal Society of Medicine*, **82**, 425–428.

—— (1991) The history of the affective disorders. In *Handbook of Affective Disorders* (2nd edn) (ed. E. S. Paykel). London: Churchill Livingstone (in press).

BOBON, D., BAUMANN, U., ANGST, J., *et al* (eds) (1983) *AMDP – System in Pharmacopsychiatry*. Basel: Karger.

—— & WOGGON, B. (1986) The AMDP-system in clinical psychopharmacology. *British Journal of Psychiatry*, **148**, 467–468.

BRITISH MEDICAL JOURNAL (1926) Discussion on manic-depressive psychosis. *British Medical Journal*, *ii*, 872–879.

CAMBRIDGE UNIVERSITY PRESS (1923) *Cambridge University Reporter*. Cambridge: Cambridge University Press.

CHASLIN, PH. (1912) *Éléments de sémiologie et clinique mentales*. Paris: Asselin and Houzeau.

CRAMPTON, C. (1978) The Cambridge School. The Life, Work and Influence of James Ward, W. H. R. Rivers, C. S. Myers and Sir Frederic Bartlett. PhD dissertation, University of Edinburgh.

DAVIES, D. R. (1972) *An Introduction to Psychopathology*. Oxford: Oxford University Press.

DEJERINE, J. & GAUCKLER, E. (1911) *Les Manifestations fonctionnelles des psychonévroses*. Paris: Masson.

DUMAS, G. (1980) Qu'est-ce que la psychologie pathologique? *Journal of Psychology and Normal Pathology*, **5**, 10–22.

EBMEIER, K. P. (1987) Explaining and understanding in psychopathology. *British Journal of Psychiatry*, **151**, 800–804.

EISDORFER, C. & KLEINMAN, A. (eds) (1981) *Models for Clinical Psychopathology*. Lancaster: MTP.

EYSENCK, H. J. (ed.) (1960) *Handbook of Abnormal Psychology*. London: Pitman.

—— (ed.) (1973) *Handbook of Abnormal Psychology* (2nd edn). London: Pitman.

FARBER, M. (1943) *The Foundations of Phenomenology*. Cambridge: Harvard University Press.

FEUCHTERSLEBEN, E. F. VON (1845) *Lehrbuch der ärztlichen Seelenkunde*. Vienna: Carl Gerold.

—— (1847) *The Principles of Medical Psychology* (trans. H. E. Lloyd & B. G. Babington). London: Sydenham Society.
FISH, F. (1967) *Clinical Psychopathology*. Bristol: Wright.
FLECK, L. (1979) *Genesis and Development of a Scientific Fact*. Chicago: University of Chicago Press.
GILLESPIE, R. D. (1929) The clinical differentiation of types of depression. *Guy's Hospital Reports*, **79**, 306–344.
GROUNDS, A. (1987) On describing mental states. *British Journal of Medical Psychology*, **60**, 305–311.
HAMILTON, M. (1974) *Fish's Clinical Psychopathology*. Bristol: Wright.
HART, B. (1916) *The Psychology of Insanity* (3rd edn). Cambridge: Cambridge University Press.
—— (1927) *Psychopathology. Its Development and its Place in Medicine*. Cambridge: Cambridge University Press.
HENRY, G. W. (1935) *Essentials of Psychopathology*. London: Baillière.
HINSIE, L. E. & CAMPBELL, R. J. (1970) *Psychiatric Dictionary*. Oxford: Oxford University Press.
JASPERS, K. (1963) *General Psychopathology* (trans. J. Hoenig & M. W. Hamilton). Manchester: Manchester University Press.
JASTROW, J. (1902) Psychopathology. In *Dictionary of Philosophy and Psychology* (ed. J. M. Baldwin). London: Macmillan.
JENNER, F. A., MONTEIRO, A. C. & VLISSIDES, D. (1986) The negative effects on psychiatry of Karl Jaspers's development of Verstehen. *Journal of the British Society for Phenomenology*, **17**, 52–70.
KENDELL, R. E. (1968) *The Classification of Depressive Illness*. London: Oxford University Press.
KRAEPELIN, E. (1896) Der psychologische Versuch in der Psychiatrie. *Psychologische Arbeiten*, **1**, 1–91.
LANGE, J. (1926) Über Melancholie. *Zeitschrift für die Ges. Neurologie und Psychiatrie*, **101**, 293–324.
LANTERI-LAURA, G. (1968) Psychologie pathologique. In *Encyclopédie médico-chirurgicale* 37032C10, pp. 1–6. Paris: Éditions Techniques.
—— (1983) La Sémiologie psychiatrique: son évolution et son état en 1982. *L'Évolution psychiatrique*, **48**, 327–363.
LEWIS, A. (1934) Melancholia: a historical review. *Journal of Mental Science*, **80**, 1–42.
—— (1970) William Mayer-Gross: an appreciation. *Psychological Medicine*, **7**, 11–18.
MALAMUD, W. (1935) *Outlines of General Psychopathology*. London: Chapman and Hall.
MASER, J. D. & SELIGMAN, M. E. P. (eds) (1979) *Psychopathology*. San Francisco: W. H. Freeman.
MAYER-GROSS, W. & GUTTMAN, E. (1937) Schema for the examination of organic states. *Journal of Mental Science*, **83**, 440–448.
MACCURDY, J. T. (1925) *The Psychology of Emotion Morbid and Normal*. London: Kegan Paul, Trench, Trubner & Co.
MCDOUGALL, W. (1919) The present position in clinical psychology. *Journal of Mental Science*, **45**, 141–152.
—— (1926) *An Outline of Abnormal Psychology*. London: Methuen.
—— (1930) William McDougall. In *A History of Psychology in Autobiography*, Vol. 1, (ed C. Murchison), pp. 191–223. New York: Clark University Press.
MCGUINESS, B. (1988) *Wittgenstein. A Life*. London: Duckworth.
MILLER, E. & COOPER, P. J. (1988) *Adult Abnormal Psychology*. London: Churchill Livingstone.
NICOLE, J. E. (1946) *Psychopathology* (4th edn). London: Baillière.
OLDFIELD, R. C. (1950) Psychology in Oxford 1898–1949. *Bulletin of the British Psychological Society, July/October*, 1–14.
PAGE, J. D. (ed.) (1966) *Approaches to Psychopathology*. New York: Temple University Publications.
PARAIN-VIAL, J. (1966) *La Nature du fait dans les sciences humaines*. Paris: Presses Universitaires de France.
PEARSON, K. (1892) *The Grammar of Science*. London: Walter Scott.
PERSONS, J. B. (1986) The advantages of studying psychological phenomena rather than psychiatric diagnosis. *American Psychologist*, **41**, 1252–1260.
QUAIN, R. (1894) *A Dictionary of Medicine*. London: Longmans & Green.
ROSS, T. A. (1923) *The Common Neuroses. Their Treatment by Psychotherapy*. London: Edward Arnold.
RYLE, G. (1929) Critical notice of Martin Heidegger's '*Sein und Zeit*'. *Mind*, **38**, 355–370.
—— (1970) Autobiographical. In *Ryle* (eds O. Wood & G. Pitcher), pp. 1–15. London: Macmillan.
SCHARFETTER, C. (1980) *General Psychopathology* (trans. H. Marshall). Cambridge: Cambridge University Press.
SHAPIRO, M. B. (1975) The requirements and implications of a systematic science of psychopathology. *Bulletin of the British Psychological Society*, **28**, 149–155.
SHEPHERD, M. (1982) Karl Jaspers: *General Psychopathology*. *British Journal of Psychiatry*, **141**, 310–312.

—— & ZANGWILL, O. L. (eds) (1983) *General Psychopathology*. Cambridge: Cambridge University Press.

SIMS, A. (1988) *Symptoms in the Mind*. London: Baillière.

SPIEGELBERG, H. (1982) *The Phenomenological Movement* (3rd edn). The Hague: Martinus Nijhoff.

TAYLOR, F. K. (1966) *Psychopathology*. London: Butterworths.

—— (1967) The role of phenomenology in psychiatry. *British Journal of Psychiatry*, **113**, 765–770.

THOMPSON, G. (1949) Abnormal psychology in relation to emotional development. In *Modern Practice in Psychological Medicine* (ed. J. R. Rees), pp. 30–48. London: Butterworths.

TUKE, D. H. (1892) *Dictionary of Psychological Medicine*. London: John Churchill.

WALKER, C. (1988) Philosophical concepts in practice: the legacy of Jaspers's psychopathology. *Current Opinion in Psychiatry*, **1**, 624–629.

WING, J. K., COOPER, J. E. & SARTORIUS, N. (1974) *The Measurement and Classification of Psychiatric Symptoms*. Cambridge: Cambridge University Press.

WINSLOW, F. (1848) Review of *The Principles of Medical Psychology*. *Journal of Psychological Medicine and Mental Pathology*, **1**, 247–263, 499–512.

15 Shell-shock

HAROLD MERSKEY

Perhaps no single topic can have had as many branches as 'shell-shock', and as many consequences for psychiatry, for medicine, and for society. The first issue arose quickly. This was the need to determine whether or not repeated exposure to high explosives without external injury produced a syndrome of emotional or 'nervous' change from organic disturbances. Within a year, the answer was clear: psychological factors were the cause, and psychiatric treatment was therefore introduced. This chapter traces the origins and evolution of the idea of shell-shock, and its subsequent decline.

The events in question weighted the views of the medical profession in favour of Freud's theory of emotional conflict in hysteria (Chapter 13), but against the notion of an infantile sexual aetiology. In addition, they left enduring effects on the profession of psychiatry, demonstrating that medical psychology could guide the selection of personnel, the prevention of nervous breakdown in battle, and the effective treatment of psychiatric casualties. Those lessons were quickly accepted (Salmon, 1917; Mott, 1919; Hurst, 1940; Miller, 1940; Grinker & Spiegel, 1943, 1945; Sargant & Shorvon, 1945; Ahrenfeldt, 1958). Like the analysis of shell-shock, they contributed to the growth and independence of psychiatry as a discipline (Brown, 1984; Stone, 1985).

These themes are important, but there is an even greater argument. In World War I, the competing armies encountered a fundamental problem in ethics and survival. The conditions of war were so bad, and the chance of death so great, that there was a risk that large numbers of men would desert or run away, unless the punishment of death for cowardice were to be employed. Serious breakdowns in morale occurred (War Office Committee of Enquiry into Shell Shock, 1922, hereafter referred to as '*Report*': see especially J. F. C. Fuller, p. 28; W. Brown, p. 43). Only one escape – illness – was available to the soldier. Yet the military authorities could not reject psychological illness: many men of proven courage, placed under protracted stress, gave way to fear. It was not acceptable to label them as cowards or to treat them as dishonourable, much less to punish them (e.g. *Report*, p. 105: comments on a holder of the Victoria Cross with shell-shock; Williamson, 1917). 'Illness' was the solution, but how could the lines of illness be drawn? If too many were accepted as ill, whole regiments would be lost and eventually, perhaps, this enormously costly war (*Report*: see J. F. C. Fuller, p. 28; W. Brown, p. 43; Lord Gort, p. 50). For a time, the medical profession at large helped to ensure the continuing operation of the military machine (Brown, 1984; Babington, 1983; Ritchie, 1986). The function of the army doctor included sustaining morale and reducing complaints of sickness, treating some 'illness' and denying other 'illness'. All this was done so that very many of his patients could return to the front to face death or severe injury. This pattern of work probably caused much stress to doctors, but the consequences for medical ethics have scarcely been examined.

Concussion and railway spine

Ideas have their origins and forces which promote them. In 1915–16, shell-shock became a tremendously powerful idea, fuelled by the instinct of self-preservation and shaped by the strongest pressures of society. The groundwork was laid in the previous half-century with a concept of 'commotion' or 'concussion' of the brain and spinal cord.

'Concussion' comes from the Latin words '*con*', meaning together, and '*quatere*', meaning to shake, strike, or dash. The *Oxford English Dictionary* cites a work by R. Copland, *Galyen's Terapeutyke* of 1541, as follows: "The solution of contynuyte called ecchymosis in greke cometh most often with concussyon and ruption", and in 1656, Ridgley in *Practical Physic* says "Concussion of the Brain is made from an external cause". Courville (1953) reviews the history of theories distinguishing between concussion, contusion and compression of the brain.

Bailey (1906) wrote (p. 91) that: "Concussion occurs in varying degrees. In the mildest form, after a blow, there is a dazing or confusion which is only momentary. . . . In the more severe degrees concussion is a much more serious matter." By comparison, contusions of the brain were described as "bruisings, by which nerve tissue, connective tissue, and blood vessels are injured."

Charles Bland Radcliffe (1880), physician to the Westminster Hospital and to the National Hospital for the Paralyzed and Epileptic, described concussion of the spinal cord in a standard textbook *A System of Medicine*, edited by Sir John Russell Reynolds, as follows (pp. 1016–1017): "Concussion of the spinal cord, like concussion of the brain, is the result of a fall or some other accident, and its symptoms vary with the intensity of the shock. . . . The appearances after death may be those of haemorrhage more or less extensive".

These opinions reflect a general view that some type of disturbance to the nervous system might be physically produced, without haemorrhage, either by temporary disablement of cells, or perhaps by the disruption of their connections. Erichsen (1866, 1886) developed the idea strongly in relation to railway accidents. With the spread of railways throughout the 19th century, accidents and collisions inevitably occurred. According to Erichsen (1886, p. 1) "These injuries of the spine and of the spinal cord occur not infrequently in civil life . . . but in none more frequently or with greater severity than in those sustained by persons subjected to the violent shock of a railway collision".

Trimble (1981) points out that one of the themes of Erichsen's book is that organic lesions can follow from relatively mild trauma. Naturally, this position supported claims for compensation for injury. Page (1883) objected. He analysed Erichsen's case histories, and often found evidence of significant physical injury such as fractured vertebrae. He argued that "purely physical causes" could explain the symptoms of general nervous shock after frightening railway accidents. Page also reasoned that those cases of a "concussion of the brain" in which symptoms persisted generally had "definite structure lesions" and that transient loss of consciousness without disruption of brain tissue would normally be followed by a full recovery. He claimed that a similar "shake" of the spinal cord would have no lasting effect. There were also some American writers (e.g. Hodges, 1881; Putnam, 1883; Walton, 1883) who were sceptical of Erichsen's theory.

Three other positions are important in this background of ideas. Russell Reynolds (1869) and Charcot (1889) had both demonstrated that hysterical symptoms could follow accidents: patients developed an illness corresponding to their idea of physical disturbance. Charcot credited Reynolds with being the first author to study this systematically. Reynolds' work actually consisted of three cases described at a meeting of the British Medical Association in 1869 and published in that year. Charcot's own contribution was to show that ideas could be implanted under hypnosis and that the patient would then have symptoms corresponding to them.

The second important position is that of Oppenheim (1889, 1911). He attributed the symptoms of concussion to functional disturbances "produced by molecular changes in the central nervous system".

Thirdly, Freud (1893–95), who was to prove the most influential writer of all on this topic, was not yet fully appreciated. He had learned from Charcot that hysterical symptoms were related to ideas, and had explained how the symptom might be produced: he saw it as the result of conflict, unconscious and repressed. Before World War I, however, these ideas were discounted. Although arguments about shell-shock helped to establish the Freudian notion that hysterical symptoms were due to emotional conflict, they also undermined the relationship which Freud alleged between these symptoms and childhood sexual experiences.

Russian doctors had also observed battle neurosis. During the Russo-Japanese War of 1904–1906, they described a condition amounting to traumatic neurosis, marked by confusional states and brief hysterical excitement, leading to irritability, fearfulness and emotional instability (Baker, 1975).

One other item contributed to the background before World War I: the effects of two well known French catastrophes. The ships *Iéna* and *Liberté* had exploded at Toulon in 1907 and 1911 respectively. Hesnard (1914) described the effects on survivors, after eliminating cases in which physical commotion of the brain or other direct organic causes might have been relevant. He recorded typical symptoms of post-traumatic psychological responses which were previously recognised and have been repeatedly observed in wars and catastrophes in this century. These included an initial state of semi-somnambulism, automatic mental activity, absorption in some trivial occupation such as an exclusive preoccupation in the attempt to save some garment, a strange lucidity and feeling of exaltation, and a period of amnesia. The rescuers also showed symptoms of disturbance for several weeks, including recapitulation of the scene, terrifying dreams, diffuse anxiety, fatigue, and various minor phobias. This knowledge of emotional change after explosions, quickly abstracted in English, became part of the contemporary climate of ideas (Brown & Williams, 1918).

The emergence of shell-shock

We will probably never know who first used the alliterative term 'shell-shock', which ultimately caught on among the forces of the British Empire like wildfire. In December 1914, Elliott described four cases of "transient paraplegia" from shell explosions. In three, he recognised significant physical injury: all three were considered to be at risk of being diagnosed as hysterical. In the fourth case, however, Elliott accepted that his patient's symptoms were indeed hysterical. He emphasised both that organic disease could be overlooked and that "functional disorders of the nervous system" were common after a "big shell explosion".

Two months later, on 13 February 1915, Myers (1915) seems to have used the term in the medical literature for the first time, although the *Oxford English Dictionary* (Murray *et al*, 1986) incorrectly states that Evans was the first to use the term in December 1915. Myers' first patient, a private, had experienced shells exploding both in front of and behind him.

> "Curiously, the one in front cut his haversack clean away, and bruised his side, and apparently it burned his little finger. His eyes burned and were blurred and he developed hysterical blindness as well as loss of the sense of taste and smell. He was cured by suggestion."

After describing this and two other patients in considerable detail, Myers writes, laconically, "Comment on these cases seems superfluous. . . . The close relation of these cases to those of 'hysteria' appears fairly certain." Viets (1917) states that Myers' article is the first recorded use of the term known to him, but that it came into use in the British Army in the latter part of 1914.

A search of *The Times* from the onset of the war to 13 March 1915 found only one reference to 'shock', on 6 February 1915 (p. 5), but without the prefix 'shell'. This related that the War Office was arranging to send soldiers suffering from shock to be treated in special wards at the National Hospital for the Paralysed and Epileptic, Queen Square.

The official history of the war (Macpherson *et al*, 1923) gives a table of functional nervous diseases from the outbreak of war to the end of December 1914 (Table 15.1). Using slightly different criteria, the following numbers of British battle casualties in France, combining officers and other ranks, were recorded as cases of shell-shock: September–December 1914, 9; January–June 1915, 141; July–December 1915, 1246; January–June 1916, 3951; July–December

TABLE 15.1
Functional nervous diseases among imperial troops, August–December 1914

	United Kingdom		France	
	officers	other ranks	officers	other ranks
Neurasthenia	20	321	65	279
Traumatic neurasthenia	–	10	–	8
Hysteria	–	50	–	11
Shock	–	15	23	114
Shell-shock	–	–	2	18
Totals	20	396	90	430

From Macpherson *et al* (1923).

1916, 16 138; January–June 1917, 3010; July–December 1917, 4038. The rise in numbers was associated with the first battle of the Somme, which took place from July to November 1916, and was not a success for the Allied forces. Colonel A. B. Soltau stated (*Report*, p. 72):

> "there were one or two cases in the fighting line in May 1915, and September 1915, but nothing which really attracted attention. . . . It was not until the Somme that it became an appreciable problem in the field ambulance. . . . We were flooded . . . with cases in the latter stages of the Somme."

The official figures by month and year also show the gradual growth of the notion. However, the fact that in the official history some cases of shell-shock are dated 1914 does not prove that they were actually given that label in 1914. These were probably patients who, having spent some time in hospital, were thus labelled on discharge.

'Shell-shock' was rare in earlier wars. The only direct evidence was an account of nervous injuries produced at a distance by the projectiles of war, given by Professor Octave Laurent, in his book *La Guerre en Bulgarie et en Turquie*, published in 1914 (*Report*, p. 109). In one chapter, Laurent (p. 367) describes a condition which he terms "Commotion Cérébrospinale" or "Nervous Injuries Produced by Projectiles". They follow the explosion of a shell and may or may not be accompanied by signs of contusion. The effects of commotion may be slight, manifesting numbness, formications and hyperaesthesia, with or without loss of consciousness, or they may be serious, provoking arrest of functions, where the injured falls into a torpor, inert as if struck by lightning, with all four limbs and the sphincters paralysed (*Report*, p. 109).

It was expected that the effects of shells might be worse in 1914 than ever before; all observers recognised that exposure to explosions had multiplied. Instead of round cannonballs which only killed where they hit, shells were available which travelled to their destination with increased velocity and better aerodynamic qualities. They carried high explosive of greater force than formerly, which would burst on impact. The gases generated by the explosion produced a shockwave in the air, more destructive than a single cannonball. In battle, men near whom a shell exploded might be seen being thrown for a distance of 15 yards (Mott, 1916*b*), while others had been seen being thrown 12 or 15 feet upwards into the air (*Report*, J. C. Dunn, p. 105). Squadron Leader W. Tyrrell (*Report*, p. 105) had observed the death of men blown up without external signs of injury. Stones, earth, walls, buildings, the ramparts or dug-outs – all might crumble. Soldiers were exposed to continuous bombardment from many guns, with numerous shells exploding in their vicinity. The prolonged noise and physical disruption of their environment could be enough to make many feel that they were being subjected to 'shockwaves'. General Lord Horne (*Report*, p. 16) commented that "shell shock became a serious factor in this war owing to the peculiar character of the war. The high explosives and the bombardments had never been known before." He added prophetically that "In moving warfare we should not experience anything like it" (J. C. Dunn, *Report*, p. 60).

Soon after the commencement of the war, French doctors also began to describe nervous changes from 'concussion' (in French '*commotion*'). Sollier & Chartier (1915) reported on the observation and treatment of 109 cases from field hospitals and from the neurological base at Lyons. Various authors made different analyses of the relationship between the physical effects of the shell bursting and the emotional changes which resulted, although some papers described the death of individuals from the bursting of a shell who had no external signs of injury (Ravaut, 1915; Mott, 1917). There were also eye-witness reports (e.g. Dunn & Tyrrell, *Report*, p. 105).

Ravaut (1915) described post-mortem findings of haemorrhages in the nervous system which could account for death, but Mott (*pace* the claim of Myers below) actually reported no relevant punctate haemorrhages in his two cases, although his second case had haemorrhage below the orbital surface of the brain. By analogy, it was thought that some cases of damage from displaced air might lead to haemorrhages which healed, leaving emotional disturbance. Shaking or disruption of neurones might occur without actual haemorrhage, and this also would cause persistent nervous sequelae. However, in cases of shell-shock, purely functional nervous disturbances were present from the outset, and organic symptoms, which were generally temporary, might be added as well (Sollier & Chartier, 1915).

Throughout 1915, and even 1916 and 1917, British papers appeared which described physical complaints following the explosion of shells. Turner (1915, 1916) was sent by the army medical services to explore the early problems of shell-shock. He reported that:

> "One of the features of the early fighting was the heavy shelling which to a large extent, accounted for the prevalence of nervous shock at that time. . . . If one studies the cases . . . it will be seen that the symptoms are widely distributed throughout the nervous system. Whatever the special symptoms may be, the patients have been subjected in most instances to prolonged and often serious general nervous strain."

Many men who were previously very stable or had given good service, broke down. This led to concern that doctors should not reject the option of invaliding for individuals with 'shell-shock' or comparable symptoms.

Turner recognised organic cases of paraplegia due to a shell exploding in the immediate vicinity of the patient, with or without an accompanying burial of the patient in the trench or resulting debris. Others who inclined to an organic view, in addition to Mott and Turner, included Parsons (1915), Milligan & Westmacott (1915), Harris (1915) and Campbell (1916) in Britain, Ravaut (1915) in France, and Gaupp (1915), Binswanger (1915), and Oppenheim (1915) in Germany.

Contrasting views

Myers (1940), who succeeded Turner (see Myers, 1940, p. 15) in duties in France, played an important role in rejecting the connection of battle neurosis with organic 'molecular' commotion in the brain. His duties were officially described as: "To select suitable cases of nervous and mental shock and neurasthenia for transference to the appropriate institutions in England for treatment." In the course of time, these duties increased: his work combined the roles of neurologist and psychiatrist, and included differentiating between cases of 'functional' and those of 'organic' disorder. He described himself (p. 12) as "one of the first to use the term 'shell-shock', which has since deservedly received adverse criticism". However, he emphasised the close relationship of these cases to hysteria, and did not suppose "as Lieutenant Colonel (the late Sir) Frederick Mott was then attempting to show, that they arose from the effects of minute cerebral haemorrhages or other microscopically visible lesions". He acknowledged that he was inclined to find an invisibly fine 'molecular' commotion in the aetiology, but said that later experience showed that emotional disturbance alone was a sufficient cause. Brown (1984) has discussed this topic in detail, showing the movement of opinion. He notes that Russel (1917), perhaps the leading Canadian author on this topic, observed that many patients had shell-shock without having been heavily shelled. Indeed, many had never even been near the front line.

In December 1915, Forsyth published one of the most cogent early assessments of the problem; he was a physician to out-patients at Charing Cross Hospital and a paediatrician. However, he was also a member of the British Psychological Society and the International Psychoanalytical Association. One of his obituarists (*British Medical Journal*, 1941) observed that "It must have needed great courage, 25 years ago, for a physician in a teaching hospital publicly to declare himself favourable to Freud's doctrines".

Forsyth wrote:

> "by far the intensest strain is shell fire, especially by high explosives. The detonation, the flash, the heat of the explosion, the air concussion, the upheaval of the ground, and the acrid suffocating fumes, combine in producing a violent assault on practically all the senses simultaneously."

He emphasised the bad effects of continued exposure to such stress or strain, and the distinction between fear, which all should expect, and self-control in battle, at which all might wish to aim. He did argue that a particular clinical case history which superficially explained events in terms of danger, fear, and injury, required further exploration, and that the patient proved on analysis to be "a case of unconscious homosexuality with well marked anal eroticism".

The Royal Society of Medicine held a "Special Discussion on Shell Shock Without Visible Signs of Injury" on 25 January 1916 in the Section of Psychiatry, presided over by Major F. W. Mott, MD, FRS. Mott (1916*a*) pointed out that:

> "the forces producing shell shock are most commonly generated by the explosion of large shells, but also by mines, aerial torpedoes, whizz-bangs, trench mortars, bombs and hand-grenades charged with high explosives. In a large number of cases, although exhibiting no visible injury, shell shock is accompanied by 'burial'. Sandbags may be dislodged from the parapet of the trench and strike the individual on the head or spine, and cause concussion without visible injury, or the roof of a dugout may fall in. While lying partially buried he may be subject to the inhalation of noxious gases, so that a combination of causes may account for the severe effects of shell shock."

The tenor of his view at that time was clearly to accept the reality of shell-shock as a frequent physical effect, even though he readily recognised alternative diagnoses.

William McDougall, William Brown, and Dr Stansfield followed with accounts of their cases. The meeting was adjourned at a late hour, and transferred for two more days to the Section of Neurology; Captain Wilfred Harris, MD, continued the discussion. He was followed by Dr Collier, Mr Walter H. Jessup, Dr Campbell Thompson, Dr Dundas Grant, Dr Fearnsides, and Dr Leonard Guthrie.

Henry Head vigorously rejected shell-shock as a category. He held it to be "a heterogeneous collection of different nervous affections from concussion to sheer funk, which have merely this much in common that nervous control has at last given way" (*Lancet*, 1916). In February and March 1916, Mott delivered three Lettsomian lectures (Mott, 1916*b*): as in January, he paid special attention to "injuries of the central nervous system without visible injury". In his civilian role, Mott was pathologist to the London County Council, serving the mental hospitals of London. He spent approximately half his first lecture describing neurones and the way in which they might respond to concussion, with histological illustrations. For the rest, he discussed such effects as the simultaneous deaths of large groups of men and the possibility of carbon monoxide poisoning in men who had been buried by high-explosive shells. In his second lecture, he discussed carbon monoxide poisoning and verified cases of damage to the spinal cord without damage to the brain, following burial from an explosion.

Finally, Mott described the varied phenomena to which shell-shock might give rise: amnesia, terrifying dreams, speech defects including mutism, headache, cardiac and vasomotor disturbance, sensory disturbances, disturbances of hearing and sight, hyperaesthesia, tremors, functional paralyses, and disorders of gait. Doctors could promise their patients' recovery by being cheerful and looking cheerful, reassuring them that they could get better, and by recommending diversion of the mind, continuous warm baths, some hypnotics, and, in general, employing common sense and taking an interest in the patients' comfort, welfare, and amusement. Having recognised the relevance of psychological factors, and having provided a good description of post-traumatic nightmares, he still adhered to the view of an organic basis. This is shown by a later paper on the microscopic examination of the brains of two men who died from *commotio cerebri* (concussion or shell-shock) without visible external injury (Mott, 1917). He thought that this was "the first description that has been given which serves to explain: (1) sudden death in shell shock, and (2) the clinical symptoms which persist for some time after the commotion of the brain in non-fatal cases". In one case, he described generalised early chromatolytic change, most affecting the small cells in which the basilar substance is partly or almost absent. In the other case, the principal phenomena were marked congestion of blood vessels, with extravasation of blood in the meninges, orbital lobe, pons, and temporal lobe.

Some clinicians investigated the cerebrospinal fluid changes. Professor Graham Brown, who had been with the forces in Salonika, had undertaken a series of examinations and concluded that, at most, 20% of patients had changes such as increased protein and cells (*Report*, p. 106).

Arguments and explanations

In France, Lépine (1919), Clinical Professor of Nervous and Mental Diseases at the University of Lyons, was the principal advocate for physical causation.

He argued that the employment of heavy artillery "has changed the conditions of the problem, without in any degree furnishing its solution" (p. 48). He claimed (p. 84): "The cases we have just described, although they had not received any visible wound, were evidently neither failures nor shammers. Without any doubt they were actually wounded, internally wounded."

Mairet & Durante (1917) induced experimental shell-shock in rabbits. Minute haemorrhages were found in the lungs, spinal cord, and nerve roots, and were held to correspond to "the symptomatology of men suffering from shell shock, especially the amnesia which may result from the anaemia in certain small areas, the neuralgias, and the pains at the emerging points of the nerves".

Some later commentators noted examples of men blown up without shell-shock (e.g., *Report*: J. Fortescue, p. 9; W. Tyrrell, p. 33; J. S. Y. Rogers, p. 62).

The 'psychological' position was most strongly espoused by Roussy (Roussy & Boisseau, 1916; Roussy *et al*, 1919; and Roussy, in *Report*, p. 110). Roussy *et al* (p. 43) quote with approval Dupré, who sees the cycle of events in the shell-shocked soldier as follows: *"Commotion, émotion, suggestion, exagération, simulation, revendication"* (shock, emotion, suggestion, exaggeration, simulation, protesting).

Lépine (1916) had supported his argument with findings in 1500 cases of shell-shock, which included evidence of haemorrhage in the cerebrospinal fluid in the early phase. In the end, Roussy and others admitted that 10–15% of the cases had a physical contribution (Roussy & Boisseau, 1916). The War Office Committee concluded from English and French evidence that 5% of cases might have had purely commotional shell-shock; perhaps 15% had a mixture of emotional and commotional shock; and at least 80% were purely emotional (*Report*, p. 112).

The literature in all languages soon emphasised that the symptoms were frequently hysterical and that almost all the chronic symptoms after shell-shock were also psychological in origin. Babinski (Babinski & Froment, 1918) had always had a rigidly sceptical attitude to the possibility of hysteria producing such persistent physical changes in the body as vesicles, etc. While he admitted (p. 45) that physical illness could cause part or all of the symptoms in the case of a definite haemorrhage, he was more sceptical about commotion.

Babinski showed that a number of supposedly hysterical symptoms persisted under chloroform: increased reflexes often occurred in the lighter stages of anaesthesia, while contractures could persist even in the deeper phase. Thus, he regarded as organic some conditions which were believed by others to be hysterical. He emphasised reflex nervous disorders which had a peripheral basis, and stressed the importance of separating these from independent or added disorders resulting from suggestion. In general, despite some inclination to believe in shell-shock as a major organic disorder, the French authors and public apparently did not accept it quite as readily as did the British.

The German authors similarly recognised even fewer full-blown cases of shell-shock than did the French, although this is not to deny that they had many cases of post-traumatic neurosis. In the early stages of the war, when the German forces were advancing successfully, they probably experienced fewer breakdowns than the retreating French and British. Nevertheless, they showed some inclination to accept the idea of shell-shock or commotion: their term (Gaupp, 1915) was *Granatkontusion* or bomb concussion. This was a notion of injury due to the effects of an explosion, but without an overt lesion. *Kontusion* means 'crushing', and the pathology was held to differ from that of *commotio*, i.e. concussion. It was also not really bruising, since it could be fatal. Aschaffenburg and Bonhoeffer (*Report*, pp. 111, 113) are reported to have emphasised the psychological causes of the syndrome. Both the German and Allied forces recognised associated factors such as air pressure, poison gas (i.e. burns or fumes from the shell), and mechanical commotion of the whole body if the soldier was thrown into the air or to the ground. Gaupp (1915) felt that "most of the writing on *Granatkontusion* is nothing other than traumatic hysteria – resembling Kraepelin's fright neurosis". He commended Schuster's observation that an explosion near a sleeping person did not cause symptoms of illness, considering that it helped in understanding the situation. Like others, he emphasised predisposition.

Lust (1916) made the impressive observation that among 40 000 war prisoners, hysterical or nervous disturbances "so common among the soldiers were found only in one among each 8,000". Oppenheim (1915) claimed new support for his original theory of traumatic neuroses. He believed that all the symptoms might be explained upon a psychogenic basis, but that the war had proved that they had a double origin. A functional disturbance from the violent impulse of the external stimuli affected the brain centres, and injury to the peripheral nerves also played a part. This position was primarily organic.

Birnbaum (1915) summarised 72 other articles (see Hoch, 1915). His focus was upon psychoses and, secondarily, upon descriptive changes. A number of reports cited Graves' disease developing after severe stress. Eissler (1986) provides valuable insight into Austrian and German views.

Elliot Smith (1916) adopted the same position as Forsyth on the immediate causes. He also took into account the views of German specialists, especially those of Gaupp (1915). Much later, Gillespie (1942, p. 180) summed up the immediate aetiology of the war neuroses as follows:

> "The outstanding cause, apart from predisposition, under actual Service conditions is undoubtedly the fear of death or disablement. The symptoms exist because the patient is afraid, and they persist so long as there is any conflict between his desire for self preservation and his sense of duty. If he is removed from duty permanently, or if he himself refuses point-blank to face danger again, . . . he loses his symptoms, sometimes in the most dramatic fashion, in a few hours."

In June 1916, Wiltshire, an assistant physician at King's College Hospital, and "late temporary Captain RAMC", rejected the term 'shell-shock'; he emphasised that the term referred to "functional nervous disease". Unlike Forsyth, he suggested that these cases of so-called shell-shock "should be invaluable for the purpose of disproving the universal application of the 'sex' theory of Freud and his followers". This seems to be the first publication of the idea that hysterical symptoms might be well explained in terms of current conflict, without invoking past sexual experiences in childhood (Wiltshire, 1916). Merskey (1979) and Stone (1985) subsequently remarked upon the part World War I played in revising the idea that hysterical symptoms were founded upon infantile sexual fixation. MacCurdy (1918, p. 15) also thought that fear was more important than sexual adjustment, but indicated that in civilian life, weaknesses in adaptability might be confined to "such demands as are essentially related to sex". Failures of adaptation in civilian life and fear in wartime were both related to "some vague constitutional defect". By early 1916, Myers (1940, p. 95) had decided that the diagnosis of shell-shock was undesirable. Grasset (1915), Myers (1915) and Smith (1916), among others, all recognised contemporaneously that the pre-morbid personality strongly predisposed to the symptoms of shell-shock.

Overwhelming stress

Despite the horrors of World War II, fewer combatants died in it than in the war of 1914–18. Others suffered more in World War II, particularly Jews at the hands of the Nazis, Stalin's prisoners in the Gulag archipelago, described by Solzhenitsyn (1973), the soldiers and others taken prisoner by the Japanese, and the Japanese civilians living in Hiroshima and Nagasaki. The horrors of Cambodia, the tortures of Latin America, and appalling natural disasters like the earthquake in Armenia in 1988, have all produced enormous suffering. However, none of these categories of people were bearing arms, nor could they escape from their danger by a retreat into hiding or into illness. In the concentration camps, illness merely hastened death. Those wounded at Hiroshima or Nagasaki needed time and medicine, but at least some of this was provided. By contrast, soldiers in the field in World War I faced intolerable conditions of danger and discomfort, but if they were ill, would be able to escape from the grave risks and profound miseries which surrounded them.

Almost every British village has a war memorial. Anyone who examines a few of these will note that the numbers killed in World War I are usually four or five times those killed in World War II. A French offensive in April 1915 against a German salient at Saint-Mihiel, south-east of Verdun, sacrificed 64 000 men to no effect. The Battle of the Somme, which lasted four months, cost the British 420 000 casualties, the French 194 000, and the Germans 440 000. It was calculated that in World War I, the Allied and associated powers mobilised more than 42 000 000 men, and lost more than 5 000 000 lives; Russia and France contributed some 60% of the dead, Britain most of the rest. Another 21 000 000 men were wounded.

In Britain, the social atmosphere which advocated persistence in the face of these awful figures was one of intense patriotism and loyal service. The misery of all and the stoicism of many emerge alike from the poetry of Wilfred Owen and the writings of men like Sassoon (1936), Graves (1960, first published 1929), and Vaughan (1981), or the historian John Keegan (1976). To the man in the ranks, the war meant being willing to serve, being ostracised, imprisoned, or shot for evasion of duty, or perhaps being 'lucky' enough to be ill. Judge Babington's book *For the Sake of Example: Capital Courts Martial, 1914–1920* (1983) describes the execution of 269 men for desertion, cowardice, or quitting the post in the face of the enemy. Illness provided a respectable escape.

Ritchie (1986) explored the attitudes of 'imperial man' to warfare. The stereotype of the good soldier or officer was of someone marked by comradeship, loyalty, the stiff upper lip, courage and endurance, who played by the rules without complaint. Doctors identified with these ideals: in fact, to function well as a medical officer, the doctor had to operate as an agent of the military purpose. His role was not simply to attend to sick men and see that they were not sent into battle, or to repair the injured. He also needed to promote self-control, moral stamina and military devotion. It was his responsibility to certify either that a man had 'shell-shock' or 'neurasthenia' and should be removed from the firing line, or that he was a coward, shirking duty, who deserved to face a court martial and even perhaps capital punishment. Babington pointed out that the medical officers were frequently more indignant about the cowardice of deserters than were other army officers. However, the medical officer himself was at least one stage less involved in battle than the men whose cowardice he was rejecting.

The War Office Committee makes the doctor's role very clear (*Report*, p. 132):

> "The doctor must get the full confidence of the patient. The persistence of symptoms often resolves itself into a *tour de force* in the struggle for ascendency between the patient's selfish and social tendencies. . . . In no type of case is there more need to maintain firm disciplinary control . . . there should be not too many inducements to prolong the stay in hospital . . . it should be avoided that any general impression obtained that the disorder is one for which invaliding from the service is bound to take place if the symptoms prove intractable."

Thus, the medical officer has to prepare the patient to be well enough to go back to face the great risk of death or mutilating injury.

In his evidence to the War Office Commission, Sir John Goodwin stated that:

> "regimental medical officers . . . can exert an influence on the regiment of incalculable benefit. The medical officers I had under me, both in the Cavalry Division and in the Guards Division . . . were splendid, the pains and trouble they took with the men; . . . they knew and worked with the men . . . and even when a young officer was put to a regiment straight away, it was astonishing how quickly he got to know the tone of the regiment, and the different companies . . . , and the extraordinarily good influence he had with them." (*Report*, p. 158).

Witnesses at the War Office Committee recognised that the state of morale in different regiments had an enormous influence on the frequency of shell-shock. The Guards had few cases, but other regiments were mentioned, though not named, as having many. Dr William Brown (p. 43) commented, for example:

> "The doctors could not help be struck by the fact that men from certain regiments came up again and again . . . where there was more 'shell shock' there was more 'skrim-shanking' . . . on one occasion he had most of the officers and men of a certain regiment in his hospital . . . it seems as if a panic arose and they all came down together."

In response to questions, Brown added that he had found it nearly impossible to decide between cowardice and shell-shock, and that after his first two or three courts martial, he found he was giving evidence in favour of the man in practically every case.

Holmes (*Report*, p. 38) observed that more cases of shell-shock occurred during prolonged engagements, especially when these were not successful, and much less frequently when the fighting was successful, for instance, during the autumn of 1918. (This is an observation which has been made in other wars also, for example by the Israeli army in comparing previous battles with those of the Yom Kippur War of October 1973.) Holmes considered that the most potent causes of shell-shock, in order of frequency, were probably: the stress of battle, exposure to the bursting of high explosives, prolonged mental stress, and prolonged service. He based these conclusions on Army Form W.3436, where the diagnosis of "shell shock, wounded", and its causes, was recorded. The incidence was also high among fresh troops, who had little training and low morale; he considered that neuropathic individuals were probably more likely to suffer. Ideas of this sort recurred repeatedly in the comments of contemporary observers and writers.

The military and medical authorities wished to recognise whatever might be called genuine illness, and also to keep out of the firing line men whose presence would encourage low morale. On the other hand, they could not accept that subjective complaints and a wide variety of dramatic symptoms (blindness, deafness, amnesia, mutism, paralysis, tremor, etc.) could be allowed to provide a means of withdrawing increasing numbers of individuals from the front. One way of solving the problem was to forbid the use of the term 'shell-shock', and this was done in 1917 (see below and also Stone, 1985, p. 258).

Shell-shock was not the only 'respectable' label to be offered during World War I. 'Disorderly action of the heart' (DAH) or 'soldier's heart' were popular diagnoses. Abrahams (1917) caustically characterised the excessive enthusiasm of many witnesses who were either greatly in favour of this diagnosis or denied its existence entirely.

The alternative diagnosis, based on cardiac symptoms, is a story in itself, told among others by Gallavardin (1917), Jarcho (1966), Skerritt (1983), Wooley (1986, 1987, 1988), and Wooley & Boudoulas (1988). Lewis (1918), who recognised the good prognosis of the disorder, seemed unwilling to admit the probable psychogenesis in most cases, and it was left to Hurst (1940) to remark that "Soldier's Heart is nothing more than a manifestation of anxiety neurosis". No one seems to have noticed that DaCosta's first case (DaCosta, 1871) had an aphonia for ten months. Today, Wooley (1988) indicates that despite the associations of 'DAH' or 'neurocirculatory asthenia' with anxiety it also has a relationship with mitral-valve prolapse and mitral regurgitation.

A great variety of treatments was used, including rest, quiet, massage, exercise, occupational management, stretching bent backs on a board (Hurst, 1940), persuasion, suggestion, more formal psychotherapy, occasional psychoanalysis and, often, disciplinary pressures. Electrical therapy was employed (Yealland, 1918) with a zest which is open to obvious criticism. In 1919 and 1929 in the aftermath of defeat Wagner-Jauregg, the leader of Viennese psychiatry and neurology and a subsequent Nobel Laureate, was accused of having used electrical stimulation to torture an invalid soldier. Freud was called upon as a witness, perhaps because he was not a direct colleague of Wagner-Jauregg, and gave evidence which helped the charges to be dismissed. Eissler (1986, p. 304) describes these events, and cites the explanation of Jellinek (1947) (p. 121) that 20 deaths of German soldiers were "due to the surprise factor". The chairman of the commission examining Wagner-Jauregg observed that the Austrian methods were gentler than the German ones (Eissler, 1986, pp. 65, 72).

The need to treat some of the patients as ill was well expressed by Williamson (1917):

> "Though very many cases of malingering and shirking are seen, in a large number of cases the symptoms are undoubtedly pathological . . . men who have received the VC, DCM and other medals, and some of the men who have been able for months to view the shell fire with the greatest possible calmness, have suffered eventually from shell shock. The symptoms may continue long after the patient is discharged from the army, and when he has no fear of further risk. . . ."

Extended discussions

In September 1916, German neuropsychiatrists meeting in Munich rejected the hypothesis of organic causation decisively, with respect to the majority of cases. This is described in English in the *Journal of the American Medical Association* (1917). Oppenheim opened the discussion and argued that a neurosis produced by psychic causes would have the same brain patterns as one due to concussion. 'Fright neurosis' and 'commotion neurosis' were both traumatic neuroses. Disturbances could be found which were not hysterical, although he admitted that he had underestimated the spread of hysteria.

Nonne opposed him strongly. Traumatic neurosis was not a distinct entity. The shell-explosion neuroses were purely functional and curable by psychological techniques. Neurasthenia could occur in stable individuals through fatigue and exhaustion. (We note this excuses illness in the brave.) Oppenheim's views were against the economic interests of the state and the therapeutic needs of the patient. Most cases were hysteria.

Gaupp and the majority of those present supported Nonne. Oppenheim retired from the argument, disappointed but without changing his view. The British meeting in January 1915 at the Royal Society of Medicine clearly achieved much less than the German one eight months later. However, understanding of the psychological basis for the symptoms was developing in Britain in 1917, and a new procedure was adopted, perhaps prompted initially by Myers (see Myers, 1940, p. 92).

Early in 1917, all cases presenting symptoms of functional nervous disorder were sent to special hospitals as 'NYD' (not yet diagnosed). If there had been direct contact with the effect of explosions, even though there was no visible external wound, a diagnosis of "shell-shock (wound)" was made, while other cases of 'nervousness' were classed as neurasthenia, hysteria, etc. After June 1917, when special neurological centres had been established in each army area, all cases of functional nervous disorder were marked 'NYDN' (not yet diagnosed, nervous) and transferred to the centres. Army Form .3346 was introduced to determine whether the man was 'wounded' or 'sick', but this procedure turned out to be unfair and unworkable.

In September 1918, it was eventually decided to abolish the classification of "shell-shock, wound" in France, and to use it only if the patient's disability was so serious as to necessitate transfer to England. There, the decision to classify the patient as a battle casualty would depend upon the recommendation of a neurological board at a special centre (*Report*, p. 119). This sequence of events and the time at which it began clearly reflect the efforts of the army medical authorities to resolve the difficult practical issues which were arising out of the concepts of shell-shock.

In time, the literature on this topic provided a series of monographs. The authors included Harris (1915), Hurst (1916), who produced two more editions of his original volume in 1918 and 1940, modifying his views each time, Hurst (1920), Smith & Pear (1917), MacCurdy (1918), Yealland (1918), Lépine (1919) (edited by Mercier) and Babinski & Froment (1918). Mott (1919) moved away from his original view that shell-shock was mostly due to organic causes.

Among American authors, Southard provided a tremendous collection of reports from all the belligerent countries, with brief comments of his own, and Fenton compiled an extensive bibliography with him (Southard, 1928). In addition to the British official war history, there was also the United States Army Report (Salmon & Fenton, 1929), and a collection by Brown & Williams (1918) which comprised a bibliography with abstracts from the different combatant countries. Fenton (1926) wrote a personal appraisal. The most notable American work was probably that by Salmon (1917), *The Care and Treatment of Mental Diseases and War Neuroses ('Shell Shock') in the British Army*. Salmon's work brought together the most important lessons of World War I, and his recommendations were applied immediately to the American expeditionary forces.

In all countries, the trend was to reject the term 'shell-shock', but, in 1922, the British government still felt it necessary to conduct an inquiry. This has provided an impressive record of the views and opinions of the doctors and soldiers of the period on the subject.

Lieutenant General Sir John Goodwin, KCB, CMG, DSO, FRCS, Director General of the Army Medical Services, said that 'shell-shock' was an unfortunate misnomer. It had covered a multitude of imperfections, and, as he understood the term, it included both shell concussion and war neurosis. That was really the same as 'commotional' and 'emotional' 'shell-shock' and included neurosis and emotional conditions occurring both in peace and in war (*Report*, p. 13). In comparison with neurosis, shell concussion was very uncommon. Witness after witness made the same comment. General Lord Horne, GCB, KCMG, told the Committee that he thought it probable that "miners and agricultural labourers, and men who lived open-air lives, such as shepherds and game keepers, were less liable to the disorder than the clerk or artisan" (*Report*, p. 16).

There was a consensus that shell-shock from commotional effects was rare, and that the condition which had been called 'shell-shock' was essentially one of fright or fear, leading to a withdrawal from the line of duty. Dr W. J. Adie, Major RAMC, Physician to the Great Northern Central Hospital and Neurologist to the Ministry of Pensions, recognised that everyone felt some fear in conditions of frontline service (*Report*, p. 17). The bravest and most decorated generals supported this view: shell-shock or neurosis was understood to be a condition in which fear overcame the ability of the individual to fulfil his military responsibilities. Several more witnesses, including Lieutenant General E. Hewlett, CMG, DSO, Late Inspector of Infantry Training, said that the term really meant the effect of the explosion of a shell so near as to "knock a man silly". He added that he had seen cases of men who apparently bore no visible outward trace of wounds, but who had been killed by shell-shock. He deplored the tendency to apply the term to forms of nervous breakdown due to mental or physical stress, or both. Like General Horne, he thought that intelligence could be a disadvantage: "A battalion of real countrymen (less intelligence) will stick out a situation which a battalion of townsmen (greater intelligence) will not" (p. 18). Commander N. D. Holbrook, VC, RN (former submarine commander) gave evidence that 'nervousness' was observed in his sailors, especially when under attack by depth charges, but not shell-shock (p. 18).

Shell-shock was largely battle neurosis, fright, or even malingering. Fifty-five distinguished witnesses concurred – gallant soldiers, distinguished physicians, and some both doctors and decorated officers. Throughout this group, there was great sympathy for men who had tried, fought, faced bombardment or other danger, and ultimately broken down. The case of a winner of the Victoria Cross was cited as an example (p. 105), among others. The term 'shell-shock' was supported because it was known that so many brave men who had fought under intolerable conditions for long periods of time had shown signs of the disorder, which would otherwise have to be called nervous.

Post-war events

In the light of the experience in Britain, France, and Germany, it is important to look at Kretschmer's observations (1948), recorded some time later in his book on hysteria. He described two primitive patterns of human behaviour which resembled the "instinctive flurry" and the "death feint" in animals; one human example is of an hysterical fugue with trembling. In discussing animals, he points out how random rapid movements may ultimately, by trial and error, release an imprisoned insect. He says "The instinctive flurry" (*Bewegungssturm*) is a typical reaction of animals to situations that threaten or interfere with their existence. It is a built-in mechanism with a biological function. Kretschmer claims that there is a link between the flurry and acute fright or the 'fear neurosis'.

This idea, fostered by the experiences of World War I, offers a biological interpretation of certain patterns of hysteria, but it has received remarkably little attention in the literature. On the whole, Kretschmer regarded the war neuroses themselves as examples of severe emotional reactions induced by fear and modified in time, sometimes consciously, by the wishes and inclinations of the patients.

Pensions became a matter for concern. MacPherson *et al* (1923, p. 56) provide figures from the Ministry of Pensions which suggest that in February 1921, 65 000 men were drawing pensions for neurasthenia and allied conditions, and that by January 1922, this number had fallen to 50 000. However, in February 1921, 14 771 men were attending either boards for assessment or clinics for treatment. The number of people in these categories increased to 16 393 by November 1921, including some who had not previously been ill. If anything, the numbers of men receiving pensions seemed to increase after 20 years, in spite of the downward trend of the initial figures quoted above, and in contradiction to the ordinary expectation that the numbers would decline by attrition caused by death and, occasionally, recovery, without being replenished. Ahrenfeldt (1958, p. 10) summarised the situation with regard to pensions in Britain, some 20 years after the end of the war, as follows:

> "In March 1939 there were about 120,000 pensioners who were still in receipt of pensions or had received final awards for primary psychiatric disability (including 'neurasthenia', 'shell-shock', effort syndrome, epilepsy and insanity). 'Neurasthenia' itself accounted for some 100,000 men, costing 10 million pounds a year, and representing about 2% of total serving troops. These 120,000 cases represented about 15% of all pensioned disabilities."

Hurst's work was republished at the beginning of World War II (Hurst, 1940), and several other volumes appeared which reviewed what had been known in the previous war (Miller, 1940; Myers, 1940; Ross, 1941; Gillespie, 1942). Strecker & Appel (1946) suggested that this knowledge had been neglected in the USA until after the start of World War II, and Ahrenfeldt (1958) indicated the same for Britain. However, it was in fact quickly applied among the British and American forces in the early years of World War II. Sargant (1959) states that published reports on the value of drug abreaction in the handling of casualties with neurosis from Dunkirk and the Blitz caused this treatment to be widely adopted in Britain and that further interest was aroused in American psychiatry by the work of Grinker & Spiegel (1943) in North Africa. In Canada Griffin (1989) described the enthusiasm of psychiatrists, led by Brock Chisholm, to introduce techniques of personnel selection from 1939 onwards. (Chalke (1954) later provided a critical assessment of the evidence for the utility of such selection.)

Effects on psychiatry

It may well be the case that the maturation of psychiatry occurred in the course of World War I; it then became a specialty with potential for the community. Rees (1945), who recalled the period well, stated that the provision for ex-servicemen "led to the establishment of clinics for civilians" (p. 29) but did not give any decisive evidence. Stone (1985) also suggested that the clinics of the Ministry of Pensions led to the development of reforms and innovations in psychiatry in Britain after World War I; those psychiatrists who qualified just before World War II, or practised during it, shared that impression. Dr Myre Sim commented (personal communication) that prominent figures like T. A. Ross, D. K. Henderson, and Millais Culpin all received an impetus to work outside the psychiatric hospitals from their own wartime experience. Nevertheless, the influence of the war upon ideas about psychiatry, which Stone observes, was weak in respect of the creation of services. There is little evidence of new provision for civilians before the Mental Treatment Act 1930. The late Sir Charles Symonds told me that he had had great difficulty in finding psychiatric help for patients in London before World War II. This was so much the case that he would occasionally select patients from his hospital practice and arrange to treat them himself, as well as he could, at his consulting rooms. He gave them psychotherapy several times a week in accordance with Freudian recommendations, and made no charge for this treatment. He gave this up because he was disappointed with the results, and felt that he was not succeeding with this technique as he should have done.

However, there was some psychiatric provision in teaching hospitals in London in the early 20th century. In 1918, Bernard Hart functioned as the first physician for mental diseases to the Out-Patient Department at University College Hospital.

Hart had pointed out to the hospital authorities the year before that departments for mental diseases already existed at St Thomas', Guys, Charing Cross, and St Mary's hospitals. In 1918, Hart wrote to the Dean of University College Hospital Medical School to draw attention to the inadequate arrangements for treating functional nervous diseases. There was only one private hospital at Brighton which could do this, but because of the problems of functional nervous disorders in the British army, special hospitals had been set up and medical officers were being carefully trained, for example at Maghull Military Hospital near Liverpool (Merrington, 1976, p. 227).

Since the Ministry of Pensions was forced to set up over 100 treatment centres in an effort to cope with the flood of 'neurasthenic' ex-servicemen, Stone argued that it was the war and the consequent mass epidemic of mental disorders which set the mechanism of psychiatric change in motion. He claimed that the major innovations between the two wars, "Psychotherapy, and the 1930 Mental Treatment Act", which promoted out-patient clinics and 'voluntary' treatment, were mainly a result of these pressures (Stone, 1985). The evidence for his contentions is still rather limited. Mayou (1989) described the history of general hospital psychiatry in Britain and showed that widespread, but very patchy, efforts at such treatment were known from the 18th century. He remarked on the interest of some other physicians in treating their patients' minds as well as their bodies but showed that out-patient clinics and general hospital provisions were very limited between the wars. Approaches to psychological management and to psychotherapy were also known before World War I, even though their bias was towards hypnosis and suggestion (e.g. Tuckey, 1891). As discussed below, the experience of the war probably did contribute to the spread of knowledge about psychological techniques but caused little institutional change. It is plausible to suppose also that another ten years from 1913 might have seen some spread anyhow of Freudian ideas and psychotherapeutic skill.

In the period between the two world wars there were competitive tensions between psychiatry and neurology. Myers expressed this frankly in an account of his relationship with Gordon Holmes: he was given a title of "Specialist in Nerve Shock", which was changed in August 1916 to "Consulting Psychologist" (Myers, 1940, p. 18). By the end of that year expert mental specialists had been appointed to the various military base hospitals which were provided with mental wards. To his surprise, Myers was given control of the shell-shock, mental and neurological cases within the Fourth and Fifth Army areas, leaving the remainder to (Lieutenant Colonel) Holmes. Holmes was appointed consulting neurologist at the same time as Myers was appointed consulting psychologist (a term used at the time for some medical practitioners). Holmes said that he felt himself responsible for the shell-shock cases, although Myers claimed that Holmes confessed that he felt "quite incompetent" to examine "mental cases".

Myers also declared that Holmes had previously told him that functional 'nervous' disorders always formed a very large part of the civilian neurologist's practice. Hence, Myers observes, "He was little disposed to relinquish in army life what was so important a source of income in time of peace, although he confessed that (like most 'pure' neurologists) he took little interest in such cases". Myers considered that in the 25 years leading up to 1916, and following the work of Janet, Prince, Freud, Janz, Adler, Hart, Rows, Jones, and many others, psychotherapy was now an established skill. He believed that Holmes should have acknowledged his own priority in this work; Myers would have been only too pleased to give up the practice of diagnosing lesions and organic diseases of the brain and cord, which he felt unqualified to perform. Myers felt – or indeed was – pushed out, and his transfer back to England was arranged. Martin (1981) described Holmes as quarrelsome (with some details).

The idea that symptoms could be motivated also often worked against patients and psychiatry to belittle both the sick and the therapist who accepted them. Morton & Wright (1987, p. 75), examining the pensions of Canadian veterans, described attitudes which are equally representative of those found in Britain (and were usually drawn from European experience):

> "Worst off were the 'functional' or 'shell-shock' cases. Whether doctors took them seriously or dismissed them as cowardly malingerers the consequences were virtually identical. Such men had subconsciously willed themselves into a primitive state [explained a neurologist, and army specialist on neurasthenia]. To give them pensions only encouraged them: 'You have thrown away the four aces'." (Morton & Wright, 1987)

It seems likely nevertheless that the war did make a difference in demonstrating the usefulness of the psychotherapeutic skills which were most developed by psychiatrists. Smith & Pear (1917) campaigned vigorously for the provision of services outside the asylums. They concluded (p. 132) that:

> "Excuses for inertia, brought forward before August 1914 can be accepted no longer. The thousands of cases of shell shock . . . have proved beyond any possibility of doubt, that the early treatment of mental disorder is successful from the humanitarian, medical and financial standpoints."

Fenton (1926) similarly argued, from the steady recovery rate to be found in the figures of the United States Army's figures, that the US Veterans' Bureau and other social organisations dealing with war neurotics, together with improved industrial conditions, and natural recovery, had made a definite impression on the problem. The British Psychoanalytical Association held its first open meeting in 1919, and psychotherapeutic ideas spread steadily throughout the 1920s. They were fostered by psychologically minded doctors such as W. McDougall, W. H. R. Rivers, William Brown, and, of course, Myers, all of whom had gained substantial wartime experience in psychotherapy.

Little was heard of shell-shock in World War II, but a new, erroneous, organic syndrome was described in Norwegian sailors under the title of the 'war sailor syndrome'. Sjaastad (1985) has given careful attention to the evidence and concludes that this syndrome, which had been attributed to an encephalopathy, was probably due to severe and prolonged stress.

Psychological breakdown was clearly well recognised in World War II (e.g. Sargant & Shorvon, 1945; Sargant, 1959; Merskey, 1979; Copp & McAndrew, 1990). Stress disorders from battle were common as well in the Vietnam War. The latter conflict led to the revision of categories for stress disorder (Figley, 1978) which were then presented in DSM–III and its revised edition (American Psychiatric Association, 1980, 1987) as 'post-traumatic stress disorder'. Today, post-traumatic stress disorder represents very well the response which was once called 'shell-shock' in soldiers, as well as an effect of other conditions in causing stress (e.g. frightening accidents). However, there is now less evidence of gross conversion symptoms than was found with shell-shock.

Doctors involved in the treatment of shell-shock displayed a striking ambivalence towards the patients, and such ambivalence persists to this day in the attitudes of many medical professionals towards hysteria. Babington (1983) noted a strong commitment by doctors in the RAMC to get their patients either to return to battle – pushing them to return to duty and denying their hesitations – or to face punishment. It is plausible that this attitude reflected some guilt that the doctors themselves were not in conditions of identical danger, even though many also faced great risks, which they tolerated bravely. But the doctor who gave in too easily to the complaints of the conscript was at risk both of endangering himself and of being fooled by 'illegitimate', albeit potentially life-saving, demands for the recognition of 'illness'. Hence perhaps the vigour with which some doctors rejected complaints (Babington, 1983, pp. 59–61) and condemned the shirker, while others (e.g. Yealland, 1918) applied unpleasant, virtually bullying treatment to the management of hysteria.

World War II seemed to escape the full force of such dilemmas, although they certainly existed. As noted earlier, conditions for most combatants were not as bad as they had been in World War I. In addition, the special barbarity of the Nazis in Germany, and of the Japanese treatment of prisoners, made fighters out of many who might otherwise have been pacifists. By the same token the force of the ethical dilemma was opposed by a moral imperative – "If I cure my patient, he may go back to be killed. But if we lose this war, who may not be killed or tortured?"

The problems encountered in Vietnam by an army composed of US conscripts may have raised the issue again in the USA. So far as I am aware, though, this immense ethical problem has not yet been tackled.

Acknowledgements

E. Tauschke helped with the German sources. M. Why provided much bibliographical help, and A. Lyubechansky searched the back issues of *The Times* for the earliest reference to 'shell-shock'. T. Copp, E. Shorter and M. Trimble drew my attention to valuable sources.

References

ABRAHAMS, H. A. (1917) Soldier's heart. *Lancet*, *i*, 442–445.

AHRENFELDT, R. H. (1958) *Psychiatry in the British Army in the Second World War*. London: Routledge & Kegan Paul.

AMERICAN PSYCHIATRIC ASSOCIATION (1980) *Diagnostic and Statistical Manual of Mental Disorders* (3rd edn) (DSM–III). Washington, DC: APA.

—— (1987) *Diagnostic and Statistical Manual of Mental Disorders* (3rd edn, revised) (DSM–III–R). Washington, DC: APA.

BABINGTON, A. (1983) *For the Sake of Example: Capital Courts Martial 1914–1920*. New York: St Martin's Press.

BABINSKI, J. & FROMENT, J. (1918) *Hysteria or Pithiatism and Reflex Nervous Disorders in the Neurology of War* (ed. E. Farquhar Buzzard). London: University of London Press.

BAILEY, P. (1906) *Diseases of the Nervous System Resulting from Accident and Injury*. New York: Appleton.

BAKER, S. L. (1975) Military psychiatry. In *Comprehensive Textbook of Psychiatry, II* (ed. A. M. Freedman, H. I. Kaplan & B. J. Sadock). Baltimore: Williams & Wilkins.

BINSWANGER, O. (1915) Hystero-somatische Krankheitserscheinungen bei der Kriegshysterie (Hysterical-somatic symptoms of illness in battle hysteria). *Monatsschrift für Psychiatrie und Neurologie*, **38**, 1–60.

BIRNBAUM, K. (1915) War neuroses and psychoses according to observations made in the present war; first résumé from the beginning of the war to the middle of March, 1915 (abstract). In *Neuropsychiatry and the War* (eds M. W. Brown & F. E. Williams). New York: National Committee for Mental Hygiene. (Kriegsneurosen und psychosen auf Grund der gegenwärtigen Kriegsbeobachtungen; erste Zusammenstellung vom Kriegsbeginn bis Mittel März, 1915. *Zeitschrift für der gesämte Neurologie und Psychiatrie*, **11**, 321–367.)

BRITISH MEDICAL JOURNAL (1941) D. Forsyth (obituary). *British Medical Journal*, *i*, 653.

BROWN, T. (1984) Shell shock in the Canadian expeditionary force, 1914–1918: Canadian psychiatry in the Great War. In *Health, Disease & Medicine, Essays in Canadian History* (ed. C. G. Roland), pp. 308–332. Toronto: The Hannah Institute for the History of Medicine.

BROWN, M. W. & WILLIAMS, F. E. (1918) *Neuropsychiatry and the War*. New York: National Committee for Mental Hygiene.

CAMPBELL, H. (1916) War neuroses. *Practitioner*, **96**, 501–509.

CHALKE, F. C. R. (1954) Psychiatric screening of recruits: a review. *Department of Veterans' Affairs Treatment Services Bulletin*, **9**, 273–292.

CHARCOT, J.-M. (1889) *Clinical Lectures on Diseases of the Nervous System. Vol. III. Delivered at La Salpêtrière* (trans. T. Savill). London: New Sydenham Society.

COPP, T. & MCANDREW, W. (1990) *Battle Exhaustion: Psychiatrists and Soldiers in the Canadian Army 1939–1945*. Montreal: McGill/Queen's University Press.

COURVILLE, C. B. (1953) *Commotio Cerebri*. Los Angeles: San Lucas Press.

DACOSTA, J. M. (1871) On irritable heart; a clinical study of a form of functional cardiac disorder and its consequences. *American Journal of the Medical Sciences*, **61**, 17–52.

EISSLER, K. R. (1986) *Freud as an Expert Witness. The Discussion of War Neuroses between Freud and Wagner-Jauregg*. Madison, CT: International Universities Press.

ELLIOTT, T. R. (1914) Transient paraplegia from shell explosions. *British Medical Journal*, *ii*, 1005–1006.

ERICHSEN, J. E. (1866) *On Railway and Other Injuries of the Nervous System*. Philadelphia: Henry C. Lea.

——— (1886) *On Concussion of the Spine, Nervous Shock and Other Obscure Injuries to the Nervous System in Their Clinical and Medico-Legal Aspects*. New York: William Wood.

EVANS, J. J. (1915) Organic lesions from shell concussion. *British Medical Journal*, *ii*, 848.

FENTON, N. (1926) *Shell Shock and its Aftermath*. St Louis: C. V. Mosby.

FIGLEY, C. R. (ed.) (1978) Introduction. In *Stress Disorders Among Vietnam Veterans*, pp. xiii–xxvi. New York: Brunner/Mazel.

FORSYTH, D. (1915) Functional nerve disease and the shock of battle. *Lancet*, *ii*, 1399–1403.

FREUD, S. (1893–95) Studies in Hysteria. In *Complete Psychological Works, Standard edn. Vol. 2*. London: Hogarth Press.

GALLAVARDIN, L. (1917) Soldiers with disordered action of the heart. *Archives des Maladies du Coeur, Paris*, **10**, 408–433.

GAUPP, R. (1915) Die Granatkontusion. *Beiträge zur klinische Chirurgie*, **96**, 277–294.

GILLESPIE, R. D. (1942) *Psychological Effects of War on Citizen and Soldier*. New York: W. W. Norton.

GRASSET, J. (1915) Clinical lecture on the psychoneuroses of war. *Medical Press New Series*, **99**, 560–563, 586–587.

GRAVES, R. (1960) *Goodbye to All That*. Harmondsworth: Penguin.

GRIFFIN, J. D. M. (1989) Interview by S. Sussman. In *Pioneers of Mental Health and Social Change* (eds D. J. Blonm & S. Sussman), pp. 70–71. London, Canada: Third Eye.

GRINKER, R. F. & SPIEGEL, J. P. (1943) War neurosis. In *North Africa: The Tunisian Campaign*. New York: Josiah Macy, Jr, Foundation.

——— & ——— (1945) *Men Under Stress*. Philadelphia: Blakiston, McGraw-Hill.

HARRIS, W. (1915) *Nerve Injuries and Shock*. London: Henry Frowde and Hodder & Stoughton.

HESNARD, A. (1914) Les Troubles nerveux et psychiques consécutifs aux catastrophes navales. *Revue de Psychiatrie*, **18**, 139–151.

HOCH, A. (1915) Review of Birnbaum (1915). *New York State Hospital Bulletin. New Series*, **8**, 287–291.

HODGES, R. M. (1881) So-called concussion of the spinal cord. *Boston Medical and Surgical Journal*, **104**, 361–365, 386–389.

HURST, A. F. (1916) *Medical Diseases of the War* (1st edn). London: Edward Arnold.

——— (1918) *Medical Diseases of the War* (2nd edn). London: Edward Arnold.

——— (1920) *The Psychology of the Special Senses and their Functional Disorders*. London: Oxford Medical Publications.

——— (1940) *Medical Diseases of War* (3rd edn). London: Edward Arnold.

JARCHO, S. (1966) Harlow Brooks on neurocirculatory asthenia in World War I. *American Journal of Cardiology*, **18**, 892–897.

JELLINEK, S. (1947) *Dying, Apparent Death and Resuscitation.* Baltimore: Williams & Wilkins.
JOURNAL OF THE AMERICAN MEDICAL ASSOCIATION (1917) Berlin Letter. *Journal of the American Medical Association*, **68**, 647–648.
KEEGAN, J. (1976) *The Face of Battle.* London: Jonathan Cape.
KRETSCHMER, E. (1948) *Hysteria, Reflex and Instinct.* Stuttgart: Trans. V. & W. Baskin. (London: Peter Owen, 1961.)
LANCET (1916) A discussion of shell shock. *Lancet*, *i*, 306–307.
LAURES, G. (1914) Troubles nerveux et mentaux consécutifs à l'explosion du cuirasse ''Liberté''. *Le Caducée*, **14**, 75–76.
LÉPINE, J. (1916) Disturbances of the nerve centers by explosion. *Bulletin de l'Académie de Médecine, Paris*, **76**, 9–11.
——— (1919) *Mental Disorders of War* (ed. C. A. Mercier). London: University of London Press.
LEWIS, T. (1918) *The Soldier's Heart and the Effort Syndrome.* London: Shaw & Sons.
LUST, F. (1916) Kriegsneurosen und Kriegsgefangene. (War neuroses among war prisoners in Germany). *München Medizinische Wochenschrift*, **63**, 1829.
MACCURDY, J. T. (1918) *War Neuroses.* Cambridge: Cambridge University Press.
MACPHERSON, W. G., HERRINGHAM, W. P., ELLIOTT, T. R., *et al* (1923) *History of the Great War Medical Services. Diseases of War. Vol. II.* London: HMSO.
MAIRET, A. & DURANTE, G. (1917) Du syndrome commotionnel. *Presse Médicale*, **25**, 478–479.
MARTIN, J. P. (1981) Reminiscences of Queen Square. *British Medical Journal*, **283**, 1640–1642.
MAYOU, R. (1989) The history of general hospital psychiatry. *British Journal of Psychiatry*, **155**, 746–776.
MERRINGTON, W. R. (1976) *University College Hospital and its Medical School: A History.* London: Heinemann.
MERSKEY, H. (1979) *The Analysis of Hysteria.* London: Baillière Tindall.
MILLER, E. (ed.) (1940) *The Neuroses in War.* London: Macmillan.
MILLIGAN, W. & WESTMACOTT, F. H. (1915) Warfare injuries and neuroses. *Journal of Laryngology, Rhinology and Otology*, **30**, 297–303.
MORTON, D. & WRIGHT, G. (1987) *Winning the Second Battle: Canadian Veterans and the Return to Civilian Life.* Toronto: University of Toronto Press.
MOTT, F. W. (1916*a*) Special discussion on shell shock without visible signs of injury. *Proceedings of the Royal Society of Medicine* (part III, suppl. 9), 1–44.
——— (1916*b*) The effects of high explosives upon the central nervous system. *Lancet*, *i*, 331–338, 441–449, 545–553.
——— (1917) The microscopic examination of the brains of two men dead of commotio cerebri (shell shock) without visible external injury. *British Medical Journal*, *ii*, 612–615.
——— (1919) *War Neuroses and Shell Shock.* London: Henry Frowde and Hodder & Stoughton.
MURRAY, J. A. H., BRADLEY, H., CRAIGIE, W. A., *et al* (1986) *A New English Dictionary on Historical Principles. Supplement* 4, 10. Oxford: Oxford University Press.
MYERS, C. S. (1915) A contribution to the study of shell shock. *Lancet*, *i*, 316–320.
——— (1940) *Shell Shock in France 1914–1918.* Cambridge: Cambridge University Press.
OPPENHEIM, H. (1889) *Die traumatischen Neurosen.* Berlin: Hirschwald.
——— (1911) *Textbook of Nervous Diseases for Physicians and Students* (trans. A. T. N. Bruce). London: Foulis.
——— (1915) The war and the traumatic neuroses. *Berliner klinische Wochenschrift*, **52**, 257–261.
PAGE, H. W. (1883) *Injuries of the Spine and Spinal Cord Without Apparent Mechanical Lesion and Nervous Shock in Their Surgical and Medico-Legal Aspects.* London: J. & A. Churchill.
PARSONS, J. H. (1915) The psychology of traumatic amblyopia following the explosion of shells. *Lancet*, 697–701.
PUTNAM, J. J. (1883) Recent investigations in the pathology of so-called concussion of the spine. *Boston Medical and Surgical Journal*, **109**, 217–220.
RADCLIFFE, C. B. (1880) Diseases of the spinal cord. In *A System of Medicine* (ed. J. R. Reynolds) (American edn, ed. H. Hartshorne). Philadelphia.
RAVAUT, P. (1915) Les hémorragies internes. *Presse Médicale*, **23**, 114.
REES, J. R. (1945) *The Shaping of Psychiatry by War.* New York: W. W. Norton.
WAR OFFICE COMMITTEE OF ENQUIRY INTO SHELL SHOCK (1922) *Report of the Committee*, Cmd 1734. London: HMSO.
REYNOLDS, J. R. (1869) Remarks on paralysis and other disorders of motion and sensation, dependent on idea. *British Medical Journal*, *ii*, 483–485.
RITCHIE, R. D. (1986) One History of Shell-Shock. PhD Thesis, University of California (San Diego).
ROSS, T. A. (1941) *Lectures on War Neuroses.* London: Edward Arnold & Co.

ROUSSY, G. & BOISSEAU, J. (1916) Nervous phenomena from explosion nearby. *Paris Médical*, **6**, 185–191.

——, —— & D'OELSNITZ, M. (1919) *Traitement des psychonévroses de guerre*. Paris: Masson.

RUSSEL, C. K. (1917) A study of certain psychogenetic conditions among soldiers. *Canadian Medical Association Journal*, **7**, 704–720.

SALMON, T. W. (1917) The care and treatment of mental diseases and war neuroses ("shell shock") in the British army. *Mental Hygiene*, *i*, 509–547.

—— & FENTON, N. (1929) *Medical Department of the United States Army in the World War. Vol. 1: Neuropsychiatry in the American Expeditionary Forces*, pp. 273–543. Washington, DC: US Government Printing Office.

SARGANT, W. (1959) *Battle for the Mind* (2nd edn). London: Pan Books.

—— & SHORVON, H. J. (1945) Acute war neurosis. *Archives of Neurology and Psychiatry*, **54**, 231–240.

SASSOON, S. (1936) *Sherston's Progress*. London: Faber.

SJAASTAD, O. (1985) The war sailor syndrome: after-effects of extreme mental stress. An organic brain syndrome or pseudodementia? In *Modern Approaches to the Dementias. Part II: Clinical and Therapeutic Aspects* (ed. F. C. Rose). *Interdisciplinary Topics in Gerontology*, **20**, 94–114. Basel: Karger.

SKERRITT, P. W. (1983) Anxiety and the heart - a historical review. *Psychological Medicine*, **13**, 17–25.

SMITH, G. E. (1916) Shock and the soldier. *Lancet*, *1*, 813–817, 853–857.

—— & PEAR, T. H. (1917) *Shell-Shock & Its Lessons*. Manchester: Manchester University Press.

SOLLIER, P. & CHARTIER, M. (1915) Shell shock and its effects upon the nervous system. *Paris Médical*, **5**, 406–414.

SOLZHENITSYN, A. (1973) *The Gulag Archipelago, Vol. I*. New York: Harper & Row.

SOUTHARD, E. E. (1928) *Shell Shock and Other Neuropsychiatric Problems* (with a bibliography by N. Fenton). Boston, MA: W. M. Leonard.

STONE, M. (1985) Shellshock and the psychologists. In *The Anatomy of Madness*, Vol. 2 (eds W. T. Bynum, R. Porter & M. Shepherd), pp. 242–271. London: Routledge.

STRECKER, E. A. & APPEL, K. (1946) Psychiatric contrasts in the two World Wars. In *Military Neuropsychiatry. Proceedings of the Association for Research in Nervous and Mental Disease* (eds F. G. Ebaugh, H. C. Solomon & T. E. Bamford, Jr), pp. 38–47. New York: Williams & Wilkins.

TRIMBLE, M. R. (1981) *Post-traumatic Neurosis from Railway Spine to the Whiplash*. London: John Wiley.

TUCKEY, C. L. (1891) *Psycho-Therapeutics or, Treatment of Hypnotism and Suggestion* (3rd edn). London: Baillière, Tindall & Cassell.

TURNER, W. A. (1915) Remarks on cases of nervous and mental shock. *Lancet*, *1*, 833–835.

—— (1916) Arrangements for the care of cases of nervous and mental shock coming from overseas. *Lancet*, *1*, 1073–1075.

VAUGHAN, E. C. (1981) *Some Desperate Glory. The World War I Diary of a British Officer*. London: F. Warne.

VIETS, H. (1917) Shell-Shock: a digest of the English literature. *Journal of the American Medical Association*, **69**, 1779–1786.

WALTON, G. L. (1883) Possible cerebral origin of the symptoms usually classed under "railway spine". *Boston Medical and Surgical Journal*, **109**, 337–340.

WILLIAMSON, R. T. (1917) Treatment of neurasthenia and psychasthenia following shell shock. *British Medical Journal*, *ii*, 713–715.

WILTSHIRE, H. (1916) A contribution to the etiology of shell shock. *Lancet*, *i*, 1207–1212.

WOOLEY, C. F. (1986) From irritable heart to mitral valve prolapse - World War I, the British experience and Thomas Lewis. *American Journal of Cardiology*, **58**, 844–849.

—— (1987) From irritable heart to mitral valve prolapse: World War I - the U.S. experience and the origin of neurocirculatory asthenia. *American Journal of Cardiology*, **59**, 1183–1186.

—— (1988) Lewis A. Conner, M.D. and lessons learned from examining four million young men in World War I. *American Journal of Cardiology*, **61**, 900–903.

—— & BOUDOULAS, H. (1988) From irritable heart to mitral valve prolapse: World War I - the U.S. experience and the prevalence of apical systolic murmurs and mitral regurgitation in drafted men compared with present day mitral valve prolapse studies. *American Journal of Cardiology*, **61**, 895–899.

YEALLAND, L. R. (1918) *Hysterical Disorders of Warfare*. London: Macmillan.

16 Mental handicap and the Royal Medico-Psychological Association: a historical association, 1841–1991

KENNETH DAY and JOZE JANCAR

In pre-industrial Britain, the mildly mentally handicapped were virtually indistinguishable in a largely illiterate general population, where unskilled manual labour was the chief occupation and the few severely handicapped who survived were cared for by the family. Some special provision, though, was made by certain religious orders, under the tradition dating back to St Vincent de Paul: Holy Cross Hospital, associated with the Chapel of St Mary Magdalene, Bath, Somerset, was probably the first such institution in Britain (Fig. 16.1). Established as a hostel for lepers in the 13th century, an inscription marking its rebuilding in 1761 indicates that it became a lunatic asylum in 1491 – the word "MOROTROPHIUM" (*moros*, stupid/feeble-minded/moron; *trophium*, a place for nursing or caring) leaving little doubt as to its function (Jancar, 1986).

The radical changes in society in general, and in family life and work in particular, brought about by the Industrial Revolution had a profound effect on the fate of the mentally handicapped. Along with the mentally ill, they joined the increasing numbers of paupers and destitutes who became confined in workhouses and prisons under the Poor Laws, vagrancy acts, and general criminal law. Public concern focused naturally on the mentally ill, who were numerically the much larger group, and in the reforms and legislation of the early 19th century – County Asylums Acts 1808, 1828; Madhouse Act 1820; Lunatics Acts 1832, 1845 – mental handicap was not separately defined. So began the association with psychiatry which has continued to this day.

The notion of specialised provision grew: firstly out of the celebrated attempts of the French physician Itard to train the Wild Boy of Averyon in 1802 (see Chapter 17); secondly, out of the work of Itard's pupil, Seguin (later to emigrate to America and help found the American Association for Mental Deficiency), who established a training school for idiots and imbeciles at the Bicêtre Hospital, Paris, in 1837 and published a textbook on the subject; and thirdly, from the Swiss physician Guggenbuhl, who established a colony for cretins (then considered to be a form of idiocy) at Abendberg in 1839.

The first British school for imbecile children was opened in 1846 at Bath, under the management of the Misses White. The first "Asylum for Idiots" in Britain – Park House, Highgate, London (Fig. 16.2) – was founded by Andrew Reed, a philanthropist who had visited Abendberg, in collaboration with John Conolly, Superintendent of Hanwell asylum, and with Samuel Gaskell (see Chapter 28), then a Lunacy Commissioner. It was opened in 1848 under the

Fig. 16.1. Holy Cross Hospital and the Chapel of St Mary Magdalene, Bath, in the early 19th century. The tablet marking its rebuilding in 1761 reads: "Anno Salutis MDCCLXI haud multo post Inaugurationem GEORGII Tertii, auspicatis fimi Regis; HOC MOROTROPHIUM. quodante ducentos et septuaginta annos; JOHANNES CANTLOW. Prior Bathoniensis Fundavit Vetustate pene collapsum i e aedificavit DUEL TAYLOR Bathoniae Rector, et hujus HospitiiMagister."

Fig. 16.2. The Asylum for Idiots, Park House, Highgate, London (date unknown)

TABLE 16.1
Some early institutions for the mentally handicapped

Year of opening	*Name*	*Location*
1846	Whites School for Imbeciles	Bath, Somerset
1848	Park House	Highgate, London
1850	Essex Hall (later Eastern Counties Asylum for Idiots & Imbeciles, eventually Turner Village Hospital)	Colchester, Essex
1854	Baldovan (now Strathmartine Hospital)	Dundee
1855	Hope Park	Edinburgh
1855	Earlswood Asylum	Redhill, Surrey
1863	Royal Scottish National Institution	Larbert
1864	Star Cross Asylum for the Western Counties	Exeter, Devon
1868	Asylum for the Midland Counties	Knowle, Birmingham
1869	Stewart Institution for Imbecile Children (now Stewart Hospital)	Dublin
1870	Royal Albert Asylum for Idiots & Imbeciles of the Northern Counties	Lancaster
1875	Darenth Institution (later Darenth Park Hospital)	Dartford, Kent
1875	Caterham Asylum (later St Lawrence's Hospital)	Caterham, Surrey

patronage of the Duke of Cambridge and the Duchess of Gloucester. Other public-subscription institutions were gradually established throughout the British Isles (Table 16.1) – another eminent member of the Medico-Psychological Association (MPA), Daniel Hack Tuke, being credited with the founding of that at Lancaster. Darenth Training School (later Darenth Park Hospital), founded in 1875, was the first pauper school for imbeciles and, more recently, one of the first hospitals to close as a consequence of new approaches to care. Special wards for idiots were also established in some lunatic asylums.

These facilities, however, only touched upon the problem: of nearly 30 000 'idiots' known to the authorities in 1881, only 3% were being cared for in appropriate settings. The resulting Idiots Act 1886 empowered local authorities to build special asylums, made the Lunacy Commissioners responsible for inspection, and applied identical conditions for admission to those for the mentally ill – further reinforcing the link with psychiatry. New institutions were built, but progress was slow and a survey of six representative areas by Dr E. O. Lewis in 1927 for the Wood Committee (see below) found that only 10% of defectives were in mental deficiency institutions, 25% in mental hospitals, and 39% in Poor Law institutions.

The first institutions were concerned with the training and education of 'idiots' and 'imbeciles', with the aim of improvement and return to the community. The Education Act of 1876 made public education compulsory. Dr Francis Warner, who had researched over 100 000 schoolchildren, together with other members of the Medico-Psychological Association, including Fletcher Beach and Shuttleworth, were instrumental in drawing to the attention of the authorities the existence of a group of children who could not satisfactorily be taught in ordinary schools but were not sufficiently defective to be certified as idiots or imbeciles. As a result a Departmental Committee of the Board of Education was appointed in 1896, reported in 1898 and in the following year the Defective and Epileptic Children (Education) Act was passed.

The beginning of the 20th century, however, saw a shift of emphasis to life-long segregated care, with recognition of the usually limited scope for improvement and the emergence of the 'feeble-minded' category as a social problem. The Mental Deficiency Act 1913 grew out of public concern about the inadequacy of control of the adult feeble-minded and its feared impact on the health, intelligence, morality and physique of the general population. This far-sighted act defined four grades of mental deficiency – idiots, imbeciles, feeble-minded persons, and moral defectives. It was applied only when an individual could not be cared for in society in the normal way, and provided both for statutory institutional care and for care in the community under guardianship or licence from the institution. It also required the establishment of local mental deficiency committees to be responsible for the ascertainment of cases, provision and inspection of institutions, and twice-yearly visits to all defectives in the community under guardianship. The Lunacy Commission was renamed the Board of Control. With minor amendments in 1929, it remained the legal basis for services until 1959.

The eugenics movement, which flourished at this time, believed that mental deficiency was inherited, insusceptible to treatment and training, and a growing danger to society. It therefore called for compulsory sterilisation, but this was rejected in the report of a Royal Commission of 1904–1908 (the precursor of the 1913 Act), which concluded that the main aim should be "the protection and happiness of the defective rather than the purification of the race". But concern about national degeneracy continued, and the matter was further considered in 1929 by the Wood Committee, which supported compulsory sterilisation, and in 1934 by the Brock Committee; this recommended sterilisation on a voluntary basis with stringent safeguards, but the policy was never put into effect by the government. The Royal Medico-Psychological Association (RMPA) was represented on these bodies by F. Turner, A. F. Tredgold, and E. O. Lewis; a vote taken in 1934 showed the membership to be overwhelmingly in favour of sterilisation by a majority of four to one (*Journal of Mental Science*, 1934, vol. 80, p. 759).

The 1913 Act also required the Board of Control to "establish and maintain institutions for defectives of dangerous or violent propensities". "Dangerous imbeciles and idiots" had been previously dealt with under the Criminal Lunatics Act 1867, which permitted their removal to county asylums. In 1920, Rampton Hospital (originally built as an overflow unit for Broadmoor) became the State Institution for Defectives. It quickly became overcrowded, and in 1933 Moss Side Hospital (originally opened for this purpose, but used instead as an epileptic colony) became the second state institution.

Community care and the psychiatry of mental handicap

The next 35 years were quiet so far as service developments were concerned. The concept of rehabilitation and care in the community, embodied in the Mental Deficiency Act 1913 and further promoted in subsequent committees (Wood, 1929; Royal Commissions, 1934, 1954), legislation, and policy statements, had little impact on services. Hospitals continued to be the main providers of care; the number of patients swelled to over 60 000 with consequent gross overcrowding, institutional regimes remained largely unchanged, and the development of community services was slow and limited.

However, the care of the mentally handicapped was precipitated into the public domain by the publication of two hospital inquiry reports (Department of Health and Social Security, 1969, 1971*a*) and a large-scale survey (Morris, 1969), which revealed that the inquiries' findings of overcrowding, understaffing, and other serious inadequacies were all too common in British mental handicap hospitals. The government acted immediately, establishing the Hospital Advisory Service in 1968 to inspect and advise hospitals on service improvements, and issuing a new policy white paper in 1971. *Better Services for the Mentally Handicapped* (Department of Health and Social Security, 1971*b*) reiterated the policy of community care for the mildly handicapped, and set targets for both hospital reduction and the development of community facilities over the next 20 years.

Mental handicap has remained high on government agendas ever since, with a series of legislative and other initiatives directed at the implementation of this policy, which has changed only in respect of the extent to which community care is now seen as the goal for many severely mentally handicapped people. By 1990, long-stay hospitals had been nearly halved, some hospitals closed, and many given closure dates, but implementation of the new policy has not been without its problems and critics. The provision of alternative services in the community has not kept pace with the reduction in hospital places, and there is concern about the adequacy of funding for the new services and about provision for those with special needs (Select Committee of the House of Commons on Community Care, 1985).

Somewhat paradoxically, though, the move from a medical to a social model of care has been accompanied by mental health legislation which once again links mental handicap with mental illness. The restrictive definitions of 'mental impairment' and 'severe mental impairment' in the Mental Health Act 1983 have excluded many mentally handicapped people from its protection. This is only partially compensated for by the provisions under the Disabled Persons Act 1981 and the white paper *Caring for People* (1989). Yet the coexistence of mental illness and mental handicap in the same patient has long been recognised (Reid, 1989). Radical policy changes in the 1970s raised questions as to how mentally handicapped people with mental illness and behaviour disorders (including offenders) should be provided for in the new service. Overshadowed initially by the massive emphasis on community care for the majority, the extent of the problem and the need for specialised services is at last being recognised. Two reports on the subject have been issued (Department of Health and Social Security, 1984; Department of Health, 1989), and some new services are beginning to be established.

Mental handicap and the RMPA

The interests of mental handicap have always been strongly represented within the RMPA and subsequently the College. John Conolly and Samuel Gaskell both wrote papers on the subject and were instrumental in establishing the first specialist asylum for the mentally handicapped. Many subsequent pioneers in the field held high office in the Association, and two Presidents, Fletcher Beach (1900–01) of Darenth Institution and Frank Turner (1933–34) of the Royal Eastern Counties Asylum, both worked exclusively in the field of mental handicap.

Mental handicap matters were much discussed during the early life of the Association. Special committees were set up to consider the Mental Deficiency Bill (1912–14) and the Medical Inspection of Children Bill (1910–14). There was a mental deficiency subcommittee of the Research and Clinical Standing Committee, which became a standing committee in its own right in 1933, when the annual meeting accepted the recommendation of a special committee, established to consider a resolution that such a committee be formed, according to the minutes, "for the purpose of including such of its members as are particularly interested in the study and treatment of the problems of mental deficiency". When the Royal Charter was gained in 1926, mental deficiency was named in the by-laws as one of the standing committees.

The Mental Deficiency Committee, whose first Chairman and Secretary were, respectively, F. Turner and E. O. Lewis, rapidly established itself as the focus of the Association's expertise on the subject; this undoubtedly paved the way for the formation of sections, established to represent specialist interests in the Association in 1946. During the first year, a pattern of regular clinical meetings was established, which has endured and has been adopted by the other specialist sections. The name was changed to "The Section for the Psychiatry of Mental Handicap" in 1983 in response to changing patterns of care, changing terminology, and, most importantly, the changing role of the specialist in mental handicap. The Section and the College in general have played a major role in drawing attention to current problems in the development of services and in shaping national policy.

In 1965, part of a legacy left to the Association on his death by Dr R. J. Blake Marsh, Medical Superintendent of Bromham Hospital, Bedford, first Secretary and subsequently Chairman of the Mental Deficiency Section, was used to "found an annual lecture of a standing equal to the Maudsley Lecture on a subject connected with mental deficiency and to be known by his name". The first lecture was delivered in 1967 and has continued to be given by distinguished national and international figures. The Natalie Cobbing Fellowship was established in 1985, with a legacy left by the Secretary of the RMPA and the College from 1958 until her death in 1984, to "further the training of specialists in mental handicap by enabling them to extend their experience through travel to appropriate centres overseas". It is awarded biannually to senior trainees and young consultants.

The influence of the Section and its members has extended well beyond the British Isles. A significant development was the founding of the International Association for the Scientific Study of Mental Deficiency in 1964 – the first international association for scientific research to be established in the field, and doubly unique because of its multidisciplinary composition. British psychiatrists played a prominent role in its birth – Alexander Shapiro (former Chairman of the Section) was a cofounder and one of its first presidents – and they have continued to be well represented in it (Clarke, 1991). Members of the Section have also played a prominent role and held office in the Mental Retardation Section of the World Psychiatric Association, since its inception.

Medical education

Mental handicap featured little in the early Diploma in Psychological Medicine (DPM) offered by the Association and by certain universities, but, in 1936, the Mental Deficiency Standing Committee drew attention to "the difficulties experienced by medical officers in mental deficiency institutions situated in the provinces in preparing and qualifying for the DPM''. The regulations of the RMPA were therefore altered to enable mental handicap to be taken as the major topic, with general psychiatry as the minor topic; representations were also made to the universities offering diplomas to do likewise. However, World War II intervened, and the first examination in its new form was not held until 1949. The new DPM also required all candidates to have clinical experience of and be examined in mental handicap, yet despite the ambitious training programmes proposed by the Association in the 1950s and 1960s, the prospect of higher training was then virtually nil. Lack of training, increasing isolation from mainstream psychiatry, and a general climate of anomie in the service as a whole led, not surprisingly, to serious recruitment problems, with up to a quarter of established medical posts vacant for lack of suitable applicants at any one time. The low point was reached around 1970, when there was a major uncertainty about the future of the service and serious questioning of the ultimate need for a medical specialist in mental handicap. From this identity crisis, emerged the 'new' and more focused specialty of the 'psychiatry of mental handicap'. Training and recruitment received a further important boost with the introduction of the MRCPsych examination and higher training in 1972.

Until recently, exposure of medical students to mental handicap was poor and patchy – often no more than a parade of rare pathological curiosities; one-third of doctors graduating in the 20 years up to 1960 reported that they had no or less than one day's exposure in their training (Holt & Huntley, 1973). A survey in 1986, though, revealed significant improvement, with an average of 11 hours of teaching in all but one British medical school and examination in the subject in two-thirds (Hollins & Bradley, 1987); students were reported to show an eagerness for information, particularly on the wider social issues. In 1986, the College published guidelines on undergraduate teaching. The establishment of academic posts was a key factor in improving teaching and training at both undergraduate and postgraduate levels and in the development of research interest. The first Chair was established in 1980, and by 1990 there were five – at St George's and Charing Cross Hospitals, London, Birmingham, Cardiff, and Nottingham as well as one combined Chair in Child Psychiatry and Mental Handicap at Leicester, with senior lecturers at nearly every teaching centre.

British textbooks on mental handicap began appearing in the latter half of the 19th century, the first comprehensive one being published in 1877 by Dr Ireland, Medical Superintendent of the Scottish National Institution for Imbecile Children, Larbert. Entitled *On Idiocy and Imbecility*, it covered definition, etiology, incidence, education, and the law. It was followed by books by Duncan & Millard (1886) and by Shuttleworth (1895), Superintendent of the Royal Albert Asylum for Idiots & Imbeciles, Lancaster. In 1908, A. F. Tredgold, Consultant Physician to University College Hospital, London, published his classic textbook *Mental Deficiency (Amentia)*, which became the *vade mecum* to all psychiatrists and other professionals working in the field, running to 12 editions over 70 years. In 1949, R. L. Penrose published *The Biology of Mental Defect*, still the most quoted reference work in the world literature, which ran to four editions.

Subsequent decades have seen the publication of an increasing number of books on specific syndromes and specialist topics, standard texts being Hilliard & Kirman's *Mental Deficiency* (first published in 1957) and *Mental Handicap – A*

Multidisciplinary Approach (published in 1985) under the editorship of Michael Craft, Joan Bicknell, and Sheila Hollins. The first British textbook on the psychiatry of mental handicap, by Andrew Reid (Strathmartine Hospital, Dundee), was published in 1982.

Articles on mental handicap appeared regularly in the *Journal of Mental Science* and latterly in the *British Journal of Psychiatry*. Three specialist journals are published in Britain – the *Journal of Mental Deficiency Research*, the *British Journal of Subnormality*, and *Mental Handicap*.

Nurse training

The Association was concerned from an early stage with the standards and training of 'keepers and attendants' in asylums. In 1885 the Association published the *Handbook for the Instruction of Attendants on the Insane*, and from 1890 issued a Certificate of Proficiency in Mental Nursing, kept a register of all nurses in training, and recognised institutions for training. By 1908, a full three-year curriculum had been developed and the first examination instituted.

The emergence of mental handicap as a separate branch of mental nursing was encouraged by the passing of the Mental Deficiency Act 1913: a separate certificate in mental deficiency nursing was introduced in 1919. Based initially on the mental nursing syllabus, the regulations for this new certificate were revised in 1920, 1923, and in 1927, when a completely independent syllabus was introduced, "in view of the special requirements of the mentally defective", for candidates "having care of that class". This innovation was adopted and continued by the General Nursing Council, when it also began to award qualifications in mental nursing. A special chapter on mental deficiency was included in the seventh edition (1923) of the now renamed *Handbook for Mental Nurses*, but was quickly recognised as inadequate, and in 1931 the *Manual for Mental Deficiency Nurses* was published – for a long time the only nursing textbook on the subject.

Until 1921, the Certificate of Proficiency was the only recognised qualification in mental nursing, and it was finally discontinued 30 years later. Regulations for the RMPA Certificate realistically reflected the nature of the work, but under the General Nursing Council, the sole examining body since 1951, an increasing emphasis on the basic sciences, with psychiatry and mental nursing relegated to the third year, led Alexander Walk (1961), in his Presidential Address to the RMPA entitled "The history of mental nursing", to lament the lack of relevance of the training to the task. The same, alas, may be said in 1991. A progressive shift of emphasis to the social aspects of care since the 1970s has led to a loss of skill in the medical and psychiatric aspects of care, at the very time when these are most needed. In 1987, the Section drew attention to the need for appropriately trained nurses to work in specialised psychiatric services and for all nurses to receive adequate training in these aspects of care. It called for "a major review of nurse training in mental handicap", but this has not taken place.

The scientific study of mental handicap

In addition to the enormous task of running, organising, and improving conditions in institutions, many doctors found time to carry out research. Early pioneers published papers on classification and descriptive features, as well as on care and treatment. In 1886, P. M. Duncan and W. Millard of the Eastern Counties Asylum published *A Manual for the Classification, Training and Education of the Feeble-Minded, Imbecile and Idiotic*, in which they proposed a behaviourally orientated classification. In the same year, John Langdon Down (Fig. 16.3), Medical Superintendent of Earlswood asylum and later of Normanfield Hospital, gave the first comprehensive description of people with mongoloid features (Down's syndrome); ten years later, he proposed a classification based on ethnic features.

The early part of the 20th century saw the development of neuropathological studies, particularly by R. M. Stewart, of Leavesden Institution. In 1929, E. O. Lewis reported the first epidemiological study – "an investigation into the incidence of mental deficit in six areas 1925–27", carried out for the Wood Committee. Research into the biological basis of mental handicap was established on a firm footing by the work of Lionel Penrose (Fig. 16.4), who in 1938 published his monumental clinical and genetic study of 1280 cases – the Colchester survey, carried out at the Royal Eastern Counties Hospital. Penrose, who held the Galton Chair of Human Genetics at London University for 20 years and was, from 1965 until his death, Director of the Kennedy Galton Research Centre, Harperbury Hospital, made an enormous impact as scientist and doctor in the development of knowledge about mental handicap, as well as in the wider fields of medicine and genetics.

The first multidisciplinary centre for research into mental handicap was established at Stoke Park Hospital, Bristol, in 1930 under the directorship of Professor R. J. Berry. Associated with the names of J. A. Frazer Roberts, R. M. Norman, R. S. Gordon, and others, the centre continues its pioneering work today and has produced over 460 publications, spanning 60 years. The

Fig. 16.3. Dr John Langdon Down (1826–96)

Fig. 16.4. Professor Lionel Penrose (1898–1972) (photo courtesy IASSMD)

Burden Research Medal and Prize was instituted in 1969 on the occasion of the diamond jubilee of the foundation of Stoke Park Hospital by the Reverend H. N. Burden to encourage research work (Wiley, 1989).

Pioneering research work was carried out in a number of centres by B. W. Richards and P. C. Sylvester (St Lawrence's Hospital, Surrey); by L. T. Hilliard, B. Kirman, L. Crome, J. Tizard, and N. O'Connor (The Fountain Hospital, London); and by Valerie Cowie at Queen Mary's Hospital, Carshalton. Mention should also be made of the Health Care Evaluation Research Centre, established by the Department of Health and Social Security under the directorship of A. Kushlick, to carry out epidemiological studies, and the Hester Adrian Research Centre, University of Manchester, under Professor P. Mittler, studying developmental and educational aspects. In 1971, the Institute of Mental Subnormality (later renamed British Institute of Mental Handicap) was established under the directorship of Professor G. Simon at Lea Castle Hospital, Kidderminster.

A link with psychology was made at the turn of the century with the introduction of intelligence testing. In the ensuing years, clinical psychologists such as Gunzburg made important contributions in the wider fields of assessment and training of social skills and the application of behavioural approaches, and more latterly in the evaluation of residential care. The work of Professors Alan and Ann Clarke and their textbook *Mental Deficiency – The Changing Outlook*, first published in 1957, had enormous influence.

Major scientific advances took place in the 1960s. New chromosomal abnormalities were discovered; many biochemical abnormalities were detected by paper and gas chromatography; electron microscopy was probing into previously unrecognisable pathologies; magnetic resonance imaging revealed hitherto undetected lesions; and the prophylactic treatment of rhesus haemolytic disease and phenylketonuria became possible. Many other branches of medicine have become involved (Eastham & Jancar, 1968).

In the 1970s, psychiatrists began to focus on the psychiatric and behavioural aspects of mental handicap, a topic which had interested earlier physicians, most notably C. J. C. Earl. He was Physician Superintendent of Monyhull Hospital, Birmingham, and was credited by Tredgold with being "the first person in this country to take a special interest in the significance of the behaviour of the unstable high grade"; in 1934, he published *The Primitive Catatonia of Idiocy*.

During the last two decades, British psychiatrists have contributed substantially to the research literature, with seminal papers on psychotic disorders, ageing, behaviour problems, offenders, and many other topics. In 1979, the College published *Psychiatric Illness and Mental Handicap*, edited by F. E. James & R. P. Snaith – the first text on the subject in Britain.

Conclusion

The contribution of the MPA and its successors to the study and care of mentally handicapped people in Britain has been long and distinguished, from the establishment of the first specialist asylums to the development of care in the community and the birth of the specialty of 'psychiatry of mental handicap' – unique in the world. The scientific study of mental handicap has yielded findings with relevance to other branches of psychiatry and to the wider field of medicine. The challenge for the future is to ensure that the service needs of the mentally handicapped and their families are properly met, and to maintain research, teaching, and training at the highest standard.

Acknowledgements

We are most grateful for the assistance given in the preparation of this chapter by Susan Floate, College Librarian, and Margaret Harcourt Williams, College Archivist.

References

CLARKE, A. D. B. (1991) A brief history of the International Association for the Scientific Study of Mental Deficiency (IASSMD). *Journal of Mental Deficiency Research*, **35**, 1–12.
DEPARTMENT OF HEALTH (1989) *Needs and Responses: Services for Adults with Mental Handicap who are Mentally Ill, who have Behaviour Problems or who Offend. Report of a Department of Health Study Team.* DoH Leaflets Unit, Stanmore, Middlesex.
DEPARTMENT OF HEALTH AND SOCIAL SECURITY (1969) *Report of the Committee of Inquiry into Allegations of Ill Treatment of Patients and Other Irregularities at Ely Hospital, Cardiff.* Cmnd 3975. London: HMSO.
—— (1971*a*) *Report of the Farleigh Hospital Committee of Inquiry.* Cmnd 4557. London: HMSO.
—— (1971*b*) *Better Services for the Mentally Handicapped.* Cmnd 4683. London: HMSO.
—— (1984) *Helping Mentally Handicapped People with Special Problems. Report of a DHSS Study Team.* London: DHSS.
EASTHAM, R. D. & JANCAR, J. (1968) *Clinical Pathology in Mental Retardation.* Bristol: John Wright.
HOLLINS, S. & BRADLEY, E. (1987) Mental handicap in context: medical undergraduate education. *Bulletin of the Royal College of Psychiatrists*, **11**, 389–391.
HOLT, K. S. & HUNTLEY, R. M. (1973) Mental subnormality: medical training in the United Kingdom. *British Journal of Medical Education*, **7**, 197–202.
JANCAR, J. (1986) The history of mental handicap in Bristol and Bath. *Bristol Medico-Chirurgical Journal*, **101**, 53–56, 79–81.
MEDICO-PSYCHOLOGICAL ASSOCIATION (1885) *Handbook for the Instruction of Attendants on the Insane.* London: Baillière Tindall, Cox.
MORRIS, P. (1969) *Put Away: A Sociological Study of Institutions for the Mentally Retarded.* London: Routledge & Kegan Paul.
REID, A. H. (1989) Psychiatry and mental handicap: a historical perspective. *Journal of Mental Deficiency Research*, **33**, 363–368.
ROYAL COMMISSION (1904–1908) *Report of the Commission.* London: HMSO.
SELECT COMMITTEE OF THE HOUSE OF COMMONS ON COMMUNITY CARE (1985) *Report of the Committee.* London: HMSO.
WALK, A. (1961) The history of mental nursing. *Journal of Mental Science*, **107**, 1–17.
WILEY, Y. V. (1989) Burden Research Medal and Prize (1969–1989). *Psychiatric Bulletin*, **13**, 701.

Further reading

BEACH, F. (1900) Presidential address. *Journal of Mental Science*, **46**, 623–653.
JONES, K. (1972) *A History of the Mental Health Services.* London: Routledge & Kegan Paul.
PENROSE, L. S. (1966) Contribution of mental deficiency research to psychiatry. The 40th Maudsley Lecture. *British Journal of Psychiatry*, **112**, 747–755.
TURNER, F. D. (1933) Presidential address. *Journal of Mental Science*, **79**, 563–577.

17 Historical influences on services for children and adolescents before 1900

CHRISTOPHER J. WARDLE

A history of child psychiatric services deserves a bold introduction full of youthful enthusiasm:

> "In all the ages of the world from the earliest dawning of society down to our own enlightened day – theologians, philosophers, and legislators, those called upon to govern and to guide mankind, have agreed as to the importance to be attached to the physical, mental, and moral training of infancy and childhood . . . The physician too . . . ought to be well acquainted with the importance of early training . . . in securing a strong, a healthy, and a powerful mind, and in dispelling predispositions to mental disease."

Thus James Crichton-Browne (1860), a 19-year-old medical student, introduced the first paper in English on "The Psychical Diseases of Early Life" to the Edinburgh meeting of the Medico-Psychological Association (MPA) in 1859.

It is the aim of this chapter to trace the influences which have led to our present attitudes, methods, and provision of services.

Earlier historical reviews

First in the field, Roberta Crutcher (1943) exemplifies the professional women of the 1920s who were involved in the beginnings of child guidance, psychology, and psychiatry. She herself had experience in all three of these, both in the USA and Britain. Starting with Rousseau's contention that the child's nature is essentially good and should be allowed to express itself, she traced this influence through Pestalozzi and Froebel to contemporary practice in education. The development of child-guidance practice had also been influenced by psychological studies of early child development and by Adolf Meyer.

Gertrude Keir's "A history of child guidance" (1952), written with the assistance of Sir Cyril Burt and other British psychologists, provides a useful account of the development of child guidance services, emphasising the psychologist's contribution but presenting a very jaundiced view of the medical one. It is important in illustrating the beginning of a polarisation of professional attitudes.

Walk (1964) and von Gontard (1988) between them present a comprehensive review of the early medical literature, while Kanner (1955, 1959) analysed developments in the USA in the first half of the 20th century, trying to identify the first child psychiatrist. Developments in the UK in this century were sketched by Cameron (1956), Howells (1965), Warren (1971), and Howells & Osborne (1980/81). Bridgeland's *Pioneer Work with Maladjusted Children* (1971) describes the evolution of services within education, while Barker (1974) dealt with the origins of in-patient work.

The medieval period to the 17th century

Early manuscripts on child nurture and education provide evidence that, in the Middle Ages, attitudes were as divided as they are today about the need for kindness or severity, encouragement or punishment. Stone's (1977) contention that all 16th- and 17th-century children were repressed, "treated with the utmost severity", and kept in "utter subordination" is to be questioned: writers of the time were likely to report the extreme cases rather than the mundane. Agnes Paston's harsh treatment of her children was not approved by her contemporaries, while Lady Jane Grey contrasted her harsh, negative, perfectionist parents with her teacher, "who teacheth me so jentlie, so pleasantlie, with soch faire allurements to learning" (Furnival, 1868).

Roger Ascham (1515–68) was stimulated to write his *Scholemaster* (published posthumously by his wife in 1570) after Sir William Cecil told him that "divers scholars of Eton be run away from the school for fear of beating". He deplored this, contrasting it with "the practice of the wise, who by gentle allurement breed them up in a love of learning", in the same way as wise horsemen train their horses to love riding. The empirical application of operant conditioning and behaviour modification would in fact have been seen daily in the training of horse, hawk, and hounds, for whom there is no effective alternative. Beating on a large scale seems to have started with the creation of very large schools like Eton in 1440; its use was less in the small free schools run by religious foundations, although bishops were not averse to the cruel government of children in their care – Wolsey was notorious.

Guides to the upbringing and training of children and youth are found in manuscripts from the 13th century onwards, with titles like *How the Good Wijf taugte hir dougtir*, *Lerne or be lewde*, or *The Babees book* (reprinted and edited by Furnival, 1868). Most of these books were addressed to children or had a section for them in rhyme, like Hugh Rhode's *Boke of Nurture* (1577), which begins "All ye that wysdom seeke to learn and would be called wyse; obedience learn you in your youth, in age avoyde you vyce" (in Furnival, 1868). Some of them would serve today as social-skills manuals. The need for 'good manners', meaning skill in recognising and deferring to the needs of others, became increasingly important, as society changed from small feudal groupings to larger urban communities. Social subordination cannot have been the aim, since the earliest books were addressed to the children of aristocrats, and were only later adopted by the bourgeoisie. However, by the 19th century, their essence was incorporated into the cultural expectations of children at all social levels.

Hugh Rhodes' introduction to his *Boke of Nurture* recognised the influence that parents and teachers had on child development and adjustment. The views he presents are not so different from those of ordinary people today. Parents should take trouble with the upbringing of their children and not leave it to others. They must choose teachers who are virtuous and sober, patient though strict with children, and who do not frighten them with harsh criticism and cruel punishments into rebellion or running away. Of clothes, he said "Apparell not your children in sumptuous apparell, for it increaseth pride and obstinacy and many other evills" and of company, "nor let your children go whither they will" – parents should know where their children are, with whom and what they are doing. The following advice has a familiar ring, "keepe them from reading of fayned fables, vayne fantasyes, and wanton stories and songs of love, which bring much mischiefs to youth".

The medieval and Tudor literature on rearing and education shows considerable understanding of children, a knowledge of common behaviour problems, and some insight into their causes and prevention. There is no evidence that children were regarded as little adults, but rather that much time, thought, and skill went into preventing the development of problem behaviour. Rhodes recommended a balance between pressure and punishment, love and respect. His advice to fathers not to show their children too much familiarity clearly did not mean they should show no love or care, because he enjoins fathers to involve themselves in all kinds of activities with their children, from "honest sports and pastimes" to reading and going to church together.

Between them, these medieval books of nurture provide a comprehensive list of familiar behavioural and emotional disorders and of problems to be avoided or eradicated. My own analysis of 14 of them, plus John Lydgate's poem on his school days (circa 1389), provided a list of 108 separate behaviour problems, most of which are familiar to clinicians today. Included were: truancy ("mecher for myfcheffe") and running away, school refusal, tics, tension and gratification habits ("nor pikyng, nor trifelynge, ne shrukkynge"), speech disorders, conduct disorder, emotional disorders including rages, depression, timidity, and anxiety, and relationship disorders including jealousy, quarrelling, and oppositional behaviour, as well as sexual problems such as exposure and open masturbation.

Aries (1962) is often misquoted as saying that medieval children were treated as little adults; what he does say is that soon after weaning, children became the natural companions of adults, mixing in all their activities and not sheltered from the violent or sexual parts of it. The result, in his view, was that adults were not as preoccupied as we are today with the physical, moral, and sexual problems of children, which is said to have started with the introduction of formal education, as it did in classical Greece. Certainly, books of nurture and grammar schools are contemporaneous.

Although punishment was more prominent then than now, there were powerful positive incentives in the conviction that virtuous behaviour would please God and Jesus, as well as being rewarded on earth by approbation of peers and social success. A good man was valued and revered, a knave abhorred and jeered. The actions children were taught to avoid demonstrates that as wide a range of behaviour problems existed then as now.

Health services

From the establishment of monasteries and convents in Saxon England, the provision of education, health, and social services was the responsibility of the church. Some of these services disappeared after the Reformation, others then became the responsibility of the parish vestry, while education became secular and dependent on endowments. In the Middle Ages, though, physicians had identified some childhood and nervous disorders as within their scope – bedwetting, nightmares, hysteria, melancholia, faulty mental habits (Osterreicher, 1540), the falling evil, terrible dreams, "watching out of measure", and incontinence (Phaer, 1546). Weyer (1560) described an epidemic of mass hysteria in a foundling hospital in Amsterdam, and Heironymus Mercurialis (1583), from Venice, discussed stammer, fears, and phobias (Walk, 1964).

Apothecaries had herbal remedies for nervous disorders, many of which had been used since classical times and which continued in use into the 19th century (Culpeper, 1826). Paracelsus and John Evelyn both believed that balm would revivify and strengthen the brain and chase away melancholy. Camomile tea was recommended for hysterical and nervous affections, to sooth and sedate, and for nightmares; fennel used to prevent witchcraft and to cure hiccough and nausea (Grieve, 1931). Children presenting with psychiatric disorders might have been treated as ill, possessed, bewitched, wilful and bad, or just have been ignored. Help might have been available from clerics, schoolmasters, counsellors, apothecaries, physicians, exorcists, or witches (Kroll, 1973).

The Reformation was followed, though, by an increasingly puritanical attitude, with greater emphasis on the innate evil of man and on hellfire, but less on Christian love and virtue. This affected child rearing negatively (Stone, 1977), leading to greater somatisation and to phobic and depressive reactions. Children were frequently drawn into the witch mania, which had started relatively late in England because of the scepticism of Elizabeth and her advisers. In 1594, the witches of Warbois were executed as a result of the evidence of two adolescent girls with severe hysterical symptoms, encouraged by their parents. In the 17th century, a wealth of severe childhood psychopathology is to be found in the accounts of trials for witchcraft, both in the accusers (gross hysteria and epilepsy) and the accused (deformities, handicaps, and hysteria) (Mackay, 1841; Wessely & Wardle, 1990). The witch mania seems to have put a stop to rational thought about psychopathology. Evil was expected, actively sought out, and attributed to the Devil and His helpers; it was believed to lead to eternal damnation and hellfire. Since the protagonists of this view either thought this was not enough or did not trust God to get it right, they provided their own hell and fire on earth for those they diagnosed evil. This caused terror, depression and mass hysteria. Yet this was the beginning of the age of reason: John Locke published his *Thoughts on Education* in 1693.

Treatment in the 18th and early 19th centuries

Early psychological approaches to treatment are heralded by Brouzet (1754), who noted the adverse effects of jealousy on children, advising parents to shift their attentions "subtly" from the rival to the ailing child. William Perfect was treating children at home from 1780; his description of an acute confusional psychosis indicates that physicians were then considering social, psychological, systemic, and cerebral factors in their assessment of cases (Walk, 1964). However, in 1781, through lack of public support, the Dispensary for the Infant Poor was closed on the death of the physician George Armstrong (von Gontard, 1988). Pauper children with psychiatric disorder or defect would most likely have been dealt with under the Poor Law, in whatever way the local church vestry and the beadle thought fit.

It seemed to be the practice for doctors to take severely disturbed children from wealthy families into their homes, if they could not be managed at home with the help of attendants. Among the long-suffering wives on this account were Mrs Hitch, wife of the founder of the MPA, and Mrs Prichard, whose husband recommended it in his treatise on insanity (1835).

During the 19th century, there were increasing numbers of reports of children treated by asylum doctors (Walk, 1964; von Gontard, 1988) – mostly cases of severe acting out, psychosis, or mental retardation. "Contemporary records suggest that at least two or three children under 14 were admitted to lunatic asylums annually"; between 1815 and 1895, over 1000 children and adolescents were recorded at Bethlem Royal Hospital (Parry-Jones, 1989).

Prichard (1835) discussed boys sent home from school for theft whom he suspected were insane and who responded to "careful moral discipline in the home of a specialist physician"; he coined the term 'moral insanity' for these cases of severe disorder in the absence of cognitive defects or dysfunction. This diagnosis became widely used for children, and resulted in more of them being treated and admitted to asylums subsequently. Adapted as 'moral imbecility' in later legislation, it led to the compulsory admission to hospitals for the mentally retarded adolescents with conduct disorder, sexual problems, or promiscuity and of children with hyperkinesis, autism, and clumsiness syndromes. Thus, the effect of this advance in understanding and humane intervention was to delay fresh thinking about these problems and to promote the institutionalisation of generations of young people who were so labelled, until the Mental Health Act 1959 abolished the category.

The great contribution of Charles West's *Lectures on the Diseases of Infancy and Childhood* (1848) was to promote separate medical services for children, and to introduce the special attitude necessary for successful work with them; he was also instrumental in establishing the first paediatric hospital and training. William Acton's book (1857) on the functions and disorders of the reproductive organs in youth drew doctors' attention to a wide range of adolescent problems, but in a most unfortunate way, attributing them to masturbation; they included idiocy, epilepsy, paralysis, and death, losing weight, spontaneity, and cheerfulness, and becoming haggard, hypochondriacal, antisocial, timid and cowardly. For some reason, the concept of masturbatory disorders was accepted uncritically by physicians, psychiatrists, and paediatricians, with disastrous consequences which lasted into the 20th century (Hare, 1962).

As mentioned above, in his paper of 1859, Crichton-Browne aleady showed a sociobiological approach to the subject, pointing out the need to take every stage of the child's existence into consideration, and to "weigh well every influence to which a being is liable from the instant of union of the spermatozoid with the ovum". He saw the excitement in "mental observation" of infancy and childhood which, apart from idiocy and imbecility and a few stray cases, "may be said to be yet uninvestigated, undescribed . . . with no systematic study or collection". He described an astonishing wealth of psychopathology, quoting numerous references and offering new interpretations. Observing that delinquency in childhood is associated with social deprivation and the behaviour of parents, he commented that "many of these young criminals are victims of disease" (kleptomania), noting in support of his statement that their "inveteracy and pertinacity, recklessness of consequences, intractability under reformatory measures and their own confessions, might have convinced those in power that it is not by the lash or by solitary confinement that these poor wanderers are to be brought back".

His own cases and descriptions from biographies include overvalued ideas, day dreams, imaginary lives and companions, and possibly some temporal lobe syndromes, all under the heading 'monomania'. The 16th-century epidemics of 'demonomania' and a case described in 1798 were attributed to exposure to "an austere and gloomy faith, dealing rather with horrors and punishments attending the lost than with rewards awaiting the blest". Crichton-Browne was clearly observing the consequences in 19th-century Scotland of family dynamics and rearing practices very similar to those described in Puritan families in 17th-century England and America (Stone, 1977). He discusses both nervous and timid children, and depression which "can and does occur": "Gloomy and taciturn they shun their former pursuits and amusements, deplore their hard fate and meditate self destruction." On the difficulty of management, he comments, "Harshness and cruelty persuade them they are outcasts whilst sympathy strengthens their belief in their wretched doom"; the cause is suggested to be unmerited severity and criticism by teacher or parent. This paper not only gives a wide-ranging account of the knowledge available in 1859, but also can tell us much about important influences on the subject at that time.

We must marvel at how well taught and well read was this 19-year-old medical student, but who influenced him? One likely candidate was Dr John Brown, a man of considerable ability and humanity who practised medicine in Edinburgh between 1833 and 1882. He was best known for the series of collected articles, *Horae Subsecivae*, of which the first instalment appeared in 1858. Of particular relevance are his articles on "Education through the senses", "Presence of mind" and "Happy guessing"; many of these articles were addressed to medical students. He laid particular emphasis on the value of wide reading outside the field of medicine and on the proper training and use of the brain.

Why did Crichton-Browne's brilliant paper fail to receive any attention, to change attitudes, to stimulate development of services for disturbed children, or to make him a pioneer child psychiatrist? Generally, the acceptance and implementation of ideas depends on the status of the protagonist, a sympathetic climate of opinion, and the readiness of others to take the idea up with enthusiasm: all these must have been lacking. Crichton-Browne himself did not recognise the importance of what he was saying, and went into neuropsychiatry.

Maudsley fails to mention the paper in his chapter "Insanity of early life" (1867), though he must have been aware of it, since he had a paper in the same volume of the *Journal of Mental Science* as Crichton-Browne. Part of his text is so similar that I suspect he used Crichton-Browne's material; if he did, he failed to recognise the gems of psychopathological understanding there, only extracting that which supported his own quite different viewpoint. Had Maudsley recognised Crichton-Browne's genius, child psychiatry might have been born then, but Maudsley was a man of his time and Crichton-Browne only a medical student.

Maudsley's attitude to children owed nothing to West either; he derides the concept of purity and innocence of the child's mind as poetic idealism:

> "The impulses which actually move it are the selfish impulses of the passions. . . . The baby is the only King, because every body must accommodate himself to him, while he accommodates to nobody. . . . Children like brutes live in the present. . . ."

His view of boys – "the most vicious of all wild beasts" – he held in common with Plato; it is not found among those who have success in helping the young. He was equally negative about insanity in childhood; "it is as the animal, and reveals its animal nature with as little shamefacedness as the monkey indulges its passions in the face of all the world."

Since Maudsley was a major influence on the development of psychiatric thinking, and his chapter the last word on child psychiatry, it is hardly surprising that in the latter part of the 19th century, services for children in Britain were developed not by psychiatrists, but by educationalists, doctors in idiot asylums, and paediatricians.

Development of a more enlightened and liberal view of children

Enlightened philanthropy and reform in the care of children, the sick, and the weak was part of the Romantic movement, started by Locke in the 17th century; the concepts of the noble savage and of the child unspoilt and innocent until corrupted by his experiences became central with Jean-Jacques Rousseau (1712–78), who borrowed extensively from Locke. The change in attitudes to children, exemplified in Wordsworth's child, "mighty prophet, seer blest", who loses insight as "the shades of the prison house" close in, derives from the 'primitivism' of Rousseau (Daiches, 1938). John Locke (1632–1704) studied, but did not qualify in medicine; his *Thoughts on Education* was widely read. Locke wanted learning to be an enjoyable process, based as far as possible on interest, and he warned against trying to teach children too much before their reason was sufficiently developed.

The publication of Rousseau's *Émile* in 1762 transformed the attitude of many parents to children, though the results were not universally approved. In 1788, Restif de la Bretonne commented on the "Rousseau infected generation":

> "Their hair straggles in a disgusting way, they are no longer checked, they deafen you with their noise, when you try to talk to their parents they choose to answer some trivial question of their darling child . . . it is Emile which is responsible for this provoking, obstinate, insolent, impudent, arrogant generation." (Jimack, 1974)

A hostile reaction to uninhibited children and adolescents, accompanied by scapegoating of anyone who offers them a more liberal understanding, is a recurring theme.

Dickens' popular writings between 1835 and 1865 probably both reflected and educated public opinion. He alerted people to abuse of children and his popular heroes were kind to children and righted social injustices, while those who perpetrated them came to sticky ends. His character studies highlighted the varieties of good and bad adult relationships with children, giving horrific descriptions of the fate of the stepchild and of all kinds of child abuse by both teachers and parents. He himself, with Lord Shaftesbury, was a member of the group of gentlemen who established the children's hospital at 47 Great Ormond Street. However, Dickens was not the only one to use novels to manipulate public opinion against social ills. Charles Kingsley (1819–1875), a 'Christian Socialist', had far more impact with *The Water-Babies* than with any of his pamphlets. Within an examination of the evils of child labour, he uses his characters to discuss the conflicts in Victorian attitudes to children. Tom's two adult carers Mrs "Do as You Would Be Done by" and Mrs "Be Done by as You Did" depict with great skill two contrasting styles of child care, leaving the reader little choice but to accept the alternative first coined by Lord Chesterfield in 1747 – "Do as you would be done by is the surest method" (*Dictionary of National Biography*, 1975).

One could guess that this conflict of attitudes to child rearing is as old as mankind; it is found in the writings of most ages and in cross-cultural studies (Meade & Wolfenstein, 1955; Whiting, 1963). To suppose that enlightened child rearing only started in this century is as nonsensical as to suppose that it is the experience of all children today; throughout the ages, the greatest differences in treatment have been between social classes. Enlightenment seldom benefits the children of those classed as inferior, or worse still as subhuman. The paradox of the 19th century was the coexistence of the horrific effects of uncontrolled urban growth and industrial exploitation on the one hand, with vigorous Christian teaching and belief, including "Love thy neighbour as thyself", on the other.

The distortion of the Christian ethic in the hands of negative parents is elegantly illustrated in Samuel Butler's ironic and autobiographical study of family dynamics, *The Way of All Flesh*, posthumously published in 1903. This must be one of the earliest accounts of two generations of negative scapegoating and perfectionist child rearing, with vivid description of its psychopathological effects. Since sarcasm and irony are not so fashionable today, some readers interpret as Butler's literal opinion passages such as "I grant that at first sight it seems very unjust that the parents should have the fun and the children be punished for it, but young people should remember that for many years they were part and parcel of their parents and therefore had a good deal of fun in the person of their parents."

The potential of moral tales was also adapted to stories specifically directed at the young. *Tom Brown's Schooldays* was influential in exposing the dangers of supposedly worthy residential institutions for the young, in publicising a great educational reformer, Thomas Arnold (1795–1842), headmaster of Rugby, and in providing the young with a model of behavioural adaptation. It depicted both heroes with obviously laudable social skills and attitudes, which children would want to imitate, and villains whose behaviour was to be avoided. *Eric, or Little by Little*, by Frederick William Farrar, was perhaps the most blatently moral of the hundreds of books that followed. Their influence on the attitudes and behaviour of children themselves lasted until the middle of this century, and would therefore have affected adult thinking about schools and children's behaviour problems in England until very recently.

The development of services for 'idiots'

Until the middle of the 19th century, there was an undifferentiated response to deviant behaviour of the children of the poor and oppressed classes. A large proportion of the insane handicapped, criminal, and destitute were taken into gaols or workhouses, or were left wandering and destitute, if not supported by their family or parish (von Gontard, 1988). The vestry had to fund the care of disabled and pauper children in their parish from local funds, and would be reluctant to take any responsibility it could avoid, so that unless there were strong local links, cases were moved from parish to parish. A fortunate few might be admitted to hospitals or charitable foundations: the 'pauper idiot asylums' provided specifically for cases from the lower social classes (see Chapter 16).

The treatment developed by Itard for Victor, 'The Wild Boy of Aveyron', was seen as the beginning of enlightened treatment for mentally handicapped and severely disturbed children by those developing services in England (Pycroft, 1882). Victor was covered with scars, suggesting that he may have been a victim of physical abuse, and Anthony (1982) hails this boy as the first child psychiatric patient, because of his response to treatment. Itard's method was applied successfully by Voisin in 1826, and by Guggenbuhl in 1842, in residential settings which aimed to create a way of life appropriate for the child's intellectual and mental state. The methods they used to awaken the children's senses amazed visitors, but Voisin's institution closed through lack of funds, and in 1840 he moved to the Bicêtre Idiot Schools. There, he recruited Seguin, who developed the approach to the treatment and education of the mentally handicapped (Seguin, 1846) which, with that of Johann Guggenbuhl, was adopted throughout Britain and the USA. The importance of philanthropists and of visits to and from these two centres, in spreading this work, is reviewed by von Gontard (1988). In England, the White Sisters were so impressed by Guggenbuhl's work that, in 1846, they opened a house in Bath, which in turn impressed Guggenbuhl, who used the good offices of Ashley Cooper (later Lord Shaftesbury) to promote the development of more such institutions (see Chapter 16).

In 1882, Pycroft, surgeon in charge of the Western Counties Idiot Asylum, addressed the annual meeting at Exeter, referring to Dr Scott, superintendent of the Exeter Deaf & Dumb Asylum and his pamphlet (the first in English, in 1848) on educating idiots. His story of Miss Plumbe illustrates how influence flowed at that time.

> "A certain Miss Plumbe had read about the success of Monsieur Seguin, in Paris, and her heart was touched, she mentioned the matter to the philanthropic Dr Reed, who had already founded three orphan asylums. She expected, of course, that the good doctor's heart would beat in unison with hers: but he was a Scotsman, cool and cautious, 'Go out, ma'am, into the streets some fine morning and see how many destitute idiots you can find.' She went, and returned with a list of twenty-eight! I think she must have included a number of fools among the number; however that may be, the doctor's cooperation was secured. Dr Conolly, and others, took the matter up warmly. Dr Scott's pamphlet was circulated widely, there was a public dinner and speeches, and the upshot of it all was that Highgate house, with eighteen acres of ground, was taken, and the second idiot industrial asylum started."

John Conolly's description of opening the ward for children in 1848 (see von Gontard, 1988) has a familiar ring; his group of 30 were running wild – "the spirit of mischief prevailed". A year later, there was "order, obedience, and authority, classification improvement and cheerful occupation", "a happy family not by coercion, but by desire''. Some of the cases admitted, to Howe's School for Idiots in Boston and by White, Conolly, and Pycroft, recovered. Their descriptions indicate they were suffering from a great variety of conditions including depression, hyperkinesis, autism, and severe emotional and behaviour disorders reactive to adverse backgrounds (Pycroft, 1882; Bridgeland, 1971). It seems that the more humane and liberal attitudes were leading to good provision and appropriate attitudes and a good model of care for psychiatrically disturbed children, but as yet there was little differentiation between those with severe intellectual handicap and those with severe psychiatric disorder and no provision for mild problems.

The beginnings of modern approaches

As the bench-book for British alienists, Maudsley's *The Pathology of Mind* indicates what a young patient referred to one might expect in the period from the first edition in 1867 to the last in 1895. He should rarely have been admitted, as Maudsley was concerned about the effect of being exposed to ''the vulgar tyranny of an ignorant attendant'' in overcrowded asylums. Maudsley advocated care in private families for cases in which 'moral treatment' required their removal from the circumstances producing the problem, or when treating the patient in his family home was difficult because ''he had become accustomed to exert authority or exact attention''. Maudsley believed that ''placing alone in a cottage under the control of one or two vulgar attendants is to be condemned'', and suggested that this had been the fate of some patients with affluent relatives.

He himself treated a girl with 'hysterical mania' by packing her in a wet sheet and applying a cloth dipped in cold water to her head; ''when this was done, she took without any difficulty a dram of tincture of henbane and after a short time slept; in the morning all the excitement had gone''. In addition to hyoscyamus, opium was used for hyperaesthesia and melancholia, bromide as a sedative, and quinine as a stimulant. He advised that purges be used sparingly, did not encourage the use of irritants, and condemned antiphlogistic treatment. At that time, bleeding was still used and leeches applied to the head. Indeed, a paper on ''Insanity in children'', given to the MPA eastern divisional meeting in 1897 (Beach, 1898), suggests that there had been little general advance in understanding of the young in British psychiatry by the end of the century. Beach thought the ''most important'' ingredient of treatment was ''the separation of the child from his friends; among strangers he will be obliged to conform to the rules of the house and carry out the treatment which has been ordered.''

Kahlbaum's ''Medical Pedagogium'' (1883) was the first fully developed system for the institutional care of mentally ill children (Harms, 1962). Some of the procedures, such as rest, free choice of activity within guidelines, harmonious combination of physical and mental activity, and promotion of character development, social-skills training, and self-control, are still only to be found in the more progressive child-care programmes. Kahlbaum's description will sound familiar to the staff of in-patient units today: mornings of instruction and mechanical and artistic occupation preceded afternoons spent on trips, gymnastics, gardening, and games.

Emminghaus, Professor of Psychiatry in Estonia, wrote an influential volume on psychic disturbances of childhood, *Die psychischen Störungen des Kindesalters* (1887), for Gerhardt's *Handbook of Paediatrics*. This was regarded by Harms (1960) as the progenitor of child psychiatry, and the first book to differentiate its scope from that of paediatrics and adult psychiatry. In it, we can recognise an important source of Adolf Meyer's later psychosocio-biological approach to the provision of child psychiatric services. Emminghaus described the majority of problems dealt with today, referring for the first time in detail to emotional and behaviour disorders, including hysteria and mass sociogenic disorders. His exhaustive list of causes included: cerebral pathology, systemic disorders, psychological stresses, social disadvantages, imitation of others, inappropriate or defective education, bad home conditions, and faults in child rearing and parental attitudes. He advocated psychotherapeutic treatment, not punishment, and emphasised the need to allow the healthy nature of the child to be "the first and best therapeutic helper" of the "growing and incomplete human being". No other comprehensive text appeared until Hector Cameron's *The Nervous Child* (1918).

In 1895, Heller, a teacher and psychologist, in co-operation with paediatricians and psychiatrists, opened an institution in Vienna for defective and neurotic children, using educational methods, hypnosis, and suggestion. Although known and used since the time of Mesmer, hypnosis has been used little in child psychiatry, and this is the only reference to its use that I have found. Whereas in the USA the initiation of services for disturbed children came from concern about juvenile delinquency, in Britain it derived from concern about children who could not fit into the new elementary schools set up from 1870, and made compulsory in 1880. Therefore, developments in the two English-speaking countries followed different courses, with influences crossing the Atlantic episodically.

As part of Galton's anthropometric study of the British Isles, Warner, a professor of anatomy and physiology in London, found that 15% of school pupils were defective physically, mentally, or morally. His methods have been criticised (Bridgeland, 1971) because he was searching for stigmata, and he measured heads, but he gave children a shilling to handle and comment on (von Gontard, 1988) – a combined projective, intelligence, and neurological test. Galton's anthropometric laboratory, started in 1894, offered advice to both parents and teachers, based on inquiry and systematic testing of the child's mental abilities. Cattell, attracted by Galton's statistical approach, became his assistant and adapted his methods when he became Professor of Psychology in Pennsylvania.

In 1896, Cattell established a clinic under the direction of Dr Lightner Witmer (1896–1940). Like Sully, Professor of Mind and Logic at University College London, and Binet in France, he insisted on the need for a co-operative team of specialists in the four main fields – psychological, social, educational, and medical (Keir, 1952). Healey gained his experience in this clinic (Kanner, 1959), which seems to have been the source of the child-guidance method. Another of Cattell's pupils, Thorndyke, had considerable influence on the development of child psychology on both sides of the Atlantic through his textbook *Educational Psychology* (1903).

Sully's laboratory, directed by McDougall and opened in 1896, offered a course in child study to teachers; he became the originator of British educational psychology (Bridgeland, 1971); Cyril Burt trained with McDougall. In *Studies in Childhood*, Sully (1895) defined three categories of educational difficulty and

TABLE 17.1
Early influences on development of attitudes, principles, and practice in child psychiatry

Year of first key publication or of starting service		*Subject of influence or pioneer work*
1300	*Bokes of Nurture*	Philosophy and theoretical principles, attitudes, education
1540	Osterreicher	Clinical description
1546	Phaer	Clinical description
1560	Weyer	Clinical description
1570	Ascham	Philosophy and theoretical principles, attitudes, education
1637	Descartes	Philosophy and theoretical principles
1693	Locke	Philosophy and theoretical principles, attitudes, education
1754	Brouzet	Clinical description, therapeutic innovations, attitudes
1762	Rousseau	Attitudes, philosophy and theoretical principles, education
1787	Perfect	Clinical description, therapeutic innovations, attitudes
1787	Tiedeman	Philosophy and theoretical principles
1798	Itard	Therapeutic innovations, philosophy and theoretical principles, attitudes
1826	Voisin	Attitudes, therapeutic innovations
1828	Arnold	Attitudes, education
1830	Froebel	Philosophy and theoretical principles, attitudes, education
1835	Prichard	Clinical description, therapeutic innovations, philosophy and theoretical principles
1836	Dickens	Attitudes
1840	West	Attitudes
1842	Guggenbuhl	Therapeutic innovations, philosophy and theoretical principles, attitudes
1846	Seguin	Philosophy and theoretical principles, therapeutic innovations, education
1848	Conolly	Therapeutic innovations
1850	Lord Shaftesbury	Attitudes
1852	Great Ormond St Hospital	Therapeutic innovations
1856	Georgen	Therapeutic innovations
1857	Acton	Attitudes
1859	Crichton-Brown	Clinical description, attitudes
1860	Peabody	Attitudes, education
1861	Sechenov	Philosophy and theoretical principles
1865	Kingsley	Attitudes
1867	Maudsley	Clinical description, therapeutic innovations, attitudes
1872	Darwin	Philosophy and theoretical principles, attitudes
1877	Galton	Philosophy and theoretical principles
1881	Preyer	Philosophy and theoretical principles
1883	Kahlbaum	Therapeutic innovations
1887	Emminghaus	Clinical description, therapeutic innovations, philosophy and theoretical principles
1890	Devine	Therapeutic innovations, education
1890	Hall	Attitudes, philosophy and theoretical principles
1893	Sully	Philosophy and theoretical principles
1895	Clouston	Clinical description

Continued

TABLE 17.1
Continued

Year of first key publication or of starting service		*Subject of influence or pioneer work*
1896	Cattell	Philosophy and theoretical principles, attitudes, education
1896	Witmer	Therapeutic innovations, philosophy and theoretical principles
1899	Manheimer	Clinical description
1900	Meyer	Philosophy and theoretical principles, attitudes
1900	Lane	Attitudes, therapeutic innovations
1902	Herbart	Philosophy and theoretical principles, education
1903	Pavlov	Philosophy and theoretical principles, therapeutic innovations
1905	Freud	Philosophy and theoretical principles, attitudes, therapeutic innovations

special need: intellectual dullness, emotional instability, and unacceptable moral conduct. He saw educational, emotional, and behavioural problems as interlocked in the unity of the child and stemming, not from pathological defect, but from "maladjustment" caused by circumstance. He advocated that education authorities should employ psychologists to work in local centres. Sully set up branches of his Child Study Society in Edinburgh, Liverpool, and Manchester; these were instrumental in starting services for children locally.

In Illinois, a separate juvenile court was established in 1899, possibly modelled on one set up in Australia in 1895, in which jurists were assisted by a team of social workers, paediatricians, and psychiatrists. In 1890, Alexander Devine founded a school at Mitcham which showed what could be done for disturbed boys by sympathy and imagination (Bridgeland, 1971). The 'Junior Republics' or 'Little Commonwealths' – therapeutic communities – were started for juvenile delinquents in the USA at the end of the century (Kennard, 1983).

Finally, in Russia, neurophysiological discoveries were being made by Pavlov (1849–1936) which were to evolve into conditioning theory and behavioural and neurophysiological approaches to the understanding and treatment of childhood behaviour disorders. Physiology was already well advanced in Russia as a result of the work of Filomafitsky, a surgeon, and of Sechenov, whose *Reflexes of the Brain* (1863) was acknowledged by Pavlov to have exerted an enormous influence. Founder of the Russian school of physiology, Sechenov advanced as early as 1861 the thesis that "the scientific definition of the organism must include the environment by which it is influenced". He distinguished inborn reflexes from acquired reflexes, and proposed that all the more complex forms of nervous activity are, by the nature of their origin, reflexes. Pavlov's report in 1903 describing the conditioning of reflexes was the practical culmination of a long train of ideas, starting with the introduction of the concept of reflexes by Descartes 250 years before (Koshtoyants, 1955).

Conclusion

Thus, at the end of the 19th century, all the components for a comprehensive assessment and advice service for children were to be found in the Western world, albeit scattered. Firstly, the need for a more positive preventive and remedial approach to juvenile delinquency had been recognised. Secondly, the establishment in Britain of universal compulsory education had uncovered a surprisingly high proportion of children who could not cope with it. Thirdly, these problems were seen to need a multiprofessional approach, and experimental clinics already existed in which doctors and psychologists worked together. Fourthly, some psychiatrists were beginning to recognise that children and adolescents had different problems from adults, and needed separate services. Fifthly, the ground was set for new ways of thinking about behaviour – behavioural, psychodynamic and psychobiological – all stemming from 19th-century doctors and 17th-century thinkers. Sixthly, the application of the scientific method to child study was leading to the development of objective methods for assessing ability, attainment, and behaviour problems. However, despite successful pioneer projects, no comprehensive psychiatric treatment centres for children of normal intelligence yet existed, and treatment methods were still very tentative. The development of child psychiatry in the 20th century is the subject of a separate publication (Wardle, 1991). It is not a story, though, of steady progress to a happy family of professionals, all working together for the common good of the children: the later stages will have to examine the development of damaging rivalry and disharmony.

References

ACTON, W. (1857) *The Functions and Disorders of the Reproductive Organs, in Youth, in Adult Age and in Advanced Life*. London.

ANTHONY, E. J. (1982) In search of the little people: the elaboration of an Irish fantasy of the past, present, and future of our child patients. In *The Child and his Family* (eds E. J. Anthony & C. Chiland). New York: Wiley.

ARIES, P. (1962) *Centuries of Childhood* (trans. R. Baldick). London: Jonathan Cape.

BARKER, P. (1974) History. In *The Residential Psychiatric Treatment of Children* (ed. P. Barker). London: Crosby Lockwood Staples.

BEACH, J. F. (1898) Insanity in children. *Journal of Mental Science*, **48**, 459–474.

BRIDGELAND, M. (1971) *Pioneer Work with Maladjusted Children*. London: Staples Press.

BROUZET (1754) *Essai sur l'education médicinale des enfans et sur leurs maladies*. Paris.

BURT, C. (1925) *The Young Delinquent*. London: University of London Press.

BUTLER, S. (1903) *The Way of All Flesh*. London.

CAMERON, H. C. (1918) *The Nervous Child*. London: Oxford University Press.

CAMERON, K. (1956) Past and present trends in child psychiatry. *Journal of Mental Science*, **102**, 599–603.

CRICHTON-BROWNE, J. (1860) Psychical diseases of early life. *Journal of Mental Science*, **6**, 284–320.

CRUTCHER, R. (1943) Child psychiatry; the history of its development. *Psychiatry*, **6**, 191–201.

CULPEPER, N. (1826) *Complete Herbal and English Physician*. Manchester: Gleave & Son.

DAICHES, D. (1938) *Literature and Society*. London: Victor Gollancz.

DICTIONARY OF NATIONAL BIOGRAPHY (1975) *Dictionary of National Biography* (compact edn). Oxford: Oxford University Press.

EMMINGHAUS, H. (1887) *Die psychischen Störungen des Kindesalters*. Nachtrag 2 to Gerhardt's Handbuch fuer Kinderkrankheiten. Tübingen.

FURNIVAL, F. J. (1868) *The Bokes of Nurture*. London: Trubner.

GRIEVE, M. (1931) *A Modern Herbal*. London: Jonathan Cape.

HARE, E. H. (1962) Masturbatory insanity; the history of an idea. *Journal of Mental Science*, **108**, 1–25.

HARMS, E. (1960) At the cradle of child psychiatry. *American Journal of Orthopsychiatry*, **30**, 186–190.

—— (1962) Karl Kahlbaum's ideas on pedagogical treatment of mentally ill children. *American Journal of Psychiatry*, **119**, 477–478.

HOWELLS, J. G. (1965) Organisation of child psychiatric services. In *Modern Perspectives in Child Psychiatry* (ed. J. G. Howells). Edinburgh: Oliver and Boyd.

—— & Osborn, M. L. (1980) The history of child psychiatry in the United Kingdom. *Acta Paedopsychiatrica*, **46**, 193–202.
Jimack, P. D. (1974) *Émile in Rousseau's Life*. London: Dent.
Kahlbaum, K. (1883) About nervously and mentally diseased children and their pedagogical treatment in institutions. *Allgemeine Zeitschrift für Psychiatrie*, **40**, 863–874.
Kanner, L. (1935) *Child Psychiatry*. Springfield: Thomas.
—— (1955) *Child Psychiatry* (3rd edn). Springfield: Thomas.
—— (1959) Trends in child psychiatry. *Journal of Mental Science*, **105**, 581–593.
Keir, G. (1952) A history of child guidance. *British Journal of Educational Psychology*, **22**, 5–29.
Kennard, D. (1983) *An Introduction to Therapeutic Communities*. London: Routledge & Kegan Paul.
Koshtoyants, Kh. S. (1955) *I. P. Pavlov: Selected Works*. Moscow: Foreign Languages Publishing House.
Kroll, J. (1973) A reappraisal of psychiatry in the Middle Ages. *Archives of General Psychiatry*, **29**, 276–283.
Mackay, C. (1841) *Memoirs of Extraordinary Popular Delusions*. London: Richard Bentley.
Maudsley, H. (1867) *The Pathology of Mind*. New York: Appleton.
Mead, M. & Wolfenstein, M. (1955) *Childhood in Contemporary Cultures*. Chicago: University of Chicago Press.
Parry-Jones, W. Ll. (1990) Annotation: the history of child and adolescent psychiatry: its present day relevance. *Journal of Child Psychology and Psychiatry*, **30**, 3–11.
Pavlov, I. P. (1903) Experimental psychology and psychopathology in animals. In *Proceedings of the Military Academy 1903*. (Trans. (1955). *Pavlov: Selected Works*. Moscow: Foreign Languages Publishing House.)
Pycroft, G. (1882) *An Address on the Education of Idiots*. Exeter: Pollard.
Rousseau, J.-J. (1762) *Émile*. Paris: À La Haye, chez Jean Neaulme.
Sechenov, I. M. (1861) Vegetative processes in animal life. *Medical Herald*, 26. (Quoted in Kostoyants, 1955.)
—— (1863) *Reflexes of the Brain*. (Quoted in Koshtoyants, 1955.)
Stone, L. (1977) *The Family, Sex and Marriage, in England, 1500–1800*. London: Harmondsworth.
Sully, J. (1895) *Studies in Childhood*. London: Longmans.
von Gontard, A. (1988) The development of child psychiatry in 19th century Britain. *Journal of Child Psychology and Psychiatry*, **29**, 569–588.
Walk, A. (1964) The prehistory of child psychiatry. *British Journal of Psychiatry*, **110**, 754–767.
Wardle, C. J. (1989) Mental health services for children and adolescents. *South West Psychiatry*, **2**, 7–16.
—— (1991) Historical influences on the development of services for child and adolescent psychiatry. The 20th century. *British Journal of Psychiatry*, **159** (in press).
Warren, W. (1971) "You can never plan the future by the past". *Journal of Child Psychology and Psychiatry*, **11**, 141–247.
Wessely, S. & Wardle, C. J. (1990) The Current Literature. Mass sociogenic illness by proxy. *British Journal of Psychiatry*, **157**, 421–424.
Whiting, B. B. (1963) *Six Cultures*. New York: John Wiley & Sons.

18 Psychiatry in Scotland

TOM WALMSLEY

In 1841, when the Association of Medical Officers of Hospitals for the Insane was formed in England with Dr Andrew Blake of Nottingham in the chair, the name of the organisation was slightly and reluctantly expanded to include asylum doctors. This can hardly have been distressing to Dr Blake, who was Medical Superintendent of Nottingham General Asylum. Nor would such a change have dismayed any Scots, who since 1781 had been going about the construction of public asylums with a zeal unknown to the English and disproportionate to their population. Indeed, in 1841, the first history of the first royal Scottish asylum – Montrose – was published by Richard Poole, and he felt able to look back on 60 years of improvement in the lot of the insane in eastern Scotland. Montrose was followed by asylums in Aberdeen (opened in 1800), Edinburgh (1813), Glasgow (1814), Dundee (1820), Perth (1826) and Dumfries (1839). In its number of public asylums at least, Scotland had an impressive record. It was also in 1841 that Thomas Carlyle published his lectures *On Heroes, Hero-worship and the Heroic in History* which made a household name of their author, a Dumfriesshire boy recently removed to London.

Poole and Carlyle make an unlikely pair: their styles of historiography are out of fashion and Poole might be said to be the ancestral voice of British asylum histories. Asylums throughout Scotland were to find their chroniclers: Rorie (1912) on Dundee, Brown (1939) on Aberdeen, and Easterbrook (1908, 1940) on Ayr and Dumfries are good examples. So far as heroes are concerned, Carlyle failed to deliver a lecture on the hero-as-physician and, perhaps more remarkably, the hero-as-lunatic, although his lectures dwelt on the hypochondriasis of Cromwell, the marital difficulties of Dante, the melancholia of Dr Johnson, and the despair of Martin Luther. However, the history of psychiatry has been coloured by idolising essays written by one doctor upon another, with varying degrees of hero worship. So far as Scottish psychiatry is concerned, French (1969) on Robert Whytt, Johnstone (1959) on William Cullen, Fish (1965) on David Skae, and Sclare (1981) on John Carswell are good examples of this historical style on a small scale, albeit modified by timing and good judgement.

The ignorance of English people concerning Scottish affairs has been remarked upon by many Scots. In fact, the Scottish medical schools made a remarkable contribution to British life in the 19th century: Victorian heroes as various as Charles Darwin, Samuel Smiles, David Livingstone, W. G. Grace, Sir Arthur Conan Doyle and Pierre Roget received education there. In psychiatry, John

Haslam (1764–1844), James Cowles Prichard (1786–1848), and John Conolly (1794–1866) were educated in Scotland (see Chapter 3). In view of this, it seems remarkable how small is the body of Scottish psychiatric history. A classic text is by Comrie (1932), but it is flawed by too much concentration on university centres of medical education, especially Edinburgh, as well as on 19th-century medical heroes. With Hamilton's general survey of Scottish medicine (1981), Comrie is not so much superseded as vitally complemented, with a correction to the emphasis on Edinburgh and an accent on the history of the provision of medical care to ordinary Scottish people.

Other forms of historiography have contributed to our understanding of Scottish psychiatry. Institutional histories of the ancient universities (Bullock, 1895; Coutts, 1909; Cant, 1946; Horn, 1967), of the royal medical colleges and societies (Duncan, 1896; Gray, 1952; Guthrie, 1954; Craig, 1976), and of psychiatric teaching in more general terms (Robertson, 1928) have served to warn and advise newcomers to the institutional complexities of Scottish medical life. Primrose (1977) chronicled the care of the mentally handicapped and Greenland (1958) Scottish lunacy legislation, while MacNiven (1960) reviewed the early work of the Scottish Commissioners in Lunacy. Only one book has considered the singular question of the history of psychiatry in Scotland: D. K. Henderson's *The Evolution of Psychiatry in Scotland* appeared in 1964 and is an interesting blend of history, antiquarianism, and autobiography. Henderson's use of the word 'evolution' should be noted: he touched on a Scottish theme of scientific dispute to which we shall return.

The social context of Scottish psychiatry

Although this chapter is concerned chiefly with events after 1841, it follows the general outlook employed by Tagliavini (1985) in her exemplary study of the origins of the Italian asylums. It was impossible, she maintained, to understand the building of those asylums without understanding the political circumstances of Italy at the time. In the 18th and 19th centuries, political change there, culminating in national unification, was generally viewed as a triumph of institutional and linguistic logic over the feudal squabbling of centuries. Quite different feelings, though, attach themselves to the political capitulation of 18th-century Scotland. Parliamentary unity with England, however sensible and advantageous in the long run, was forever tainted with duplicity, corruption, and deceit. The key Scottish political events of the 18th century were the Parliamentary union with England in 1707, the Jacobite rebellions in 1715 and 1745, and the last battle fought on 'British' soil – Culloden, in 1746. So far as medical practice was concerned, these events had little effect on everyday life. Indeed, it was a Scot, James Thomson, who wrote the words of "Rule, Britannia", and a medical graduate of the University of Aberdeen, John Arbuthnot, who invented the 'John Bull' motif for England. Yet the unification of Parliaments robbed Edinburgh of its political clout and left a social vacuum, to be filled from the legal and academic worlds. The importance of this process, usually called the 'Scottish Enlightenment', should be set against the social and economic facts of the time; and the central fact of Scottish life was its poverty. Indeed, since the work of Smout (1969, 1986), Scotland has been as fortunate in its historians as it has been unfortunate in its history.

In 1841, Smout (1986) indicates, the population of Scotland was 2.6 million and growing rapidly – it had doubled since 1775. Not only was it growing, but in a peculiar way: some rural areas had actually experienced a fall in numbers while Glasgow, with a population of 275 000, was 12 times larger than it had been in 1775. Edinburgh was now only half the size of Glasgow, despite the construction of its New Town. Yet only a third of Scottish people were urban dwellers, without immediate answer to the minister or laird, and the poverty of the rural Highlands was breathtaking. The tax returns of 1842/43 gave a figure of 12*s*. per head for the annual rentable value of the average Scottish house; but in Skye and the Outer Hebrides, the figure was 5*d*. These were the 'black houses', built of rough stone and turf, thatched with heather, without ceiling, paved floor, windows, or chimney. The diet of fish and potatoes could support life, but could not continue as a viable way to live off the land; the population of the Highlands had fallen by the census of 1851, and was to continue to fall in every census for the next century.

The Universities of Edinburgh and Glasgow stood amid some of the worst housing in Europe. In 1842, Chadwick's celebrated report on the condition of the labouring population of Scotland was full of striking examples of poverty in cities. Alexander Miller, a gynaecologist attached to the Royal Dispensary in Edinburgh, was asked to describe the dwellings of the poorer class. He replied:

> "The dwellings of the poor are generally very filthy. Those of the lowest grade often consist of only one small apartment, always ill-ventilated, both from the nature of its construction and from the densely peopled and confined locality in which it is situated. Many of them, besides, are damp and partly underground. A few of the lowest poor have a bedstead, but most make up a kind of bed on the floor with straw, on which a whole family are huddled together, some naked and others in the same clothes they have worn during the day." (Chadwick, 1842)

Some inhabitants of these dwellings in Edinburgh and Glasgow actually hoarded their own excrement, to help to pay their rent in dung. Dr Neil Arnott in Glasgow commented:

> "This picture is so shocking that, without ocular proof, one would be disposed to doubt the possibility of the facts."

As the century progressed, things got worse. Between 1841 and 1911, the population of Glasgow grew from 275 000 to 784 000, and that of Edinburgh from 164 000 to 401 000. Smout (1986, p. 40) quotes *The Builder* of 1861 as saying of Edinburgh that every visitor will carry away two impressions:

> "a sense of its extraordinary beauty and a horror of its unspeakable filth. . . . We devoutly believe that no smell in Europe or Asia – not in Aleppo or Damascus in the present day – can equal in depth and intensity, in concentration and power, the combination of sulphurated hydrogen we came upon one evening about 10 o'clock in a place called Toddrick's Wynd."

Along with poverty came the problems of alcohol and prostitution. Drink was consumed in enormous quantities. Smout (1986, p. 138) quotes the Edinburgh physician, Dr George Bell:

> "From the toothless infant to the toothless old man, the population of the Wynds drinks whisky. The drunken drama that is enacted on Saturday night and Sabbath morning beggars description. The scene is terrible . . . it is impossible to say how much is expended on the chronic drinking of whisky."

Nevertheless, Bell did try to calculate how the people could afford to buy so much alcohol. In fact, they could not; on the reasonable assumption that every resident of Blackfriar's Wynd drank four gallons of whisky a year, he concluded that they must resort to theft, begging, and prostitution. An intuition of the association of insanity with sexual promiscuity caused some doctors to take an interest in this social problem. In 1842, Dr William Tait published a study of 'Magdalenism' in Edinburgh, claiming that 800 girls were involved. (Smout, 1986, p. 162), while in 1843, Wardlaw gave a series of lectures on female prostitution in Glasgow (Smout, 1986, p. 162), though these and other doctors failed to locate the precise link between sexual behaviour and general paralysis. For the time being, medicine was to take on a scientific mantle rather than a social one; and science was to be had in the Scottish medical schools.

Scottish medical schools and insanity

The 18th century saw a massive expansion of Scottish medical education, particularly in Edinburgh. In the half-century 1650–1700, only 36 British doctors graduated from Scottish universities; between 1750 and 1800, the number had risen to 2594. The comparable figures for Oxford and Cambridge were 933, falling to 246. This reversal of academic medical interest moved against the currents of political control. More importantly, Scottish medicine was in the ascendant at the precise moment in which insanity became a matter of medical interest.

In Edinburgh, Robert Whytt (1714–66) occupied the Chair of the Institutes of Medicine from 1747 until his death. In 1765 he published his observations on nervous, hypochondriacal, and hysterical disorders, to which he prefixed remarks on the sympathy of the nerves. It was this doctrine of the nerves, which Whytt exemplified by concepts of sensibility and irritability in an early formulation of the 'reflex', which sought to supplant the spiritual notions of Stahl and the doctrine of the humours. In doing this, Whytt, always a careful scientist, delivered the human body from mere mechanism as much as from magical theistic fantasies. William Cullen (1710–90), who played a major part in founding the medical school in Glasgow, followed Whytt, translating 'nervous' into 'neurotic' in 1784 in his *First Lines in the Practice of Physic*. Pinel was the first to translate Cullen's book into French (in 1785), and Cullen's neurocentric physiology found an important admirer in Chiarugi (1793/94) who considered him to have brought most light to the obscure subject of insanity in his *Della Pazzia in Genere*.

The importance of Whytt and Cullen – and their opinions – lay in their pupils. From England, Arnold and Trotter, from America, Benjamin Rush, and to Russia, Alexander Crichton (1798), who ensured the worldwide dissemination of the views nurtured by the socially conscious Scottish Enlightenment of Hume, Ferguson, Boswell, and Adam Smith. Lawrence (1979) has argued powerfully that for 18th-century Edinburgh, the nervous system appeared to provide a metaphor of organisational harmony, which political Scotland yearned to achieve. It was to Edinburgh that Spurzheim came in 1815, with his phrenological doctrines and secular notions of self-improvement, which chimed in nicely with the decay of religious belief among its educated, middle-class elite. These doctrines, amplified by the method of the public dissection of the brain, provided medical men with their notions of social responsibility and improvement which they found irresistible in the face of unreasoning insanity.

It is frequently emphasised that the Enlightenment was a Scottish achievement as much as it was Edinburgh's. This is well exemplified by the career of Robert Macnish (1802–37). Macnish was born in Glasgow, where he obtained a master's degree in surgery. In a short life, unadorned by clinical innovation, he set out a kind of psychiatric agenda for the 19th century. His main work was *The Philosophy of Sleep* (1836), but his doctoral dissertation, which concerned states of intoxication, was published as *The Anatomy of Drunkenness*; and towards the end of his life, he published an introduction to phrenology. Had Macnish lived longer, he might well have become a founding father of psychiatry in Scotland.

The foundation of Scottish psychiatry

W. A. F. Browne was born at Stirling on 24 June 1805. Easterbrook (1940) and Harper (1955) have provided brief accounts of his life. Named after his father (William Browne) and two paternal uncles (Alexander and Francis), he lost his father when only a year old. Lt Browne of the Cameronian Regiment was drowned when the ship on which he was being transported to the Peninsular War was wrecked on the Goodwin Sands off the Kent coast. The boy was then brought up in the family home by his mother – who died in 1861 – and his paternal grandparents at The Enclosure in Stirling. Two maternal aunts also took a hand in his upbringing, and William was educated at the High School of Stirling. He proceeded to study medicine at the University of Edinburgh, where he showed an unusual quickness of thought and facility of expression; in 1825, he was elected Fellow of the Royal Medical Society and President for the academic year 1827/28, having qualified as a Licentiate of the Royal College of Surgeons in 1826.

Such a beginning in life would seem to have assured Browne a future in the Edinburgh medical establishment, in the ascendancy of the Victorian era, but as an undergraduate, he came under the influence of George Combe, the internationally famous teacher of phrenology, by whom his mind seems to have been turned towards the study of psychology. Dr Browne contributed to the *Phrenological Journal* and assisted Combe's brother Andrew in endocranial casting and cranioscopy, in time becoming one of the trustees of the Combe estate. In 1828, Browne left Edinburgh for France, where he studied under Esquirol (but not, as Easterbrook states, under Pinel, who had died in 1826) and where he acquired a fluency in French. In 1830, he returned to Scotland, settling in medical practice in Stirling, but achieving success as a specialist in mental disorders at Edinburgh.

In 1834, the managers of Montrose Royal Asylum, carrying out the wishes of Mrs Carnegie, decided to advertise for a medical superintendent. Andrew Combe applied for the post, but on receiving a request for a testimonial from

Browne, withdrew his application and warmly endorsed his former pupil, who was elected to the post by a majority vote. In the same year, Browne married Magdalen Balfour, a daughter of Dr Andrew Balfour of Edinburgh – a well known physician and publisher who had assisted Sir David Brewster in the production of the *Edinburgh Encyclopaedia* (1810–30).

Browne was to prove a fortunate choice for Montrose, as his earliest reports demonstrate. As well as studying and publishing reports of religious mania, Browne conceived the idea that one of the duties of a medical superintendent was to instruct the asylum managers as to the known facts concerning insanity. In 1837, he published five lectures under the general title *What Asylums Were, Are and Ought To Be*, and the effect was catalytic. In their anthological masterwork, Hunter & Macalpine (1963) state that Browne laid out a manifesto for Victorian psychiatry. Certainly, in modesty of claim, scientific caution, and practical consideration, Browne quickly established himself as the model of the asylum doctor. The effects were personal also. Mrs Elizabeth Crichton of Friars Carse by Dumfries was attempting to endow a fifth Scottish university with her family fortune. When, on advice, she decided to devote her philanthropy to an institution for the insane, a primary stipulation was that there should be a physician superintendent; Browne's lectures were brought to her attention and, after a brief interview, she knew him to be the man for the task. Philanthropy had scarcely known such extension before: Mrs Crichton's endowment was £100 000, which makes Henry Maudsley's gift of £30 000 to London County Council (Chapter 4) seem almost niggardly (though of course it was not). Browne remained Physician Superintendent of the Crichton Royal Institution from 1838 until 1857 when, after the passage of the Lunacy (Scotland) Act, he was appointed one of the first Medical Commissioners for Scotland. He then created the role of Medical Commissioner in much the same way as he had become the first Medical Superintendent at Montrose. His reports were exemplary in their courtesy, constructive criticism, and literary style. In 1864, he published his thoughts on "the moral treatment of the insane", encouraged by the admiration of Thomas Laycock, then Professor of Medicine at the University of Edinburgh. He received an MD from Heidelberg and an honorary LLD from Wisconsin. He was elected a Fellow of the Royal Society of Edinburgh – an honour bestowed on few psychiatrists – and was President of the Medico-Psychological Association in 1866.

In 1870, Browne suffered an accident while on official circuit in East Lothian and following this his eyesight deteriorated, probably because of glaucoma. He resigned as Commissioner in the same year, returning to Dumfries, where he spent the remaining 15 years of his life as a psychological consultant to the Crichton Royal Hospital, tended by his wife and daughters and devoting attention to various literary projects including the "Religio Psycho-Medici" (1877). He died quite suddenly in March 1885, survived by two sons and two daughters. His eldest son, James Crichton-Browne (1840–1938), Lord Chancellor's Visitor in Lunacy, was created a Knight Bachelor within a year of his father's death; the younger surviving son, John Hutton Balfour Browne, KC (1845–1921), was the leader of the Parliamentary bar in his day. Madeline and Buntie Browne were their father's affectionate companions during his years of affliction, Buntie moving to Norwich in 1897 and dying there in 1940.

Browne and Charles Darwin

Browne's abilities as an orator and administrator were evident during his studentship at Edinburgh. In 1829, Coldstream wrote to Darwin that the only news in Edinburgh was the success of the Plinian Society, to which Browne "lent his matured experience". This society, fostered by Professor Jameson and devoted to natural history, had seen the first scientific address given by the young Charles Darwin. On the same evening, Browne gave the other paper, in which he proposed that all mental activity was material and that the mind itself was a mode of biological organisation. Browne's overt materialism led to uproar and all records of the meeting were suppressed (Darwin, 1974). It has been suggested that Darwin's horror of scientific controversy stemmed from this episode (Miller, 1982). In view of this, when Darwin turned to asylum cases for the provision of evidence for his *Expression of the Emotions in Man and the Animals* (1872), he first chose to approach Henry Maudsley. Maudsley, in turn, recommended Sir James Crichton-Browne, with whom Darwin had a fruitful collaboration; but Darwin failed to remark on his close acquaintance with Sir James' father when both were students at Edinburgh.

Browne and the Lunacy (Scotland) Act 1857

Dorothea Lynde Dix (1802–87) was the daughter of an alcoholic preacher in New England who abandoned his family early in her life, so that she had to take care of her younger siblings. Later, she became a social reformer in the style of Elizabeth Fry, Octavia Hill, and Florence Nightingale. Her interests centred on the care of the insane, and she was appalled by what she found in America, Scotland, Russia, and elsewhere. Browne seems to have regarded her as something of an irritation to the smooth regulation of the administrative process (he called her "that interfering woman"), but, in general, he supported the drift of her reforming zeal. In 1855, Dix visited Scottish asylums and asked the Home Secretary of the day to undertake a review of the care of the insane in Scotland. Browne and Skae gave extensive evidence to the Committee of Enquiry, whose findings were translated into the Lunacy (Scotland) Act of 1857.

The 1857 Act

The main provisions of the act included the establishment of the General Board of Commissioners in Lunacy for Scotland, with an unpaid chairman, two paid medical commissioners, and not more than three other unpaid legal commissioners. In addition, there were to be two paid deputy medical commissioners, a secretary, and a clerk to the General Board. The powers of the General Board included:

(a) the superintendence, management, direction, and regulation of all matters arising in relation to lunatics; and to public, private, and district asylums and to every house in which a lunatic was kept or detained under order of the sheriff

(b) the granting or refusing or recalling of licences to the proprietors of private asylums

(c) the making and enforcing of rules and regulations for the good order and management of all private and district asylums and for the conduct of their officers and servants
(d) the making and enforcing of the rules and regulations in relation to the books at each asylum; and to the returns of the entries therefrom to be made to the General Board
(e) the regulation of the visitation and inspection of asylums and houses – to be made twice yearly by the paid commissioners, who were to make entries in the "Patients' Book", to be kept in each asylum or house, of the condition of the patients and asylum and of any coercion or restraint imposed on any lunatic and of the way in which asylum registers were kept
(f) the visitation of houses, private houses, prisons and poorhouses detaining lunatics or alleged lunatics
(g) the institution of inquiries and the summoning and examination on oath of witnesses.

The act also provided that, on the expiry of five years as from January 1858, the General Board should cease to exist, and that the two paid Commissioners should become Inspectors-General in Lunacy for Scotland and exercise all the powers of the General Board, except the granting of licences, to be vested in the sheriff. Other official inspections were also to be allowed. Sheriffs and justices of the peace were authorised to visit and inspect any asylum or any house detaining a lunatic.

The act empowered sheriffs to order the reception of lunatics into any public, private, or district asylum or house, on a petition by a party applying for the same, accompanied by certificates by two qualified medical persons specifying the facts upon which the opinion of insanity was based. The act also empowered the superintendent of any asylum to receive and detain for not more than 24 hours, without a sheriff's order, any lunatic duly certified by one medical person to be a case of emergency. The act also authorised the reception and detention of a patient in any private house for temporary care and treatment, not exceeding six months and with a view of the patient's recovery under the certificate of a medical person to that effect and without any petition or sheriff's order.

Next, the act decreed that asylums licensed for 100 or more patients should have a resident medical attendant; those for more than 50 patients should be visited daily by a medical person; those licensed for 50 patients or fewer should be visited at least twice weekly by a medical person.

Ministers and relatives and other friends of lunatics detained in any asylum or house were authorised to visit them. The General Board might grant orders for such visits. Furthermore, there was to be provision for the proper protection of the property of lunatics by application to the Court of Session for the appointment of a judicial factor ('curator bonis').

Provision was also made for punishment of the wilful abuse, ill-treatment, or neglect of any lunatic or alleged lunatic. A fine up to £100 or imprisonment up to six months, without prejudice to any civil action by or on behalf of the lunatic, was provided. Special provisions were made for the commitment of dangerous and criminal lunatics and of prisoners who became insane during sentence. Provision was also made for the transfer of lunatics from one asylum to another and for their discharge from asylums. Also, provision was made for the keeping of asylum registers, including a Register of Lunatics and Register of Deaths in which the details of the date and cause of death were required to be entered.

Lastly, the act divided Scotland into 'lunacy districts', combining groups of counties and the appointment of district boards. The General Board was, after inquiry, to require the district boards to prepare plans and estimates for district asylums where required and then to provide for these district asylums.

The district asylums and their doctors

The implementation of the Lunacy (Scotland) Act 1857 resulted in the construction of 19 district asylums by 1910, the first of them opening at Lochgilphead in 1863. Sir John Sibbald, a pupil of Skae's at Morningside and a fellow student of Clouston, was appointed Superintendent of the Argyll and Bute Asylum. He stayed for about eight years, until his preferment to a medical commissioner post. Perthshire District Asylum at Murthly did equally well with the appointment of William Carmichael M'Intosh (1838–1931), whose duties towards the pauper lunatics of Perthshire did not obstruct his passion for marine invertebrates. His exhaustive monograph on this subject, illustrated by his sister, resulted in his election to Fellowship of the Royal Society, shortly before his resignation from Murthly to take up the Chair of Natural History at St Andrews in 1882.

The ancient 'Royal' asylums continued in their own ways, fortified by their auxiliary role as district asylums. Thus, the Crichton Royal Institution at Dumfries incorporated the Southern Counties Asylum, and frequently admitted pauper lunatics from other parts of Scotland, pending completion of their own facilities. Here, James Rutherford, who had previous experience at Lochgilphead and Woodilee (Glasgow District Asylum) proved an exemplary superintendent and, in collaboration with Lockhart Robertson of the Sussex County Asylum at Haywards Heath, translated the works of Griesinger into English. At Morningside, Clouston succeeded Skae in 1873 and put an end to the long animosity between the university (where Professor Laycock lectured on medical psychology) and the Royal Edinburgh Asylum. No longer did Laycock's pupils have to travel to Stirling or Dumfries for clinical demonstrations. In 1879, Clouston was appointed University Lecturer on Mental Diseases, the first lectureship to be established, but quickly followed by Argyll Robertson's appointment in Diseases of the Eye. Extramural teaching, forced on Edinburgh by the rejection of Sir Alexander Morison's scheme for a chair in mental diseases, was carried on by Sir John Batty Tuke and Sir John Macpherson, who used Stirling and West Lothian for their clinical material. Batty Tuke had been the first Superintendent of Fife & Kinross Asylum at Stratheden, but quickly moved to Edinburgh to manage a private asylum at Saughton, before his election to Parliament as the Member for the Universities of Edinburgh and St Andrews (Rankin, personal communication).

By the end of the 19th century, as in England, the asylums provided a network of medical positions which were sufficient to support a growing number of specialists in insanity. But unlike their English colleagues, Scotland's specialists found considerable support in the universities and in the Royal College of Physicians. The University of Edinburgh founded its Diploma in Psychiatry in 1912, while Clouston had been elected President of the College in 1902. Nevertheless, asylum-centred psychiatry was already in question and the impulse for reform already active.

Asylum reform

In his Maudsley lecture, John Carswell (1924) summarised the case for reform of the asylums. He had studied under Rutherford at Woodilee Hospital before his appointment as medical officer to the Barony Parish in Glasgow. Here, he noted class differences in certification and in 1887 set up two lunacy wards at the Parochial Hospital; his thinking seems to have been influenced by Griesinger, the relationship of lunacy to alcohol, criminal behaviour, and urban deprivation being matters of central concern to him. The themes which recur in Carswell's writings are the social causes of insanity, the early recognition of individual cases by the use of observation wards and without certification, and the care of the mentally handicapped outside hospital. In addition, there was the hope of prevention of illness.

In this, Carswell closely paralleled the work in England of Helen Boyle, who saw him as an earlier exponent of much of her own practice (1905), while, in Edinburgh, George Robertson took pride in the 'hospitalisation' of the asylum. Robertson had introduced the villa system while superintendent at Murthly (1892–99); he brought generally trained nurses into the asylum, encouraging female nurses to work in male wards, and recognised the special importance of night nursing. At the end of World War I, he was appointed to the newly established Chair of Psychiatry in the University of Edinburgh. Here, he found a chain of nursing homes organised by the military for shell-shocked soldiers of the officer class, some of them patients of W. H. R. Rivers; Robertson developed these as wards in the community for the treatment of doubtful or early cases of insanity, which hardly required certification. In 1929, the Jordanburn Nerve Hospital was opened to provide similar facilities for the poor, as did the Lansdowne Clinic established by Yellowlees in Glasgow.

This adaptation of the Scottish asylums did much to ensure their survival. In 1896, Clouston and Batty Tuke had founded the Central Pathological Laboratory of the Scottish Asylums. Its first Director, Ford Robertson, was a powerful teacher, whose emphasis on the neurological basis of insanity greatly influenced pupils like Lewis Bruce and Dods Brown. Similar research initiatives took place in Glasgow and Dumfries. As lately as 1923, the first Henderson Trust Lecture – "The old and the new phrenology" – was delivered by Elliot Smith (1924), and the Trustees included the Professors of Anatomy, Psychology, and Psychiatry at Edinburgh. Yet this neurological emphasis did not blind Scottish psychiatry to psychosocial processes. In 1915, Stoddart had startled his audience with an abrupt account of psychoanalysis, and Rivers' wartime work at Craiglockhart was more quietly assimilated (perhaps because Rivers had a stammer), through figures such as Fairbairn and Angus Macniven. It was this eclecticism, described and personified by Sir David Henderson, which came to dominate the inter-war psychiatry of Scotland. Ironically, the eclectic clinical style was to marginalise the neuropsychiatry of Lewis Bruce, to isolate the distinguished psychoanalyst Ronald Fairbairn, and to cause Winifred Rushforth to open the Davidson Clinic for psychotherapy in 1940.

Nor was the asylum era entirely concluded. Baird (personal communication) states that, in the early 1930s, consideration was given to establishing a special facility for criminal lunatics in Scotland. Construction of a new hospital for offender patients began on a greenfield site at Carstairs Junction, and the first offenders were transferred there in 1948. In 1958, the last patients left Perth Prison to be admitted to the State Hospital at Carstairs.

Conclusion

In this procession, we can find progress in the lot of the mentally ill in Scotland since Susan Carnegie had transferred the pauper lunatics from the Tolbooth of Montrose to a local asylum in 1781, yet the progress was patchy. Scotland's early achievements in the provision of asylums (with seven 'Royal' asylums by 1839) were ahead of the English constructions enabled by her Lunacy Acts of 1808 and 1845, but the general uniformity of asylum construction and reform throughout the British Empire, Europe, and North America, as the Industrial Revolution took hold, is more striking. Similar institutional efforts are to be seen in the prisons, railways, and major schools of the period. But Scotland was poorer and less populous than England, and placed a higher premium on education. The asylum doctors had an easier way with the medical schools and the medical royal colleges. In its early exponents – Browne, Carswell, and Clouston – Scottish psychiatry found an intellectual eloquence unbettered by its many richer neighbours. The recognition of this heritage has been slow in coming.

References

BOYLE, A. H. (1905) Provision of suitable accommodation. *Journal of Mental Science*, **51**, 676–710.

BROWN, R. D. (1939) *Aberdeen Royal Mental Hospital*. London: British Medical Association.

BROWNE, W. A. F. (1837) *What Asylums Were, Are and Ought To Be*. Edinburgh: Adam and Charles Black.

—— (1864) The moral treatment of the insane. *Journal of Mental Science*, **10**, 309–327.

—— (1877) Religio psycho-medici. *Journal of Psychological Medicine*, **3**, 17–31, 215–231.

CANT, R. G. (1946) *The University of St Andrews*. Edinburgh: Oliver & Boyd.

CARLYLE, T. (1841) *On Heroes, Hero-Worship and the Heroic in History*. London.

CARSWELL, J. (1924) Some sociological considerations bearing upon the occurrence, prevention and treatment of mental disorders. *Journal of Mental Science*, **70**, 347–357.

CHADWICK, E. (1842) Reports on the sanitary condition of the labouring population of Scotland. *House of Lords Papers*, **28**.

CHIARUGI, V. (1793/94) *Della Pazzia in Genere e in Specie*. Firenze: publisher unknown.

COLDSTREAM, J. (1829) Letter. In *The Correspondence of Charles Darwin*, pp. 77–78. Cambridge: Cambridge University Press.

COMRIE, J. D. (1932) *History of Scottish Medicine*. London: Baillière, Tindall and Cox.

COUTTS (1909) *A History of the University of Glasgow*. Glasgow: University of Glasgow.

CRAIG, W. S. (1976) *History of the Royal College of Physicians of Edinburgh*. Oxford: Blackwell.

CRICHTON, A. (1798) *An Inquiry into the Nature and Origin of Mental Derangement*. London: Cadell and Davies.

CULLEN, W. (1784) *First Lines in the Practice of Physic*. Edinburgh: Elliot.

DARWIN, C. (1872) *The Expression of the Emotions in Man and the Animals*. London: Murray.

——— (1974) *Early Writings* (eds. P. H. Barrett & H. E. Gruber), pp. xi, 219. Chicago: University of Chicago Press.

DUNCAN, A. (1896) *Memorials of the Faculty of Physicians and Surgeons of Glasgow 1599–1950*. Glasgow: Maclehose.

EASTERBROOK, C. C. (1908) *Ayr District Asylum*. Ayr: Privately printed.

——— (1940) *The Chronicle of Crichton Royal, 1833–1936*. Dumfries: Courier Press.

ELLIOT SMITH, G. (1924) *The Old and the New Phrenology*. Edinburgh: Oliver & Boyd.

FISH, F. J. (1965) David Skae, M.D., F.R.C.S. *Medical History*, **9**, 36–53.

FRENCH, R. K. (1969) *Robert Whytt, the Soul and Medicine*. London: Wellcome Institute.

GRAY, J. (1952) *History of the Royal Medical Society*. Edinburgh: Edinburgh University Press.

GREENLAND, C. (1958) One hundred years of Scottish lunacy legislation. *Public Health*, **72**, 147–155.

GUTHRIE, D. J. (1954) *The Medical School of Edinburgh*. Edinburgh: Edinburgh University Press.

HAMILTON, D. N. H. (1981) *The Healers: A History of Medicine in Scotland*. Edinburgh: Canongate.

HARPER, J. H. (1955) Dr. W. A. F. Browne. *Proceedings of the Royal Society of Medicine*, **48**, 590–593.

HENDERSON, D. K. (1964) *The Evolution of Psychiatry in Scotland*. Edinburgh: Livingstone.

HORN, D. B. (1967) *A Short History of the University of Edinburgh*. Edinburgh: Edinburgh University Press.

HUNTER, R. & MACALPINE, I. (1963) *Three Hundred Years of Psychiatry 1535–1860*, pp. 865–869. London: Oxford University Press.

JOHNSTONE, R. W. (1959) William Cullen. *Medical History*, **3**, 33–46.

LAWRENCE, C. (1979) The nervous system and society in the Scottish Enlightenment. In *Natural Order* (eds B. Barnes & S. Shapin). London: Sage Publications.

MACNISH, R. (1836) *The Philosophy of Sleep* (3rd edn). Glasgow: McPhun.

MACNIVEN, A. (1960) The first commissioners: reform in the mid-nineteenth century. *Journal of Mental Science*, **106**, 451–471.

MILLER, J. (1982) *Darwin for Beginners*. London: Writers and Readers.

POOLE, R. (1841) *Royal Lunatic Asylum, Infirmary and Dispensary of Montrose*. Montrose: Nichol.

PRIMROSE, D. A. (1977) The development of mental deficiency hospitals in Scotland. *Health Bulletin*, **35**, 63–67.

ROBERTSON, G. M. (1928) History of the teaching of psychiatry. *Edinburgh Medical Journal*, **35**, 192–205.

RORIE, J. (1912) *History of Dundee Royal Lunatic Asylum*. Dundee: Matthews.

SCLARE, A. B. (1981) John Carswell: A pioneer in Scottish psychiatry. *Scottish Medical Journal*, **26**, 265–270.

SMOUT, T. C. (1969) *A History of the Scottish People 1560–1830*. London: Collins.

——— (1986) *A Century of the Scottish People*. London: Collins.

STODDART, W. H. B. (1915) The new psychiatry. *Edinburgh Medical Journal*, **14**, 244–260, 339–359, 443–461.

TAGLIAVINI, A. (1985) Aspects of the history of psychiatry in Italy in the second half of the nineteenth century. In *The Anatomy of Madness, Vol. 2* (eds W. F. Bynum, R. Porter & M. Shepherd), pp. 175–196. London: Routledge.

19 Irish psychiatry. Part 1: The formation of a profession

MARK FINNANE

Irish psychiatry was formed in the work of the public lunatic asylum: like its companions in Britain and other parts of Western Europe, it was marked especially by its function as an administrative practice in a specialised medical institution. Among its leading practitioners were some highly dedicated and professional officers who combined their asylum duties with a keen interest in the advancement of the knowledge of psychological medicine. While none were among the leading English-speaking psychiatric writers and thinkers in the 19th century, the history of Irish asylum doctors is instructive in understanding the ways in which specific forms of scientific knowledge and practice are formed, disseminated, and applied. Hence, Irish psychiatry in that century offers an insight into both the institutional and intellectual contexts in which psychiatric knowledge was later dispersed in administrative and social life by the early 20th century.

Medical politics and the emergence of Irish alienism

The formation of Irish psychiatry was the outcome of a struggle for domination between two groups of medical men in the middle of the 19th century. Rules for the management of Irish lunatic asylums had prescribed in 1843 that the medical oversight of the institutions was to be placed in the office of 'Visiting Physician' (see Finnane (1981) for the development of public asylums in Ireland). From the 1840s, however, the trend to appointment of medically qualified asylum managers created substantial tensions over the management and medical supervision of asylum inmates. To the extent that psychological medicine was being formed at this time in the medical practices of the asylum, the role of the visiting physician was becoming redundant. Indicative of the changing climate was the first number of Forbes Winslow's *Journal of Psychological Medicine*, which criticised the absence of resident physicians in Irish asylums: a system employing visiting physicians encouraged irregular medical attendance and was disruptive to the institution (Winslow, 1848).

By 1850, the *Dublin Journal of Medical Science* was able to welcome the appointment of a medically qualified manager to the Carlow Lunatic Asylum, suggesting that the practice of appointing physicians was now so general that the title 'manager' should be discontinued. Titular reform should be extended to the institutions themselves, with 'lunatic asylums' becoming 'hospitals for the insane'. The important Royal Commission into lunatic asylums in Ireland agreed that the resident physician was now so general that new regulations were required; for example, that such appointees be disqualified from private practice (Commissioners of Inquiry, 1857/58).

In the consolidation of the institutional authority of the medical superintendent of the public asylum, the Medico-Psychological Association had a crucial role to play: although an Irish division of the Association was not formed until 1872, Irish alienists were members much earlier than this. Robert Stewart, resident physician at the Belfast asylum and author of anonymous reviews on insanity in the *Dublin Journal of Medical Science* from 1846, was present at the 1851 annual meeting of the Association under the chairmanship of John Conolly. The Association gathered other Irish members during the 1850s, and in turn supported their case for resident medical superintendents. The 1857 annual meeting of the Association urged Dublin Castle to appoint only medical officers as managers, taking the

> "opportunity to show the government and the public, that lunacy is the result of disease. Unfortunately, an opinion was too prevalent that lunacy is out of the category of disease; and they found as a consequence, that medical men were degraded to the point of mere keepers of mad houses." (*Journal of Mental Science*, 1857)

The concerns of both Irish doctors and the Association generally in this struggle were not only with matters of medical practice and autonomy, but also with the attendant concerns of salary and status. The tone of the struggle is well captured by John Bucknill's 1860 review of a pamphlet by Joseph Lalor, the first resident physician of the Richmond Lunatic Asylum in Dublin. Bucknill strongly endorsed Lalor's appeal for the subordination of the visiting physician to the resident, remarking that the lay managers had been supplanted, "according to Mr. Darwin's theory of the origin of species, by a class possessed of far more vitality and usefulness, to wit, the resident physician" (*Journal of Mental Science*, 1860).

Subsequently, the Association's support for the Irish members was affirmed in their election of Lalor as the President for 1861 and a decision to hold the 1861 annual meeting in Dublin. At that meeting, it was John Conolly himself who moved the Association to resolve that the responsibility for management of asylums and for the treatment of patients should be given to resident medical officers, with visiting physicians reverting to merely a consulting role (*Journal of Mental Science*, 1861).

The Irish alienists won the day in 1862, when the Privy Council in Ireland endorsed new rules drawn up by the Secretary of State for Ireland, Sir Robert Peel, who had received a deputation from the Association during the 1861 annual meeting in Dublin. The new rules established the undisputed authority of the resident medical superintendent in the Irish public asylums. As a qualified physician and surgeon, the superintendent was to be responsible for the medical and moral treatment of all patients and for the domestic management of the asylum. The visiting physician was reduced to the role of consultant, whose visits to the asylum were to be made only with the superintendent's consent (Inspectors of Lunatics in Ireland, 1862).

The consolidation of the professional and employment status of Irish alienists was achieved through a war of pamphlets and medical journalism, given weight by the organised strength of the Medico-Psychological Association (MPA). The MPA continued to provide the major forum for consideration of questions affecting asylum medical and managerial practice, as well as the development and dissemination of the science of psychological medicine itself.

The emergent specialty

The intellectual and scientific interests of the Irish members were for the most part somewhat marginal to their work, certainly in comparison to some of their English and Scottish colleagues. Their outlook was dominated not by an articulated theory of insanity and its treatment, but by the institutional conditions of their practice. However, by establishing the distinctive nature of the asylum physician's vocation, some impetus was given to an informal education in 'mental disease'.

From the late 1860s, informal classes for the study of insanity ''both systematically and clinically'' were being conducted by physicians in Dublin and Edinburgh (*Dublin Journal of Medical Science*, 1867). The principal mode of attaining specialised knowledge, however, was service in an asylum. In Ireland this was difficult, since there were few medical appointments below the level of superintendent. In 1875, only four of the 22 public asylums had assistant medical officers – a situation regarded as one of the ''obstacles to the advancement of psychological medicine in Ireland'' (*Journal of Mental Science*, 1875). Additional appointments in later years meant that an assistantship in an asylum became a means of gaining an education in mental diseases, in the absence of formal training in the medical schools. Although the government sometimes appointed direct from dispensary or general practice, there was a tendency to look to those with some asylum training.

Moreover, career histories make clear that those who had experience of an assistantship came to dominate the psychiatric profession in Ireland in later years. E. M. Courtenay, later an Inspector of Lunatics in Ireland, topped his medical class at Trinity before continuing his psychological studies at the reputable West Riding asylum in Yorkshire under the leading alienist, Dr James Crichton-Browne. Subsequently, he served as an assistant medical officer at the Derby asylum, before appointment as superintendent at the Limerick asylum in 1873. Ringrose Atkins, the major reviewer for many years of works on insanity for the *Dublin Journal of Medical Science*, was appointed superintendent at Waterford in 1878, following two years as assistant at Cork. Conolly Norman, President of the MPA in 1894, and editor of the *Journal of Mental Science* in the 1890s, went immediately to an assistantship at Monaghan, following his graduation in 1874. After five years there, he spent two years working under Dr George Savage at Bethlem in London, before his first appointment as superintendent at Castlebar in 1882. Norman (1853–1908) came from a prominent Derry family. Among his contributions to the development of the profession should also be added his nomination of the first woman member of the MPA, Dr Eleanora Fleury, in 1894. Dr Fleury was at the time a clinical assistant at the Richmond Asylum in Dublin (*Journal of Mental Science*, 1894).

By the 1880s, this progression had become so common that the MPA felt it should be a condition of appointment as superintendent that the appointee have had the "special training afforded by residence as a medical officer" in an asylum. Dublin Castle was unperturbed by the MPA's resolution to this effect, replying that it agreed with this view and had already put it into practice.

The MPA contributed in other ways to medical education and training, by initiating the Certificate in Psychological Medicine in 1885, following the report of an Association committee on the matter of the training of medical officers in asylums. Conolly Norman and Dr James Eames, of the Cork asylum, became the first Irish examiners for the certificate. The Irish university colleges, however, had already taken some steps in the right direction. In 1875, the President of Queen's College, Cork, arranged for the first time to have the Cork asylum superintendent deliver a series of lectures to the Cork medical students. By 1885, the Royal University in Dublin was examining in mental diseases for the MD degree. These developments, according to Eames, delivering the presidential address to the MPA in 1885, were ahead of those in England. Perhaps Eames was referring to the lack of support for the contemporaneous initiative in England: in 1879 the *Medical Press and Circular* reported that no students had attended the classes in psychological medicine at University College Hospital or Westminster Hospital during the previous summer session (Eames, 1885).

Such advances in professional autonomy and training contributed significantly to the Irish psychiatrists' confidence and professional standing. By the time of Conolly Norman's stewardship of the Irish Division of the Association, relations with non-asylum physicians had resolved to the point where it was meeting regularly in the College of Physicians in Dublin. The final step in the consolidation of the position of the Irish psychiatrists in fact came in 1892, when the post of visiting physician was abolished by new rules drafted by the Inspectors of Lunatics, one of whom was now E. M. Courtenay. Norman answered some press criticism of the step, observing in the Dublin *Daily Independent* (26 April) in 1892 that insanity was a bodily disease, and that its treatment was a matter for specialists who devoted all their time to the subject; it was a vigorous and public defence of the new specialty of psychological medicine.

Mind, matter and society

When Dr Joseph Lalor (1861), the first Irish president of the Association, cited "the well-known though mysterious connexion between mind and matter", he touched on the weakness of the alienist's theoretical apparatus. Irish psychiatry, as represented in the debates and papers in the medical press and journals, was not highly distinguished. But it reflected some of the dominant concerns of the emerging profession of psychiatry (as it was coming to be known from the 1880s). Within these limited parameters it is instructive to identify some of the ways in which contemporary psychiatric thought was received and reproduced in the ranks of the Irish members of the Association.

Three issues are worth noting: the physiology/psychology debates, the role of hereditarianism, and the question of an increase in insanity. In the first case, the best of the Irish psychiatrists played a role in translating the debates into discussion at a local level; in the second, they tended to take a somewhat more sceptical view than many of their British colleagues; and on the last, they had good reason to be pondering the evidence before their own eyes of the often dramatic increases in asylum populations in the later 19th century.

British psychiatry in the late 19th century variously explored the physiological and psychological approaches to the study of insanity. The basic postulate of the medical approach to insanity was that the brain was the organ of the mind. A persistent theme in the work of the alienists was the search for what Henry Maudsley called a ''physiology of mind''. However, the significant achievements of physiology lay more in the understanding of motor disorders, with the development of the neurophysiology of Hughlings Jackson and others (Young, 1970).

The problems posed by the failure of medicine to discover a somatic basis for most of the symptoms of the patients in asylums meant that more interest was taken in the development of a clinical understanding of individual cases. Attempts by somaticists like Skae to establish a 'somato-aetiological' classification were criticised by many for their lack of scientific basis – the causes of so many cases were unknown (Skae, 1875). In the debate over proper classification of disease entities in insanity, Irish psychiatrists like Conolly Norman particularly supported the new contributions of German psychiatry. Norman found the older classifications ''essentially metaphysical''; but the proposed somatic taxonomies were no advance. Skae's system simply did not have pathological or physiological significance for many cases. Before a medical audience in Ireland in 1887, Norman gave examples of case histories which could have encompassed mania, melancholia, and dementia. He himself was beginning to favour the German distinction (he cited Krafft-Ebing) between psychoneuroses and the more serious conditions of mental derangement (Norman, 1887). Norman played an important role too in transmitting the work of Kraepelin to his colleagues in Ireland and Britain. The German impact was evident not only in the increasing use of the term 'psychiatry', but in the emphasis on the total clinical picture, rather than on the classification of symptoms, which had dominated earlier asylum practice. The measure of Kraepelin's influence was evident in the inclusion from 1891 of a section devoted to ''Clinical psychiatry'' in Ringrose Atkin's long-running ''Report on nervous and mental diseases'' in the *Dublin Journal of Medical Science* (Atkin, 1891).

Later, other Continental influences showed their impact on Irish psychiatric practice: psychoanalysis, imperfectly understood in Britain and Ireland before World War I, was nevertheless affecting some psychiatrists' clinical approach towards patients. Dr Graham of the Belfast asylum reminded his listeners in 1911 that the summary methods of the past were useless – ''such phrases as 'strange behaviour', 'incoherent talk', did not throw much light on the individual's mental state''. He recommended attention to Professor Freud's technique for ''the discovery of the psycho-genesis of delusions'' (*Journal of Mental Science*, 1911).

While many psychiatric debates centred on the development of clinical work, others went beyond the individual patient to explore the possibility that insanity was in effect a social disease. Under the impact of Herbert Spencer and Charles Darwin, a preoccupation with explanations of the incidence of insanity in civilised society became an important part of psychiatric thought. Whether biological versus sociological or hereditarian versus environmentalist, the contrasting accounts had special pertinence for a medical specialty which was centred on an institution that seemed to concentrate many of the disorders of modern society.

In spite of the enthusiasm of some for hereditarian explanations and eugenic solutions to the incidence of insanity, Irish psychiatrists – like others – were divided. At a forum at the Royal Academy of Medicine in Ireland in 1900, Conolly Norman took exception to the generalities of a eugenics speaker who postulated the concept of an "insane predisposition" in some – that was something, said Norman, which "we all have". Dr William Dawson, from a Dublin private asylum, agreed with Norman in 1900 "as to the excess to which the theory of heredity is carried now-a-days" (*Dublin Journal of Medical Science*, 1900). Dawson's consideration changed over time however. In 1901, he explained that while heredity might be relevant in particular cases, "what is inherited is, not a disease, but a diathesis which may manifest itself by the occurrence not only of insanity, but of other nervous diseases" (*Dublin Journal of Medical Science*, 1901).

A decade later, at the height of the Edwardian enthusiasm for eugenics, Dawson, now an Inspector of Lunatics in Ireland, regretted the difficulties of extending the mental deficiency bill to Ireland, since hundreds of defectives were being allowed to produce an ever-increasing crop of degeneracy (*Dublin Journal of Medical Science*, 1913). Dawson by now was citing the discoveries of the Eugenic Society, "that feeble-minded people produced rather larger numbers of children than did the sound-minded" (*Journal of Mental Science*, 1911). In spite of this strong advocacy from a leading Irish psychiatrist and administrator, the hopes of the eugenists in Ireland collapsed with the failure of mental deficiency legislation and the lack of public support for eugenics in the country (Finnane, 1981).

The speculative methods which dominated eugenic and hereditarian discussions in psychiatry were shared by those who postulated a greater role for environmental explanations of the increase of insanity. But the pages of the medical journals which record debate on this problem, principally in the *Journal of Mental Science*, show some refinement of method in describing and accounting for the incidence and distribution of insanity. One of the most distinguished essays in the epidemiology of insanity before World War I was William Dawson's account of the incidence of insanity in Ireland, which drew attention to the important differences between counties and regions in the rate of incarceration (Dawson, 1911). Irish psychiatrists were as ready as their British colleagues to enter the 'increase of insanity' debate, stressing the contribution of the imbalances brought about by modern civilisation. Thus Dr James Duncan, another Irish President of the MPA, considered the increase of insanity in his 1875 presidential address. Modern conditions of life favoured the development of a state of mind predisposed to insanity: the congregation in cities, the greater mental activity, the loosening of family bonds, the upsetting of parental authority – all contributed. Such a state of mind, he suggested (instancing the Paris Commune as an outbreak of madness on a large scale), lay "at the very root of Socialism". The greater amount of "brain work" required by modern life and the breakdown in moral values (a "higher principle" than self-interest was needed) predisposed individuals to insanity. Duncan's explanation of the increase of insanity quickly dissolved from analysis of the insane populations and its context into a general anxiety about the direction of modern life.

The very immensity of the problem seen from this perspective made psychiatrists especially inclined to advocate state responsibility for the insane. Individuals frequently had little control over the onset of insanity, and required appropriate care and protection; alternatively, society needed to protect itself. In 1861, Lalor, of the Richmond asylum in Dublin, wanted to see the insane poor maintained out of state funds because a large proportion of the insane in Ireland were detained in public asylums, "not for their own advantage but for the protection of society". The causes of insanity were more often of a general than a local nature and could be "diminished or advanced by general social advancement or deterioration" (*Journal of Mental Science*, 1861).

In their everyday contact with a population which was undoubtedly among the most outcast of the outcast poor of 19th-century Ireland and Britain, the psychiatrists of both countries were constantly caught in the dilemma of whose interests they served. The medical psychologist's role, said James Crichton-Browne in his 1878 presidential address to the Association, was to aid "in warding off the evils with which the body politic is threatened". The difficulty was, he, added, that in their own work in asylums, medical men "have to oppose evolution, promoting the survival of the unfittest, of weakly and crippled beings".

A generation later, in an even more hostile political climate marked by eugenics and anxieties about national efficiency, Conolly Norman also reflected on the same dilemma. There was a strong prejudice against asylums, he remarked, for their expensive maintenance of those whom some thought should be allowed to perish by natural processes. For Norman, this was too narrow. The "more extended and philosophical view" was that "the care of the unfit subserves some greater ulterior developmental end, and is – to take no higher view of it – the necessary step towards the attaining of a more perfect social state" (Norman, 1904).

Conclusion

Irish psychiatry was not remarkably distinguished in the 19th century, and there were certainly branches of Irish medicine which developed a much higher profile nationally and internationally, obstetrics above all. Its interest, though, lies in the way in which its development can be charted through the history of the public hospital for the mentally ill, and then through the stimulus to debate and reflection on medical and institutional practice which came through the Medico-Psychological Association. The brief review above of some of the areas in which contemporary psychiatric thought and politics were registered in Ireland suggests that medical opinion was fluid at a time when the parameters of psychiatry were still being developed. In this instance, the Irish story is one primarily of the mechanisms of transmission rather than of initiation, but, for this very reason, it is instructive for our understanding of the formation of the specialty of psychiatry.

References

Atkin, R. (1891) Report on nervous and mental diseases. *Dublin Journal of Medical Science*, **91**, 54.

Commissioners of Inquiry into the Treatment of the Insane in Ireland (1857/8) Report. *House of Commons Papers*, **27**.

CRICHTON-BROWNE, J. (1878) Presidential address. *Journal of Mental Science*, **24**, 345–373.
DAWSON, W. (1911) On the relation between the geographical distribution of insanity and that of certain social and other conditions in Ireland. *Journal of Medical Science*, **57**, 571–597.
DUBLIN JOURNAL OF MEDICAL SCIENCE (1850) *Dublin Journal of Medical Science*, **10**, 421.
—— (1867) *Dublin Journal of Medical Science*, **44**, 91.
—— (1900) *Dublin Journal of Medical Science*, **110**, 145–146.
—— (1901) *Dublin Journal of Medical Science*, **112**, 1–2.
—— (1913) *Dublin Journal of Medical Science*, **135**, 161–167.
DUNCAN, J. (1875) Presidential address. *Journal of Mental Science*, **21**, 461–465.
EAMES, J. A. (1885) Presidential address. *Journal of Mental Science*, **31**, 321–325, 432–435.
FINNANE, M. (1981) *Insanity and the Insane in Post-Famine Ireland*. London: Croom Helm.
INSPECTORS OF LUNATICS IN IRELAND (1862) *Eleventh Annual Report. House of Commons Papers*, **23**, 56.
JOURNAL OF MENTAL SCIENCE (1857) *Journal of Mental Science*, **3**, 9–11.
—— (1860) *Journal of Mental Science*, **6**, 52–58.
—— (1861) *Journal of Mental Science*, **7**, 44–49, 324–325.
—— (1894) *Journal of Mental Science*, **40**, 156–157, 691.
—— (1911) *Journal of Mental Science*, **57**, 628, 634.
LALOR, J. (1861) The President's address. *Journal of Mental Science*, **7**, 318–326.
NORMAN, E. M. C. (1887) *Dublin Journal of Medical Science*, **83**, 228–229.
—— (1904) *Dublin Journal of Medical Science*, **118**, 162–163.
SKAE, D. (1875) *Journal of Mental Science*, **21**, 339–365.
WINSLOW, F. (1848) *Journal of Psychological Medicine*, **1**, 151–154.
YOUNG, R. M. (1970) *Mind, Brain and Adaptation in the Nineteenth Century*, pp. 208–209.

Other sources

This chapter draws on unpublished material from Chapter 6 of the author's PhD thesis (ANU, Canberra, 1979) and is based mainly on a reading of the *Journal of Mental Science* and other medical journals of the 19th century, especially the *Medical Press and Circular* and the *Dublin Journal of Medical Science*.

20 Irish psychiatry. Part 2: Use of the Medico-Psychological Association by its Irish members – *plus ça change*!

DAVID HEALY

The initial list drawn up by the founder members of what was later to be the Medico-Psychological Association (MPA), intended to include asylum superintendents in the United Kingdom, was to be sent to 83 prospective members; of these, 21 were in Ireland. Only three of the 21 letters were to named individuals – a Dr Kidd in Armagh, and Drs Thomson and Stewart in Belfast. In the other cases the letters were sent to both visiting physicians and resident superintendents at Ballinasloe, Carlow, Cork, Dublin, Limerick, Londonderry, Tipperary, Waterford, and Maryborough.

There were apparently no replies, and this group of non-replies formed a large proportion of the total. Whether this was caused by delays in the postal system is not certain. It is also possible that Irish asylum politics, as outlined below, may have militated against replies.

In all, there were only eight attenders at the third annual meeting of the Asylum Society. Of these, one was Robert Stewart, the resident physician of the District Hospital for the Insane in Belfast. At the fifth annual meeting, in 1847, Stewart was co-opted as Secretary, in the absence of the designated secretary; Dr Flynn of Clonmel was also elected at this meeting. In 1849, Stewart was made the Honorary Secretary for Ireland, a post that he was to hold in the subsequently constituted MPA until 1874, at which point he was the last survivor of the original members of the Society.

When the MPA was first formed, there were 12 Irish members. In 1862, of 200 members in the Association, 26 were Irish, while in 1875, 30 were Irish. This was possibly as high a proportion of the total membership of either the MPA or Royal College of Psychiatrists as has ever been Irish, except for at the annual general meeting in 1919, at the Retreat at York, when the then President, Colonel Keay, in a post-prandial speech claimed that almost all the membership was Irish!

From 1860, it was acknowledged by the Treasurer that Irish members were contributing handsomely to the balance sheet of the Association. They were, however, somewhat under-represented at meetings, a fact that was attributed by Irish members to difficulties in being able to leave the asylums, as there were no assistants to deputise for the resident superintendent. The lack of resident assistants was also cited by Irish members as a contributing factor to their lack of scientific input to the meetings. Compared with medicine in general, where the names of Graves, Corrigan, and others (O'Brien, 1983) had earned a worldwide stature for Irish medicine during this period, there are no significant names from the field of Irish psychiatry (Chapter 19).

The Irish, however, were not merely sleeping members of the Association. Through the opportunities thrown up by Ireland's peculiar political situation, they exploited their membership far more, it would seem, than their mainland counterparts. This point can be illustrated by considering the contents of the addresses to the MPA by Irish presidents at annual general meetings between 1860 and 1885, as well as the subsequent discussions at those meetings.

Asylum politics

In the 1850s, the dominant issue for Irish alienists was not, to judge by their pronouncements, the nature of mental illness – all three Irish presidential addresses concur in the belief that mental disorders are diseases, and assert that this was now generally accepted – but rather the practical question of who ran lunatic asylums. This was not an issue of whether the asylums should be run by lay or medical superintendents, but rather an internal struggle within the medical profession itself. Irish asylums were under a code of rules established by the Lord Lieutenant and Privy Council of Ireland in 1843 (Flynn, 1861; Finnane, 1981), which were designed to regulate the conversion of workhouses into asylums for the treatment of mental illness. Under these rules, there was no obligation for a doctor to be appointed to the position of superintendent, partly because this would have led, at that time, to a number of workhouse superintendents being dismissed. There was, however, a requirement for all asylums to have a visiting physician, and not unnaturally where medical matters were concerned, the visiting physician had seniority.

After 1845, while it remained a theoretical possibility that the Lord Lieutenant's coachman could be appointed to the position of asylum superintendent, as the resident medical superintendents complained, it was invariably the custom that a medical man was in fact appointed. The difficulties arose insofar as the visiting physician remained essentially the medical superior to the resident superintendent. These doctors also remained privileged, in that they could, for instance, absent themselves for two weeks, having given due notice, whereas a resident superintendent had to apply to the Board of Governors even for overnight leave (Flynn, 1861).

This matter was taken up by the Commissioners in Lunacy in 1856, when a majority of them supported giving seniority to the resident medical superintendent (O'Brien, 1983), whereas Sir Dominic Corrigan wanted the status quo maintained. In reply, Joseph Lalor, then the Superintendent of the Richmond asylum, wrote a pamphlet castigating Corrigan for his position, which no doubt raised professional awareness about the issues involved (Bucknill, 1859). But this was only Lalor's first move.

In 1859, the Irish members applied to have the annual general meeting held in Dublin, but it had to be deferred owing to renovation work then being undertaken at the Richmond asylum, where it was proposed to meet. At the annual general meeting of 1860, a further proposal to have the next one held in Dublin was put forward, specifically mentioning that it would be useful in supporting the Irish members on this issue. However, there was opposition to

Dublin, with a number of members, notably the Treasurer, Thomas Ley, arguing that difficulties in travelling would lead to poor attendance, in addition to which the Association was trying to avoid being seen as provincial. The issue was keenly debated, but in the end it was decided to go to Dublin in 1861, and Joseph Lalor became President-Elect.

In Dublin, Lalor duly became the eighth President of the MPA and its first Irish one, but of those present at the meeting, only eight were from the mainland, bearing out Ley's fears. Twelve of the 14 Irish resident medical superintendents were present, but only two visiting physicians. Lalor's presidential address has a surprisingly contemporary note, in comparison with many of the time (Lalor, 1861). While recognising the importance of social science in mental illness, he defended the claims of medicine to deal with disorders of the intellect, on the basis of the intimate connections between body and mind and the reciprocal influences of diseases on passions and of the passions on diseases. He went on to claim that there was, therefore, no one so well placed to study the relationship of mind and matter as those who were already – by education, opportunity, and habits of thought – trained to study the material constitution of man.

After touching on the need for good asylum staff and on the need for the state funding of the care of mental illness, he came to the nub of his speech – the status of resident asylum superintendents in Ireland, compared with their counterparts on the mainland. Noting the common interests of Irish and mainland asylum superintendents, he hoped that the efforts of the Association generally could be directed towards resolving this anomaly. The subsequent discussion focused on the issues of the relative seniority of the two medical officers, infringement of the rights of visiting physicians to various payments or patronage, and potential espionage by them. It is on this latter point that Corrigan had claimed it would be wise to maintain the policy of having a visiting physician to ensure that any abuses of the system would be detected earlier – a point that Edward Mapother was to endorse many years later (O'Brien, 1983).

A week after the meeting, the Irish members of the Association headed by Lalor, along with several English members, visited the Chief Secretary, Robert Peel, at Dublin Castle to make representations to him (Deputation, 1861). Lalor then presented the recommendations drawn up at the annual general meeting. In fact, new rules for the governing of mental asylums in Ireland were steered by Peel through the Irish Privy Council in January 1862 (*Journal of Mental Science*, 1862). These made the resident medical superintendent the superior of the two medical officers.

Assistant medical officers

The next major issue for the Irish members of the Association was the question of having assistant medical officers appointed to support the resident medical superintendent. This issue was taken up in 1875, when the second Irish meeting of the MPA was held in Dublin. On this occasion, there was no dispute beforehand as to whether Dublin was an appropriate venue. There was good attendance from the mainland, which included Hack Tuke, Henry Maudsley, and Thomas Clouston. James Duncan assumed the Presidency during the course of the meeting.

Duncan began his presidential address by mentioning that the holding of annual meetings in Ireland and in some of the other provincial centres was of great benefit, as it provided a motive to exertion for improvement in those institutions which, by their remoteness, might seem especially to need it (Duncan, 1875). Like Lalor, he argued that as insanity was a disease, doctors were "the best fitted to unravel the mysteries of their phenomena, to investigate the intricate chain of circumstances connected with their origin, to discriminate the relative importance of their various symptoms and to estimate the effect of remedies". That the Irish contingent of the Association had done little for the advancement of mental science he put down to a lack of professional help: only four of the 22 asylums in the country then had a second resident medical officer. This militated against superintendents being able to attend meetings or to engage in any scientific consideration of the issues facing them.

Duncan went on to stress that such a consideration was urgently needed, as the incidence of mental disorder appeared to be on the increase. This he attributed to the confinement of lunatics, increasing recognition of mental disorders, and the changes in society brought about by the Industrial Revolution. "Civilisation is evidently an artificial state of existence and the more widely our habits of life diverge from what is natural, the more it is certain to be followed by a corresponding retribution in the shape of disease or death". He felt that the incessant mental activity of the age must inevitably produce the consequences to be seen in the ever-greater filling of asylums, but asylum doctors had a large contribution to make in the area of preventing insanity. He preached the virtue of a preventive medicine, which, contrary to what the cynics might say, would be a truly disinterested service - one that would run counter to the interest of medical men themselves, who might be expected to wish to profit out of the increase in business.

The subsequent discussion at this particular meeting focused on the intertwined issues of medical assistants to the superintendent, the teaching of psychological medicine to medical students, and the fostering of mental science by the MPA. James Stewart, Robert's son, had a resolution adopted which deplored the lack of assistant medical officers in Irish asylums and supported the sending of a deputation to wait on the Chief Secretary of Ireland to draw his attention to these facts (Stewart, 1875). There were subsequent representations by the Irish branch of the MPA to the government in Ireland on this issue, and these were successful, just as the earlier ones regarding the position of medical superintendents had been. By the time J. A. Eames came to address an annual general meeting of the MPA in Cork in 1885, the third to be held in Ireland, all asylums had residential medical assistants.

English neglect of the Irish experiment

These examples indicate that the Irish members of the MPA were able to use the Association effectively to further their ends. However, it must not be thought that this was simply a case of an underdeveloped country struggling to keep pace with a more developed neighbour. The situation in Ireland was more complex than this. The government of Ireland by Lord Lieutenant and Privy Council enabled many experiments to be undertaken in areas that might have proved too risky on the mainland. This was particularly likely to be the case when the officers in question were of a liberal inclination.

One such development was the existence in Ireland of a facility for the criminally mentally ill, at Dundrum. This, it was noted, was "admirably circumstanced in all essential respects . . . [and provided a] relief to all other hospitals for the insane in Ireland". This first reference to Irish affairs in the Association records was noted by members who were keen to see a comparable development in England, although there is no record that the English members actually used this Irish example to further their ends.

A more striking example occurred during the decade between 1875 and 1885. At the annual meeting in Dublin in 1875, Clouston presented a proposal on the desirability of making teaching in psychological medicine a compulsory part of medical education (Clouston, 1875). Those present supported him, demurring only at the inclusion of the word 'compulsory', on the tactical grounds that this might prejudice the case.

When J. A. Eames came to address the annual meeting in 1885 (Eames, 1885), he noted that although assistants had been appointed to Irish asylums since 1875, Irish members were still not able to contribute satisfactorily to the development of mental science, for the most part owing to the ever-growing increase in insanity. The position of the medical superintendent was becoming more managerial, and of necessity more concerned with the mechanics of how to ensure the hygiene of such a large number of inmates. He argued that the only way to stem this increase was to detect insanity in its earliest stages, in primary care. To do this effectively would require general practitioners to be soundly trained in psychological medicine.

There had, however, been no progress on the mainland in the matter of the inclusion of psychological medicine in general medical education. In contrast, there had been compulsory lectures in psychological medicine at Queen's University, Cork, since 1875, and more generally in all the constituent colleges of the Royal University of Ireland, following its institution in 1883 (Eames, 1885). In 1885, furthermore, the Royal University had instituted the Henry Hutchinson Scholarship in Psychological Medicine, the first such prize to be offered in the United Kingdom (Eames, 1885). There is no record, however, that this Irish example was used in any creative manner by mainland asylum doctors in their efforts to promote medical education in England.

Plus ça change . . .

Thus, the Irish members of the MPA were more creative in their use of the contrasting situations between England and Ireland than were their English counterparts. English interest in Ireland was confined to considering the scientific question of why the general increase in insanity in the latter part of the 19th century appeared to be accelerated in Ireland (Drapes, 1894; Tuke, 1894). Otherwise, there appears to have been a great deal of ignorance on the part of the English regarding the actual state of affairs in Ireland. The records of these annual meetings show that Englishmen constantly had to be informed about the practical details of how the Irish system operated – a situation probably quite comparable with the one which pertains today.

The first regional quarterly meeting of the Royal College of Psychiatrists to be held in Ireland was that in Galway in 1990. Doubts were expressed beforehand that sufficient numbers would attend to make it a viable meeting (Fahy, personal communication), yet, in the event, it was one of the best-attended quarterly meetings. At this meeting, the chairman of the Irish Division, in the presence of an Irish Minister of Health, drew attention to significant failings in the postgraduate educational programme for Irish psychiatrists. The support of the attending UK membership and the example of training in the UK were used to bring home his point – in a manner quite comparable to that of Joseph Lalor in 1861.

In contrast, at the time of a changing health system in the UK, with uncertainty as to what the future may hold for it, the English members are probably not aware that for decades there has been a significantly different mix of private and public provision in the Irish health services. In this context, the psychiatric services – if not psychiatric education – have flourished, with a substantially better ratio of psychiatrists to patients in Ireland than in the UK, and in many respects a better development of community services. However, the practical details of these arrangements are virtually unknown in the UK.

The broader political realities of the day have never been excluded from the discussions of the MPA, with, for example, the British forces in the Crimea being toasted in 1856. A number of members commented after World War I that it should serve to make British alienists more cautious in paying heed to the pronouncements of German psychiatric thinkers.

The political differences between Ireland and England have, however, been noticeably absent in the recorded discussions of the Association, with only passing mention being made to the virus of Irish nationalism as possibly contributing to the excess of insanity to be found in Ireland (Drapes, 1894). Even in the period from 1916 to 1922, when Ireland was at war with the rest of the UK and finally left it, Council, educational, annual general, and other MPA meetings were noticeably devoid of comment on the Irish situation: the question of Irish members leaving the Association did not arise. The union of Irish and British asylum doctors has always, it would appear, transcended such differences, with even today Irish members readily joining a *Royal* College of Psychiatrists. The example of the Irish branch of the MPA and subsequently the College would therefore seem to indicate that – for Irish members at least – the political and social importance of professionalism has outweighed that of nationalism.

Acknowledgements

The author wishes to acknowledge the assistance of Margaret Harcourt Williams and Susan Floate in researching this piece.

References

BUCKNILL, J. C. (1859) Review of observations on the offices of resident and visiting physicians of district lunatic asylums in Ireland, by Lalor, J. *Journal of Mental Science*, **6**, 520–528.

CLOUSTON, T. (1875) The clinical teaching and study of insanity. *Journal of Mental Science*, **21**, 458–460.

DEPUTATION OF MEDICAL OFFICERS OF ASYLUMS AND HOSPITALS FOR THE INSANE TO SIR ROBERT PEEL, BART, MP (1861) *Journal of Mental Science*, **7**, 339–342.

DRAPES, T. (1894) On the alleged increase of insanity in Ireland. *Journal of Mental Science*, **40**, 519–548.
—— (1896)
DUNCAN, J. F. (1875) President's address. *Journal of Mental Science*, **21**, 313–338.
EAMES, J. A. (1885) Presidential address. *Journal of Mental Science*, **31**, 315–327.
FINNANE, M. (1981) *Insanity and the Insane in Post-Famine Ireland.* London: Croom Helm.
LALOR, J. (1861) The president's address. *Journal of Mental Science*, **7**, 318–326.
FLYNN, J. (1861) Annual general meeting. *Journal of Mental Science*, **7**, 332–333.
JOURNAL OF MENTAL SCIENCE (1862) Revised rules of the Irish Government for the better control of district lunatic asylums in Ireland. *Journal of Mental Science*, **8**, 119–132.
O'BRIEN, E. (1983) *Conscience and Conflict: A Biography of Sir Dominic Corrigan*. Dublin: Glendale Press.
STEWART, J. (1875) The position of medical superintendents of asylums in Ireland. *Journal of Mental Science*, **21**, 461–465.
TUKE, D. HACK (1894) Increase of insanity in Ireland. *Journal of Mental Science*, **40**, 549–558.

Other sources

Minutes from the annual meetings of the Asylum Society, held in the Library of the Royal College of Psychiatrists, were reviewed in the preparation of this chapter.

21 The drive towards the community

DOUGLAS BENNETT

Where does the history of community psychiatry begin? It seems inaccurate to attribute its beginnings to the introduction of phenothiazine medication in the 1950s, as Brill & Patton believed (1962) – a view denied by Ødegaard (1964). Nor can it realistically be described as "psychiatry's third revolution", as suggested by Bellak (1964). Instead, it is better seen as the present phase of the continuously changing view of how people with psychological disorders should be cared for, where they should be treated, and by whom. One theme of this story is of the development of treatment, while the other is concerned with the relationship of the individual who has psychiatric disorder to his/her own society. There is a technical medical element, linked to changes in medicine and to scientific progress, but also a social element, which is the expression of the social attitudes of the time in relation to such matters as pauperism, slavery, and prison reform or to crime, social welfare, and civil rights.

It is appropriate to start with the belief common in the 1850s that the elimination of abuse in workhouses, by separating the mentally ill from other social deviants, would lead to the better care of all patients, even the incurable. At times, this illustrated the third law of sociodynamics which suggests that for every advantage from change, there is an equal and opposite disadvantage. At the beginning of the 19th century, there had been a change in those ideas which traditionally give a shape and meaning to life. It had been brought about by industrialisation, dramatically altering the conditions under which many of the population lived. The change itself was one of enlightened sensitivity to human deprivation, and manifested itself largely as a concern about poverty. But other views exerted their influence: for instance, the members of the Select Committee set up in 1857 to inquire into the state of criminal and pauper lunatics included Rose, who was interested in poverty, Wilberforce, preoccupied with slavery, and Romilly, who was a prison reformer; Wynn alone was concerned with lunacy reform (Jones, 1960). At this time, relatively little interest was shown by the doctors; medical registration would not be established until 1858, and the profession was disparate and unorganised before that.

However, by the mid-1840s, the asylum was coming into its own, having been conceived in hope by concerned and dedicated reformers of the early 19th century, who believed that such progressive agencies would offer clean and tranquil protection to those unfortunates whom they could not cure. But the general belief was that many, if not most of those admitted would be cured.

Even at this time, however, there were honest doubters as to whether asylum was the correct solution for the care of most of the mentally ill, although they were in a minority. In 1839, Conolly had been appointed to Hanwell asylum as resident physician; he visited Gardiner Hill and Charlesworth at the Lincoln asylum and within four months had put their views on non-restraint into practice (see Chapter 3). This became the prevailing ideology at Hanwell, representing a new attitude and a new management approach to the mentally ill; it was celebrated in the first article, entitled "Prospectus", in the first issue of the *Asylum Journal*, published in 1853, where Conolly was credited with having established "a new school of special medicine". He felt that for certain patients, "confinement is the very reverse of beneficial for it renders permanent the temporary excitement or depression, which might have passed away, in actual insanity". No doctor had the right to restrain the mentally disordered person any more "than to imprison a man for being short sighted or a little lame in one leg". The "safety and liberty of men was not lightly to be trifled with". To Conolly, using no restraint meant that "no patient should be confined to a Lunatic Asylum except on the particular representation of the relative or friend that he could not have proper care and attention out of it" (Conolly, 1830). Non-restraint was close to community care, for he believed that once signs of insanity appeared, notice of this should be given at the asylum and that medical officers from within that establishment should visit immediately; a register of all patients in or out of the asylum should be kept and recent cases should be visited once in seven days, or once in 15 days if they were chronic. Conolly (1830) believed that smaller houses in the neighbourhood of the asylum should be provided for the reception of one or two lunatics; none should be allowed to remain in a workhouse or private house. If Conolly thought in 1830 that these liberal views would advance his reputation, he was disappointed, for his suggestions were denounced and generally ignored for many years.

Subsequent improvements took much time. By 1859 Arlidge, a pupil of Conolly, was lamenting that "many asylums had grown to such a magnitude that, in these colossal refuges for the insane, a patient may be said to lose his individuality". A little later, Neuschler (1867), in a letter to the editors of the *Journal of Mental Science*, asked "who among us that has lived for years in a public asylum has not often been filled with sympathy for the sad condition of its inmates and for the many restrictions which they endured". While there was some recognition of the dangers of institutionalisation, asylums continued to increase in size and became far larger than had been contemplated by their innovators. Troublesomeness in the community rather than curability had become the criterion for admission: people entered asylums mainly if their mental disorder was so severe that relatives could no longer care for them, or if they had no relatives.

There was another side to this picture; in 1856, at the Devon lunatic asylum, Bucknill as the superintendent had relieved pressure on his overcrowded asylum by opening a temporary branch at a seaside house in Exmouth and by housing patients in cottages in the neighbourhood. There was opposition from residents, of course (*Journal of Mental Science*, 1857), but later it was agreed that this opposition had been groundless (Bucknill, 1858). This system offering "free social life differing little from a large private family" was repeated in both England and Scotland, where variants of the family system were tried (Parry-Jones, 1981).

In 1869, the Reverend Hawkins, a clergyman working at Colney Hatch Asylum, was concerned that female patients had difficulty when discharged in re-establishing themselves. Influenced by Bucknill's ideas, Hawkins made him President, with Lord Shaftesbury as Patron, when he established the Mental Aftercare Association (Hawkins, 1871). The work of this society proceeded slowly and patiently, but it continued to play an important part in the development of community psychiatry in Britain.

In spite of these positive ideas, criticisms of overcrowding were becoming more frequent. James Davey, also a former pupil of Conolly, and afterwards Superintendent at Hanwell and Colney Hatch, said at an annual meeting of the Medico-Psychological Association (MPA) in 1867 that "such asylums were not adapted by their magnitude and arrangment for the cure of mental disorders". He proposed that a hospital with 250 beds – "otherwise it can be no hospital but simply an asylum" – should be built in the neighbourhood of London, with "all those means and appliances held essential, either directly or remotely to the relief and cure of the disordered mind". This was to include an out-patient department. The London County Council (LCC), which had been established in 1889, took up the idea with vigour, but the subcommittee involved had an animosity towards asylums and indeed to all mental specialists. They wished the hospital to be staffed by visiting non-specialist physicians who, they were convinced, were more likely to cure mental illness (Walk, 1962). The idea of such a hospital was, however, eventually abandoned for lack of funds and instead, several large new asylums were built in the Epsom area to provide for the needs of the still rising population of London. At the same meeting of the MPA Dr Belgrave (1867) suggested that incipient cases would be best treated as out-patients. This was not well received, in part because it was not understood, and a Dr Henry Munro asked, in a puzzled way, whether the out-patients were insane or persons suspected of going insane; he wondered how one could persuade such patients to come for treatment.

Both these proposals for moving the treatment of 'curable' patients from the overcrowded asylum therefore languished, and it was not until 1890 that the first out-patient clinics were opened – at St Thomas's Hospital and the Wakefield asylum. Thus, the end of the 19th century was characterised by some discontent with asylum care and mechanical restraint, as well as by tentative efforts towards after-care and the beginning of out-patient treatment. Society too was changing; the passage of the Second Reform Bill 1867 gave working men the vote and this was followed by the first Education Act and the rise of Fabianism.

The 20th century

With the beginning of the 20th century, some evidence of a new spirit was abroad. In their separate report to the 1909 Commission on the Poor Law, Beatrice Webb and three others insisted on the state's responsibility to secure a national minimum of civilised life for all citizens, of both sexes and all classes. It is uncertain, though, whether they saw this as specifically including the mentally ill. At about this time, Henry Maudsley, a successful private psychiatrist who had by then become a retired recluse (Chapter 28), influenced by his friend Mott, who had visited Kraepelin's clinic in Munich, wrote to the LCC, offering them £30 000 to build a mental hospital (Chapter 4). Maudsley too had grown disillusioned with the large public asylums and favoured the establishment of a hospital, on the lines set out by Davey, which should not be a "receptacle for the insane but specifically a clinic designed for psychiatric research" (Bynum *et al*, 1988). Curable patients were to be admitted without any kind of legal restraint, and would receive early treatment. Out-patient treatment, with male and female patients seen on different days, commenced when the Maudsley Hospital, which during World War I had been used as military hospital, opened in 1923 (Chapter 4).

The practice of the Maudsley Hospital had an effect on the views of the Royal Commission on Lunacy and Mental Disorder, which was set up in 1924 to examine and allay the public unease about the treatment of the mentally ill in asylums. It reported in 1926 and recommended that voluntary treatment without legal commitment should be available to all. It stressed both psychiatry's relationship to general medicine and the need for the after-care of discharged patients in the community. It also recommended that the connection between mental illness and the Poor Law should be abandoned. The Mental Treatment Act 1930, which followed, introduced voluntary treatment and legitimised the spending of money by local authorities on out-patient care; it also recommended the after-care being developed voluntarily by the Mental Aftercare Association (Rooff, 1957). It was at about this time that malarial treatment for general paralysis of the insane (GPI) also reinforced these changes in the care of mental hospital patients. Patients suffering from the disease who needed laboratory investigation and medical treatment were often transferred to general hospitals, where legal controls did not apply; this led to a realisation that such controls might be less necessary than had been thought. A follow-up of demented patients treated in the Mott clinic at Horton Hospital between 1942 and 1952 showed that good pre-illness personality, dependable and sympathetic support, and the availability of some occupation were the determinants of optimal community adjustment (Bree, 1960).

While voluntary treatment had been introduced in 1930, relatively small numbers of patients were admitted under its dispensations in the years before World War II. Dr Thomas Beaton, who was appointed medical superintendent of the Portsmouth lunatic asylum in 1926, was an exception to this trend (Freeman, 1962). He opened an out-patient department in the voluntary general hospital soon after his appointment, and it was expanded after the 1930 Act; a quarter of the admissions to his asylum were voluntary. He had good relations with the general practitioners in the area, and so a service for both neurotics and psychotics, for in-patients and out-patients, was provided, while doors were opened on some wards. However, Beaton did not believe in the introduction of psychiatric beds in local general hospitals. Like other services, that in Portsmouth was a casualty of the tripartite organisation which was to follow World War II, when the National Health Service (NHS) was established.

World War II and after

Psychiatrists in World War II made their own contribution in the drive towards community psychiatry – mainly by innovations in treatment, but particularly by the selection procedures for the armed forces, which aimed to ensure that only men who were mentally suitable for combat were selected, as had been recommended by the Soughborough Committee in 1922. In spite of selection, cases of 'soldier's heart' occurred and led indirectly to the growth of therapeutic communities, as recommended by Main (1946) and practised by him and Maxwell Jones (1952). Programmes of rehabilitation and repatriation were dealt with in an intelligent and thoughtful manner (Ahrenfeldt, 1958); there was an explosive development at Northfield Hospital of group methods of treatment, which greatly influenced psychiatric practice when the war ended (Bion, 1946; Foulkes, 1948).

The post-war period saw many further changes. Blacker (1946) was impressed that some psychiatrists had developed new growing points of service in the previous 20 years, based in what to institutional psychiatry was the 'outside world'. Like Hill (1969), he feared a schism between a restrictive closed psychiatry, limited to the care of those suffering from psychosis and mental deficiency, and an extramural psychiatry – often known as psychological medicine or medical psychology – in the teaching and voluntary hospitals, concerned mainly with neurotic patients, industrial psychiatry, and prevention. Blacker felt that Beaton had overcome this difficulty with his pioneering efforts in Portsmouth.

With the ending of the war, it became the practice increasingly for mental hospitals to open their doors: this happened first at Dingleton, Warlingham Park, and Mapperley Hospitals. Warlingham Park was an open hospital by 1949, although there is no clear description of how this was achieved. At Dingleton, changes which were introduced by Dr Bell in 1945 were completed in 1950 (Bell, 1955). Ratcliff (1962) considered that the open-door regime had proved as safe for the in-patients and for the community in the Scottish Borders as the service given by other Scottish mental hospitals, as well as encouraging patients from the catchment area to make fuller use of the hospital.

In a number of ways, most mental hospitals were no longer as isolated as they had been; more and more of their patients were being admitted and discharged relatively quickly. Rehabilitation and the 'therapeutic community' were established at Belmont Hospital by Maxwell Jones, in a unit funded by the Ministry of Labour. His ideas of democratisation, permissiveness, communalism, and reality confrontation were a reaction against current institutional beliefs and practices. These ideas had an important effect on thinking about hospital treatment, not only in Britain, but in America (Jones, 1952; Rapaport, 1960).

General improvements in hospital regimes were also taking place. Rees had introduced 'habit training' for incontinence at Warlingham Park Hospital, using the method described by the chief nurse (Symons, 1951). Attempts to study this by using a control group measured the improvement in terms of the number of wet sheets – a comment on the care of chronic psychosis, even in advanced hospitals, at that time (Bennett & Robertson, 1955). This was an era primarily of physical treatment, and there was some reluctance to take social psychiatric management seriously. However, Freudenberg *et al* (1957) examined the relative importance of both physical and social methods in the treatment of schizophrenia and found that the outcome for severely ill patients with schizophrenia was not influenced by the period of physical treatment, although phenothiazenes had not been introduced at that time. More importantly, perhaps, they found a preponderance of patients with schizophrenia from densely populated areas, in contrast to those with affective disorders. They also found that additional improvements could be effected by community social measures in chronic schizophrenic patients, beyond those previously achieved with habit training. In 1946, Joshua Bierer had started the Marlborough Day Hospital in London, believing that it avoided the trauma and stigma of in-patient treatment (Bierer, 1951). Since those days, the number of day patients has increased steadily, as have the attendances of the more disabled mentally ill in day centres provided mainly by local authorities. Thus, day treatment and day care expanded the alternatives to hospital admission, as out-patient treatment and after-care had in earlier days. While day hospitals are not substitutes for the whole of hospital in-patient care, over the years, the contribution of these facilities to the spectrum of psychiatric care has grown enormously.

Perhaps the greatest change of this period, however, was in the development of the Welfare State, which, in 1948, included the establishment of the NHS. This took over responsibility for mental hospitals from the local authorities, who had been running them until that time. Other aspects of health and welfare provision integrated out-patient care and in-patient treatment, as well as replacing public assistance with social security benefits; only when such insurance liabilities are extended can extramural services develop nationally (Mangen, 1985). Mangen goes on to say that the introduction of the phenothiazines, which in Britain were a catalyst for the discharge of patients from hospitals to the community, did not have such clear-cut effects elsewhere in Europe; this is an interesting interaction between the effects of changes in medical treatment and in social and political conditions. Thus, in Britain, in a way not achievable in other countries, it was possible to integrate all the alternatives to mental hospital care into what, in the 1950s, was termed 'comprehensive care'. However, the chronic psychiatric patient was excluded from community treatment, once the home became too strained for him to go on living there (Macmillan, 1958). In a study at Napsbury Hospital, Bott (1976) found that there had been a change in the pattern of admission as far back as the mid-1930s; "a new pattern of population started coming into the hospital, a population which left more readily as well as coming in more readily". Carse *et al* (1958) reported that the continuing increase in admissions, together with serious overcrowding within the mental hospital, meant that they could not meet this demand, so that there was a need to expand out-patient and other extramural treatment facilities. This was the origin of the 'Worthing Experiment'. Experience after only ten months convinced Carse that such an out-patient service could do much to ease the strain on the mental hospital, which nevertheless was still seen as the centre of the service. This service and others in Croydon, Nottingham, York, and elsewhere were medically directed and were found most often in county boroughs (Macmillan, 1956; Bowen & Crane, 1957). In these cases, the medical superintendent re-established co-operative relationships with the staff of the borough's mental health service, of which he had often been a member before the local authority had been divested of responsibility for the mental hospital by the NHS in 1948. These developing ideas were sustained in York by Bowen, who had worked in Beaton's service in Portsmouth.

In 1954, the Royal Commission on the Law Relating to Mental Illness and Mental Deficiency was established, and it reported in 1957. The implementation of the NHS had emphasised the contrasting position of patients in mental hospitals with those in general hospitals, to the disadvantage of the former (Busfield, 1986). The Royal Commission reported that in almost all forms of psychiatric illness, there was "an increasing emphasis on the forms of treatment, training and social service which could be given to patients without bringing them into hospital or which made it possible to discharge them much sooner than in the past". Although no financial provision was made for such developments, the Royal Commission's ideas were embodied in the Mental Health Act 1959, which established informal admission and greatly diminished the numbers of patients who were legally committed to hospital. If patients were admitted compulsorily, reasons had to be given why these people were a danger to themselves or others and could not be treated outside hospital. As a result, the number of compulsorily detained patients diminished in the early 1960s to one-tenth of the number in the late 1950s; it also had a profound effect in encouraging the discharge of patients from mental hospitals.

This was a period of great confidence and enthusiasm in the psychiatric services; change seemed possible, and to some extent was possible. In 1961, Tooth & Brooke forecast the rate at which the existing long-stay population of the mental hospitals might decline. This forecast was statistically unsophisticated and hedged with caveats, but it marked the beginning of the active involvement of politicians in community care. Enoch Powell in an oft-quoted speech, said that however tentative, however qualified, and however much in need of revision the plan might be, he had told hospital authorities that in 15 years' time, they might only need half as many beds in mental hospitals. He recognised that there would be resistance from those who had laboured devotedly through years of scarcity and neglect: "It would be more than flesh and blood to expect them to take the initiative in planning their own abolition, to be the first to set the torch to the funeral pyre" (*sic*) (Powell, 1961). In spite of the objections raised to Tooth & Brooke's assertions, their prognostications were eventually proved correct, if somewhat delayed. Planning in relation to both hospital and community care followed; first came the 'Hospital Plan' (Ministry of Health, 1962), and in the following year, a 'National Plan' for community care. These were significant for psychiatric patients, since for the first time, their treatment and care were being considered in the context of general health and social services. Yet since the plans involved no financial commitments, they had little effect on the activities or achievement of local authorities.

There was, however, a feeling of movement. For example, in 1961, the chief male nurse at Warlingham Park Hospital reported the first use of a psychiatric out-patient nursing service, which was the precursor of community psychiatric nursing (Moore, 1961). More rehabilitation was being practised, more patients were being resettled (Bennett, 1983), and relationships between patients and professionals were changing to some extent. In the 1960s there were more television and radio programmes and "a significant heightening of the salience of mental illness in terms both of overt political activity and broader social awareness" (Martin, 1984). Enthusiastic and innovative psychiatrists in many parts of Britain developed and described new services. In Croydon, May & Gregory (1963) described district psychiatry as "following from the emphasis on community care implicit in the Mental Health Act of 1959". The principles of comprehensive district care were further developed in Lancashire, which had a relatively large number of county boroughs whose general hospitals each had a psychiatric observation ward. When the NHS began, the Manchester Regional Hospital Board found that its mental hospitals were relatively few, grossly overcrowded, and neglected. They decided to use the general hospital observation units to develop local psychiatric services (Downham, 1967; Freeman, 1983). Day hospitals, which had been a new development in the 1950s, had by then proved themselves useful and were proliferating (Harris, 1958). By the early 1980s, there were 15 000 places available, although 19% of those individuals using them were in-patients: 3800 patients were day visitors to in-patient wards (Department of Health and Social Security, 1984*a*,*b*). Local authorities, however, provided fewer places in day centres (Department of Health and Social Security, 1983*a*,*b*), and their number was still below the number proposed in the government's paper on *Better Services for the Mentally Ill* (Department of Health and Social Security, 1975).

Planning of services, which had been related largely to the populations of mental hospitals, changed during the 1960s with the establishment of a number of cumulative registers of psychiatric contacts with residents of defined areas, the first being in Camberwell in south London. These made it possible to measure the use of services, to examine patterns of contact over time, to monitor changes, to estimate future trends, to indicate researchable issues, and above all to act as a sampling frame for more intensive study of specific issues, such as the prevalence of schizophrenia (Freeman & Alpert, 1986). Case registers not only promote scientific work, but also produce findings which have important practical applications (Wing & Hailey, 1972). This research probably played a large part in the formation of government policy and in changing the direction of hospital functions. In the case of the Maudsley Hospital, it took on responsibility for the surrounding catchment area, including chronic patients, 50 years after the hospital had pioneered early and voluntary treatment of selected patients.

Social work too had been changing. In 1951, there were only eight full-time psychiatric social workers (PSWs) employed by local authorities in England, and their numbers had only increased to 24 by 1959 (Titmuss, 1963). These social workers did not undertake the after-care of psychotic patients discharged from hospital (Harris, 1958), and even in 1962, of a sample of 100 patients discharged from London mental hospitals, only four had been visited by a social worker in the follow-up year (Parkes *et al*, 1962). The Seebohm Committee believed that human needs could not be divided between different social workers, some of whom dealt with child-care, others with the aged and physically disabled, and still others with the mentally ill and mentally handicapped. They recommended that social workers should give up their specialisation, and, with the exception of probation officers, form a unified profession (Committee on Local Authority and Allied Personal Social Services, 1968). These recommendations were ratified in the Social Services Act 1970, whose results have been far from satisfactory, since there has been a considerable loss of specialist mental health training and the diversion of resources to child-care (Bennett & Wing, 1972). This fall in social work involvement in mental health after-care almost certainly stimulated the development of the work of community psychiatric nurses.

In the 1970s, there was a steady reduction in mental hospital populations, but there was a spread of housing in the community for those who were mentally disabled, and increasing numbers of day hospitals and day centres as part of the network of services (Bennett, 1978). Research was directed particularly at epidemiology, at hospital effectiveness, and at the relations between family members and their psychotic relatives, research which showed important replication of earlier findings (Brown, 1959; Brown *et al*, 1972); this led on to intervention work with the families of schizophrenics (Leff & Vaughn, 1980; Kuipers *et al*, 1989), which is likely to provide an important model for services in the future. Even so, the impetus of the earlier years somewhat diminished, and the ensuing period was well summed up by Martin (1984) as "undramatic progress along lines already well established".

However, in the white paper on hospital services, the Department of Health and Social Security (1971) indicated that improvements in treatment and care made it possible to treat all psychotic patients in district general hospitals. The government's broad policy objectives were set out in *Better Services for the Mentally Ill* (1975), but expenditure on the mentally ill by health and social services respectively was still in a ratio of about 23 : 1. Attempts were made by joint financing to alter this and to transfer services and fund developments by the local authorities, but with only modest results. In the 1980s, there was more action in determining priorities, both in the financing and managing of services, by a government anxious to reduce expenditure. *Care in Action* was an indication of government policy on closing mental hospitals, while *Care in the Community* was a consultation document, seeking views on specific ways of transferring money from health to local authorites (Department of Health and Social Security, 1981*a*,*b*). This led to the ministerial decisions which were set out in *Care in the Community and Joint Finances* (Department of Health and Social Security, 1983*b*). Then, the Mental Health Amendment Act 1982 made small changes to the Mental Health Act 1959, which was felt by some to infringe the civil liberties of a minority of committed patients.

One of the most influential reports on community care came from the House of Commons Social Services Committee (1985), which examined services in both Britain and elsewhere, and recommended that adequate community-care policies for the mentally handicapped and mentally ill would be achievable only with increased expenditure. They recommended that nobody should be discharged from hospital without a jointly devised and practised individual care plan. Although it got a poor response from the government, this important report was followed by another from the Audit Commission (1986), pointing out that every year, £6 billion of public funds is spent in providing long-term support for elderly, mentally ill, or mentally and physically handicapped people, excluding the cost of acute hospital and general practitioner services. They believed that the NHS would inevitably remain the prime authority responsible for care. However, the Griffiths' report (1988) recommended that local authorities should be responsible for the delivery of packages of care to individuals and act as the designers, organisers, and purchasers of services in the community. After some delay, the government response indicated that while local authorities would become responsible for packages of care to the mentally handicapped, the elderly, and the physically handicapped, health services will continue to have responsibility to a greater extent for the community care of those individuals disabled by psychiatric illness (Department of Health & Department of Social Security, 1989). While some mental hospitals are closing or are planning to close, the arrangements for planning and financing community care have been handicapped by these delays.

The present and the future

There is considerable anxiety about the burdens of community care on families. Alarming statements have been made about the numbers of homeless people, including a high proportion of those with chronic mental illness, and these were only partly answered by a Salvation Army study (Chant, 1986). Beliefs about the 'transcarceration' of former asylum patients to prison life have also been challenged by Bowden (1990) and Fowles (1990). Certainly, adequate plans for individual resettlement (Wing, 1982), special provision for the care of chronic patients who require some sort of hospital care (Bennett, 1980), adequate monitoring of medication and self-care, and a 24-hour crisis service will be needed everywhere. Community psychiatry will have to overcome many such difficulties, for in this long process of change, there can be no turning back to the model of the pauper lunatic asylum. The drive to community psychiatry must and will continue, though inevitably with pauses, deviations, and temporary reverses (Bennett & Freeman, 1991).

References

AHRENFELDT, R. H. (1958) *Psychiatry in the British Army in the Second World War*. London: Routledge & Kegan Paul.

ARLIDGE, J. T. (1859) *On the State of Lunacy and the Legal Provision for the Insane, with Observations on the Construction and Organization of Asylums*. London: J. & A. Churchill.

ASYLUM JOURNAL (1853) Prospectus. *Asylum Journal*, **1**, 1.

AUDIT COMMISSION (1986) *Making a Reality of Community Care*. London: HMSO.

BELGRAVE, T. B. (1867) Discussion on Dr Davey's paper. *Journal of Mental Science*, **13**, 399–400.

BELL, G. M. (1955) A mental hospital with open doors. *International Journal of Social Psychiatry*, **1**, 42–48.

BELLAK, L. (1964) Community psychiatry: the third psychiatric revolution. In *Handbook of Community Psychiatry and Community Mental Health* (ed. L. Bellak). New York: Grune & Stratton.

BENNETT, D. (1978) Community psychiatry. *British Journal of Psychiatry*, **132**, 209–220.

—— (1980) The chronic psychiatric patient today. *Journal of the Royal Society of Medicine*, **73**, 301–303.

—— (1983) The historical development of rehabilitation services. In *Theory & Practice of Psychiatric Rehabilitation* (eds D. H. Bennett & F. N. Watts). Chichester: Wiley.

—— & ROBERTSON, J. P. S. (1955) The effects of habit training on chronic schizophrenic patients. *Journal of Mental Science*, **101**, 664–672.

—— & WING, L. (1972) Social work services. In *Evaluating a Community Psychiatry Service* (eds J. K. Wing & A. M. Hailey). London: Oxford University Press.

—— & FREEMAN, H. L. (eds) (1991) *Community Psychiatry, The Principles*. London: Churchill Livingstone.

BIERER, J. (1951) *The Day Hospital*. London: H. & K. Lewis.

BION, W. R. (1946) The leaderless group project. *Bulletin of the Menninger Clinic*, **10**, 77–81.

BLACKER, C. P. (1946) *Neurosis in the Mental Health Services*. London: Oxford University Press.

BOTT, E. (1976) Hospital and society. *British Journal of Medical Psychology*, **49**, 97–140.

BOWDEN, P. (1990) New directions for service provision: a personal view. In *20th Cropwood Conference, Institute of Criminology*. Cambridge: Cambridge University Press.

BOWEN, W. A. L. & CRANE, C. B. (1957) *1st Report York Mental Health Service, 1953–1957*. Privately printed.

BREE, M. H. (1960) *The Dement in the Community*. Epsom: Horton Group Management Committee.

BRILL, H. & PATTON, R. E. (1962) Clinical-statistical analysis of population changes in New York State mental hospitals since the introduction of psychotropic drugs. *American Journal of Psychiatry*, **119**, 20.

BROWN, G. W. (1959) Experiences of discharged chronic schizophrenic patients in various types of living group. *Milbank Memorial Fund Quarterly*, **37**, 105–131.

——, BIRLEY, J. L. T. & WING, J. K. (1972) Influence of family life on the course of schizophrenic disorders: a replication. *British Journal of Psychiatry*, **121**, 241–258.

Bucknill, J. C. (1858) Description of a new house at the Devon county lunatic asylum, with remarks upon the sea-side residence for the insane, which was for a time established at Exmouth. *Journal of Mental Science*, **4**, 317–328.

Busfield, J. (1986) *Managing Madness: Changing Ideas and Practices*. London, Hutchinson.

Bynum, W. F., Porter, R. & Shepherd, M. (1988) *The Anatomy of Madness, Vol. III The Asylum and its Psychiatry*. London: Routledge.

Canter, D., Drake, M., Littler, T., *et al* (1989) *The Faces of Homelessness in London*. Interim report to the Salvation Army. Guildford: Department of Psychology, University of Surrey.

Chant, J. (1986) Making ends meet: a continuum of care. In *The Provision of Mental Health Services in Britain: The Way Ahead* (eds G. Wilkinson & H. Freeman), pp. 18–29. London: Gaskell.

Carse, J., Panton, N. & Watt, A. (1958) A district mental service: the Worthing experiment. *Lancet*, *i*, 39–41.

Committee on Local Authority & Allied Personal Social Services (1968) *The Seebohm Report*, cmnd 3703. London: HMSO.

Conolly, J. (1830) *An Inquiry Concerning the Indications of Insanity with Suggestions for the Better Protection and Care of the Insane*. London: John Taylor.

Davey, J. G. (1867) On the insane poor in Middlesex and the asylums of Hanwell and Colney Hatch. *Journal of Mental Science*, **13**, 314–319.

Department of Health and Social Security (1971) *Hospital Services for the Mentally Ill*. HM 97. London: HMSO.

—— (1975) *Better Services for the Mentally Ill*, cmnd 6233. London: HMSO.

—— (1981*a*) *Care in the Community: A Consultative Document on Moving Resources for Care in England*. HC(81). London HMSO.

—— (1981*b*) *Care in Action: A Handbook of Policies and Priorities for the Health and Social Services in England*. London: HMSO.

—— (1983*a*) *Health Care and its Costs*. London: HMSO.

—— (1983*b*) *Health Service Development: Care in the Community and Joint Finance*. London: HMSO.

—— (1984*a*) *Facilities and Services in Mental Illness and Mental Handicap Hospitals in England 1980–81*. London: HMSO.

—— (1984*b*) *Caring for People: Community Care in the Next Decade and Beyond*, cmnd 849. London: HMSO.

—— (1989) *Caring for People: Community Care in the Next Decade and Beyond*, cmnd 849. London: HMSO.

Downham, E. T. (1967) The Burnley psychiatric service. In *New Aspects of the Mental Health Services* (eds H. Freeman & J. Farndale). Oxford: Pergamon.

Foulkes, S. H. (1948) *Introduction to Group-analytic Psychotherapy*. London: Heinemann.

Fowles, A. J. (1990) The mentally abnormal offender in the era of community care. *20th Cropwood Conference, Institute of Criminology*. Cambridge: Cambridge University Press.

Freeman, H. L. (1962) The Portsmouth mental health service 1926–1952. *Medical Officer*, **107**, 149–151.

—— (1983) Concepts of community psychiatry. *British Journal of Hospital Medicine*, **30**, 90–96.

—— & Alpert, M. (1986) Prevalence of schizophrenia in an urban population. *British Journal of Psychiatry*, **149**, 603–609.

Freudenberg, R. K., Bennett, D. H. & May, A. R. (1957) The relative importance of physical and community methods in the treatment of schizophrenia. In *Report of Second International Congress of Psychiatry, Congress Report*, vol. 1, pp. 157–178. Zurich: Orell Füssli Arts Graphiques.

Griffiths, R. (1988) *Community Care: Agenda for Action*. London: HMSO.

Harris, A. (1958) General adult psychiatric services outside the mental hospital. *Hospital and Health Management*, **21**, 405–407.

Hawkins, H. (1871) A plea for convalescent homes in connection with asylums for the insane poor. *Journal of Mental Science*, **17**, 107–116.

Hill, D. (1969) *Psychiatry in Medicine*, London: Nuffield Provincial Hospitals Trust.

House of Commons Social Services Committee (1985) *Community Care with Special Reference to the Adult Mentally Ill and Mentally Handicapped People*. London: HMSO.

Jones, K. (1960) *Mental Health and Social Policy*. London: Routledge & Kegan Paul.

Jones, M. (1952) *Social Psychiatry: A Study of Therapeutic Communities*. London: Tavistock.

Journal of Mental Science (1857) Annual reports for the county lunatic asylums for 1856–1857. *Journal of Mental Science*, **3**, 477–478.

Kuipers, L., MacCarthy, B., Hurry, J., *et al* (1989) Counselling the relatives of the long-term adult mentally ill. II A low-cost supportive model. *British Journal of Psychiatry*. **154**, 775–782.

Leff, J. P. & Vaughn, C. E. (1980) The influence of life events and relatives' expressed emotion in schizophrenia and depressive neurosis. *British Journal of Psychiatry*, **136**, 146–153.

MACMILLAN, D. (1956) An integrated mental health service. *Lancet*, *ii*, 1094–1095.

——— (1958) Community treatment of mental illness. *Lancet*, *ii*, 201–204.

MAIN, T. F. (1946) The hospital as a therapeutic institution. *Bulletin of the Menninger Clinic*, **10**, 66–70.

MANGEN, S. P. (1985) Psychiatric policies: development and constraints. In *Mental Health Care in the European Community* (ed. S. P. Mangen). London: Croom Helm.

MARTIN, F. M. (1984) *Between the Acts: Community Mental Health Services 1959–1983*. London: Nuffield Provincial Hospital Trust.

MAY, A. R. & GREGORY, E. (1963) An experiment in district psychiatry. *Public Health*, **78**, 19–25.

MINISTRY OF HEALTH (1962) *A Hospital Plan for England and Wales*, cmnd 1604. London: HMSO.

MOORE, S. (1961) A psychiatric out-patient nursing service. *Mental Health*, **20**, 51–55.

NEUSCHLER, E. (1867) A visit to Gheel. A letter to the editors of the Journal of Mental Science. *Journal of Mental Science*, **3**, 20–43.

ØDEGAARD, O. (1964) Pattern of discharge from Norwegian psychiatric hospitals before and after the introduction of the psychotropic drugs. *American Journal of Psychiatry*, **120**, 772–778.

PARKES, C. M., BROWN, G. W. & MONCK, E. M. (1962) The general practitioner and the schizophrenic patient. *British Medical Journal*, *i*, 972–976.

PARRY-JONES, W. H. (1981) The model of the Gheel lunatic colony and its influence on the nineteenth-century asylum system in Britain. In *Madhouses, Mad-Doctors and Madmen: The Social History of Psychiatry in the Victorian Era* (ed. A. Scull). London: Athlone Press.

POWELL, E. (1961) *Opening Speech at Annual Conference*. London: National Association for Mental Health.

RAPAPORT, R. N. (1960) *Community as Doctor: New Perspectives on a Therapeutic Community*. London: Tavistock.

RATCLIFF, R. A. W. (1962) The open door: ten years' experience at Dingleton. *Lancet*, *ii*, 188–190.

ROOFF, M. (1957) *Voluntary Societies and Social Policy*. London: Routledge & Kegan Paul.

ROYAL COMMISSION ON LUNACY AND MENTAL DISORDER (1926) *Report*. London: HMSO.

ROYAL COMMISSION ON THE LAW RELATING TO MENTAL ILLNESS & MENTAL DEFICIENCY (1957) *Report*, cmnd 169. London: HMSO.

ROYAL COMMISSION ON THE POOR LAW (1909) *Report*. London: HMSO.

SYMONS, J. J. (1951) The nursing of the deteriorated patient. *Mental Health*, **11**, 18–21.

TITMUSS, R. M. (1963) Community care – fact or fiction? In *Trends in the Mental Health Services* (eds H. Freeman & J. Farndale). Oxford: Pergamon.

TOOTH, G. C. & BROOKE, E. M. (1961) Trends in the mental hospital population and their effect on future planning. *Lancet*, *i*, 710–713.

TURNER, T. (1988) Henry Maudsley: psychiatrist, philosopher and entrepreneur. In *The Anatomy of Madness, vol. 3, The Asylum and its Psychiatry* (eds W. F. Bynum, R. Porter & M. Shepherd). London: Routledge.

WALK, A. (1962) Mental hospitals. In *The Evolution of Hospitals in Britain* (ed. F. N. L. Poynter). London: Pitman.

WING, J. K. (ed.) (1982) Long-term community care: experience in a London borough. *Psychological Medicine* (monograph suppl. 2).

——— & HAILEY, A. M. (eds) (1972) *Evaluating a Community Psychiatric Service: The Camberwell Register 1964–1971*. London: Oxford University Press.

22 The anti-psychiatry movement

DIGBY TANTAM

'Anti-psychiatry' was a term first used by Beyer (1912, cited by Szasz, 1979*a*) but revived by Cooper (1967) and defined by him as the attempt to end the "game" that the bourgeois psychiatrist plays with his "victim" (patient) to reduce him "to nothing more than the wretched, forsaken condition into which the psychiatrist himself has fallen". The game is expressed in diagnosis, especially in the use of the term 'schizophrenia', in the use of those "Abortifacients of the Spirit" the neuroleptics, in the non-reciprocity that exists between patient and doctor, and in the wish of the psychiatrist to "close experience down rather than open it up".

Cooper graduated in medicine in Cape Town and trained as a psychiatrist in Britain. His critique of psychiatry, unlike that of some of the American and French critics of the profession (Scheff, 1966; Foucault, 1973; Rosenhan, 1973), was from the inside, and, again unlike theirs, his concern – at least initially – was to find alternative treatments which might be better. It was an essential characteristic of Cooper the anti-psychiatrist that he was also a psychiatrist.

A small number of other psychiatrists were making similar criticisms, notably Cooper's collaborators, Laing and Esterson in Britain, Szasz in the United States, and Basaglia in Italy. Together, they constituted the anti-psychiatry movement, with the addition perhaps of a few successors such as Berke in Britain and Deleuze and Guattari in France (Turkle, 1981). Basaglia's work has influenced British psychiatry only recently and is therefore considered towards the end of this chapter, while Deleuze and Guattari have had negligible influence in Britain, and are not considered at all. Szasz is included, despite his repudiation of the term 'anti-psychiatry', because he has had considerable impact on a generation of British psychiatrists, even if he does not enjoy an association with "base rhetoricians" and those who are "picking the taxpayers' pockets" (Szasz, 1979*a*).

Basic premises

Siegler *et al* (1969) detected three "models of madness" in Laing (1967): a psychoanalytic one, a conspiratorial one, and a psychodelic one. In fact, all three models share four interconnected premises.

(a) Schizophrenia (and by extension, all madness) is not an illness but a label arbitrarily fixed by society and confirmed by psychiatrists.
(b) The symptoms of schizophrenia (and by extension all madness) are understandable as communications: the 'praecox feeling' that some psychiatrists identify exists in the psychiatrist and not in the person with schizophrenia.
(c) What psychiatrists call schizophrenia is either a reaction to a disturbed family (the conspiratorial model) or a healing voyage which would be of benefit if it could be completed without interference (the psychodelic model).
(d) Psychiatrists and psychiatric hospitals degrade people, and create mad behaviour.

The anti-psychiatry movement in Britain, unlike its more politicised progeny in France and the United States, has never had a manifesto. Furthermore, the views of Laing and of Cooper diverged from each other and from those of their colleagues in the Philadelphia Association. Each moved on: Cooper to the *Dialectics of Liberation* (Cooper, 1976), Laing to mysticism and the lingering effects of the birth trauma, and both to telling people how to live their lives. Both revised some of their earlier positions. However, the four assumptions derived from *The Politics of Experience* continue to be the most well known and most influential formulation of British anti-psychiatry, and each is examined in turn.

(a) Schizophrenia is not an illness

The status of schizophrenia is an embarrassment for anti-psychiatrists for, as Szasz (1979*a*) has witheringly pointed out, it is absurd for them to discuss the causes and treatment of something that does not exist, and yet they do so, at considerable length. His own position is that schizophrenia is bad behaviour, or behaviour that someone else dislikes, or a performance designed to get help (Szasz, 1960, 1972), and that the only response that a doctor should consider is to agree to a contract, if the patient requests one, to have a series of conversations about it, for which the doctor will be paid (Szasz, 1979*b*).

Social scientists have been some of the most influential critics of the diagnostic process. Scheff (1966) argued that mentally ill people are labelled as deviant because they have broken 'residual' rules of their society, rules which are not explicitly stated but concern the etiquette of public behaviour. He considers four sources of residual rule-breaking: organic causes, psychological causes, external stress, and "volitional acts of innovation or defiance".

There have always been cases in which a 'volitional act' was misinterpreted as a mad one: the Rosenhan experiment provided examples which were later taken as particularly damning confirmation of the anti-psychiatrists' case. In this experiment (Rosenhan, 1973; Crown, 1975), research assistants made fraudulent claims to a doctor that they experienced auditory hallucinations; they were admitted to mental hospitals where their attendants, as expected, continued to interpret their behaviour as confirmation of a psychosis. Here was evidence not just of the gullibility of some psychiatrists or of the reliance of psychiatrists on history: for the anti-psychiatrist, it was a re-enactment of the normal process of diagnosis, and but a step from the mistaken psychiatrist to the persecutory psychiatrist who created madness *ex nihilo*.

Szasz (1960, 1972) had provided an account of hysteria based on simulation and the use of metaphorical communication which he extended, with much less justification (Smith, 1985), to schizophrenia. Laing tackled schizophrenia more directly. His first book, *The Divided Self* (1960), is dismissed by Szasz (1979*a*) as a "virtual repetition of the classic psychiatric view of the schizophrenic as a 'split personality' ", but it anticipates much of Szasz (and derives much from Sartre – Laing and Cooper (1964)). The schizophrenic is "often making a fool of himself and the doctor. He is playing at being mad to avoid at all costs the possibility of being held responsible" (p. 179), but the schizophrenic also converts "existential truths into physical facts" (p. 212). Laing remains conventionally psychoanalytic in accepting that schizophrenia is a disorder of ego identity, but in his next book, *The Self and Others* (1971), the split inside the self is changed to the fragmentation of relationships by conflicting or paradoxical demands by others, and from this interpersonal perspective emerges a new theory of schizophrenia in *Sanity, Madness and the Family* (Laing & Esterson, 1970): the odd behaviour of the schizophrenic becomes normal when examined in detail in the family context. This contention is mirrored in the style of the third book which, as Sedgwick (1972) pointed out, completely omits any quotations from patients which betray thought disorder, although these are common in *The Divided Self*.

Having established that some symptoms of schizophrenia, and many symptoms of hysteria, could be understood as strategies to deal with unusual or intolerable situations, the anti-psychiatrists made the bold claim that they had thereby established that schizophrenia was only an interpersonal strategy, not an illness at all. As Szasz (1972) put it, personal conduct can never be anything other than "rule-following, strategic, and meaningful". In retrospect, it is difficult to see why this assertion was so widely accepted. What of alcohol- or drug-induced disturbance, let alone mental illness?

Scheff (1966) quotes his own research into commitment proceedings, in which he discovered a hasty readiness to commit patients to hospital from court clinics in the Midwest of the United States which was disturbing. But he has no data on what a more thorough investigation of these people would have shown. The reader is invited to conclude that there were no grounds for assuming that any of these people were ill, and consequently there is no discussion of the possibility that some of them suffered from the organic causes or external stressors that Scheff recognised as causes of residual rule-breaking. Scheff's argument is directed only at the damaging effects of 'labelling', and loses much of its force if what is 'labelled' is an underlying bodily disturbance which can be treated.

This has in fact been the position of many psychiatrists, whose apparent commitment to the physical welfare of their patients has not spared them from the anti-psychiatrists' interpretation of their response as a wish to hang onto the power that diagnosis confers on doctors. Although Szasz (1979*c*) argues that the presence of disease does not justify involuntary treatment under any circumstances, both he and Laing accept that it is acceptable to diagnose the presence of a disease when there is bodily disturbance, but only then. Since their position is that schizophrenia is not a name for a disease but merely a label for bad behaviour, consistency dictates that they try to discredit the evidence for the association of the label with bodily factors, and that they independently dismiss the relevance of both genetic and biochemical abnormalities.

Kendell (1975), Wing (1978), and Roth & Kroll (1986) have all provided the contrary arguments for schizophrenia being a brain disease, and Laing at least admitted to second thoughts. He is reported as saying that "something along this line may turn up for some people currently diagnosed as psychotic", but "I find it very difficult to discuss succinctly what I take to be the basic principles of current opinion in these respects" (Evans, 1976; pp. 16, 19).

The similar signs and symptoms of schizophrenia and some organic psychoses could arise because doctors shape the presentation of psychosis to make it fit their conception of an organic psychosis, or because, as Scheff suggests, psychotic behaviour is learnt by exposure to cultural stereotypes, or 'faked', as Szasz

Fig. 22.1. R. D. Laing (photography by HAG)

sometimes states. An alternative possibility, which receives no recognition by the anti-psychiatrists, is that symptom similarity indicates similar underlying brain states; this would suggest that not just one, but both underlying brain states are abnormal.

Moral and empirical claims

The concept of disease, although it receives considerable attention from both anti-psychiatrists and the defenders of traditional psychiatry, does not really seem to be the basis of the argument between the two camps. Empirical consequences of the disease theory receive scant attention. Although the existence of organically caused symptomatic schizophrenia makes it difficult for any doctors, whether or not they are anti-psychiatrists, to dismiss the need for a diagnostic assessment, Laing, Cooper, and Szasz remain silent about this.

On the other hand, it is striking how often personal experiences are introduced into the debate. Laing admits (1985) that one of the families described in *The Divided Self* was his own, while Szasz (1975) has edited an anthology of biography and fiction about being, or being taken for, mentally ill. Sedgwick (1981) cites the case of his aunt, in an article critical of Foucault. The debate about whether or not something is taken to be a disease or to be merely residual rule-breaking thus seems to be conducted by and with the anti-psychiatrist less on empirical grounds than on moral ones. What matters is how the person is regarded as a result of being 'labelled'. Anti-psychiatrists are in no doubt: the disease theory is a way "to stamp out experience we do not think people should have, whether they think so or not" (Laing, 1982, p. 39). To make a diagnosis is, according to the anti-psychiatrists, to substitute a disease for a patient.

There *is* something frightening about treating as mad someone who is in fact sane. There is also something very disturbing about treating someone who is mad as if they were responsible: Kingsley Amis (1984) has given a convincing account of the effects in a recent novel. Unfortunately, the recognition that each case therefore needs to be judged on its merits is rarely made.

Empirical considerations

The neglected empirical dimension to the debate has been most clearly stated by the 'labelling theorists', whose work derives from Lemert (1951). He makes the following propositions (Scheff, 1966). Once a label is applied to residual rule-breaking, the individual is inclined to accept the offer of a role (proposition 8) which he/she has learnt from childhood (proposition 4) and has had reinforced subsequently (proposition 5): the role of the 'mentally ill' person. There are strong social rewards for staying in this role (proposition 6) and punishments for abandoning it (proposition 7).

Each of these propositions has the merit of being testable. If each is true, then it would be expected that the behaviour labelled in our culture as a 'mental illness' would be rarer and less often associated with other behaviour characteristics of that mental illness (strong prediction) in cultures without a stereotype of that illness, or (more weakly) that mentally ill behaviour would be less long-lived and less incapacitating in these latter cultures. The strong prediction has had the virtue of stimulating cross-cultural research, which has demonstrated that there are some culture-bound syndromes of which it is in fact true: multiple personality disorder in the United States, neurasthenia in China, and anorexia nervosa in industrialised societies, for example. It does not seem to be true of schizophrenia (Murphy, 1976) or depression (Goldberg & Tantam, 1991).

The weak prediction has been claimed to be true of schizophrenia, too (Waxler, 1979), but this has been contested (Gove, 1970). It is now generally accepted that the effects of all potentially chronic mental illness can be adversely influenced by social expectations, and that social conditions do sometimes conspire to maintain a person in the role of a mentally ill person ('secondary deviation' in the language of labelling theory). However, the effects of secondary deviation in psychiatry have been less dramatic than its effects in other conditions whose ascertainment is less controversial, for example intelligence in children (Rosenthal & Jacobson, 1968), stuttering (Lemert, 1967), or blindness (Scott, 1969); there is even some evidence for a beneficial effect of labelling in psychosis (Warner *et al*, 1989).

(b) The symptoms of schizophrenia are intelligible

Laing distinguishes (in *The Divided Self*) between people with acute schizophrenia, whose psychotic symptoms he professes difficulty in eliciting, and the person with chronic schizophrenia whose company provokes "that uncanny 'praecox' feeling" (p. 214). The latter position is abandoned later by Laing, Cooper and Szasz, who all deny any special difficulty in understanding people with schizophrenia as long as they are not considered to be ill. In fact, Laing and Cooper increasingly locate the communication difficulty in the psychiatrist, parent, or other 'normal' person who makes the language of psychosis unintelligible by attributing it to 'inhuman processes' rather than experiencing it directly. It is hard to refute this. Intelligibility clearly does require a communicative effort by both parties, and who is to say whether enough effort has been made in any particular case? However, it does not fit with many people's experience, including that of some anti-psychiatrists. Schatzman (1972), a psychotherapist committed to anti-psychiatry, writes of the Kingsley Hall residents' experience of a fellow resident, Joseph: "What did his behaviour mean? Was it worth the nuisance or the risk to us to let him live with us while we tried to find out?"

Anti-psychiatrists claim that psychotic discourse can be made intelligible by (i) taking the attitude that it is intelligible (Laing), which may reduce the deliberate concealment of meaning that is typical of schizophrenia (Laing, Szasz); (ii) interpreting symptoms as consequences (Laing, Esterton, Cooper), re-enactments (Cooper, Laing), or metaphorical representations (Cooper, Szasz) of social relationships; (iii) interpreting behaviour as covert or ambivalent self-assertion (Laing, Cooper, Esterson); and (iv) appreciating the 'mad' feelings that result from conflicting demands or threats to identity made by others.

All of these are interesting suggestions that are not dissimilar to interpretations of other psychoanalysts, but are sufficiently concrete to be usable. There is, however, no instance given anywhere of a conversation with a psychotic person which is carried on using these principles, although they are applied to a previously published American case history in Laing (1971). It is not, therefore, possible to know whether they are actually the key to the abnormal communication of the person with schizophrenia.

(c) Schizophrenia is either a reaction to a disturbed family or a healing voyage

From 1958 to 1967, Laing was involved with Esterson and other collaborators in research into families, at first at the Tavistock Institute for Human Relations and then as a Fellow of the Foundations Fund for Research in Psychiatry. One aspect of this research was to develop a measure of couples' assessment of themselves, of themselves as they thought the other person saw them, and of what they thought the other person would think they knew about the other person's views of them. For all the complexity of the measure, the research design was a conventional one, and resulted in the Interpersonal Perception Method (IPM) – a 720-item questionnaire given independently to each partner. The IPM was validated in 12 disturbed and 10 normal couples (Laing *et al*, 1966).

The second aspect of the research was a detailed study of patients with families who were consecutively admitted to Villa 21 (men) and another, unidentified hospital. No control group was included in the final study, although it appears to have been planned to do so, and the IPM was not used, although it was, presumably, originally designed for this purpose.

Forty-two patients with schizophrenia diagnosed by other psychiatrists were given milieu therapy, family therapy, and (in 28 cases) modest doses of neuroleptic medication. There were 20 men and 22 women; 20 out of the 42 were in their first admission. Thirty-three patients were discharged home, and 32 went back to work. Outcome was assessed by means of the readmission rate (17% in the first year), which was compared with the readmission rate (43% in the first year) in a completely different sample of men with schizophrenia collected by the Medical Research Council's Social Psychiatry Unit (Laing *et al*, 1965). The paper contains little reference to families being the cause of schizophrenia, but is clearly intended to be a validation of the author's approach to schizophrenia. There is little in it, though, that corresponds to the fog of invective that was gathering about the family in the more populist books and articles by the same authors: only a reference to the "patterns of communication which we take to be 'schizogenic' within the family", and in the discussion, a mention of the first report of high emotional involvement being associated with increased relapse (Brown *et al*, 1962).

The reference to Brown *et al* is followed by the statement, "Of the five women readmitted, two were not living with their families, and of the two men readmitted, one was living away from his family". It is unclear why this sentence is included, unless it is to suggest that families are pathological; because more patients are readmitted from parental homes than from other accommodation. This inference is not borne out by their own data: 6% of men and 19% of women living at home were readmitted, but the readmission rate of men and women living in hostels or other accommodation was much higher – 33%.

This evidence of a possible protective effect of living with a family is never seriously considered. The authors only seem to be aware of the destructive side of family life, the side which drove Cooper some years later to proclaim *The Death of the Family* (1970) and to write that "the family must be abolished to enable people to love each other".

Laing, Esterson, and Cooper's views about families and mental illness are based on 'clinical experience' and on very detailed, qualitative study of some of the families of the 42 cases reported in the 1965 paper. The families of 11 of the women are reported in Laing & Esterson (1970), with between 14 and 50 hours of interview being given to each case: one family is described in even more detail in a separate book by Esterson (1967), and the family of a man with schizophrenia by Cooper (1967).

A control group was not studied, although it was planned, because, the authors say, they did not "set out to test the hypothesis that the family is a pathogenic variable in the genesis of schizophrenia" but to see "if we look at the same experience and behaviour [associated with a diagnosis of schizophrenia] in their original family context they are liable to make more sense" (Laing & Esterson, 1970, p. 12). However, by the time of publication of *The Politics of Experience*, Laing (1967) considered that this study matched findings in the United States that "*no* schizophrenic has been studied whose disturbed pattern of communication has not been shown to be a reflection of, and reaction to, the disturbed and disturbing pattern characterizing his or her family of origin" (p. 95).

Many readers agreed with Laing that a plausible account of symptoms in terms of disturbed family communication was tantamount to proving that disturbed family communication caused symptoms. *The Politics of Experience* was written at the height of 1960s rebellion by young people against their parents' generation. It was the apogee of flower power and a year before the Paris *événements*. Drug-induced mysticism was fashionable and was presented as a voyage of self-discovery. It was tempting to pretend that schizophrenia was not only intelligible, but intelligent. Bateson (1961) reprinted an autobiographical account of madness which, a hundred years before, had possibly already influenced reforming psychiatrists (Tantam, 1989), and in his introduction he hinted that madness may have a healing effect. Laing (1967) emphasised this more strongly in his account of a friend's psychosis, and it was taken up by other anti-psychiatrists who, Szasz acidly commented (1979*a*), sought to glamorise distress.

Looking back, untouched by the intoxication of those times, the research evidence for schizophrenia being a reaction to familial or social pathology is not compelling. The study reported in *Sanity, Madness and the Family* (Laing & Esterson, 1970) is methodologically weak. No attempt was made in it to ensure that knowing the symptoms did not prejudice the researchers in favour of finding the disturbed communication: some abnormality would surely be expected to surface after so many hours of interview. The authors' judgement that "reliability studies . . . add nothing relevant to this particular study, so they are not included" seems faulty now, as does the omission of a control group of families not containing a schizophrenic member who, as has since been shown (e.g. Hirsch & Leff, 1975), often show similar abnormalities. Finally, no attempt was made to consider the effect on a family of an abnormal member. Even if there was an increased frequency of abnormal communication in these families, how often was it a reaction to abnormal behaviour on the part of the patient?

Whether it was a leaning to psychoanalysis, a distrust of family life, or for some other reason, the anti-psychiatrists were always led to consider the damage that families could do to individuals, never the damage that individuals could do to families.

(d) The degradation of psychiatric patients and the creation of mad behaviour

The damage done by 'labelling' is just one facet of the central concern of anti-psychiatry – the 'violence' done to people by psychiatrists and psychiatric institutions. In the later work of Cooper and Laing, as of Foucault, Scheff, Basaglia and Szasz, the pathological effect of social association goes beyond the family to the whole of society. Psychiatrists are viewed at best as the policemen of society and at worst as a "small part in an extensive system of violence" (Cooper, 1976, p. 55). The evidence for this is the use of electroconvulsive therapy (ECT) and other treatments with the potential of serious harm, and in the use of involuntary treatment. Potentially dangerous treatments are common in medicine, but the anti-psychiatrists attribute a special degree of unpleasantness and 'violence' to ECT and psychosurgery.

Involuntary treatment provokes particular rage in Szasz, who claims that it is never in the patient's interests, but only undertaken to control a person on behalf of others. He and other anti-psychiatrists also claim that much informal psychiatric treatment is actually carried out involuntarily, because the psychiatrist is acting on behalf of the patient's family who, it is assumed, have interests in opposition to those of the patient. Because mature people expect to have control over their lives, anti-psychiatrists argue that coercive psychiatric treatment, which denies this, results in infantilisation (Szasz, 1974), an exacerbation of the alienatory symptoms that the patient is already experiencing (Laing, 1967), and a backlash of retaliatory violence on the part of the patient (Lovell & Scheper-Hughes, 1986).

Anti-psychiatrists have various explanations of why psychiatrists practise in this way: that they are unable to tolerate regression or that they have fallen into a "wretched, forsaken condition" are two examples from Cooper (1976). The most frequent explanation is a political one: that psychiatrists belong to the middle class and that it is in their interest to preserve the orderliness of a society which benefits them and their families and friends.

Psychiatrists enjoy some of the status accruing to other doctors, but this status contrasts painfully with the low status of being mentally ill or being a psychiatric patient. One of Laing's recurring images is of the case conference: the high-status psychiatrist, surrounded by acolytes, confronts the patient, who is stripped of status, even that of a private person. "It is a ceremonial of control, control of mind, body and conduct" and its effect is to alienate the patient from autonomy, with the result that "We are no more chained, tortured, cut-up, and taken apart. We are mentally dismembered. Raw data go into the machine, as once raw human meat into the mouth of Moloch" (Laing, 1982, p. 36).

Laing's perception of institutional psychiatry receives some support from observational studies of mental hospitals, the most celebrated being Goffman's (1961), and many psychiatrists would probably accept that some features of institutions and institutional psychiatry are open to abuse of this kind. The anti-psychiatrists are not merely suggesting reforms, however. They assert that unless the whole medical process of diagnosis, treatment, involuntary detention, and prognosis is abandoned, violence will continue to be done by psychiatrists to patients.

In *The Voice of Experience* (1982), Laing apostatises Jaspers for suggesting that there is an abyss between the psychotic and the psychiatrist. There is no *objective* abyss, according to Laing. It exists only in the experience of the psychiatrist, who has been trained to feel and think differently from the patient – trained, Laing might have said, to alienate him/herself from the patient, to be, in fact, an alienist. The violence done by psychiatry is thus made to be the explanation for the inaccessibility of chronically ill people, like Julie, whom Laing had described in *The Divided Self* as inducing in him the feeling that there was "no one there".

The demonstrable existence of many thousands of disturbed and socially handicapped people who have symptoms which an orthodox psychiatrist would attribute to psychosis is an embarrassment to an anti-psychiatrist denying the existence of mental illness. Psychiatric violence provides the anti-psychiatrist with an explanation: these long-stay patients, hostel residents, recidivists, and bag-ladies are the victims of psychiatric oppression. Without psychiatry, therefore, there would be no chronic mental illness.

Empirical claim

Basaglia's formulation of the "circuit of control" (Basaglia, 1981) is a succinct statement of the effects of psychiatric violence, which is susceptible to empirical testing. This circuit is said to lead (Lovell & Scheper-Hughes, 1986) from material and affective deficits to violence and dangerousness, to admission to hospital and consequent loss of autonomy, and so to further violence and material disadvantage. This model predicts that violence (including suicide) would fall if rates of hospital admission, particularly involuntary admission, were reduced. The conventional model, however, is that hospital admission prevents suicide and violence, and so predicts the opposite.

Basaglia's principles were the inspiration for the passage in Italy of a new law (180) which restricted compulsory admissions, prevented admissions to mental hospitals, and limited the number of beds available in general hospitals for psychiatric patients (Papeschi, 1985; Mangen, 1989). This has provided a natural experiment to test the circuit-of-control hypothesis. There has in fact been a considerable reduction of involuntary admissions since the passage of the law in 1978, and suicide is said not to have increased (Tansella, 1987), but an increase in violence has also been reported (Jones & Poletti, 1985). Social control of mental illness has not been abolished by changing the use of mental hospitals to 'hotels' and community facilities, and it has been argued that the circuit of control has not therefore been completely broken. Some effect of such a major change in hospital provision would be expected even so, and psychiatric practice elsewhere may yet be considerably influenced by the results of the Italian experience and thus, indirectly, by anti-psychiatry – although the reforms have, so far, influenced British psychiatry less than some other developed countries (Ramon, 1989).

Anti-psychiatry and treatment

Cooper and Laing were both committed to the development of 'anti-hospitals' (Cooper, 1965) to put anti-psychiatric principles into practice. Cooper developed a therapeutic community for young men, two-thirds of whom had schizophrenia

(Cooper, 1967), in a converted insulin coma unit, Villa 21, at Shenley Hospital to the north of London in 1962. He left in 1966, concluding that the surrounding hospital confined the work of the ward too much, and the ward closed in 1967.

Laing and Cooper were founder members of the Philadelphia Association which opened a hostel, Kingsley Hall, to run as a community on anti-psychiatric lines. Laing (1977) reported that from its foundation up to 1971 (he left in 1972), there had been 194 residents in Kingsley Hall and other hostels which opened subsequently, of whom 81 had previously been psychiatric in-patients. Most stayed for between one week to a month, and eight required readmission to hospital while in residence.

The most celebrated account of life at Kingsley Hall is by Barnes & Berke (1971). This dramatic story is written as two narratives, one from the point of view of the patient (Barnes) and the other that of the psychiatrist (Berke). It is quoted as a vindication of Laing's conception of madness as a voyage which, if only it can be completed, is ultimately healing. The evidence is actually more equivocal. Although Ms Barnes did leave Kingsley Hall after five years "a woman miraculously cured of madness, a gifted painter", in Szasz's (1979*a*) ironical words, she was also "on her way toward fame as a goddess in the Church of Anti-psychiatry", who was not "discovered to be a 'gifted painter' but merely was declared to be one". Ms Barnes had not, in fact, been mad when she went to Kingsley Hall, although she had had treatment for a condition diagnosed as schizophrenia (Barnes, 1989). She had subsequently recovered and was working in a hospital when she heard of Laing and asked him if he would treat her, and then waited for Kingsley Hall to open before going there; she continued to go to work from Kingsley Hall for some time, until her behaviour became too regressed (Schatzman, 1972).

The Philadelphia Association and the Arbours Association, a breakaway group led by Mary Barnes' therapist, continue to run communities (Berke, 1987), although they are now more tolerant of residents' involvement with conventional psychiatry and drug treatment. No formal evaluation of their work has been published, nor is it clear what proportion of their clients have experienced psychoses or even formal mental illness.

The legacy of anti-psychiatry

The emphasis of the anti-psychiatrists on the inadmissibility of diagnosis was one impulse for the very considerable refinement of psychiatric diagnosis in recent years. If the use of the anti-psychiatrists' term for diagnosis, 'labelling', is any guide, then anti-psychiatry has also made individual psychiatrists more sensitive to the disadvantages of 'labelling' patients by making their diagnosis public. Both of these developments are beneficial. The contemptuous dismissal of psychiatric diagnoses as mere 'labels' and the aversion to any diagnosis because it would 'just be a label' are less desirable, if not less frequent, consequences.

The anti-psychiatry movement has made other important contributions. *The Divided Self* is an impressive account of the experience of schizoid personality and schizophrenia which does make these conditions more intelligible. The observation that psychotic behaviour can be made more understandable when located in the correct context was also an important one, which would today be considered unexceptionable. The Interpersonal Method anticipates attribution theory in its emphasis on the influence of the expectations and reactions of others on one's own behaviour. Szasz's communication-theory approach to hysteria is equally illuminating in that field.

Anti-psychiatrists joined with other more research-orientated psychiatrists, sociologists, and historians of society in emphasising the shortcomings of institutional psychiatry. However, they pressed their criticism further, and concluded that people cannot but be harmed by conventional psychiatric practice, because it alienates them from their humanity. Overcoming alienation by means of alternative therapy, self-help, the abolition of the distinction between professional and patient, and the levelling of hierarchy became the programme of radical psychiatry (Radical Therapist / Rough Times Collective, 1974) which, although it has proved vulnerable to internal faction-fighting, still survives.

The anti-psychiatrists' critique also appealed strongly to non-medical mental health professionals who had reason to resent psychiatrists' monopoly over diagnosis, drug treatment, and involuntary treatment (Treacher & Baruch, 1981). Many of these professionals found that they had more freedom from psychiatric control in community practice, and radical mental health movements have therefore also espoused 'community mental health', particularly as provided by the community mental health centre to which people may have direct access without referral from a doctor.

The usefulness of some of the anti-psychiatrists' criticisms may have received less acknowledgement than they deserved because of the polemical tone of the discourse in which they were embedded. The anti-psychiatrists were moralists first, and scientists second: it is noteworthy in this connection that Laing's first paper after starting at the Tavistock Clinic was on Tillich's theology (Laing, 1957). Critics of their position were 'enemies', not discussants. This made acceptance of their views an act of faith, which many psychiatrists, not surprisingly, felt reluctant to undertake. A further obstacle to scientific debate was the promiscuous inclusion of fact, imagination, and fiction in anti-psychiatric writing. Szasz includes fictional biography in his anthology of reactions to psychiatry, without intimating that the actual psychiatrist cannot be judged by the attitudes or behaviour of his fictional counterpart. He also shifts from witch trials to contemporary psychiatry (1973), implying that what is true of one is true of the other.

Foucault has an almost ahistorical approach (Merquior, 1985), maintaining that what medieval burghers did still reflects on psychiatrists today. One device which assists him to do this is 'the ship of fools' on which mentally ill people are crowded and sent from one Rhineland town to another. This is his paradigm of the asylum, but he fails to say that it was merely a literary device, even in the medieval period: ships were never actually used for this purpose (Roth & Kroll, 1986). Laing goes even further. He quotes from a radio commentator talking about twins being aborted so that their mother's racing career would not be damaged, and then writes, "I thought at first he was talking about a woman athlete but he was talking about a racehorse. However, a racehorse today a woman tomorrow what's the difference?" (1977, p. 96).

Guilt by association is an accepted rhetorical technique, but it generates strong feeling. Anti-psychiatry generated, indeed continues to generate, considerable anger among many psychiatrists, but in public debate it was usually the anti-psychiatrists who came off best. One reason for this has been the anti-psychiatrists' commitment to and familiarity with moral argument. However, there is another, deeper reason for the anathema of one by the other. The anti-psychiatrists presumed that psychiatric science was not only wrong, but also it was misapplied. Their position is reminiscent of that of the creationists. The Bishop of Oxford objected to Huxley's exposition of evolution not because it was false, but because it made out that apes were the ancestors of men. The anti-psychiatrists' case does not rest on the falsity of, say, the genetic theory of schizophrenia, but on repugnance to it.

Repugnance to some aspects of previous psychiatric practice has led to improvements in the environment of many mental hospitals, to legislative attention to mental health law, and to the espousal of community care. But it has also led to closure of psychiatric units without alternative provision, to internecine struggle between different mental health professions, and to a great deal of wishful thinking. As Scull, no friend of psychiatry, writes: "sociologists have encouraged two fatally mistaken notions: first, the romantic idea that madness was all a social construction, a consequence of arbitrary labelling . . . and second, that existing mental hospitals were so awful that *any* alternative must somehow represent an improvement. Sadly, 'it just ain't so' " (Scull, 1986).

Nineteenth-century romantic psychiatrists, like anti-psychiatrists, considered that diagnosis has "nothing to do with name-giving; it is finding a key that will make the symptoms intelligible" (Ellenberger, 1970, p. 214). They were also responsible for introducing some of that century's most barbaric treatments. This should not be a surprise. It is a consequence of the failure to distinguish value and fact and, having done so, to follow Weber's (1917) advice and make clear which statements are statements of value – weighed on their moral implications – and which are statements of fact – evaluated empirically. This, Flew (1985) considers, is "an imperative of intellectual honesty and respect for truth" (p. 139). Mental illness is not a hybrid of morals and brain disease, as has been suggested (Eisenberg, 1988), but it has both a moral and an empirical dimension. Value determines which topics need study, but inquiry must itself be value free. In studying highly emotive topics, such as those chosen by the anti-psychiatrists, "the desire to tell the truth, letting the chips fall where they may, needs to be much stronger" (Flew, 1985, p. 146).

The anti-psychiatrists have identified, indeed continue to identify (Szasz, 1988), topics which do need further investigation. It is lamentable that at the same time, in their own inquiries, they have fostered value saturation rather than value freedom. Szasz (1979*a*, p. 55) quotes Martin, a critic of Laing, approvingly: "His method consists in random accusation and sloganized virulence, which destroys the possibility of discussion" (Martin, 1973). This statement would seem to be applicable to any of the anti-psychiatrists, including Szasz himself. It is a style of argument that is easier to spot in others than in oneself, and psychiatric opponents of anti-psychiatry have also repeatedly failed to be aware that whenever they rejected anti-psychiatry because its proponents presented their ideas disagreeably, they had themselves sacrificed facts to emotions. *Caveat lector*!

References

AMIS, K. (1984) *Stanley and the Women*. London: Hutchinson.

BARNES, M. (1989) *Something Sacred*. London: Free Association Books.

—— & BERKE, J. (1971) *Mary Barnes: Two Accounts of a Journey into Madness*. London: MacGibbon & Key.
BASAGLIA, F. (1981) Breaking the circuit of control. In *Psychiatry and Anti-psychiatry* (ed. D. Ingleby). Harmondsworth: Penguin.
BATESON, G. (1961) *Perceval's Narrative. A Patient's Account of his Psychosis*. Palo Alto: Stanford University Press.
BERKE, J. H. (1987) Arriving, settling-in, settling-down, leaving and following-up: stages of stay at the Arbours Centre. *British Journal of Medical Psychology*, **60**, 181–188.
BROWN, G. W., MONCK, E. M., CARSTAIRS, G. M., *et al* (1962) Influence of family life on the course of schizophrenic illness. *British Journal of Preventive and Social Medicine*, **16**, 55–68.
COOPER, D. G. (1965) The anti-hospital: an experiment in social psychiatry. *New Society*, 11 March.
—— (1967) *Psychiatry and Anti-psychiatry*. London: Tavistock.
—— (ed.) (1968) *The Dialectics of Liberation*. Harmondsworth: Penguin.
—— (1970) *The Death of the Family*. Harmondsworth: Penguin.
—— (1976) *The Grammar of Living*. Harmondsworth: Penguin.
CROWN, S. (1975) On being sane in insane places: a comment from England. *Journal of Abnormal Psychology*, **84**, 453–455.
EISENBERG, L. (1988) The social construction of mental illness. *Psychological Medicine*, **18**, 1–10.
ELLENBERGER, H. (1970) *The Discovery of the Unconscious: The History and Evolution of Dynamic Psychiatry*. New York: Basic Books.
ESTERSON, A. (1967) *The Leaves of Spring: A Study in the Dialectics of Madness*. London: Tavistock Press.
EVANS, R. I. (1976) *R. D. Laing: The Man and his Ideas*. New York: Dutton.
FLEW, A. (1985) *Thinking About Social Thinking*. Oxford: Blackwell.
FOUCAULT, M. (1973) *Madness and Civilization*. New York: Vintage Books.
GOFFMAN, E. (1961) *Asylums*. New York: Doubleday.
GOLDBERG, D. P. & TANTAM, D. J. H. (1991) Mental diseases. In *Oxford Textbook of Public Health* (2nd edn) (eds W. Holland, R. Detels & E. G. Knox). Oxford: Oxford University Press.
GOVE, W. R. (1970) Societal reaction as an explanation of mental illness: an evaluation. *American Sociological Review*, **35**, 873–884.
HIRSCH, S. & LEFF, J. P. (1975) *Abnormalities in Parents of Schizophrenics*. London: Cambridge University Press.
JONES, K. & POLETTI, A. (1985) Understanding the Italian experience. *British Journal of Psychiatry*, **146**, 341–347.
KENDELL, R. E. (1975) The concept of disease and its implications for psychiatry. *British Journal of Psychiatry*, **127**, 305–315.
LAING, R. D. (1957) An examination of Tillich's theory of anxiety and neurosis. *British Journal of Medical Psychology*, **30**, 88–91.
—— (1960) *The Divided Self*. London: Tavistock.
—— (1967*a*) *The Politics of Experience*. Harmondsworth: Penguin.
—— (1967*b*) *The Bird of Paradise*. Harmondsworth: Penguin.
—— (1971) *The Self and Others*. Harmondsworth: Penguin.
—— (1977) *The Facts of Life*. Harmondsworth: Penguin.
—— (1982) *The Voice of Experience*. Harmondsworth: Penguin.
—— (1985) *Wisdom, Madness and Folly: The Making of a Psychiatrist 1927–1957*. London: Macmillan.
—— & COOPER, D. G. (1964) *Reason and Violence*. London: Tavistock.
——, —— & ESTERSON, A. (1965) Results of family-orientated therapy with hospitalized schizophrenics. *British Medical Journal*, *ii*, 1462–1465.
——, PHILLIPSON, H. & LEE, A. R. (1966) *Interpersonal Perception*. London: Tavistock.
—— & ESTERSON, A. (1970) *Sanity, Madness and the Family*. Harmondsworth: Penguin.
LEMERT, E. M. (1951) *Social Pathology*. New York: McGraw-Hill.
—— (1967) *Human Deviance, Social Problems and Social Control*. Englewood Cliffs, New Jersey: Prentice-Hall.
LOVELL, A. M. & SCHEPER-HUGHES, N. (1986) Deinstitutionalization and psychiatric expertise: reflections on dangerousness, deviancy, and madness. *International Journal of Law and Psychiatry*, **9**, 361–381.
MANGEN, S. (1989) The politics of reform: origins and enactment of the Italian 'experience'. *International Journal of Social Psychiatry*, **35**, 7–20.
MARTIN, D. (1973) *Tracts Against the Times*. Guildford: Lutterworth Press.
MERQUIOR, J. G. (1985) *Foucault*. London: Fontana.
MURPHY, J. (1976) Psychiatric labeling in cross-cultural perspective. *Science*, **191**, 1019–1028.
PAPESCHI, R. (1985) The denial of the institution. A critical review of Franco Basaglia's writings. *British Journal of Psychiatry*, **146**, 247–254.

Radical Therapist/Rough Times Collective (1974) *Radical Therapist*. Harmondsworth: Penguin.
Ramon, S. (1987) The implications of cultural construction of mental distress on psychiatric policies in Britain. *International Journal of Social Psychiatry*, **33**, 149–153.
——— (1989) The impact of the Italian psychiatric reforms on North American and British professionals. *International Journal of Social Psychiatry*, **35**, 120–127.
Rosenhan, D. L. (1973) On being sane in insane places. *Science*, **179**, 250–258.
Rosenthal, R. & Jacobson, L. (1968) *Pygmalion in the Classroom*. New York: Holt, Rinehart & Winston.
Roth, M. & Kroll, J. (1986) *The Reality of Mental Illness*. Cambridge: Cambridge University Press.
Schatzman, M. (1972) Madness and morals. In *Psychiatry and Anti-psychiatry* (eds R. Boyers & R. Orrill). Harmondsworth: Penguin.
Scheff, T. J. (1966) *Being Mentally Ill*. Chicago: Aldine.
Scott, R. (1969) *The Making of Blind Men*. New York: Russell Sage Foundation.
Scull, A. (1986) Mental patients and the community: a critical note. *International Journal of Law and Psychiatry*, **9**, 383–392.
Sedgwick, P. (1972) R. D. Laing: self, symptom and society. In *Psychiatry and Anti-psychiatry* (eds R. Boyers & R. Orrill). Harmondsworth: Penguin.
——— (1981) Michel Foucault: the anti-history of psychiatry. *Psychological Medicine*, **11**, 235–248.
Siegler, M., Osmond, H. & Mann, H. (1969) Laing's models of madness. *British Journal of Psychiatry*, **115**, 947–959.
Smith, A. C. (1985) *The Myth of Mental Illness*: T. S. Szasz. *British Journal of Psychiatry*, **147**, 89–90.
Szasz, T. (1960) The myth of mental illness. *American Psychologist*, **15**, 113–118.
——— (1972) *The Myth of Mental Illness*. London: Granada.
——— (1973) *The Manufacture of Madness*. St Albans: Granada.
——— (1974) *Law, Liberty, and Psychiatry*. London: Routledge & Kegan Paul.
——— (ed.) (1975) *The Age of Madness*. London: Routledge & Kegan Paul.
——— (1979*a*) *The Theology of Medicine*. Oxford: Oxford University Press.
——— (1979*b*) *The Myth of Psychotherapy*. Oxford: Oxford University Press.
——— (1979*c*) *Schizophrenia: The Sacred Symbol of Psychiatry*. Oxford: Oxford University Press.
——— (1988) Letter: Koryagin and psychiatric coercion. *Lancet*, **8610**, 573.
Tansella, M. (1987) Editorial: the Italian experience and its implications. *Psychological Medicine*, **17**, 283–289.
Tantam, D. J. H. (1989) Samuel Gaskell and his family. *Transactions of the Unitarian Historical Society*, **19**, 228–237.
Treacher, A. & Baruch, G. (1981) Towards a critical history of the psychiatric profession. In *Psychiatry and Anti-psychiatry* (ed. D. Ingleby). Harmondsworth: Penguin.
Turkle, S. (1981) French anti-psychiatry. In *Psychiatry and Anti-psychiatry* (ed. D. Ingleby). Harmondsworth: Penguin.
Warner, R., Taylor, D., Powers, M., *et al* (1989) Acceptance of the mental illness label by psychotic patients: effects on functioning. *American Journal of Orthopsychiatry*, **59**, 398–409.
Waxler, N. E. (1979) Is outcome for schizophrenia better in nonindustrial societies? *Journal of Nervous and Mental Disease*, **167**, 144–158.
Weber, M. (1917) The meaning of 'value-freedom' in sociology and economics. In *The Methodology of the Social Sciences* (eds. E. A. Shils & H. A. Finch) (trans E. A Shils, 1949). Glencoe, Illinois: Free Press.
Wing, J. K. (1978) *Reasoning about Madness*. Oxford: Oxford University Press.

III. People

23 Whatever happened to Henry Maudsley?

HENRY R. ROLLIN

Henry Maudsley will be remembered for all time as the founder of one of the world's most prestigious hospitals for the treatment and study of psychiatric disorders – the Maudsley Hospital in south-east London – and for little else. That it is possible for a man to achieve immortality and yet, at the same time, to fade quietly and reclusively into obscurity is an enigma to which this chapter addresses itself.

Henry Maudsley (pictured in Fig. 23.1) had the singular good fortune to live in the golden age of Victorian affluence, an affluence characterised as much by material success as by a wealth of intellectual creativity unmatched since the time of Isaac Newton. The lead-players who crowded the stage at this time included Michael Faraday, James Clerk Maxwell, Charles Darwin, Thomas Carlyle, Alfred, Lord Tennyson, John Ruskin, Matthew Arnold, Herbert Spencer, and John Stuart Mill. Paradoxically, perhaps, there was an associated upsurge of social unrest and spiritual discontent: doubts were openly expressed by scholars and scientists as to the validity of Christian dogma and the tenets of fundamentalism. The literal biblical chronology of the history of the Earth, for example, was seriously challenged by geologists and palaeontologists; they offered proof of the immensity of geological time, in the context of which the Creation happened only yesterday. The same iconoclasts showed that the Earth had previously been inhabited by species of plants and animals now long extinct.

Paramount among the philosophical preoccupations was that of evolution, the theoretical explanation of man's origins – a theory patently at odds with the time-honoured story of his origins as told in Genesis. The two main protagonists of evolution were Alfred Russel Wallace and Charles Darwin, but there was at least one important difference between them: whereas Wallace postulated that the human mind could not have originated by evolutionary processes, Darwin believed the very opposite. Maudsley, probably the outstanding philosopher-psychiatrist of the 19th century, could not avoid being caught up in this momentous debate. He threw his weight behind Darwin, and it is important to emphasise that such was his standing among naturalists and philosophers alike that his views were listened to with respect. Thus, Darwin saw fit to quote Maudsley

Based on a paper read at the inaugural meeting of the History of Psychiatry Group of the Royal College of Psychiatrists at Robinson College, Cambridge, 6 October 1988.

frequently in his writings, particularly in *The Descent of Man* and *The Expression of the Emotions*.

For one who deserves to be placed in the front rank of 19th-century intellectual gliterati, it would have been reasonable to expect that there would be an abundance of biographical, or autobiographical, material. Unfortunately, exactly the opposite is the case; A. J. A Symons' *Quest for Corvo* was child's play, compared with the quest for Maudsley. A recent biography (Collie, 1988), although exceedingly useful for bibliophiles concerned with Maudsley the writer, adds little to our knowledge of Maudsley the man. The only autobiographical material is that contained in a document discovered in the archives of the Bethlem Royal and Maudsley Hospitals by Sir Aubrey Lewis, on which he drew for his Maudsley lecture, "Henry Maudsley: his work and influence" (Lewis, 1951). This autobiographical snippet, together with an introduction, has been published in full (Turner, 1988). For the rest, Alexander Walk's scholarly monograph "Medico-Psychologists, Maudsley and the Maudsley" (Walk, 1976), again, adds little to the corpus of biographical detail. Nor do the various obituaries published in the medical press, for example, those in the *Lancet*, the *British Medical Journal*, and *Munk's Roll* – a collection of obituaries of fellows of the Royal College of Physicians of London, which is remarkable for its brevity, a mere 400 words or so.

Why is there such a paucity of biographical material? Trevor Turner (1988) suggests that Maudsley deliberately destroyed his private papers at some time before his death; support for this contention is contained in Maudsley's own writing. In his last work, *Religion and Realities*, published in 1918, he writes in his cynical, uncompromising way: "comical, almost pitiful at times is the ludicrous display of vanity by men of great eminence . . . they leave behind them carefully preserved letters and elaborate memoirs of what they thought and felt." The act of destruction of the private details of his life, however, could be interpreted as a symbolic gesture of self-destruction, consonant with the depression which he very likely suffered in the twilight of his life.

An honourable exception to Maudsley's other obituarists was Sir George Henry Savage, Resident Physician to Bethlem Hospital from 1878 to 1888 and co-editor of the *Journal of Mental Science* after Maudsley's retirement in 1888. Savage (1918), a long-standing friend and colleague, is the only obituarist who bears witness to Maudsley as a sentient human being, rather than as a cardboard cut-out. Even so, the halo effect which clouds all obituaries has to be taken into account. From the available sources the following sketchy biography can be extracted.

Henry Maudsley was born on 5 February 1835 (though he himself gives the year as 1834) on a farm in the parish of Giggleswick, in the West Riding of Yorkshire. He describes himself as being descended from yeoman stock, who had farmed in those parts for generations. His mother, also of farming stock, died when Maudsley was seven years old, which, he writes, "all things considered was not to be wondered at, seeing that she had eight children – the last two twins – at intervals of two years". Apart from her over-fecundity, she seems to have suffered from chronic invalidism and "much from headaches". Despite Maudsley's virtual negation of environmental factors in psychological development, it would be most difficult to ignore completely the adverse effects of a chronically sick mother who disappears from the scene when he was at such an impressionable age. Added to this is his melancholic comment on his childhood after her death: "Still it was a succession of sombre and dreary years, for my

Fig. 23.1. Henry Maudsley.

father was so profoundly afflicted by my mother's death, to whom he was ardently attached, that his natural silence was increased and hardly a word passed between us boys and him except when absolutely necessary". In terms of predisposition to psychological illness, this is piling Pelion on Ossa.

However, Maudsley himself would probably have disagreed with any idea of such circumstances predisposing to psychological illness – and with some vehemence. In his mini-autobiography, he declares himself convinced that genetic factors alone are responsible for his mental make-up. Thus, he says, "It was from my mother's family that I inherited chiefly the emotional part of my nature". In the same vein he goes on, "My intellectual faculties savour most of my father's family", although, "As for my physical features and gestures, they have been singularly mixed". He chances his arm even further, genetically speaking, when reflecting that "I presumably hark back to my grandfather, who was notable in the countryside for his sayings, sardonic and sarcastic; so much so as to have earned him the soubriquet of 'the old philosopher'." Certainly, Maudsley could himself be both sardonic and sarcastic, so that he came to be dubbed by

Sir John Bucknill, the first editor of the *Asylum Journal*, "the young philosopher". But to what extent these attributes are grandpapa's responsibility is a matter for conjecture. A further illustration of Maudsley's overwhelming enthusiasm for genetic factors in both psychological and physical development is his assertion in the mini-autobiography (he was then 72 years of age) that his "sound arteries, bespeaks his paternal texture".

Maudsley received his early education at Giggleswick School, where he was day boy "who had to walk over two miles to the school and back daily in summer and winter, in rain and snow". He was taught on the (even then) old-fashioned lines of Greek and Eton Latin Grammar – without in the least understanding what the words meant. Similarly, in the upper school, he was taught arithmetic and part of the first book of Euclid without any comprehension of the nature of the problems. And that was all. At the age of 14, Maudsley was transferred as a private pupil to the Reverend Alfred Newth at Oundle, where he benefited immensely from the new academic horizons that were opened up to him. He discovered, obviously to his relief, that "there was a meaning in Euclid's problems". The first proof of Maudsley's superior academic potential is reflected in the results of the London University Matriculation Examination, in which he passed in the first division.

Having decided on a career in medicine, Maudsley was apprenticed in 1850 to University College Hospital for five years; he was attached to Mr J. T. Clover, of anaesthetic fame, who was then resident medical officer. However, his relationship with his teacher was an unhappy one, which may not have been entirely Clover's fault. Maudsley was, on his own admission, not the most enthusiastic of medical students. He ascribes this to the fact that "I was self-assertive and stubbornly rebellious against all control, as I have always been". Could this perhaps be attributable to lack of parental control as a child? Professor Sharpey, the distinguished physiologist, commented that "Maudsley has great abilities but he has chosen to throw them into the gutter". To this Maudsley tersely retorted, "Happily I managed to pick some of them up again before they entirely rotted". As evidence of this successful retrieval, he could point to the scholarship he was awarded, not to mention an array of gold medals. Savage related that Maudsley "felt rather ashamed of winning medals and prizes as they did not represent real knowledge, but only accurate (i.e. photographic) memory". His prodigious memory allowed him to quote large chunks from Shakespeare, the Bible, and his favourite poets.

After qualification, he intended to become a surgeon but because of "a trivial accident", the "purposed tenour of my life was completely changed". He therefore decided to enter the service of the East India Company which, remarkably for those times, required him to have spent six months working in a lunatic asylum. And so, much more by virtue of a "trivial accident" than by design, one of Britain's most distinguished psychiatrists was launched on his career. He was fortunate in obtaining a post at Wakefield Asylum, Yorkshire, as assistant to the deputy medical superintendent, Dr John Davies Cleaton, where he served in all for nine months. There followed a brief and unhappy spell at the Essex County Asylum, Brentwood.

The explanation of his unhappiness is to be found in his autobiographical sketch, and it exhibits either Maudsley's somewhat paranoid parochialism or, possibly, the extent of the north–south divide as it existed at that time. He expresses himself unambiguously thus:

> "I may fairly say that I got on so well with my congenial Yorkshire countrymen that they were sorry to lose me. Returning to London, I was for a short time appointed Assistant Medical Officer to the Essex County Asylum (Brentwood), where I never felt at home, the character of the Essex people, sly, secret and insincere, being distasteful to me."

His alienation in the flat-lands of Essex was not to last for long, however. Thanks to Dr Cleaton's recommendations to the governors of the Manchester Royal Lunatic Asylum (Cheadle Royal) he was appointed medical superintendent of that institution.

His comments on this crucial appointment are well worth repeating, if only because they reflect Maudsley's insightful analysis of his own psychological make-up and of the elements to which he ascribes its complexity and apparent contradictions:

> "I was only twenty three years old, and I think now it was a somewhat rash appointment to make, especially to such a self-assertive character as myself and curiously not self-sufficient, for I am a tormenting critic of myself – this ascribable perhaps to the paternal judgement censoring the maternal impulsion. I have always thought and said that the paternal and maternal were never vitally 'welded' in me, but only 'rivetted'."

This is yet another exposition of Maudsley's unshakeable belief in the vital importance of genetic factors in the genesis of personality, but when it came to ascribing precisely any particular attribute to either parent, he hedges his bets.

Despite his youth and his self-doubts, Maudsley was an outstanding success in the job. Nevertheless, after three years, he wrote, "I became restless and desirous of change and resigned my appointment and threw myself on London, without any definite notion of what I should do there". In 1862, Maudsley took lodgings in Camden Town, even in those days not one of the most salubrious districts of the capital. But he did not remain there long. If having the right address is an index of success, then Maudsley soon succeeded mightily. In the archives of the Wellcome Museum are four letters written by him to a Dr Henry Bastian from rooms he presumably rented in Cavendish Square, Queen Street, Mayfair, Hanover Square and finally from his country home, Heathbourne in Bushey Heath, Hertfordshire. It seems likely, therefore, that it was not long after coming to London that he captured a good deal of the available 'carriage' trade, thus enabling him to amass wealth in plenty.

One most important event in the context of the mystery of whatever became of Maudsley towards the end of his life relates to the great John Conolly, who thought very highly of the young Maudsley, largely because of his erudite literary publications on such subjects as Hamlet and Edgar Allan Poe. Although the precise details of how it came about are unknown, the fact remains that Maudsley married Conolly's youngest daughter, Ann Caroline, in 1862. It is of some consequence to note that an older daughter married Dr Harrington Tuke, proprietor of a private madhouse – the Manor House, Chiswick – and a prominent member of the Medico-Psychological Association. The importance of his marriage lies in the fact that Maudsley succeeded in quarrelling bitterly with his brother-in-law, but his attitude to his father-in-law also changed dramatically, and there is a thinly veiled hostility towards Conolly expressed in his memoirs. To break with both father-in-law and brother-in-law lends weight to the argument that Maudsley was, or could be, a most difficult man to keep as a friend.

So much for the documented biographical detail of this brilliant and, according to all accounts, physically handsome and elegantly dressed man. But further data are unfortunately meagre, and what exist are often contradictory. Sir George Savage, in his long obituary in the *Journal of Mental Science*, is of some assistance here as is, to a lesser extent, Sir Frederick Mott (1918) in the same issue of the *Journal*. Savage begins with a percipient statement: "As to the man Maudsley, as he said of himself, he was a man of two temperaments, two distinct and original differences". This is consonant with Maudsley's own self-analysis, referred to above, in which he describes himself as being at the same time self-assertive and yet curiously not self-sufficient. Savage goes on to describe him as "cynical and rather unfriendly: a man who seemed to prefer solitude and contemplation to social life". But Mott writes that, "To those who had not the privilege of knowing him intimately he might seem cynical and satirical . . . but beneath a seemingly hypercritical manner was a most kindly disposition". Again, Savage illustrates and emphasises a further blatant contradiction: "To the outside world he appeared to be a materialist and a pessimist with no basis of any religious faith, yet I have known him repudiate the accusation of being opposed or antagonistic to religion". It would seem that Maudsley accepted agnosticism for himself, although he conceded that religion and faith might serve as a help for others. Another contradiction is that although allegedly not a clubbable man, Maudsley belonged to at least one dining club in addition to membership of the Reform and the Savile – both of them prestigious and expensive clubs. If he merely had need of a good London address, for social or professional reasons, surely one club would have sufficed.

Yet another apparent contradiction is that in spite of the munificence of his offer in 1907 to the London County Council of £30 000 towards the establishment of a hospital for mental diseases in London (Chapter 4), he could perhaps at the same time be accused of stinginess, or at any rate of lacking in the accepted courtesies of a man in his position. This possibility is based on a letter in the Wellcome archives, dated 15 May 1902, written from 12 Queen Street, Mayfair, to a colleague, Dr Henry Bastian (1837–1915), and referring to a proposed visit by Bastian to Maudsley's country house, Heathbourne. Giving instructions for the journey, Maudsley writes: "The distance from Harrow Station is 3 miles – uphill – an hour's easy walk; from the Metropolitan a mile more – i.e. – 4 miles – the extra mile on the level". It seems strange to me that Maudsley, now living the part-time life of a country gentleman and boasting, as he did, a pair of horses, did not offer to meet his guest, or send a servant to meet him in his carriage, at one of the two stations mentioned. At the time Bastian would have been aged 65, and such a walk would have been no mean undertaking.

There is still one more inconsistency. It might seem incompatible for a man of Maudsley's scholarly, reclusive habits to be concerned with sport, even cricket. Yet from his student days onwards, he was fascinated by the game and could lay claim to be a considerable authority. Although not a member of the MCC, he is recorded to have paid professionals at Lords to bowl at him. Further evidence of his towering enthusiasm is the fact that when he was over 70, he journeyed across the world to Australia for the purpose, as he said, of "seeing how cricket was played".

However, of all the mysteries that engulf the would-be researcher into the nature of this great man, none is so tantalising or frustrating as the attempt to piece together a picture of what became of him in the twilight of his life. He seems to have gone to earth, leaving very little that can be construed as a trail behind him. He effectively retired from medical practice in 1903, but in 1890 had resigned from the Medico-Psychological Association, with which he had been so closely identified since he joined in 1858. He never rejoined, although he was elected an Honorary Member in 1912. Contributions from him to the *Journal of Mental Science* continued, but they were infrequent and their content increasingly abstruse and esoteric. The key to the mystery may perhaps be concerned with the deteriorating physical and mental health of his wife and her eventual death. Of the circumstances of Maudsley's marriage we know nothing. Was it a *mariage de convenance*, entered into by an aspiring, ambitious young man? Or was it a *coup de foudre*? What we do know is that shortly after Conolly's death in 1866, Maudsley and his wife moved into Lawn House, Hanwell, which had served as Conolly's home and as a small, select, private madhouse, accommodating up to six ladies. What course the marriage ran is equally uncertain, apart from the fact that the union was not blessed with children – of which Maudsley's obituarists made much play. Savage, for example, writes that "Maudsley was a home-lover and I feel, with others, that if he had had children he would have gained and that his sympathies would have been wider". This is pure conjecture, albeit that there is no known reason why the marriage was childless. Although six years Maudsley's senior, Ann would have been only 33 at the time of their marriage and, therefore, well within child-bearing age. Was she infertile or, indeed, was Maudsley impotent or sterile? We just don't know.

The clue, remote as it may be, in support of my theory about Ann, is contained in her death certificate, one document Maudsley could not destroy. She died at the marital home in Bushey in the presence of her husband, at the age of 81. The cause of death is given as "Senile Decay", with "Heart Failure" as a secondary cause. It is my belief that Ann's dementia was a drawn-out affliction and that Maudsley voluntarily withdrew from society in order to look after and act as companion to his stricken wife. It is likely that he became depressed as a result of watching the inexorable process of decay in a loved one, and that he reacted to her eventual death, as his father had done before him to the loss of his wife, with manifest clinical depression. "Implicitly in his nature the wills of his forefathers have silently acted from all eternity to make him what he is", he writes in *Essays on Religion and Realities*.

Are there any other clues? I believe there is one other and that it is to be found in the directions Maudsley gives in his will (another document he could not destroy) for the disposal of his mortal remains. Ann, it must be remembered, had been cremated and her ashes kept at Golders Green crematorium until Maudsley himself was cremated there in 1918. He instructed that the ashes of himself and his wife be mixed and buried or scattered to the winds together.

This is a deeply touching, if somewhat macabre, gesture of devotion, the togetherness of lovers beyond the grave.

Although there is a minimum of hard evidence in support of this theory, that does not make it untenable. I call to the stand in support of my case Hilaire Belloc Esq., who will aver:

> "Oh! let us never, never doubt
> What nobody is sure about!"

Acknowledgements

I would like to express my sincere thanks to Patricia Allderidge, Archivist, Bethlem Royal and Maudsley Hospitals, who, apart from acting as my mentor, as she has done so often in the past, let me have copies of Maudsley's will and of his wife's death certificate.

References

COLLIE, M. (1988) *Henry Maudsley: Victorian Psychiatrist. A Bibliographical Study*. Winchester: St Paul's Bibliographies.

LEWIS, A. (1951) Henry Maudsley: his work and influence. *Journal of Mental Science*, **97**, 259–277.

MOTT, F. (1918) Obituary of Henry Maudsley. *Journal of Mental Science*, **64**, 125–129.

SAVAGE, G. H. (1918) Obituary of Henry Maudsley. *Journal of Mental Science*, **64**, 118–123.

TURNER, T. (1988) Henry Maudsley – psychiatrist, philosopher and entrepreneur. *Psychological Medicine*, **18**, 551–574.

WALK, A. (1976) Medico-psychologists, Maudsley and the Maudsley. *British Journal of Psychiatry*, **128**, 19–30.

24 Thomas Clouston and the Edinburgh School of Psychiatry

ALLAN BEVERIDGE

On the morning of 20 July 1911, Thomas Clouston left his residence at 26 Heriot Row to present himself at Holyrood Palace, where King George V was to confer a Knighthood upon him. The letters of congratulations which arrived at the Clouston home in the New Town reflected the belief of his contemporaries that he was receiving a fitting honour for half a century's toil in the field of lunacy. As expected, many medical colleagues sent complimentary messages to the new Sir Thomas, but they also came from nursing assistants who had worked for him, from the Edinburgh student association who remembered his exciting lectures, and from patients who recorded their gratitude for his kind treatment. These numerous telegrams and letters testified to the impact Clouston had made on a very large number of people throughout his professional life. For 35 years, he had combined the post of managing Scotland's largest and most prestigious asylum with a career as writer of a multitude of books, papers, and popular articles, in which he had grappled with the major social concerns of the day. Clouston's ability to unite the practical with the philosophical typifies what Davie (1973) has considered characteristic of the Scottish outlook. Thus any study of Thomas Clouston has to reflect both his day-to-day medical activity and his more speculative, literary pursuits, but in the context of the overall development of Scottish psychiatry as well as that of the Edinburgh medical world in which he moved.

Early life

Very little is known about Thomas Clouston's early life, though his son Storer Clouston (1948) gave a brief sketch of his background in *The Family of Clouston*. Thomas was born in 1840 at Nisthouse in the Orkneys and was the youngest of four brothers. His father, Robert, was 54 years old at the time of Thomas' birth, and Storer Clouston, who appears to have imbibed his father's views of heredity, pictures Robert as a weak link in the line of the family. An Orkney laird, he allowed his estates to deteriorate by "indulging in commercial ventures"; one of these was the purchase of a distillery in Stromness, which ended in failure and eventually had to be sold. It is interesting to speculate what effect this would have had on the young Thomas. Indeed, Margaret Thompson (1984) has even suggested that his father may have been a drunkard, thus firing the son's later crusade for moderation, but this must remain an open question. It is known, though, that Robert Clouston eventually had to sell all the family property, except for Nisthouse, and died 'in straitened circumstances' in 1857. Thomas would have been 17 years old at the time, and just beginning his medical studies at the University of Edinburgh. Later in life, he said that he spent his student days in total abstinence from alcohol, thus lending some credence to Thompson's theory of parental dissipation.

Storer Clouston gives a much more favourable account of Thomas' mother. Described as "an exceptional beauty", Janet Smith of Stromness came from a family of engineers and "developed into a woman of quite remarkable character". She was "rigidly pious, judging all things by a Heavenly and never a worldly standard, yet with immense influence on her sons". From his mother, the young Thomas received "constant injunctions to be 'humble' and think only of serving God, and the Heaven awaiting us if we served faithfully". He was later to claim that any "vigour or ability" that he possessed had been inherited from his mother, and it is interesting that in his medical writings, he was to stress the importance of maternal over paternal heredity.

In assessing Clouston's later intellectual development, his religious background is of great significance. It is known that he was baptised by the Reverend W. McGowan, secession minister in Sandwick. Clouston later told a correspondent of the *Orkney Herald* (1925, 28 January) that his father had been of "the Old Church" and his mother of United Presbyterian (UP). The great cataclysmic event in Victorian Scotland's cultural and religious life was the Disruption of 1843, which had resulted in several denominations seceding from the Established Church (Boyd, 1980; Smout, 1986; Brown, 1990); the largest of these was the Free Church. The UP Church had seceded in 1847 and was the first of the churches to liberalise its Calvinist heritage. Clouston felt that the Disruption had taken a great toll in the Orkneys, and he blamed the drunkenness and dissipation of the clergy of the Established Church, whose unholy example had provoked the congregation to join the seceding denominations.

Religion played a deeply influential role in Clouston's upbringing; a Scripture notebook, kept by him at the age of 14, reveals his thorough immersion in Christian teaching. Furthermore, it remained important throughout his days. On his death, the minister of St Cuthbert's parish spoke of his "profoundly reverent frame of mind" and his regular attendance at church (*The Scotsman*, 1915, 5 May). Exactly how he accommodated his religious outlook with his scientific viewpoint is examined below.

Practically nothing is known about Clouston's childhood; his son's account scarcely mentions it, but a biographical fragment, entitled "Dr. Clouston", from an untraced newspaper in Clouston's collection at the Archive Centre in Edinburgh, gives a brief glimpse of his boyhood days. It relates that he spent his school holidays investigating nature: "with a *vasculum* on back or geological hammer in hand to study the secrets or beauties of nature, to prove or disprove textbook definitions. Or again, nights spent with the fishing fleet enabled him to lay up vast stores of knowledge, on which he drew . . . in composing his thesis." How much this picture of the embryonic scientist and schoolboy Darwin is romanticised, though, it is impossible to say.

However, it is known that Clouston attended the West End Academy in Aberdeen, which necessitated his living away from home; he remained there until the age of 16, when he enrolled as a medical student at Edinburgh. Thus far, the picture of Clouston is very sketchy: an elderly father, failed in business, a deeply pious mother, later somewhat idealised by her son, a rural childhood, and schooldays in the city. Of his three older brothers, all would be dead by the time Thomas was 25 and it seems quite possible, as Storer Clouston implies, that he felt personally responsible for the future family fortunes.

Medical studies

Clouston was not unusual in going to university at the age of 16 and it was only later, as a result of pressure to follow the English system of education, that the entrance age was raised (Davie, 1961). He would have found an Edinburgh Medical School that was still outstanding. His near contemporary Crichton-Browne (1938) remembered "an unusually brilliant galaxy of medical professors": Bennet, Syme, Christison, Goodsir, Playfair and Laycock were all teaching during Clouston's student days (Comrie, 1927). He would have been likely to have found his fellow students industrious and diligent. Describing his Edinburgh student days of the late 1850s, Kenneth MacLeod (1907) claimed that medical students were "a hard-working, well-behaved lot", very few of whom "led an idle or a fast life". Clouston himself was evidently very industrious, collecting several prizes and medals.

As a student, Clouston attended lectures by two men who were to influence him greatly – David Skae and Thomas Laycock. Skae was the Physician Superintendent of the Royal Edinburgh Asylum and provided a course of two lectures a week during the summer term, with a weekly visit to the asylum. Clouston (1879*a*) found that the course was "full of interest and much practical instruction". From Skae (1861) Clouston would have been apprised of the dictum that, "Insanity is a disease of the brain affecting the mind".

An even greater influence was Thomas Laycock, Professor of the Practice of Medicine, who had just initiated a course on medical psychology; for Clouston, these lectures were highly stimulating. Laycock lectured on "medical psychology in the largest sense", as opposed to "technical lectures on insanity" (Clouston, 1894*c*). Clouston (1881*c*) found this "most suggestive, original and instructive". Crichton-Browne (*Journal of Mental Science*, 1881), who also attended these lectures, described Laycock as "the greatest teacher of medical psychology" he had known, and regarded him as the best of all the Edinburgh professors. However, the lectures by Skae and Laycock were not compulsory, and it gives some indication of Clouston's enthusiasm for the subject that he did in fact attend them.

Another important influence was John Goodsir, the Professor of Anatomy, who supervised Clouston's MD thesis. Goodsir, whose investigations of cellular structure influenced Virchow, was described by Clouston (1894*d*) as "one of the greatest histologists of his time". He remembered Goodsir poring over his specimens of the nervous ganglion of the lobster and declaring his admiration of Clouston's preparation. Clouston was, in fact, awarded a gold medal in 1861 for his thesis, entitled "Contributions to the Minute Anatomy and Physiology of the Nervous System as illustrated in the Invertebrata".

In choosing such a subject, Clouston had been caught up by the general scientific excitement of the time. The first half of the 19th century had seen a revolution in the understanding of the structure and function of the nervous system (Clarke & Jacyna, 1987), which achieved a primacy in physiological research. Comparative anatomy had a respectable intellectual heritage, and studying lower animals to settle questions of human anatomy was well established: "comparative studies were the royal road to enhanced knowledge in all departments of biology" (Clarke & Jacyna, 1987). With his thesis, Clouston was thus placing himself firmly in this tradition and was clearly excited by its potential, declaring at the outset that, "No purely anatomical subject bears such an important relation to the Science of Medicine as the structure of the Nervous System". He continued:

> "The nervous system stands in intimate relation to the higher functions of the body, and to the faculties of the mind. Its diseases are the most obscure and the most interesting, and every advance in our knowledge of its structure, leads directly to an explanation of some of its disorders."

Clouston's MD thesis is an interesting document. Though he was barely 21 years old, his writing is confident, accomplished, and gives a foretaste of his later literary flair. From an early age, he had identified what was to be his lifelong interest.

At this stage, he apparently had the opportunity to work with Virchow but financial considerations impelled him to find paid work as an asylum doctor. Though this is a fascinating and crucial point in Clouston's career, the relevant information is entirely based on a few lines in the unidentified biographical article "Dr. Clouston". He was said to have "deplored" the missed opportunity; perhaps his father's financial difficulties had placed pressure on him to earn money quickly. Whatever the circumstances, Clouston was not to follow a career in pure science.

Early medical career

Having completed his medical studies in 1860 and worked for a spell as a demonstrator in anatomy, the young Dr Clouston, with his gold medal and Presidency of the Hunterian Medical Society secured, began work as an assistant physician with Skae at the Royal Edinburgh Asylum in 1861. Clouston (1873*c*) was later to speak of Skae, as "my old teacher and chief, whose genial friendship and whose massive intellect I had admired". The word 'genial' is in fact the most commonly used adjective in descriptions of Skae; Fish's (1965) sympathetic account portrays him as a well liked, amiable physician, who presided over the Morningside asylum for 30 years.

Clouston's colleagues at the asylum were John Sibbald, who had drawn the illustrations for his thesis, and David Yellowlees. Both remained his lifelong friends and both achieved some eminence in their field – Sibbald as a Commissioner in Lunacy and Yellowlees as a Superintendent of the Gartnavel Royal Asylum. Yellowlees (1915) has left an account of the early years at the Edinburgh asylum:

> "We first met in the Autumn of 1861, and we lived in close association as fellow-assistants in the Royal Edinburgh Asylum for about 18 months . . . In those months of daily intercourse we came to know each other well, and intimate friendship was the result. Our able and genial chief, Dr. Skae, trusted his assistants entirely and gave them a sense of responsibility which made them do their best, and thus our work became a constant and engrossing pleasure. Our sitting room was in common, and many a mental, moral and spiritual theme was discussed there, often far into the night. Clouston was a forcible and fluent speaker, often more forcible the less sure he was of his own view."

Skae encouraged original work in medicine and Clouston quickly began publishing his research. His first publication, in 1863, was a shortened version of his thesis, describing the nervous system of the lobster. The reprint in the Royal Edinburgh Hospital library is inscribed to "Dr. Skae with Dr. Clouston's best thanks and kindest regards". The same year, Clouston published his first paper, in the *Journal of Mental Science*, entitled "The connection between tuberculosis and insanity". While revealing what would become his characteristic command of detail and industrious capacity to amass information, the paper is atypical in one respect – the extensive references to foreign literature. In later years, Clouston paid less attention to foreign writers and was criticised for not reading the European literature (Savage, 1915). In this, his first paper, he was understandably keen to parade his wide reading and to add weight to his own findings by citing recognised authorities, but in later years he was to rely much more heavily on his own clinical experience.

The Carlisle years

In 1863, Clouston was appointed Medical Superintendent of the Cumberland and Westmorland asylum at the impressively early age of 23. As he later recalled, he was "a sort of boy physician, the youngest ever appointed" (*Journal of Mental Science*, 1910). The asylum, which had opened in 1862, was situated on a hill three miles from Carlisle and housed 200 patients. Clouston was in charge of a staff of 30, including officials, attendants, and workmen. He remained in Carlisle for ten years and saw the asylum population double during his period of office. The annual asylum reports which he composed during the ensuing decade reflected his development as a superintendent and his growing confidence in the management of the institution. Clouston also quickly recognised the report as a means of communicating with the outside world. As he wrote in 1869:

> "An annual report of an Asylum circulates among three classes of persons who each look in it for quite different information. The magistrates, to whom it is addressed, like it to be short, and to contain only official matters; the public generally look for sensational incidents and a readable account of things, which they regard with mingled interest and aversion; the medical profession seek an accurate history of the diseases treated in it."

An article published in 1865 is very revealing of Clouston's style of management, despite its rather unprepossessing subject matter. Entitled *Sewage*

Exhalations, the Cause of Dysentery, it described an outbreak of dysentery in the asylum, which was "caused by the effluvia from a field irrigated with sewage". Less than a year after he had taken up his new position, dysentery had broken out, which by March of the following year had struck 31 people, killing 20. This was an extremely daunting development for any newly appointed clinician, but especially for Clouston (1876*b*), who was later to write that "the Superintendent should look on any death as a discredit to himself, and an affront to his profession". Nevertheless, this paper and the asylum reports of 1864 and 1865 displayed a superintendent very much in charge. With conscientious thoroughness, Clouston investigated the cause, enrolled the services of the local meteorologist to chart the direction of the wind, assessed barometric pressure, and personally performed 16 of the post-mortems. This reflected Clouston's philosophy that medical management should involve itself with all matters concerning the running of the asylum, and demonstrated how meticulous and energetic he was in putting his views into practice. These writings also reflected Clouston's frank nature in making public what others might have preferred to have kept hidden.

The ten years at Carlisle were formative for Clouston, and he evidently used his time there both to develop his clinical abilities and to further his career. He felt (1870) that asylum doctors had a great opportunity to study patients – a captive population who could be subjected to endless observation and tabulation (Bynum, 1989). Laycock (1869) had suggested that much could be done in the way of empirical observation in asylums and Clouston produced a steady stream of papers, detailing his clinical observations (Clouston, 1864, 1865, 1868*a*,*b*, 1870, 1872, 1873*a*). His studies on the effects of drugs reflected his careful and methodical approach and were innovative in their precise delineation of dosage, duration, and response. Clouston wanted to improve on subjective, anecdotal reports of drug benefits and provide a more objective, 'scientific' account of the effects of medicine. He was awarded the Fothergillian Gold Medal in 1870 for his paper "Observations and experiments on the use of opium, bromide of potassium, and cannabis indica in insanity" (Clouston, 1871).

In 1872, following the resignation of John Sibbald, Clouston became co-editor, with Henry Maudsley, of the *Journal of Mental Science*. He greatly admired Maudsley, whom he described as "creating a new literary era in our department. His eloquence, his boldness of thought, his philosophical insight place him 'facile princeps'" (Clouston, 1894*c*). This co-editorship represented another important advance in his career, and it was apparent that he was ambitious. In 1865, he had applied for the senior post in the new Surrey asylum, and, although unsuccessful, he had consoled himself that, at 25, he was the youngest man on the short list. Eight years later, when the post at the Royal Edinburgh Asylum became vacant following the death of Skae, Clouston was not only short-listed, but was offered the job.

Return to the Royal Edinburgh Asylum

When Clouston returned to Edinburgh, he was 33 years old and was by now a rising star in the psychiatric firmament. He had become superintendent of the most prestigious asylum in Scotland, was publishing papers in the medical journals, was co-editor of the *Journal of Mental Science*, and had received the Fothergillian Gold Medal. In addition, the ailing David Skae had asked him initially to read over his Morisonian Lectures on Classification, and then subsequently to complete them when the old superintendent's health deteriorated further. This last act must have had poignant, symbolic meaning – the dying chief handing on the torch of Morningside wisdom to his successor. Skae had stated that he was to be judged by this work. It was obviously an emotional time for Clouston, coming as it did when he was in the midst of applying for the Edinburgh post and being far from "calm and undistracted". Clouston (1873*c*) admitted that he felt "greatly honoured", and this request may go some way to explaining Clouston's continuing allegiance to Skae's system of classification, long after it was rejected by most British authorities. Certainly, Crichton-Browne felt that emotional factors were important in this respect. In his savage attack on Skae's system, published in 1875 in the *Journal of Mental Science*, he wrote:

> "Dr. Skae's old pupils, with a fervour, that speaks volumes for his influence, rally round . . .. Its great principles have been pronounced binding by the oecumenical council of Morningside."

When Clouston took up his post in 1873, he was a man with a mission: the physician was to be "the priest of the body and the guardian of the physical and mental qualities of the race" (Clouston, 1880). He immediately set out to transform the asylum. As Hayes Newington (1915*a*), who was on the staff at the time, recalled, Morningside had become "stagnant", owing to the enforced absence of Skae through illness. The system was to change dramatically under Clouston (1896*a*), who aimed to bring in a regime of "discipline, order, a life under medical rule". In keeping with his contemporaries, he felt that the asylum architecture itself affected patients' mental well-being, and he proceeded to rearrange the very fabric of the institution, knocking down and rebuilding wards, kitchens, and recreation rooms. As he later recounted, "We have never been out of the mortar tub" (Clouston, 1883).

Staff looked on uneasily as Clouston had the tall, prison-like walls of the old airing courts torn down, the refractory ward for the most dangerous inmates closed, and its patients dispersed around the asylum. By such measures, he was following the thinking of his contemporaries; Sibbald had taken down the airing courts in the Argyllshire District Asylum in 1868, and Batty Tuke had introduced the 'open-door' system to the Fife and Kinross asylum in 1870. Even so, it took some boldness on Clouston's part, and he was aware of the impact that he was making. "A young Physician Superintendent comes and turns everything upside down, changing the entire system, and pulling the whole building to pieces," he was later to write (Clouston, 1883).

For his model, Clouston (1879*b*) had taken "a first class hotel, not an asylum" and intended that it should be "bright, airy and broken up". To realise his plan, he (1882*a*) made use of the hospital architect, Mr Moffat, with whom, as he freely admitted, he was "most exacting and unceasingly interfering". To a small degree, he also emulated the example of the Gheel colony in Belgium by providing several cottages where attendants lived with patients (Clouston, 1894*e*; Parry-Jones, 1981). Clouston sought to build the best asylum imaginable – one which would incorporate all that was best and most up to date in contemporary thinking.

He travelled to Europe and America, inspecting and contemplating the latest models in care, concluding that, "If mental disease is largely the penalty of the faults of civilisation, as it unquestionably is, then it is the clear duty of that civilisation to apply its best resources to undo and mitigate the evil that has mingled with its good" (1866*b*).

Clouston's grand scheme achieved reality in 1894, with the opening of Craighouse, a spectacular Gothic mansion, catering for the upper classes (Fig. 24.1). With obvious pride, he (1894*f*) claimed that "No man, sane or insane, can walk over it without feelings of admiration". It consisted of self-contained wards, each providing for a different type of patient, and each luxuriously appointed and designed to evoke a homely ambience.

The day-to-day running of the asylum was also to change under Clouston, with order, discipline, and medical rule becoming the professed ethos of the institution. He introduced formal case-note sheets and "demanded a high standard of medical and administrative care" (Henderson, 1964), which junior assistants could find quite exacting (Robertson, 1915). So far as the moral prerequisites for asylum work were concerned, he declared that: "It needs for its proper working a combination of gifts, a single-minded sense of duty, with much self-denial, in many of its offices, and the exercise in a right proportion of discipline, tact, kindness of tone and applied medical ideas in its management" (1884*a*). Thus, by discipline and routine, the asylum would bring stability to the disordered brain. The Clouston (1881*a*) regime favoured work, exercise, fresh air, and diet. When he had assumed his post in 1873, only a third of patients went out of doors, but under the new management, any patient who was physically able was taken out to participate in the daily walking expeditions. Exercise was held to provide a "rational, physiological outlet" for "morbid muscular energy" and to "distract the mind from morbid humours". Clouston (1876*b*) expounded lyrically that "Work on the land, digging mother earth [is] the simplest and most healthful toil for restoring tone to exhausted brain cells". As Haley (1978) demonstrated in *The Healthy Body and Victorian Culture*, exercise and fresh air were considered to be remarkably efficacious; countless individuals outside the asylum were also pursuing a similarly energetic path to health.

Fig. 24.1. Craighouse, Edinburgh, Clouston's asylum for the upper classes

Clouston (1881*a*) also advocated "The Gospel of Fatness" – his belief that plumpness led to mental recovery. "Fatten your patient and you will improve him in mind", he advised. Of the treatment of one of his patients, a 21-year-old student, Clouston (1896*a*) cheerfully reported:

> "The treatment from the beginning consisted of his being compelled to take an enormous quantity of milk and eggs in liquid custards, flavoured with nutmeg, and with half a glass of sherry in each. He took usually in the day 12 eggs and 6 pints of milk."

In his simplest definition of mental disease, Clouston (1896*a*) averred that: "Sanity is self-control, and insanity is the want of it". He believed that civilised society depended for its survival on all of its members exercising self-control over their baser instincts. Insanity represented a breakdown in this mechanism, and it was the role of the asylum to help an inmate regain mastery over his rebellious thoughts and actions. Clouston (1896*a*) extolled its overall benefits:

> "In an institution . . . under certain definite rules of living, and where there is obviously the means of enforcing medical orders, a patient must be very insane not to conform to the orders given as to his treatment, and to the general way of living of the place. This is very often seen when patients come to asylums. At home they had been difficult to manage, or very obstinate, while from the moment they came into the institution they give very little trouble."

Clouston and his patients

An American journalist who visited Clouston at the Morningside asylum in the 1890s reported to his readers that "Dr. Clouston appeared as a ministering angel . . . and a wise and benevolent healer" (Talcott, 1891). In considering how he approached his patients, there are three sources contributing to the picture of Clouston at work. Firstly, the asylum reports which Clouston assiduously composed and which were read by the general public and reviewed in the newspapers; secondly, his clinical textbooks and papers, intended primarily for a medical audience; and thirdly, the Royal Edinburgh case notes themselves, which reflected how the Clouston regime perceived and processed its clientele.

In the asylum reports, Clouston displayed his most sympathetic disposition towards his patients. He appeared genuinely interested in them and intrigued by their stories. As he wrote in 1883:

> "These are really bits of strange biographies. When lately for a medical purpose, I had occasion to spend many hours, evening after evening, in reading many hundreds of our old cases, I used to get so into the spirit of the false beliefs and strange conduct of the person described, that on getting up I had to rub my eyes and recall myself to the actual things of life, just as one has to do after a vivid dream."

He drew many touching portraits of the 'characters' of the asylum, warmly describing their eccentricities and mourning their passing. Clouston felt that society was becoming less tolerant of mental and social aberration, and that the

Fig. 24.2 (above). Thomas Smith Clouston, who occupied the first lectureship appointed in Edinburgh, that in mental diseases, in 1879.

Fig. 24.3 (above right). Sir Alexander Morison, credited with instituting the first course of lectures on mental diseases in Britain.

Fig. 24.4 (right). Thomas Laycock, Professor of the Practice of Medicine at Edinburgh.

asylum was becoming a refuge for such misfits. In one extraordinary sketch, he described a patient whom he thought was without original sin, a man whose complete lack of guile or malice made him unfit for the outside world. For this Prince Myshkin of Morningside, the asylum had become his haven (Clouston, 1896a).

In his medical writings, though, Clouston was more detached. His widely read *Clinical Lectures on Mental Diseases* contained countless case histories and reflected his attitude to his charges; in many of the clinical encounters, the struggle between doctor and patient was evident. The patient, wrote Clouston (1896*a*): "must not always have his own way. Quite the contrary. In most instances another will must overcome his own and to be substituted for it.'' The case histories detailed many battles between asylum staff and patients. A whole battery of techniques was used to quell the patient – enforced walks, baths, blisters, stomach pumps, drugs, and electricity. Of one patient, a young man who was described as ''violent, destructive and unmanageable'', Clouston (1896*a*) reported that: ''I got a first-rate, strong, trained attendant and we gave him two baths of about 104°, with cold to his head . . . between baths he was taken out into the open air and walked about for several hours, until he was pretty nearly exhausted.'' Of a 44-year-old married lady, Clouston (1896*a*) wrote:

> ''On the fifth day, having refused food altogether, she was fed with the stomach pump. This was done with extreme difficulty, on account of her holding her teeth together most closely. The steel mouth opener, though padded with tape, she crushed with a tooth by the force with which she bit it. This caused a good deal of inflammation in the gums and jaws, spreading back to the parotid gland, which became enormously swollen and suppurated.''

The Royal Edinburgh case notes throw into even greater relief the opposition which sometimes arose between patients and staff. Patients were expected to behave and to participate in the asylum routine of work, exercise, and feeding: those who did not conform were frequently derided as 'troublemakers', 'nuisances', or, even worse, 'scoundrels' (Barfoot & Beveridge, 1990). Female patients appear to have been regarded as particularly troublesome, often being castigated for vanity, laziness, mischief-making, silliness, and immodesty. Male patients were frequently suspected of the vice of masturbation, especially if they were wilful or not getting better; comments such as 'Probably a terrible masturbator'' were frequently recorded.

An assessment of Clouston and his patients is thus very complex and has to take into account several factors to reflect both his high-minded and sincere aspirations and the often oppressive and judgemental nature of his asylum regime.

The Edinburgh School of Psychiatry

When Thomas Clouston (Fig. 24.2) was appointed Lecturer in Mental Diseases at Edinburgh University in 1879, it was the culmination of a campaign which had begun in the early part of the century to achieve academic recognition for the study of insanity. The story begins in 1823 with Sir Alexander Morison (Fig. 24.3), who had approached the university to create a chair in mental diseases, with himself as the occupant (Blackhall-Morison, 1921; Robertson, 1928). The request was rejected, and similar approaches by Morison to the Royal Edinburgh Asylum, the Royal College of Physicians, and the town council also ended in failure. Undeterred, Morison went ahead anyway with a lecture course, and has since been given credit for instituting the first course of formal lectures in mental diseases in Britain. The initial historic lecture took place on 21 November 1823, to an audience of six people. In his diary, Morison (1823/24) recorded disappointedly that he had spoken too quickly and too monotonously. Morison is a curious figure in early British lunacy. Hailed by Henderson (1964) as a pioneer, forging links between French and Scottish psychiatry, he was portrayed by Macalpine & Hunter (1969) as an ambitious, well connected physician, exploiting the emerging specialty of mental disease to further his own career. Scull (1979) dismissed his lectures as "an unoriginal mélange of ideas, uncritically assembled from existing works in the field" and even his obituary in the *Journal of Mental Science* (1866) admitted that he lacked "great mental power". On the other hand, Morison did display dogged endurance in continuing his lecture course, and for the next 30 years he lectured in both Edinburgh and London on mental diseases (Hunter & Macalpine 1963).

David Skae

According to Clouston (1911*b*), Dr William MacKinnon, the first Superintendent of the Royal Edinburgh Asylum, had provided elementary lectures for medical students during his period of office. In 1850, the Royal College of Physicians of Edinburgh passed a motion suggesting that formal instruction in mental disease should be provided at the Morningside asylum. The impetus had originated from the East India Company, which required its doctors to have some knowledge of mental disease. The Asylum Board of Management eventually approved the scheme, and on 7 May 1853, David Skae (pictured in Fig. 3.5, p. 47), who had succeeded MacKinnon, gave his first lecture (Skae, 1853).

Skae's 1853 course involved a clinical lecture on a Saturday and thrice-weekly tours of the asylum in the company of one of the medical officers, who would demonstrate interesting patients, encountered *en passant*. By Clouston's time, at the end of the decade, Skae was giving two lectures weekly but the asylum visit had been reduced to one each week. According to Laycock (1869), Skae's class depended for its numbers upon the army and navy requirement of certificates of competence in mental disease. When their respective boards abolished this requirement, the numbers fell and Skae was forced to abandon the class.

Skae taught that mental diseases were brain diseases and was interested in organic disorder, moral insanity, and medicolegal problems (Skae, 1858, 1860, 1861, 1867; Clouston, 1873*b*). As indicated above, Skae (1863) felt that his major contribution was his classification of mental diseases, a system which even his most sympathetic biographer, Fish (1965), admits was "best forgotten". It is not appropriate to give a detailed consideration of Skae's system here, but it is worth noting the clinical significance it held for Clouston (1895), who was to write:

> "In large degree it is founded on bodily causation – 'the somato-etiological'. Its great merit is that it helps the practising physician in his efforts to discover the causes of the insanity and also assists him in his treatment and prognosis. It seizes on the bodily and constitutional relationships of the mental symptoms, and groups the latter accordingly."

Skae's classification met with much opposition at the time (e.g. Tuke, 1870; Crichton-Browne, 1875; *Journal of Psychological Medicine and Mental Pathology*, 1877). Crichton-Browne had pronounced it "Philosophically unsound, scientifically inaccurate and practically useless". Browne also used the opportunity to castigate the entire Edinburgh School, and seized upon a remark Clouston had made about the classification, "excluding everything mental". Crichton-Browne saw this as an example of Morningside's antipathy to the mental and metaphysical aspects of man. He scoffed that: "The physician who limits himself to the outside view of humanity must remain below the level of an intelligent dog". However, despite the hostility and its lack of general acceptance (Robinson, 1988), Clouston (1876*a*) continued to defend the classification; as late as 1894, he was claiming that Skae's system was "the most useful yet devised".

Thomas Laycock

The most important figure in Edinburgh psychiatry at this time was undoubtedly Thomas Laycock, Professor of the Practice of Medicine (Fig. 24.4). Laycock had been elected to the Chair in 1855 and became the first Englishman to occupy the senior professorship in medicine at Edinburgh. He had previously worked in York, where he greatly influenced Hughlings Jackson, the eminent neurologist, and Danziger (1982) has lauded him as the most original of all the British mid-century psychologists. Laycock was among the first to argue that a science of mental life was possible – that the mind could be studied using the principles of physiology. In his classic book, *Mind and Brain* (1860), he sought to develop a "scientific Cerebral Psychology" which would unite philosophy and physiology. He believed that medicine and biology, not metaphysics, represented the proper foundation for psychology (Hearnshaw, 1964). Laycock argued that the mind/body problem was resolvable in terms of a psychophysical parallelism; that consciousness could accompany brain processes, but did not interact with them. An important concept in this grand synthesis was the reflex, and he was the first thinker to extend the reflex function to the brain (Smith, 1970, 1981; Jacyna, 1980*b*, 1981). Clouston (1894*c*) was later to write of him:

> "He promulgated the law of reflex action of the brain, and in my opinion anticipated Spencer and Darwin. He was a daring speculator and thinker. He was not afraid of startling conclusions, tried to include all mental phenomena, in animals and man, in health and disease, within his generalizations, and was the most suggestive writer on the subject at the time."

Laycock did much to improve the study of insanity. In 1857, he obtained a sanction from the university for putting a question on mental diseases in the MD degree, for the first time in Britain (Clouston, 1879*a*). In 1861, he instituted an examination for those studying mental diseases. Seven years later, he called for a formal course of lectures and examinations for doctors wishing to pursue an asylum career, in an attempt to improve both the standards and morale among asylum doctors, but, unfortunately, this came to nothing (*Journal of Mental Science*, 1861; Laycock, 1866, 1868, 1869).

Laycock's most important contribution was the introduction of a specialised course of lectures on 'medical psychology', the first of its kind within a British university medical school (Smith, 1970). As Laycock wrote (1871):

> "The rapid development of a new school of cerebral physiology and pathology (in which I had my share) rendered it year by year necessary for me to

> introduce into practice something more intelligible than the old empiricism as to mental diseases, until at last at Edinburgh during the Winter session 1857–8 . . . I set apart one lecture in each week for a distinct course of Practical Psychology. In the Summer of 1858, I was requested by the Senatus Academicus to give a Summer course of lectures on Medical Psychology, which I did in the following year (1859). To this course I subsequently added the practical study of mental diseases in an asylum.''

Laycock had intended to use the Morningside asylum for teaching, but its superintendent, Skae, refused him access; no doubt Skae was defending his territory, and resented the intrusion of another lecturer. For his part, Laycock could often be difficult and quarrelsome; rebuffed by Skae, he took his class to Millholm Private Asylum in Musselburgh. Clouston recounts that there were about 40 students, and practice was given in signing lunacy certificates. However, within a month of the death of Skae in April 1873, Laycock was once again requesting permission to use the Morningside asylum, and this time, it was agreed that he could teach during the summer term. When Clouston arrived in August of that year, Laycock approached him about teaching, and Clouston (1879*a*) recalled that he ''made very flattering and earnest overtures to me''. The new superintendent readily accepted, and the minutes of the University Senate recorded that Dr Clouston was ''to receive Dr. Laycock and his class at the Asylum and to give also Clinical Instruction at visits twice a week during the Summer session. Dr. Clouston will also give demonstrations from time to time to Dr. Laycock's class in the Pathological Anatomy of Insanity and Cognate diseases of the Nervous System.'' It was also recorded that as a result of this new university connection, Clouston was to withdraw from the Extra-Academical School, his place being filled later by Dr Batty Tuke (Guthrie, 1965).

Clouston (1879*a*) greatly valued his contact with Laycock, and in his later writings, frequently referred to him and employed many of his fundamental ideas. ''My association with him'', he reminisced, ''was a source of the utmost pleasure and much instruction to me''.

Clouston as lecturer in mental diseases

The 19th century witnessed great changes in the Scottish university system (Anderson, 1983), which Davie (1961) has seen as a process of the steady 'anglification' of traditional Scottish values. Of the many Scottish University Commissions which deliberated in that century, the one of 1877 recommended the creation of lectureships. In 1879 the University Senate instituted a Lectureship in Mental Diseases, the first lectureship at Edinburgh, and Thomas Clouston was appointed to the post. It is clear that he was a success in his new position, and contemporaries were unanimous in their praise of him as a gifted speaker. Robertson (1928) wrote that he was ''one of the most brilliant lecturers we have had at the University''. Phrases such as ''dazzling'', ''freshness of outlook'', and ''novelty of phraseology'' were employed to describe Clouston in action (Robertson, 1915; *Lancet*, 1915; *British Medical Journal*, 1915; *Journal of Mental Science*, 1915).

As his son, Storer Clouston, recalled: ''It was really his personality . . . that left the deepest impression. His animation, his slight frame, quivering with energy, the extraordinarily bright and piercing eyes''. An impression of Clouston's lecturing style can also be gained from his textbook, *Clinical Lectures on Mental Diseases*, which was based on his talks to students. On one occasion, he proclaimed to them:

> ''I am able to present to you, some of the most remarkable personages that have ever lived. Here is Jesus Christ, and here are the Prophet Elias, the Emperor of the Universe, the Universal Empress, the Empress of Turkey, the only daughter of God Almighty, Queen Elizabeth, four Kings of England, one King of Scotland, the Duke of Kilmarnock, the inventor of perpetual motion, a man who has discovered the new elixir of life . . . and a lady who daily and nightly has delightful conversations with the Prince of Wales.'' (Clouston, 1896*a*)

He was evidently something of a showman, on occasions resembling a ring master in a circus of performing lunatics. In one lecture, he promised to produce ''a one legged dressmaker of 40 . . . with no personal charms'', and in another, fretted that he had no really good specimens of 'microcephalics' to show his audience.

Clouston has left a very clear account of his teaching methods in *The Teaching of Psychiatric Medicine*, originally delivered to the International Medical Congress in 1881. He wrote:

> ''My course is a Summer course of 3 months, and by far the majority of students are in their fourth year . . . I give 12 systematic lectures in the University, one a week; the students come out to the asylum twice a week for clinical instruction and towards the end of the course I give four systematic demonstrations from specimens and diagrams, two being macroscopic and two microscopic, on the pathology of insanity'' (Clouston, 1881*c*).

He maintained that illustrative clinical cases would ''rouse the attention of every student, in the sultriest day when it was flagging''. The most important part of the course was the clinical demonstration, which he described as ''the backbone of teaching''. Clouston had found the Skae method of wandering around the asylum, in search of interesting patients, too haphazard and unsystematic. Instead, he preferred to bring patients into the lecture room and interview them in front of the students, explaining that ''I try to direct and concentrate their attention on the one point to be illustrated by each case. My object is to create in each student's mind a vivid sense of the direct connection of brain derangement with . . . mind''. Discussion of the case usually occurred after the patient had left the room. Students were also expected to see patients on their own, make a diagnosis, and sign a medical certificate of lunacy.

Clouston's lecture course was popular with the students and it was well subscribed. An article in the Edinburgh *Student* magazine of 1907 gives a mockingly affectionate tribute to Clouston the lecturer, depicting him in his frock coat and striped trousers.

> ''Here is Clouston as you see,
> Warbling of Insanity,
> . . .
> Thomas, garrulous and kind,
> Gives them Hygiene of the Mind.''

During his tenure, Clouston also fought to make the study of mental diseases part of the medical curriculum, and in 1890 he put this to the Scottish Universities Commission. In 1893, psychiatry was made a compulsory subject for all medical students by the General Medical Council, which Clouston (1911*b*) greeted as the "charter for our real and full incorporation into general medicine".

Throughout his career, Clouston participated in medical meetings and conferences, particularly those of the Medico-Psychological Association (MPA). The 19th-century journals gave very full accounts of these meetings, detailing not only the papers presented but also the ensuing discussions. From these records, Clouston emerges as a dominant and articulate contributor to the proceedings, ever ready to comment and unequivocally state his point of view. The *Medical Press* (1886, 8 September) commented that Clouston's "word coinage is a monomania and he cannot resist a catching phrase". His colleagues were evidently slightly in awe of his "gladiatorial skills" (*The Scotsman*, 1902, 20 February), and considered him a "bold and fearless" thinker. Yellowlees (1915) remembered that he was "eager to generalise, and apt to be impatient of facts which disturb the symmetry of a generalisation". Clouston's description of Laycock as a great speculator applied equally well to himself, and at times his contemporaries found some of his propositions hard to accept. For example, following Clouston's 1888 Presidential Address to the MPA, Dr Ireland (*Journal of Mental Science*, 1888) complained that his "generalizations were difficult to seize and they were certainly novel".

Clouston the writer

Thomas Clouston was a prolific author, producing a wide range of material for medical journals, textbooks, asylum reports, pamphlets, newspapers, and letter columns. He wrote two clinical books, *Clinical Lectures on Mental Diseases* (1896*a*) and *The Neuroses of Development* (1891*a*), and four popular works: *The Hygiene of Mind* (1906), *Unsoundness of Mind* (1911*c*), *Before I Wed* (1913) and *Morals and Brain* (1914). His numerous clinical papers appeared regularly in all the leading British journals and also, to a lesser extent, in the American and European ones. His work embraced all the major 19th-century psychiatric concerns, with papers on alcohol, general paralysis of the insane, asylums, and medicolegal problems (Morton, 1988; Thompson, 1988). From his early empirical observations of clinical practice, Clouston increasingly moved to consider the wider implications of mental disease to society. His asylum reports increasingly became an opportunity to speak directly to the population and *The Scotsman* (1902, 25 February) was to greet his later reports as "the moral and physical stock-taking of the community".

Although he frequently lifted complete passages to repeat in subsequent articles and although he reiterated the same arguments time and again, Clouston has nevertheless left a substantial body of work, and it is only possible to provide a brief sketch of his writings.

Clinical writing

Clouston's most widely known book is his *Clinical Lectures on Mental Diseases*, which appeared in 1883 and ran to six editions. Changing little throughout its successive editions, it represents the best account of his clinical approach. On its first appearance, the *Journal of Mental Science* (1884) hailed it as "the best book from a clinical point of view, published in Great Britain". The reviewer noted that, "Inhibition, like evolution and localisation strongly appeals to our author" – an observation which provided a succinct summary of the book.

From evolutionary theory, Clouston argued that mental disease represented an example of incomplete development or of 'reversions' to a more primitive type of brain and mind. From physiology, which had demonstrated that higher centres of the nervous system controlled lower ones by 'inhibition', Clouston reasoned that a similar system operated to control man's mental life. Cerebral localisation, as demonstrated by David Ferrier (Young, 1970*a*), completed the triad which formed the foundations of Clouston's conception of mental disease. The influence of Laycock, Skae, and Hughlings Jackson permeated the book, while Maudsley's concept of the "tyranny of organisation", with its implications of the inevitability of biological fate, recurred throughout the pages.

For Clouston, as it had been for Skae before him, mental disease was brain disease. The multiple case histories which filled the book served to illustrate the numerous ways the 'brains' of individuals could become disordered. For example, Clouston described the case of a 15-year-old girl who had become 'depressed' following a religious sermon: "I need hardly say that the 'cause' assigned – viz., the sermon she heard – had in reality less to do with the disease than the brain she took to church, predisposed by heredity, exhausted by study and unnatural life at a boarding school, starved of fresh air, and rendered unstable by the physiological crisis of commencing menstruation." This typifies Clouston's style, and also catalogues the misfortunes he felt could befall a young female brain. His perspective was a somaticist one, and he paid less attention to the psychological aspects of his patients than to the indications of how they had compromised the healthy working of their brains through an ill-advised mode of living. Throughout the book, Clouston was conversational, mixing the 'latest scientific advances' with homilies on beef tea and living in the country.

By the appearance of the sixth edition, Clouston was being described as the 'Grand Old Man' of Scottish psychiatry, but there was also a feeling that his book was becoming out of date. The reviewer of the *Journal of Mental Diseases* complained that he had not kept abreast of the latest advances, particularly those emanating from Germany. While respecting Clouston's contribution, the reviewer consigned the Edinburgh sage to a bygone era of psychiatry (Pickett, 1905).

In *The Neuroses of Development* (1891*a*), Clouston brought together a potent mixture of evolutionary, degenerationist, and criminal anthropological theories to account for the casualties of civilisation (Bynum, 1984). Nature's grand design could be disrupted, resulting in a motley collection of misfits – the insane, the poor, and the criminal – each of whom displayed the physical stigmata of their flawed humanity. In particular, Clouston held that the shape of the palate gave an indication of its owner's developmental integrity, and he argued that the degenerate classes tended to have palatal deformities. In support of his thesis, Clouston, with his typical industry, had examined all the prisoners in the Edinburgh gaol as well as nearly 600 patients in the Morningside asylum. He had also attempted to examine the inmates of the local poorhouse, but had found that they were too old and frail to permit proper study. Clouston's findings seemed to indicate that the human social hierarchy was mirrored in nature, and that society's lower orders were physically of an inferior mould to that of the higher classes. Describing the prisoners in Edinburgh, he wrote that: "Fully two thirds were in face and stature and appearance, far below the average standard of human development".

Many of his contemporaries felt that Clouston's most significant contribution to psychiatry was his description of the "Insanity of adolescence" (MacPherson, 1915; *British Medical Journal*, 1915; Newington, 1915*b*). He originally described the condition in the Morisonian Lectures of 1873, at that time calling it the "Hereditary insanity of adolescence". Clouston (1894*a*) defined the disease as "a developmental instability due to hereditary weakness. It occurs at the last stage of development 22–25 years". He noted the tendency of the illness to result in 'dementia' (Berrios, 1990), by which he meant "permanent mental weakening in volition, in emotion, in reasoning, in memory, in observation, in imagination, in reactiveness to the environment" (Clouston, 1888). He was considered to be the earliest British author to recognise the connection between adolescent insanity and later deterioration. In subsequent years, his concept was overshadowed by Kraepelin's delineation of 'dementia praecox', and Henderson (1964) relates that Clouston became "somewhat fretful and aggrieved that Kraepelin had not accorded him greater recognition". In a letter to the *Lancet* in 1905, Clouston complained that he had "seldom been given credit" for his clinical description. He remained critical of the concept of dementia praecox, and felt that the term 'dementia' was misleading (Clouston, 1905*a*).

Clouston's general philosophy

"Modern Science may succeed in doing what all the great philosophers, moralists, and religious teachers of the past have been trying to do for six thousand years". So rang the opening page of Clouston's 1906 book, *The Hygiene of Mind*. For him, science was on the brink of resolving all the philosophical problems of mankind: the 'gospel of science' would lead man to a Promised Land of mental and physical salvation. He declaimed that: "A necessity is laid on Modern Science to bring morals, conduct and even religion under fixed laws and to harmonise with the reign of law everywhere apparent in the universe".

Clouston's optimistic faith in 'science' was very much in keeping with the intellectual climate of the times. As Turner (1974) has observed: "Not since . . . the 17th century . . . had so many eloquent voices praised the cause of science". In the second half of the 19th century, an influential group of individuals, including T. H. Huxley, John Tyndall, Herbert Spencer, Francis Galton, and G. H. Lewes came to espouse what has been called 'scientific naturalism'. This was the view that nature, including man, was subject to fixed laws, whose mechanism science had revealed. Clouston was thus participating in the heady, intellectual excitement of the day (Irvine, 1955; Smith, 1977; Jacyna, 1980*a*).

James Ward, a Cambridge philosopher and psychologist writing at the end of the century, identified three fundamental theoretical assumptions of scientific naturalism: "1) Nature is ultimately resolvable into a single vast mechanism 2) Evolution is the working of this mechanism 3) the theory of psychophysical parallelism or conscious automatism . . . mental phenomena occasionally accompany but never determine the movements and interactions of the material world'' (Turner, 1974).

Clouston (1880) accepted a mechanical model of the universe, in which the quantity of energy remained finite: the principle of the conservation of energy had important implications for both society and the individual. One generation could expend more than its fair share of 'energy', thus depleting the supplies of the next generation, and, on an individual basis, each person could dissipate his pre-allotted fund of brain 'energy', thus courting nervous disintegration. ''Woe to the man who uses up his surplus stock'', warned Clouston (1896*a*), ominously.

Clouston remained committed to the evolutionary doctrines of Darwin, Lamarck, and Spencer. As Young (1970*b*) has shown, evolutionary theory offered a ''doctrine of unlimited progress, sanctioned by the laws of nature''. Clouston believed that mankind was evolving from a lower to a higher stage of development.

The third strand of scientific naturalism concerned the mind/body relation: ''man was a 'bit of nature' . . . brain and its highest function mind, work through natural laws as sure and unvariable as the law of gravitation'' (Clouston, 1906). Of the relationship between mind and body, Clouston (1875) held that: ''Every joy, each mental manifestation has a corresponding physical action''. In later years, he (1911*c*) identified himself with the theory of 'psychophysical-parallelism', but was often inconsistent with regard to the connection between mind and body. In his *Clinical Lectures*, with its inventory of brain disorders, he approached an almost materialist stance – ''the brain is the man''. As *The Times* (1906, 16 November) had noted in its review of *The Hygiene of Mind*, Clouston seemed confused about mind/body relationships and ''had a tendency to run with the metaphysician and hunt with the physiologist''. Clouston was often appealing to a popular audience, and he was less concerned with rigorously working out the logic of his philosophical position than with pursuing a 'practical' approach. Thus his writing was frequently polemical in style, and eschewed philosophical niceties.

Despite his advocacy of the 'New Nature', Clouston remained a Christian and attended weekly services of the Church of Scotland, as described above. However, how did he equate his religious outlook with the secular implications of science? As Young (1970*b*) has observed, the conflict between God and Science in 19th-century debate has been overstated: for many, the question was ''not whether God governed the Universe but how''. The answer increasingly came to be 'by law', and Clouston (1874) spoke of ''the Divine Author and exemplar of the law of love''. Withrington (1988) has argued that the 'science versus religion' debate had been played out in Scotland between Robert Chambers and Hugh Miller a decade before Darwin's *Origin of Species* appeared in 1859 and that, consequently, evolutionary arguments caused less difficulty for Scottish Christians than might have been anticipated. Miller, the geologist and Free Church disciple, had concluded that the newly revealed design in geological evolution argued in favour of a 'Grand Designer'. For Clouston, as for many of his contemporaries, the dictates of religion and science were not incompatible. Clouston's 'psychophysical parallelism' could accommodate a physiological view of brain, alongside a spiritual view of mind.

Given the premise that man was subject to the same, fixed, universal laws which applied in nature, it was logical that Clouston felt entitled, if not impelled, to enter contemporary debate about the problems of society. As a scientist, he could discern nature's purpose and was therefore in a position to advise, or rather to order the rest of mankind in the paths of rectitude. "Science – the commanding voice of the inexorable law – Do this and thou shalt live", he boomed (1899). A brave new world was at hand, if humanity would only obey the laws of nature, as revealed to them by the men of science, but when Clouston (1887) surveyed society, he saw everywhere evidence of the transgression of natural law. Thousands were flocking in a "Moloch rush, year by year from the country to the city", where vice, "mental excitement" and overcrowding prevailed. Clouston (1888) warned that:

> "The continual process of too sudden adaptation to new environments and new conditions that is going on in our modern life constitutes one of the great dangers of mental development. Nature's hereditary laws provide for development on old lines with slow changes."

With Morel, Clouston (1884*b*) saw that the cities were creating an ever-enlarging army of 'degenerates', who were woefully weighing down society. From his vantage point as asylum keeper, Clouston (1901, 1904*b*) witnessed the increasing incidence of alcohol-induced disease and of general paralysis of the insane, and concluded that the city populations were becoming "more immoral". If this continued it would be "the very death of the race". The better classes were not left unscathed by the ever-accelerating juggernaut of modern living, with its "hurry, competition, newspapers and telegraphs" and a "nervous constitution" was increasingly being found among the ranks of the well-to-do (Clouston, 1900). As Clouston (1906) observed, "The finer the instrument, the more likely it would go out of tune in families of distinction".

Women were at particular risk: their physiology, with the relentless cycle of menarche, menstruation and the climacteric, rendered women especially vulnerable (Showalter, 1985). In addition, modern society with its 'forcing-house' method of education was encroaching upon women's natural stores of energy, and thereby weakening their ability to reproduce the race (Clouston, 1882*b*, 1911*a*).

What was to be done to avert disaster? "We need at present another Jeremiah to denounce the sins against physiological law" (Clouston, 1887), and increasingly, Clouston came to see himself in the role of 'physiological prophet', declaiming against unhealthy living. Doctors were, after all, "the priests of the body and the guardians of the mental and physical qualities of the race". Clouston used 'hygiene of mind' to describe his programme of moral and physical regeneration. "The highest aim of mental hygiene," he wrote, "is to increase the power of mental inhibition amongst all men and women. Control is the basis of law" (Clouston, 1906).

Mental inhibition was "self-control"; without it, the way led to insanity and anarchy. Clouston's (1891*a*) prescription for healthy living included: building up the bone, fat, and muscle, plenty of fresh air and exercise, and the avoidance of alcohol and nervous stimulants. He advised:

> "Do not cultivate, rather restrain, the imaginative and the artistic faculties and sensitiveness and the idealisms generally, in cases where such tend to appear too early or too keenly . . . cultivate and insist on orderliness and method in all things . . . Fatness, self-control, orderliness, are the three most important qualities."

Much of Clouston's advice, especially his depreciation of the imagination, coincided with the views of the leading British medicopsychologists of the time such as Maudsley, Mercier, Hack Tuke, and Bevan Lewis (Clark, 1988). The term 'mental hygiene' had been in use for several decades – Laycock and W. A. F. Browne had both employed it, though it had gained its greatest currency in America, with the mental hygiene movement. Clouston's philosophy had many similarities with American writers such as Beard and Jacobi, and it is quite possible that he was influenced by them. He certainly had many contacts with America, having married an American and made several trips to the United States. Barbara Sicherman's (1981) thoughtful analysis of the American movement is pertinent to Clouston. She points out that many 'mental hygienists' came to professional maturity in the 1860s and 1870s, and thus had to reconcile their childhood religious beliefs with the scientific values they learned in adult life: "By working for mental hygiene they reintroduced traditional values – always under a cloak of science – and asserted their right, as physicians, to lead others to the desired goals".

In his later years, the fusion between religious and scientific precepts became more explicit in Clouston's writing, and the maxims of science were increasingly couched in the language of the Bible. He called for a "Health Apostolate" of medical and lay preachers, who would teach the ways of "physical righteousness" and denounce "health sin" (Clouston, 1903*a*,*b*, 1904*a*, 1905*b*). With admonitory zeal, he preached that, "To break nature's law would be a sin, to be followed by contrition and amendment". The country needed the creation of a 'health decalogue' and facts about health should no longer be buried in specialised journals, but should be available to all – "The press must be our pulpit" (Clouston, 1903*b*). By letters and articles to the newspapers, by books such as *Morals and Brain* and *Before I Wed*, and by the newly created Council for Public Morals, Clouston exhorted the public to seek redemption through health (*Lancet*, 1915).

It is possible to detect in Clouston's intellectual development a gradual change in outlook. Earlier in his career, he had eloquently defended the rights of the insane (1886*a*). "One poem of the highest kind," he had written, "one great impulse of humanity for good, or one great invention by one of the sufferers, might repay the world for all the care and cost it has bestowed on the mentally afflicted". In later years, he was attracted to the eugenic movement (MacKenzie, 1981), with its programme of genetic manipulation. He dismissed his previous defence of 'the mentally afflicted' and argued that the increasing burden of the insane outweighed any benefits from the occasional production of an associated genius. He felt that mental disorder should become a 'notifiable' disease, and called for the prevention of the marriages of those deemed 'unfit' (Clouston, 1907). Jacyna (1980*b*, 1982) has seen in eugenics "the clearest form of the application of a naturalistic outlook" and also an expression of medical aspirations for power. In his final years, Clouston was certainly increasingly eager for the state to intervene, along the lines stipulated by medical science, in the lives of its citizens.

Clouston's men

"A man with the Morningside stamp, rarely turns out bad metal" opined Clouston (1881*b*) of his junior medical staff. When he retired in 1908, over 35 junior assistants had worked with him and he calculated that nearly 200 papers had been produced during his reign at Morningside (*Journal of Mental Science*, 1910). The majority of the papers by 'Clouston's men' reflected the general somaticist approach to mental disease of British psychiatry during this period (Clark, 1981). Thus, there were many clinical and pathological reports on epilepsy (Newington, 1877), general paralysis of the insane (McLaren, 1874), alcohol (Newington, 1874), puerperal mania (Clark, 1884*a*), and brain tumours (Mitchell, 1883). There were also accounts of physical treatments such as sulphonal (Johnstone, 1892), galvanism (Mitchell, 1894), and dietetics (Clark, 1887). MacPherson (1892) described the successful treatment of myxoedema by thyroid grafting and Clouston (1892) was heartened that it gave justification to the physical approach to mental disease.

Several other publications were also of note. Clark (1884*b*), following Clouston's lead, described the training of asylum attendants, while MacPherson (1899) put forward a new system of classification. Elkins (1892), in a revealing account of visitors to the Morningside asylum, found that a large number fortified themselves with drink to reduce their fear of entering. George Robertson (1892*a*,*b*) was interested in the new treatment of psychotherapeutics, and reported on his visit to Charcot and Bernheim in France. While sympathetic to the therapy, Clouston concluded that it would not be so effective with "the steady and unexcitable Scotch brains" (Clouston, 1891*b*).

Later developments in Edinburgh psychiatry

As the century drew to a close, there emerged a growing feeling that Scottish psychiatry was lagging behind that of Europe, particularly Germany. British psychiatry, though, had followed a different course (Bynum, 1983, 1985). Whereas British alienists had developed independently of general medicine, and to a great extent had become administrators of large asylums, German physicians were part of a neuropsychiatric tradition and had a place in the clinics of university hospitals. Research rather than practice was their interest. There was an uncomfortable awareness that most of the original work was coming from Germany. As John MacPherson (1901) complained: "We have long been content to rely on the knowledge from work done in these clinics [in Germany]". Lewis Bruce (1901), an asylum superintendent at Murthly, observed plaintively that asylum doctors were too burdened with their administrative duties to compete with their German counterparts, who were able to devote all their time to the study of insanity. The response in Edinburgh to this perceived deficiency was twofold: it involved calls both for a pathological laboratory and for the creation of wards in the Edinburgh Royal Infirmary for the reception of early cases of mental disorder (*Journal of Mental Science*, 1901; Clouston, 1902).

The Edinburgh psychiatric profession had been impressed not only with German research work, but also with the laboratory at Claybury, under Mott, which had been opened in 1895. Bevan Lewis' *Textbook of Mental Diseases* from the Wakefield Asylum Laboratory had, according to Clouston (1911*b*), stimulated "the psychiatric conscience" as to the importance of pathological work. With Clouston's encouragement, several asylums joined together to fund the Scottish Asylum Laboratory, which was opened in 1897 at 12 Bristo Place and rented temporarily from the Royal College of Physicians (Ritchie, 1953). The laboratory was under the direction of Ford Robertson who had worked as a pathologist at the Royal Edinburgh Asylum. The aim of the new venture was to encourage pathological research among asylum doctors and provide slides for clinical demonstrations (*Journal of Mental Science*, 1898a,*b*). In 1900, Ford Robertson produced his *Pathology of Mental Diseases*, which he dedicated to Clouston for his encouragement.

However, the campaign for a psychiatric ward in the Royal Infirmary proved less successful. MacPherson (1901) had stated that: "Until Edinburgh has a department for the study of acute cases, it will not be abreast of the better equipped German Universities". During the previous 30 years, several Edinburgh doctors such as Laycock, Sibbald, Mitchell, and Batty Tuke had called for a ward in the Royal Infirmary for early cases of mental disorder. Sibbald (1871), who had visited Griesinger at his clinic in the Charité Hospital, Berlin, was eager to set up a similar ward in Edinburgh. By the end of the century, there was a feeling that asylums possessed many limitations. In a thinly veiled criticism of Clouston's Craighouse, Batty Tuke (1900) condemned the building of "palatial residences" for chronic patients, when there was no provision for those with early symptoms of mental disorder.

A special meeting of the Edinburgh Medico-Chirurgical Society was convened in February 1902 to press for a psychiatric ward in the Royal Infirmary. Most members of the capital's psychiatric establishment were present, including Clouston, Batty Tuke, Sibbald, and MacPherson (*Journal of Mental Science*, 1902*a*,*b*; Sibbald, 1902). The meeting felt that the current arrangements for psychiatric teaching at Morningside and the extramural clinic in Stirling were inadequate, as students had to travel too far. A ward in the Royal Infirmary, situated in the centre of town, would be more easily accessible; such a ward would cater for early cases of mental disease and stigma would be lessened. The teaching of psychiatry would improve, as students would gain experience of the early cases which they would be more likely to meet in their future practice, rather than the more severe cases found in asylums. The meeting closed by formally proposing that the Royal Infirmary provide a facility for mental patients. The proposal was later rejected by the Board of Management of the Infirmary, which has continued to hold out against such a suggestion to the present day.

Conclusion

Looking back over his career after his retirement from the Royal Edinburgh Asylum, Thomas Clouston commented that his "ideal" had been "to connect his administrative duties with the scientific study of brain and mental disease'' (*Journal of Mental Science*, 1910). Unlike his English contemporaries, such as Maudsley, Bucknill, and Hack Tuke (Turner, 1988; Collie, 1988), who had fairly quickly forsaken asylum work for the more congenial life of writing and private practice, Clouston continued in the onerous role of physician superintendent. Highly regarded by his medical peers, Clouston could easily have found employment outside the asylum, for example as a Lunacy Commissioner. That he chose to continue in work which he admitted was difficult, irksome, sometimes unpleasant, and frequently the occasion of much anxiety, is a reflection of his basic attitude to his vocation. His son had observed of his father that: ''the word most frequently on his lips was 'duty'. It was the very quintessence of his life''. This sense of duty, combined with what he perceived as the high moral calling of the physician as 'priest' and 'guardian', must account to a large extent for Clouston's decision to remain within the asylum.

Russell's (1988) picture of the higher echelons of the asylum medical profession retreating from direct clinical contact with patients does not apply to Clouston, who continued to make daily visits to the wards of Morningside. In general, the bleak vistas of late-19th-century English asylums – vast and unwieldly, custodial and therapeutically stagnant – have less relevance for the Edinburgh asylum. Clouston (1894*b*), who admitted that his visits to the 'gigantic' country asylums south of the border had left him depressed about the future of psychiatry, contended that Scotland offered a superior standard of care, both in terms of its asylum management and in the workings of its lunacy laws. He could point to the many visitors from America and Europe, who made the pilgrimage to the 'Mecca' of Morningside (Savage, 1915) and were favourably impressed. Despite the yearly increase in the asylum population and the lack of any really effective treatment, Clouston remained a self-confessed optimist (*Journal of Mental Science*, 1910). If, in the words of Bynum *et al* (1988), the asylum became ''an imperial colony to be managed with justice, economy and administrative flair'', Clouston was the highly competent viceroy of Scotland, whose governance others sought to emulate.

Yet the demands of a well managed institution for order and organisation could have countertherapeutic results for its inmates. Storer Clouston, in describing his father, observed that ''his word – even his nod – was law; a not uncommon characteristic of advanced Liberals, holding strongly democratic theories''. This *aperçu* of the domestic disciplinarian beneath the humanitarian rhetoric was reflected in Clouston's asylum management. While evincing a genuinely felt philanthropic concern, Clouston could be, in practice, a stern and somewhat foreboding ruler. His successor, George Robertson (1922), recognised that rigid routine could affect the patient adversely, and he introduced a less restrictive asylum milieu. To his credit, Clouston accepted that each generation had to make its own decisions about the care of the mentally disturbed and that this often meant overturning the received wisdom of the past.

Clouston was very much a product of his time and culture, and his writings represented a bold and populist synthesis of the leading currents of Victorian thought (Houghton, 1957). A grand speculator and spinner of theories, he reflected in many ways Buckle's (1861) description of the ''Scotch Intellect'', with its tendency to proceed from the general to the particular. However, the intellectual foundations upon which Clouston built his world view began to crumble in later years. The new physics of Rutherford and Einstein rendered the naturalistic model of the universe untenable, while the work of Weismann on the continuity of the germ plasm undermined hereditary and degenerationist theories. As many commentators have observed (McCandless, 1981; Clark, 1982; Showalter, 1985), the tenets of Victorian psychiatric thought were often little more than the conventional codes of morality, expressed in the language of 'science'. Certainly, much of Clouston's writing echoed the popular assumptions of the Victorian middle classes. But, as Bynum (1984) indicates, to dismiss Clouston as a mere mouthpiece of the interests of his class and profession is facile, and ignores his sincere belief in science to improve the lot of humanity. What shines through Clouston's writing is his optimistic faith in mankind's potential for change.

Acknowledgements

I am very grateful to Dr Michael Barfoot of the Medical Archive Centre for his assistance in the preparation of this work. I am also very grateful to Thomas Clouston's relatives, in particular Mr David Wallace and Mrs Ann Wallace for their co-operation and for generously allowing me access to the private papers of the Clouston family. I would also like to thank: Dr Howarth, Garlands Hospital; staff at Royal Edinburgh Hospital; Edinburgh University Library; Royal College of Physicians; National Library of Scotland; The Orkney Library, and Cumbria County Council Record Office.

References

ANDERSON, R. D. (1983) *Education and Opportunity in Victorian Scotland.* Oxford: Oxford University Press.

BARFOOT, M. & BEVERIDGE, A. W. (1990) Madness at the crossroads: John Home's Letters from the Royal Edinburgh Asylum, 1886–87. *Psychological Medicine*, **20**, 263–284.

BERRIOS, G. (1990) Memory and the cognitive paradigm of dementia during the 19th century: a conceptual history. In *Lectures on the History of Psychiatry: The Squibb Series*, (eds R. M. Murray & T. H. Turner), pp. 194–211. London: Gaskell.

BLACKHALL-MORISON, A. (1921) *Biography of Sir Alexander Morison, M.D.* Edinburgh: Royal College of Physicians.

BOYD, K. M. (1980) *Scottish Church Attitudes to Sex, Marriage and the Family 1850–1914.* Edinburgh: John Donald.

BRITISH MEDICAL JOURNAL (1915) Obituary of Sir Thomas Smith Clouston. *British Medical Journal*, *i*, 744–745.

BROWN, C. G. (1990) Religion, class and church growth. In *People and Society in Scotland, II, 1830–1914* (eds W. Hamish Fraser & R. J. Morris), pp. 310–335. Edinburgh: John Donald.

BRUCE, L. C. (1901) The teaching of psychiatry (letter). *The Scotsman*, 6 July.

BUCKLE, H. T. (1861) *On Scotland and the Scotch Intellect.* Chicago: University of Chicago Press (1970 edn, ed. H. J. Hanham).

BYNUM, W. F. (1983) Psychiatry in its historical context. In *Handbook of Psychiatry 1: General Psychopathology* (eds M. Shepherd & O. L. Zangwill), pp. 11–38. Cambridge: Cambridge University Press.

—— (1984) Alcoholism and degeneration in 19th century European medicine and psychiatry. *British Journal of Addiction*, **79**, 59–70.

—— (1985) The nervous patient in eighteenth and nineteenth century Britain: the psychiatric origins of British neurology. In *The Anatomy of Madness, vol. 1. People and Ideas* (eds W. F. Bynum, R. Porter & M. Shepherd), pp. 89–102. London: Tavistock.

—— (1989) Victorian origins of epidemiological psychiatry. In *The Scope of Epidemiological Psychiatry. Essays in Honour of Michael Shepherd* (eds P. Williams, G. Wilkinson & K. Rawnsley). London: Routledge.

——, Porter, R. & Shepherd, M. (eds) (1988) *The Anatomy of Madness, Vol. III. The Asylum and its Psychiatry*. London: Routledge.

Clark, A. C. (1884*a*) *Clinical Illustrations of Puerperal Insanity*. Glasgow: David MacLure & Son.

—— (1884*b*) The special training of asylum attendants. *Journal of Mental Science*, **29**, 459–466.

—— (1887) Experimental dietetics in lunacy practice. A record of investigations and results. *Edinburgh Medical Journal*, **33**, 301–308.

Clark, M. J. (1981) The rejection of psychological approaches to mental disorder in late nineteenth century British psychiatry. In *Madhouses, Mad-doctors, and Madmen: The Social History of Psychiatry in the Victorian Era* (ed. A. Scull), pp. 271–312. London: Athlone Press.

—— (1982) The data of alienism: Evolutionary Neurology, Physiological Psychiatry and the Reconstruction of British Psychiatric Theory, c. 1850–c. 1900. DPhil thesis, University of Oxford.

—— (1988) 'Morbid introspection', unsoundness of mind, and British psychological medicine, c. 1830–c. 1900. In *The Anatomy of Madness, Vol. III. The Asylum and its Psychiatry* (eds W. F. Bynum, R. Porter & M. Shepherd), pp. 71–101. London: Routledge.

Clarke, E. & Jacyna, L. S. (1987) *Nineteenth Century Origins of Neuroscientific Concepts*. London: University of California Press.

Clouston, J. S. (1948) *The Family of Clouston*. Kirkwall: Private Circulation. The Orkney Library.

Clouston, T. S. (1861) Contributions to the Minute Anatomy and Physiology of the Nervous System as illustrated in the Invertebrata. MD thesis, University of Edinburgh.

—— (1863) The minute anatomy and physiology of the nervous system in the lobster (*Astacus marinus*). Reprinted from the *Edinburgh New Philosophical Journal*, New Series, for January 1863.

—— (1863) The connection between tuberculosis and insanity. *Journal of Mental Science*, **9**, 36–65.

—— (1864) Illustrations of phthisical insanity. *Journal of Mental Science*, **10**, 220–229.

—— (1865) *Sewage Exhalations. The Cause of Dysentery. An account of an outbreak of dysentery in the Cumberland and Westmorland Asylum, which was caused by the effluvia from a field irrigated by sewage.* Carlisle: T. W. Arthur.

—— (1868*a*) Observations on the temperature of the body in the insane. *Journal of Mental Science*, **13**, 34–49.

—— (1868*b*) Experiments to determine the precise effects of bromide of potassium in epilepsy. *Journal of Mental Science*, **14**, 305–321.

—— (1870) The medical treatment of insanity. *Journal of Mental Science*, **16**, 24–30.

—— (1871) Observations and experiments on the use of opium, bromide of potassium, and cannabis indica in insanity, especially in regard to the effects of the two latter given separately. Reprinted from the *British and Foreign Medico-Chirurgical Review* (October 1870, and January 1871). Bartholomew Close: J. E. Adlard.

—— (1872) Tumours of the brain and their relation to its mental functions. *Journal of Mental Science*, **18**, 153–173.

—— (1873*a*) The local distribution of insanity and its varieties in England and Wales. *Journal of Mental Science*, **19**, 1–19.

—— (1873*b*) Obituary of David Skae, M.D. *Journal of Mental Science*, **19**, 323–324.

—— (1873*c*) The Morisonian Lectures on Insanity for 1873 by the late David Skae. Edited by T. S. Clouston. *Journal of Mental Science*, **19**, 340–355.

—— (1874) Physician Superintendent's annual report for the year 1874. In *Sixty-second Annual Report of the Royal Edinburgh Asylum for the Insane*. Edinburgh: Royal Edinburgh Asylum.

—— (1875) Lecture on mental health. *The Morningside Mirror*, February and March (reprint). Edinburgh: Royal Edinburgh Asylum.

—— (1876*a*) Skae's classification of mental diseases. *Journal of Mental Science*, **21**, 532–550.

—— (1876*b*) Physician-Superintendent's annual report for the year 1876. In *Sixty-fourth Annual Report of the Royal Edinburgh Asylum for the Insane*. Edinburgh: Royal Edinburgh Asylum.

—— (1879*a*) *The Study of Mental Disease: Being the Introductory Lecture in the University of Edinburgh, on the Institution of the Lectureship on Mental Diseases, May, 1879*. Edinburgh: Oliver & Boyd.

—— (1879*b*) *An Asylum, or Hospital Home, for Two Hundred Patients: constructed on the principle of adaptation of various parts of the house to varied needs and mental states of inhabitants; with plans etc.* Boston: Rand, Adberg & Co.

—— (1880) Puberty and adolescence medico-psychologically considered. *Edinburgh Medical Journal*, **26**, 5–17.

—— (1881*a*) Review of Dr Kirkbride's work on the construction etc. of insane hospitals. *Journal of Mental Science*, **27**, 66–74.

—— (1881*b*) Physician-Superintendent's annual report for the year 1881. In *Sixty-ninth Report of the Royal Edinburgh Asylum for the Insane*. Edinburgh: Royal Edinburgh Asylum.

—— (1881*c*) *The Teaching of Psychiatric Medicine*. London: Kolckmann.

—— (1882*a*) Physician-Superintendent's annual report for the year 1882. In *Seventieth Report of the Royal Edinburgh Asylum for the Insane*. Edinburgh: Royal Edinburgh Asylum.
—— (1882*b*) *Female Education from a Medical Point of View. Being two lectures delivered at the Philosophical Institution*. Edinburgh: MacNiven & Wallace.
—— (1883) Physician-Superintendent's annual report for the year 1883. In *Seventy-first Report of the Royal Edinburgh Asylum for the Insane*. Edinburgh: Royal Edinburgh Asylum.
—— (1884*a*) Physician-Superintendent's annual report for the year 1884. In *Seventy-second Report of the Royal Edinburgh Asylum for the Insane*. Edinburgh: Royal Edinburgh Asylum.
—— (1884*b*) *The Effects of the Use of Alcohol on the Mental Functions of the Brain. The Lecture delivered to Students of the University of Edinburgh, 19th December, 1883, under the auspices of The Edinburgh University Total Abstinence Society*. Edinburgh: Andrew Elliot.
—— (1886*a*) Physician-Superintendent's annual report for the year 1886. In *Seventy-fourth Report of the Royal Edinburgh Asylum for the Insane*. Edinburgh: Royal Edinburgh Asylum.
—— (1886*b*) *Preliminary Report by Dr. Clouston to the Managers and Medical Board of the Royal Edinburgh Asylum, in regard to the proposed erection of a new department on the Craighouse estate for the patients who pay the higher rates of board, in substitution for the East House, whose site and grounds are too circumscribed, and have become overlooked by tenement houses, and disturbed by the suburban railway*. Edinburgh: Royal Edinburgh Asylum.
—— (1887) *How Pleasant Surroundings and Conditions affect the Health and Happiness. Edinburgh Health Society*. Edinburgh: MacNiven & Wallace.
—— (1888) Secondary dementia, Presidential address to the Medico-Psychological Association. *Journal of Mental Science*, **34**, 325–348.
—— (1891*a*) *The Neuroses of Development being The Morisonian Lectures for 1890*. Edinburgh: Oliver & Boyd.
—— (1891*b*) Physician-Superintendent's annual report for the year 1891. In *Seventy-ninth Report of the Royal Edinburgh Asylum for the Insane*. Edinburgh: Royal Edinburgh Asylum.
—— (1892) Physician-Superintendent's annual report for the year 1892. In *Eightieth Report of the Royal Edinburgh Asylum for the Insane*. Edinburgh: Royal Edinburgh Asylum.
—— (1894*a*) The developmental aspects of criminal anthropology. *Journal of the Anthropological Institute*, February, 215–225.
—— (1894*b*) Modern medico-psychology and psychiatry III. Legislative and state measures and their effects. *The Hospital*, **16**, 25.
—— (1894*c*) Modern medico-psychology and psychiatry V. The men who have made modern psychiatry. *The Hospital*, **16**, 114.
—— (1894*d*) Modern medico-psychology and psychiatry IV. The men who have made modern psychiatry (continued). *The Hospital*, **16**, 159.
—— (1894*e*) Modern medico-psychology and psychiatry VII. The men who have made modern psychiatry. *The Hospital*, **16**, 203.
—— (1894*f*) Physician-Superintendent's annual report for the year 1894. In *Eighty-second Report of the Royal Edinburgh Asylum for the Insane*. Edinburgh: Royal Edinburgh Asylum.
—— (1895) Modern medico-psychology and psychiatry. The clinical classification of the insanities. *The Hospital*, **17**, 91.
—— (1896*a*) *Clinical Lectures on Mental Diseases*. London: Oliver & Boyd.
—— (1896*b*) Physician-Superintendent's annual report for the year 1896. In *Eighty-fourth Report of the Royal Edinburgh Asylum for the Insane*. Edinburgh: Royal Edinburgh Asylum.
—— (1899) Science and nature. The modern doctor. *The Scotsman*, 17 January.
—— (1900) Science and nature. Temperament. *The Scotsman*, 6 February.
—— (1901) The dangers to the brain from alcohol. The young abstainer. *Edinburgh Supplement*, **3**.
—— (1902) The possibility of providing suitable means of treatment for incipient and transient mental diseases in our great general hospitals. *Journal of Mental Science*, **48**, 697–709.
—— (1903*a*) An address on the Scottish Medical Corporations and the Public Weal: how they might develop a health conscience. *British Medical Journal*, *ii*, 61–63.
—— (1903*b*) Science and nature. Physical education and improvement. *The Scotsman*, 29 December.
—— (1904*a*) 'Physical righteousness'. The relation of drink and insanity. *Daily News*, 5 October.
—— (1904*b*) Physician-Superintendent's annual report for the year 1904. In *Ninety-second Annual Report of the Royal Edinburgh Asylum for the Insane*. Edinburgh: Royal Edinburgh Asylum.
—— (1905*a*) The prognosis of adolescent insanity (letter). *Lancet*, *i*, 386–387.
—— (1905*b*) Wanted, a health conscience (letter). *The Spectator*, 30 December.
—— (1906) *The Hygiene of Mind*. London: Methuen & Co.
—— (1907) Psychiatry as a part of public medicine. A discussion. *Journal of Mental Science*, **53**, 704–723.

—— (1911*a*) The psychological dangers to women in modern social developments. In *The Position of Woman: Actual and Ideal* (preface by O. Lodge), pp. 103–117. London: James Nisbet & Co.
—— (1911*b*) The diploma in psychiatry. *Journal of Mental Science*, **57**, 207–218.
—— (1911*c*) *Unsoundness of Mind*. London: Methuen.
—— (1913) *Before I Wed*. London: Cassell & Co.
—— (1914) *Morals and Brain*. London: Cassell & Co.
COLLIE, M. (1988) *Henry Maudsley: Victorian Psychiatrist. A Bibliographical Study*. Winchester: St. Paul's Bibliographies.
COMRIE, J. D. (1927) *History of Scottish Medicine to 1860*. London: Baillière, Tindall & Cox.
CRICHTON-BROWNE, J. (1875) Skae's classification of mental diseases. A critique. *Journal of Mental Science*, **21**, 339–365.
—— (1938) *The Doctor Remembers*. London: Duckworth.
DANZIGER, K. (1982) Mid-nineteenth century British psycho-physiology: A neglected chapter in the history of psychology. In *The Problematic Science: Psychology in Nineteenth Century Thought* (eds W. R. Woodward & M. G. Ash), pp. 119–146. New York: Praeger.
DAVIE, G. E. (1961) *The Democratic Intellect. Scotland and her Universities in the Nineteenth Century*. Edinburgh: Edinburgh University Press.
—— (1973) *The Social Significance of the Scottish Philosophy of Common Sense*. Edinburgh: T. &. A. Constable Ltd
ELKINS, F. A. (1892) Concerning the kinsmen and friends of insane patients. *Edinburgh Medical Journal*, **37**, 834–840.
FISH, F. (1965) David Skae, M.D., F.R.C.S., Founder of the Edinburgh School of Psychiatry. *Medical History*, **9**, 36–53.
GUTHRIE, D. (1965) *Extramural Medical Education in Edinburgh and the School of Medicine of the Royal Colleges*. Edinburgh: Livingstone.
HALEY, B. (1978) *The Healthy Body and Victorian Culture*. Cambridge, Mass: Harvard University Press.
HEARNSHAW, L. S. (1964) *A Short History of British Psychology, 1840–1940*. London: Methuen.
HENDERSON, D. K. (1964) *The Evolution of Psychiatry in Scotland*. Edinburgh: Livingstone.
HOUGHTON, W. E. (1957) *The Victorian Frame of Mind, 1830–1870*. New Haven: Yale University Press.
HUNTER, R. & MACALPINE, I. (1963) *Three Hundred Years of British Psychiatry 1535–1860: A History Presented in Selected English Texts*. London: Oxford University Press.
IRVINE, W. (1955) *Apes, Angels, and Victorians: A Joint Biography of Darwin and Huxley*. London: Weidenfeld & Nicolson.
JACYNA, L. S. (1980*a*) Scientific Naturalism in Victorian Britain: An Essay in the Social History of Ideas. PhD thesis, University of Edinburgh.
—— (1980*b*) Science and social order in the thought of A. J. Balfour. *Isis*, **71**, 11–34.
—— (1981) The physiology of mind, the unity of nature, and the moral order in Victorian thought. *British Journal for the History of Science*, **14**, 109–132.
—— (1982) Somatic theories of mind and the interests of medicine in Britain 1850–1879. *Medical History*, **26**, 233–258.
JOHNSTONE, J. C. (1892) Some notes on the use of sulphonal as a sedative and hypnotic. *Journal of Mental Science*, **38**, 55–71.
JOURNAL OF MENTAL SCIENCE (1861) Class of medical psychology and mental diseases in the University of Edinburgh. *Journal of Mental Science*, **7**, 286–288.
—— (1866) Obituary of Sir Alexander Morison M.D. *Journal of Mental Science*, **12**, 296–297.
—— (1881) Notes and News. The International Medical Congress. *Journal of Mental Science*, **27**, 447–453.
—— (1884) Review of *Clinical Lectures on Mental Diseases* by T. S. Clouston. *Journal of Mental Science*, **30**, 273–279.
—— (1888) Notes and News. Report of the M.P.A. annual meeting. *Journal of Mental Science*, **34**, 458.
—— (1898*a*) Occasional notes of the quarter. The Laboratory of the Scottish Asylums. *Journal of Mental Science*, **45**, 105.
—— (1898*b*) Notes and News. Scottish Division. *Journal of Mental Science*, **45**, 204–205.
—— (1901) The Scottish universities and psychiatry. *Journal of Mental Science*, **47**, 779–780.
—— (1902*a*) The proposed psychiatric clinique in Edinburgh. *Journal of Mental Science*, **48**, 329–330, 381–383.
—— (1902*b*) Insanity and toxaemia. *Journal of Mental Science*, **48**, 533–536.
—— (1910) Presentation portraits to Dr. Clouston. *Journal of Mental Science*, **56**, 375–377.
—— (1915) Obituary of Sir Thomas Smith Clouston. *Journal of Mental Science*, **61**, 333–338.

JOURNAL OF PSYCHOLOGICAL AND MENTAL PATHOLOGY (1877) Skae's classification of mental diseases. *Journal of Psychological Medicine and Mental Pathology*, **2**, 195–237.

LANCET (1915) Obituary of Sir Thomas Smith Clouston. *Lancet*, *i*, 936–937.

LAYCOCK, T. (1860) *Mind and Brain: or, the correlations of consciousness and organisation; with their applications to philosophy, zoology, physiology, mental pathology, and the practice of medicine*. Edinburgh: Sutherland & Knox.

—— (1866) A plea for the conjoined study of mental science and practice. Being the introductory lecture to a course of medical psychology. *Journal of Mental Science*, **12**, 174–188.

—— (1868) A memorandum on the pay, position, and education of assistant medical officers of asylums. *Journal of Mental Science*, **13**, 587–589.

—— (1869) The objects and organisation of the Medico-Psychological Association: the anniversary address. *Journal of Mental Science*, **15**, 327–343.

—— (1871) The teaching of psychological medicine and mental pathology at Edinburgh (letter). *British Medical Journal*, *i*, 293.

MACALPINE, I. & HUNTER, R. (1969) *George III and the Mad-Business*. London: Allen Lane.

MCCANDLESS, P. (1981) Liberty and lunacy: the Victorians and wrongful confinement. In *Madhouses, Mad-doctors and Madmen: The Social History of Psychiatry in the Victorian era* (ed. A. Scull), pp. 339–62. London: Athlone Press.

MACKENZIE, D. A. (1981) *Statistics in Britain, 1865–1930: The Social Construction of Scientific Knowledge*. Edinburgh: Edinburgh University Press.

MCLAREN, J. (1874) On a case of general paralysis of the insane of unusually long duration. *Edinburgh Medical Journal*, **20**, 296–302.

MACLEOD, K. (1907) Reminiscences of Edinburgh fifty years ago. *Caledonian Medical Journal*, **7**, 414–429.

MACPHERSON, J. (1892) Notes on a case of myxoedema treated by thyroid grafting. *Edinburgh Medical Journal*, **37**, 1021–1024.

—— (1899) *Mental Affections: An Introduction to the Study of Insanity*. London: MacMillan.

—— (1901) The teaching of psychiatry. *The Scotsman*, 4 July.

—— (1915) Obituary of Clouston. *British Medical Journal*, *i*, 745.

MITCHELL, R. B. (1883) Two cases of brain tumour. *Edinburgh Medical Journal*, **29**, 296–302.

—— (1894) The treatment of prolapsus recti by galvanism. *Lancet*, *ii*, 572–573.

MORISON, A. (1823/24) *Diaries*. Edinburgh: Royal College of Physicians.

MORTON, M. J. S. (1988) Sir Thomas Clouston: Medical Practice and Polemic in the Alcohol Debate. MPhil thesis, University of Edinburgh.

NEWINGTON, H. H. (1874) Observations on mania a potu. *Edinburgh Medical Journal*, **20**, 493–500.

—— (1877) Case of an extraordinary number of convulsions occurring in an epileptic patient, with remarks on nutrient enemata. *Journal of Mental Science*, **23**, 89–95.

—— (1915*a*) Obituary of Clouston. *British Medical Journal*, *i*, 745.

—— (1915*b*) Obituary of Clouston. *Journal of Mental Science*, **61**, 495–496.

PARRY-JONES, W. L. (1981) The model of the Gheel lunatic colony and its influence on the nineteenth century asylum system in Britain. In *Madhouses, Mad-doctors and Madmen: The Social History of Psychiatry in the Victorian era* (ed. A. Scull), pp. 201–217. London: Athlone Press.

PICKETT, W. (1905) Review of *Clinical Lectures on Mental Diseases* by T. S. Clouston. Sixth edition. *Journal of Nervous and Mental Diseases*, **32**, 143–144.

RITCHIE, J. (1953) *History of the Laboratory of the Royal College of Physicians of Edinburgh*. Edinburgh: Royal College of Physicians.

ROBERTSON, G. M. (1892*a*) Hypnotism at Paris and Nancy. Notes of a visit. *Journal of Mental Science*, **38**, 494–531.

—— (1892*b*) Psycho-therapeutics. Another fragment. *Lancet*, *ii*, 657–658.

—— (1915) The late Sir Thomas Clouston. *British Medical Journal*, *i*, 787.

—— (1922) *The Hospitalisation of the Scottish Asylum System: The Presidential Address of the Medico-Psychological Association*. London: Alard & Newman.

—— (1928) The history of the teaching of psychiatry in Edinburgh: and Sir Alexander Morison. *Edinburgh Medical Journal*, **35**, 192–205.

ROBERTSON, W. F. (1900) *A Text-Book of Pathology in Relation to Mental Diseases*. Edinburgh: William F. Clay.

ROBINSON, A. D. T. (1988) A century of delusions in South West Scotland. *British Journal of Psychiatry*, **153**, 163–167.

RUSSELL, R. (1988) The lunacy profession and its staff in the second half of the nineteenth century, with special reference to the West Riding Lunatic Asylum. In *The Anatomy of Madness, Vol. III. The Asylum and its Psychiatry* (eds W. F. Bynum, R. Porter & M. Shepherd), pp. 297–315. London: Routledge.

Savage, G. H. (1915) Obituary of Thomas Smith Clouston. *Journal of Mental Science*, **61**, 495.

Scull, A. T. (1979) *Museums of Madness. The Social Organization of Insanity in Nineteenth Century England.* London: Allen Lane.

Showalter, E. (1985) *The Female Malady. Women, Madness and English Culture, 1830–1980.* London: Virago Press.

Sibbald, J. (1871) Clinical instruction in insanity. A necessary element in medical education. *Journal of Mental Science*, **16**, 528–537.

—— (1902) The treatment of incipient mental disorder and its clinical teaching in the wards of general hospitals. *Journal of Mental Science*, **48**, 215–226.

Sicherman, B. (1981) The paradox of prudence: mental health in the gilded age. In *Madness, Mad-doctors, and Madmen. The Social History of Psychiatry in the Victorian Era* (ed. A. Scull), pp. 218–40. London: Athlone Press.

Skae, D. (1853) Clinical lectures on insanity in the Royal Edinburgh Asylum. *Monthly Journal of Medical Science*, **16**, 558–567.

—— (1858) Remarks on that form of moral insanity called dipsomania and the legality of its treatment by isolation. *Edinburgh Medical Journal*, **3**, 769–783.

—— (1860) Contributions to the natural history of general paralysis. *Edinburgh Medical Journal*, **5**, 885–905.

—— (1861) The legal relations of insanity. *Edinburgh Medical Journal*, **6**, 867–890.

—— (1863) On the classification of the various forms of insanity. *Journal of Mental Science*, **9**, 309–319.

—— (1867) The legal relations of insanity: The civil incapacity and legal responsibility of the insane. *Edinburgh Medical Journal*, **12**, 811–829.

Smith, R. (1970) Physiological Psychology and the Philosophy of Nature in Mid-Nineteenth Century Britain. PhD thesis, University of Cambridge.

—— (1977) The human significance of biology: Carpenter and Darwin, and the vera causa. In *Nature and the Victorian Imagination* (eds V. C. Knoepflmacher & G. B. Tennyson), pp. 216–230. Berkeley: University of California Press.

—— (1981) *Trial by Medicine: Insanity and Responsibility in Victorian Trials.* Edinburgh: Edinburgh University Press.

Smout, T. C. (1986) *A Century of the Scottish People 1830–1950.* London: Collins.

Talcott, D. R. (1891) Letter, *The Conglomerate*, 28 October.

Thompson, M. S. (1984) The Mad, the Bad and the Sad: Psychiatric Care in the Royal Edinburgh Asylum (Morningside). PhD thesis: Boston University.

—— (1988) The wages of sin: the problem of alcoholism and general paralysis in nineteenth century Edinburgh. In *The Anatomy of Madness, Vol. III. The Asylum and its Psychiatry* (eds W. F. Bynum, R. Porter & M. Shepherd), pp. 313–340. London: Routledge.

Tuke, B. J. (1870) A pathological classification of mental disease. *Journal of Mental Science*, **16**, 195–210.

—— (1900) On the teaching of insanity. *The Scotsman*, 5 May.

Turner, F. M. (1974) *Between Science and Religion. The Reaction to Scientific Naturalism in Late Victorian England.* New Haven: Yale University Press.

Turner, T. (1988) Henry Maudsley: psychiatrist, philosopher, and entrepreneur. In *The Anatomy of Madness, Vol. III. The Asylum and its Psychiatry* (eds W. F. Bynum, R. Porter & M. Shepherd), pp. 151–189. London: Routledge.

Withrington, D. (1988) 'A ferment of change'. Aspirations, ideas and ideals in nineteenth century Scotland. In *The History of Scottish Literature, Vol. III* (ed. D. Gifford), pp. 23–43. Aberdeen: Aberdeen University Press.

Yellowlees, D. (1915) Obituary. Sir Thomas Smith Clouston. *Journal of Mental Science*, **61**, 494–495.

Young, R. M. (1970*a*) *Mind, Brain and Adaptation in the Nineteenth Century: Cerebral Localization and its Biological Context from Gall to Ferrier.* Oxford: Clarendon Press.

—— (1970*b*) The impact of Darwin on conventional thought. In *The Victorian Crisis of Faith* (ed. A. Symondson), pp. 13–35. London: SPCK.

Other sources

Medical Archive Centre, Edinburgh University Library, Royal Edinburgh Hospital Records, and Senate Minutes of Edinburgh University. Papers relating to Clouston family, in the Orkney Library, Orkney Islands Council. Cumbria County Council Record Office, Carlisle; Cumberland and Westmorland Asylum papers and reports. Private papers of the Clouston family, care of Mr D. Wallace and Mrs A. Wallace.

25 The West Riding asylum and James Crichton-Browne, 1818–76

JOHN TODD and LAWRENCE ASHWORTH

The West Riding Pauper Lunatic Asylum at Wakefield was opened on 23 November 1818, when it accommodated 75 men and 75 women patients. It owed its existence in no small measure to two influences – the abuses uncovered by the West Riding magistrate Godfrey Higgins at the York asylum (opened in 1777), then the only institution in Yorkshire into which paupers could be admitted, and the enlightened attitude of the governors of the Retreat (opened in 1796). The County Asylums Act 1808 (Wynn's Act) was the instrument through which the Wakefield building was made possible; this was not a mandatory measure, but authorised asylum care for the insane poor. There was the most pressing need for this institution, since many poor people with mental disorder in Yorkshire were in workhouses or prisons, or had to be cared for by relatives, often in conditions of extreme misery and privation. Wakefield was the sixth county asylum to be built in England.

The influence of the Retreat is seen in the advice given by Samuel Tuke to the West Riding magistrates when the design of the asylum was being contemplated, which was based on some 20 years' experience of the Retreat. His advice was accepted by them, and he was invited to instruct the architects and supervise their work. In 1819, Tuke's *Hints on the Construction and Economy of Pauper Lunatic Asylums* (written specifically with the Wakefield asylum in mind) was printed and published, along with the architect's drawings and plans. Some 40 architects submitted plans, from which those of Watson & Pritchett of York were selected. No doubt the site was chosen for its relatively central position in the West Riding, availability of well drained land, and abundant supply of water. It was then some distance from the nearest habitation, in Wakefield, and was therefore quiet and secluded.

After making inquiries to the various parish overseers (appointed at quarter sessions to look after the welfare of the poor), the magistrates were satisfied that accommodation for 150 patients would be quite adequate. Indeed, it appeared at first that this would be more than adequate, since the cost to parish overseers (sometimes as low as 6*s*. 6*d*. per week) was more than that of maintaining a patient in a workhouse, and they were therefore reluctant to send paupers into the asylum until they became unmanageable. This problem deeply concerned the early medical directors, who commented on it frequently in their annual reports, since it caused much hardship and misery, as well as reducing the chances of improvement in many cases (Bolton, 1928).

The first medical director was Dr William Charles Ellis, his wife acting as matron. Ellis had received some notice from his *Letter to Thomas Thompson, M.P.* (1815) on the abuses in the treatment of the insane, with suggestions for amelioration, and there is little doubt that he attempted, both at Wakefield, and later at Hanwell, where he was also the first director, to carry these principles into effect. He was knighted in 1835.

From the first, the asylum was operated on the basis of self-help, the whole of its manual tasks being undertaken by patients, under the supervision of staff. Cooking, baking, brewing, gardening, engineering, and domestic duties were all by patient labour. As a result, the costs of the asylum were kept very low, but these activities were also believed to be therapeutic. A weaving industry was established in 1819 which not only provided all the clothing, sheets, and pillow cases for the Wakefield asylum, but also for Hanwell in later years.

The hospital was designed to be run on humane principles, and from the first had at its head a kindly man in Dr Ellis. In 1829, he commented on the high proportion of paupers admitted during the previous 11 years who had been insane for months or even years. The hospital records include the case of a woman admitted from Barnsley Workhouse, where she had been chained in a cell for 36 years, and of the admission of a man who had been under the care of his father and had been locked in a space under the stairs for 11 years, and his limbs had assumed grotesque shapes. Since bleeding was then a common medical procedure, many cases had almost bled to death before admission. Physical restraint was discouraged from the beginning, although its abandonment (except in rare cases) was attributed to Dr Alderson in 1853. Ellis was a devout Methodist, sincerely believing that his work at the asylum was divinely inspired and personally conducting its religious life.

Dr Charles Caesar Corsellis followed Ellis in 1831. He greatly admired Ellis, and made every effort to emulate his example in the treatment of the patients under his care. With the exception of the building of the acute asylum (later Pinderfields General Hospital) in 1900, the most extensive additions to the 1818 buildings in its history were during this term of office. His wife acted as matron, but this kind of partnership was never repeated. During his term, the cholera epidemic struck the asylum. The manner of his leaving is shrouded in mystery; it seems to have been rather sudden, and few of the usual expressions of regret are recorded. Corsellis was succeeded in 1853 by Dr John Septimus Alderson, who had been medical superintendent of the York asylum. He did not enjoy good health while at Wakefield, and little is known of his activities there, except that he was credited with the discontinuance of restraint as a form of treatment. He died shortly after retirement through ill-health, in 1858.

Described by Professor Shaw Bolton (1928), a later director, in his Presidential Address to the Royal Medico-Psychological Association, as a brilliant medical administrator – "perhaps the best our specialty has ever known" – Dr John Davies Cleaton was appointed director in 1858. There was still only one asylum in the West Riding then, though by 1866 the patient population had risen to 1128. The need for a further asylum in the south of the Riding was being keenly felt, and plans were being made for one to be built near Sheffield. Cleaton, however, was not to benefit from the temporary relief that this would bring to the overcrowding at Wakefield, as, in 1866, he was invited by the Lord Chancellor to take up the post of Lunacy Commissioner. He later visited his old asylum on two occasions in that capacity. Thus, on Dr James Crichton-Browne's appointment to fill Cleaton's post, the asylum at Wakefield provided the only professional psychiatric care for the whole of the West Riding.

The original building must have presented a very pleasant aspect: it had simple yet graceful proportions, and stood in well laid out gardens and grounds, which extended to some 25 acres, surrounded by plantations of trees. However, after a few years, it became evident that the original estimates of the need for accommodation had been far too low; subsequent additions to the buildings, though, were made piecemeal and with complete disregard for aesthetic considerations. Industrial grime covered the cream bricks with which the original building had been clad, and by the middle of the 19th century, the whole complex retained very little of architectural merit.

James Crichton-Browne

> "A great-hearted and gifted physician, psychologist, reformer, scientist and author who occupied a unique place in the medical, scientific and literary annals of his time." (Obituary, *Edinburgh Medical Journal*, April 1938)

Cleaton was succeeded by Dr J. C. (later Sir James) Browne in August, 1866; he later preferred to be called Crichton-Browne (Fig. 25.1). During his stewardship of the asylum, it became internationally renowned as a seat of learning, research, and academic excellence. Born in Edinburgh on 29 November 1840, Crichton-Browne had the advantage of being the son of an exceedingly well read and intellectual mother and of Dr W. A. F. Browne, medical director of the Crichton Royal Institute (later Lunacy Commissioner in Scotland), an alienist of considerable eminence who had delivered a series of five lectures (Browne, 1837) before the managers of the Montrose Royal Lunatic Asylum, later published under the title *What Asylums Were, Are, and Ought To Be.*

Crichton-Browne was educated at Dumfries Academy, Trinity College Glenalmond, and the University of Edinburgh. He qualified LRCS in 1861 and graduated MD in 1862 with a thesis entitled "On Hallucinations", which was highly commended. In 1861 he had taken first place in the class of "Medical Psychology & Mental Diseases" given by Thomas Laycock, Professor of Practical Medicine. In later life he described Laycock as a "biological Socrates", developing his ideas on cerebral physiology throughout his subsequent career. After short periods of service in selected asylums, culminating in a medical directorship at Newcastle-on-Tyne Borough Asylum, he applied for the post at Wakefield. The short-list of eight candidates included T. S. (later Sir Thomas) Clouston and F. (later Sir Frederick) Needham, both later Presidents of the Medico-Psychological Association, as was Crichton-Browne himself (Bolton, 1928). The quality of this list was a compliment, perhaps, to its retiring medical director, yet Crichton-Browne was appointed with only "one dissentient vote"!

The improvements which took place in the asylum's buildings, the quality of life of the patients, and the working conditions of the staff during Cleaton's term of office were complemented by his successor's achievements in the spheres of research and academic psychiatry. Discussing Crichton-Browne's preface to the first volume of the *West Riding Lunatic Asylum Medical Reports* and his administration

Fig. 25.1. Sir James Crichton-Browne, pictured in 1935, at the age of 94.

of the asylum, Viets (1938) wrote that "Far from assuming the humdrum institutionalized life of the average medical director of a lunatic asylum, this energetic and forceful doctor flatly rejected the current implication that no scientific work could be accomplished in public asylums." As Crichton-Browne himself wrote (1871), "It has been an often repeated accusation that the medical officers of these establishments are so absorbed in general or fiscal management, in farming or in devising ill-judged amusements for their charges, that they have no time or energy left to devote to professional research. And it has been further asserted that when these medical officers have by any chance ventured to enter the field of original investigation, they have, as a rule signally failed in achieving any useful result."

In fact, Crichton-Browne lost no time in putting himself and the Wakefield asylum in a position to dispel these misconceptions about asylums and their medical staff. His flair for recognising potential talent enabled him to recruit a medical staff of exceptional ability, while he used his persuasive charm to obtain a positive response to invitations to eminent or promising colleagues to read papers at the annual conversaziones which he arranged. He also encouraged doctors whom he thought specially gifted to engage in clinical and pathological research, whether or not they were members of the staff, and to submit papers for the *West Riding Lunatic Asylum Medical Reports*. He was the initiator and editor of these publications annually between 1871 and 1876.

At the same time, Crichton-Browne was a most effective administrator, devoting much time to the interests of the patients and staff and to the solution of such problems as shortage of accommodation and a contaminated water supply. Apart from his skill as a psychiatrist and administrator, he also had an exceptional aptitude for literary expression, both written and oral, and throughout his professional life, his services as a speaker were in constant demand both by specialist societies and the general public. His interests were far ranging, and he was equally at home when addressing sanitary inspectors on matters of public health as when delivering a eulogy on Burns to an audience interested in literature.

Crichton-Browne's role as an instigator of research and medical teacher

The chief actors in the drama of Crichton-Browne's remarkable reign as medical director of the Wakefield asylum are considered in turn.

David Ferrier, MA, MD, FRCP, FRS

The most important research carried out at the Wakefield asylum during Crichton-Browne's period of office was almost certainly that by Ferrier. Ferrier (later Sir David) had graduated from the University of Aberdeen with first-class honours in classics and philosophy, before undertaking medical training at the University of Edinburgh and graduating MB in 1868. As a postgraduate student, he gained a gold medal for an MD thesis on the corpora quadrigemina in 1870. Crichton-Browne invited Ferrier, a fellow Edinburgh graduate who was at the time Professor of Forensic Medicine at King's College Hospital, to undertake research at the Wakefield asylum, putting laboratory and other facilities at his disposal. Ferrier's electrical experiments on the brains of small animals paved the way for his later research on the brains of apes, at King's College, London.

The results of Ferrier's work at Wakefield were first published in the *West Riding Lunatic Asylum Medical Reports* under the title "Experimental researches in cerebral physiology and pathology" in 1873 (vol. 3, pp. 30–96). This paper attracted great attention and was described in more detail in his Croonian Lectures to the Royal Society in 1874 and 1875. Ferrier's research enabled him to make a major contribution to the clarification of problems connected with the localisation of function in the brain, thereby taking the work of Fritsch and Hitzig a stage further, and verifying the ideas of Hughlings Jackson. Ferrier wrote two other papers for the *Medical Reports* – "Pathological illustrations of brain function" (1874, vol. 4, pp. 30–62) and "Labyrinthine vertigo. Ménière's disease" (1875, vol. 5, pp. 24–29). He received numerous honours and awards during his career, being the Royal College of Physicians' Goulstonian Lecturer in 1878 and giving the Marshall Hall and Harveian Orations in 1883 and 1902 respectively, and the Lumleian Lecture in 1906. He was a royal medallist of the Royal Society in 1890 and was awarded the Baly and Moxon Gold Medals by the Royal College of Physicians. He received a knighthood in 1911.

Thomas Clifford Allbutt, MA, MD, FRCP, FRS, KCB

At the Wakefield asylum, Crichton-Browne developed a close and important relationship with T. C. (later the Right Honourable Sir Clifford) Allbutt, a Yorkshireman, born at Dewsbury in 1836 and educated at St Peter's School, York. After leaving school, he demonstrated his academic brilliance by taking a first in the Natural Sciences Tripos at Cambridge in 1860. He completed his medical training at St George's Hospital, London, taking his MB in 1861 and MD in 1869. After a period of study in Paris, he embarked on a highly successful career at the Leeds General Infirmary (1864–84). He practised there until 1889, and during this time was closely linked with the West Riding Lunatic Asylum, where he carried out important research. In 1868, he read a paper at the Royal Medical & Chirurgical Society of London entitled "The state of the optic nerves and retinae as seen in the insane", and in 1871 wrote an "epoch-making monograph" (Rolleston, 1929) on *The Use of the Ophthalmoscope in Diseases of the Nervous System and of the Kidneys, and also in Certain General Disorders*. Much of the investigation for these two dissertations was carried out at Wakefield with the encouragement of Crichton-Browne, whose help Allbutt never failed to acknowledge. He wrote two papers for the *Medical Reports* – "The electric treatment of the insane" (1872, vol. 2, pp. 203–222) and "On the obscurer neuroses of syphilis" (1873, vol. 3, pp. 223–284). The first of these is a detailed account of the results of applying an electric current to the head or in a few cases to the neck of selected patients in the asylum; in this, Allbutt was assisted by Crichton-Browne's clinical assistant, Dr H. C. Major. Since the strength of the current was too weak to produce a convulsion, Allbutt and Major must have come fairly near to anticipating the very important discovery made later by Cerletti and Bini in 1938. Despite Allbutt's hope of "more intensive investigations to come", 66 years were to elapse before the Italians were to show that electroshock could be used as a treatment for affective disorders.

Although an outstanding general physician, Allbutt had a persistent interest in psychiatry (Crichton-Browne, 1931). Largely under the influence of Crichton-Browne, now a close friend, he temporarily and surprisingly abandoned his prestigious career in 1889 to accept the post of Commissioner of Lunacy, returning to the fold of general medicine as Regius Professor of Physic at Cambridge in 1892. In 1882, Allbutt had become a magistrate for the West Riding of Yorkshire and a member of the Wakefield asylum's Committee of Visitors, which managed the asylum. As a Lunacy Commissioner, he also visited the asylum and made some valuable suggestions in his reports. His interest in psychiatry and his respect for Crichton-Browne's ability are further shown by the paper he read to the Psychological Section of the British Medical Association in 1891 entitled "The proposed hospitals for the treatment of the insane". In this, he referred to Crichton-Browne as "one of the ablest superintendents of our day", but did not hide his scepticism concerning his friend's opinion that "more medicinal treatment of insanity may raise the percentages of cures by 10 per cent". In fact, he suggested that "the hundreds and thousands of prescriptions given daily for organic nervous diseases in the towns and cities of Great Britain are but amulets whose combinations of arsenic, zinc, belladonna, ergot, nitrate of silver, strychnia, physostigmine, and so forth are as useful as crabs' eyes and pounded newts, and really come after all under the head of hygienic uses of the imagination''. (However, Crichton-Browne and Allbutt were of the same opinion in their antipathy to psychoanalysis and the 'brain forcing' of schoolchildren, a practice much in vogue in Japan.) He left no doubt about his own viewpoint on the usefulness of drugs for the cure of mental illness by observing that ''the more we know of insanity, the less medicine do we give'', but favoured the placing of asylum patients ''under the most favourable external conditions of light, air, food, temperature, exercise, rest, protection, control, sympathy, fellowship, amusement, occupation and so forth''. Since such a programme of common sense and kindness would come under the heading of 'moral treatment', Allbutt is likely to have had a great deal of sympathy for Ellis's opinions on the treatment of mentally ill patients.

In this connection, Crichton-Browne's observations some 12 years earlier merit attention. In his annual report dated 1869, he wrote:

> ''The medicinal treatment of the patients during last year has been conducted on the same wide basis as has been formerly intimated. Our drug accounts will show that we have not been affected here by the paralyzing influence of that scepticism as to the usefulness of remedies that has been fashionable of late. On the contrary the results of our daily trials and observations, stimulates us to more vigorous therapeutic efforts, and convince us more and more of the curability of insanity by medical agents.''

However, Crichton-Browne's enthusiasm for medicinal treatment did not mean that he had lost faith in the value of moral treatment (including employment), for in the same report he stated that moral treatment ''has been extended and improved in 1868 as opportunities have permitted . . . . To those unfamiliar with Asylum life it is impossible to convey any notion of the amount of thought, tact, and ingenuity expended in the organization of moral treatment.''

Crichton-Browne's approval of moral treatment is also illustrated by comments in his report of January 1872:

> ''A few kind and well chosen words, a little judicious firmness, a hope suggested, a fear allayed, or a new line of thought pointed out, is sometimes as beneficial as 'poppy and mandragora'.* The Medical Officers are really dispensing medicines when chatting with their patients.''

However, since he also believed in recourse to drugs when such a course of action seemed to offer the best hope of improvement, his views on treatment were clearly eclectic.

In 1921, Allbutt opened a discussion on visceral syphilis at the annual meeting of the British Medical Association at Newcastle upon Tyne. Paying tribute to the generous help he had received from Crichton-Browne, he said: ''When in 1868, I first described syphilitic arteritis, with dispersed granuloma of the brain, it was in a specimen sent to me by Dr. Crichton-Browne''. Among Allbutt's numerous achievements, two others deserve mention. In 1867, he had designed

---

**Mandragora officinarum*, a plant found in Mediterranean regions with a narcotic and emetic action, and believed by the ancients to have magical properties. ''Not poppy, nor Mandragora, / Nor all the drowsy syrups of the world . . .'' (Shakespeare, *Othello*, III. iii. 331–332).

a clinical thermometer, made on his behalf by Harvey & Reynolds; it was originally six inches long, but in later productions only three inches. However, it fell out of favour: "The experiment of marking it with the Centigrade scale, introduced by Celsius in 1742, instead of the Fahrenheit scale, for which Allbutt expressed disapproval, at once stopped its sale" (Rolleston, 1929). It is ironic, therefore, that clinical thermometers using the centigrade scale have now displaced the Fahrenheit thermometers. A second major achievement was his editorship of the famous *System of Medicine* (1896–99) in eight volumes, which was "probably his greatest literary service to medicine" (Rolleston, 1929). Allbutt was the inspiration behind the inauguration of the Diploma of Psychological Medicine at Cambridge in 1912 (Mott, 1925).

When reminiscing about his friend, Crichton-Browne (1931) wrote:

> "As a physician in Leeds, Clifford Allbutt was from the first an undeniable success. He lectured like a Trousseau in the medical school, now part of the University, and no wealthy manufacturer in the West Riding could die without seeing him. He had a singular clarity of intellect and charm of manner, and was popular with all classes." (p. 243)

Allbutt's close association with the West Riding Asylum was most fortunate for it, as he was a physician of outstanding merit who gained many honours, including a knighthood in 1907 and membership of the Privy Council in 1920. He gave the Goulstonian Lecture in 1884, the Harveian Oration in 1900, the Fitzpatrick Lectures in 1909/10, and the Linacre in 1914. He was elected FRS in 1880 and FRCP in 1883.

Allbutt died in 1925. It was fitting that, some five years later, although 89 years old, Crichton-Browne should have been invited to unveil a plaque to his deceased friend in the Allbutt Library at Cambridge; he used the opportunity to give a most moving panegyric about him.

John Hughlings Jackson, MD, FRCP, FRS

Hughlings Jackson wrote five papers for the *West Riding Lunatic Asylum Medical Reports* – "Observations on the localisation of movements in the cerebral hemispheres, as revealed by cases of convulsion, chorea and aphasia" (1873, vol. 3, 175–195), "On the anatomical, physiological, and pathological investigation of the epilepsies" (1873, vol. 3, 315–339), "On a case of recovery from double optic neuritis" (1874, vol. 4, 24–29), "On temporary mental disorders after epileptic paroxysms" (1875, vol. 5, 105–129), and "On epilepsies and on the after effects of epileptic discharges (Todd & Robertson's hypothesis)" (1876, vol. 6, 266–309). Jackson's contributions to the *Medical Reports* were a great compliment to the repute of Crichton-Browne and enhanced the prestige of the *Reports*, since Jackson was later described by the renowned neurologist Henry Head as "The greatest scientific clinician of the nineteenth century in this country" (McNalty, 1965), and by common consent, "The father of English Neurology". Seeking information from Crichton-Browne about the manifestation of auras in the case of epileptic lunatics, Jackson received the following reply:

> "When auras are present in epileptic lunatics they are almost invariably general in character and consist in indescribable feelings in the head (vertigo) or abdomen, spreading thence over the body, or in universal creeping,

> tingling, thrilling of the skin. Of course, special warnings are occasionally encountered, but in the great majority of cases there is no warning of any kind." (Taylor *et al*, 1931)

Crichton-Browne (1895) revealed his admiration, when observing that Jackson's "guesses in neurology were more valuable and enlightening than most other men's lifelong observations and carefully reasoned conclusions" (extract from Crichton-Browne's Cavendish lecture to the West London Medico-Chirurgical Society.) Although essentially a neurologist, Jackson made some challenging observations on the aetiology of insanity (Dewhurst, 1982) and remained in close contact with Crichton-Browne professionally, long after the latter had left the Wakefield asylum. Jackson was the Goulstonian Lecturer in 1869, Croonian Lecturer for 1884, Lumleian Lecturer for 1890, and winner of the Moxon Gold Medal in 1903. It is a sad reflection both on society and the medical profession that he was never publicly honoured.

Thomas Lauder Brunton, MD, DSc, FRCP, FRS

A valuable contribution to the *Medical Reports* was made by T. Lauder (later Sir Lauder) Brunton, entitled "On inhibition, peripheral and central" (1874). A reviewer for the *Lancet* (1875, *iii*, 312) commented on Brunton's paper that: "A very able as well as interesting paper on 'Inhibition, Peripheral and Central' by Dr. Lauder Brunton appears in a journal – the *West Riding Lunatic Asylum Medical Reports* – that, under the editorship of Dr. Crichton-Browne, has in the fourth year of its publication, attained a high position for the numerous and excellent original essays it contains." Brunton assisted Ferrier, and Fothergill in his researches at Wakefield for his paper "Cerebral anaemia" (1874, vol. 6, pp. 179–222). An oil painting of Sir Lauder is to be found in the Wellcome Historical Museum in London.

Brunton had gained prizes, gold medals, and honours as a medical student, qualifying MB, CM with honours at Edinburgh in 1866, and proceeding MD (with gold medal) in the same year. In 1868, he gained the Baxter Natural Science Scholarship and the DSc in 1870. At the time of writing his paper for the *Medical Reports*, he was a physician and pharmacologist on the staff of St Bartholomew's Hospital. In 1885, the first edition of Brunton's *Textbook of Pharmacology & Therapeutics* was published, and this was followed by many others. He was knighted in 1900 and received a baronetcy in 1909; he died on 16 September 1916. Brunton's discovery of the dilating effect of amyl nitrite on the coronary arteries was mentioned in an obituary notice written by Clifford Allbutt: "In 1867, Brunton made one of the most beneficial discoveries ever achieved in the cure of disease, namely, the relief of angina pectoris by the nitrites: a discovery deserving to rank with that of the Peruvian bark in the cure of the ague."

John Milner Fothergill, MD, MRCP

Fothergill's four contributions to the *Medical Reports*, namely, "The heart sounds in general paralysis of the insane" (1873, vol. 3, pp. 113–128), "Cerebral anaemia" (1874, vol. 4, pp. 94–151), "Cerebral hyperaemia" (1875, vol. 5, pp. 171–187) and "Notes on the therapeutics of some affections of the nervous system" (1876, vol. 6, pp. 254–265), are notable for the fact that the first three were based on research and observations undertaken at the Wakefield asylum. This was with the permission and encouragement of Crichton-Browne, since Fothergill was a visitor and not a member of staff.

The son of a surgeon, Fothergill was born in Westmorland in 1841, graduated MB, CM at the University of Edinburgh, and proceeded to the MD in 1865. He was a physician of exceptional talent, who was awarded the Hastings Gold Medal of the British Medical Association in 1870 (Fothergill, 1871) and the Forthergillian Prize of the Medical Society of London in 1878. He obtained specialist appointments at the City of London and West London Hospitals, publishing many papers in addition to those appearing in the *Medical Reports*. His most notable contributions were probably ''An essay on the action of digitalis'' (1871) and ''The antagonism of therapeutic agents and what it teaches'' (1878). Fothergill's obituarist (*Dictionary of National Biography, 1921/22*) stated that ''In his writings his expressions about those with whom he did not agree are violent'', and that ''he was a man of enormous weight, with a large head and very thick neck.'' Unfortunately, he was *un homme maudit*, as he was fated to die prematurely in 1888 from obesity, gout, and diabetes.

Henry Sutherland, BA, DM, MA, MRCP

The four papers by Henry Sutherland published in the *Medical Reports* were ''Arachnoid cysts'' (1871, vol. 1, pp. 218–232), ''Menstrual irregularities and insanity'' (1872, vol. 2, pp. 54–72), ''The change of life, and insanity'' (1873, vol. 3, pp. 299–314) and ''Cases on the borderland of insanity'' (1876, vol. 6, pp. 108–119). A resident assistant medical officer at the asylum for seven months, he had studied at the University and Addenbrooke's Hospital in Cambridge, obtaining a BA in 1867. He later attended Oxford University and St George's Hospital, London, taking the BM and MA in 1869; in 1870, he obtained the MRCP and proceeded DM in 1872. His father and grandfather had been physicians who cared for the insane at St Luke's Hospital, London; both had outstanding medical qualifications and were Fellows of the Royal Society. Crichton-Browne referred to Sutherland's distinguished medical kinsmen, on his arrival at the asylum, in his *Report* dated January 1872: ''Dr. Churchill Fox, who has since become Assistant Medical Officer in the Stafford County Asylum, at Lichfield, was replaced as Clinical Clerk here, in February last, by Dr. Henry Sutherland, who not only acquitted himself in that capacity in a manner worthy of his name and antecedents but rendered admirable service while acting as Assistant Medical Officer in the Male Division, in the interval between Mr. Thompson's departure and Dr. Burman's arrival.'' Sutherland had been educated both at two public schools (Westminster and Radley) and two universities (Oxford and Cambridge). He achieved the status of Lecturer on Insanity at the Westminster Hospital Medical School and Physician to St George's Hospital, London. In addition to those he contributed to the *Medical Reports*, he was the author of articles appearing in Hack Tuke's celebrated *Dictionary* (1892); other papers of particular interest by Sutherland were ''The asylums of Paris'' (1873) and ''Prognosis in cases of refusal of food'' (1883). He died in 1901, aged 59 years.

Thomas William McDowall, MD, LRCS

A paper by T. W. McDowall (1873, vol. 3, pp. 129–152) for the *Medical Reports* entitled "On the power of perceiving colours possessed by the insane" was of special interest because his appointment had been the first of its kind in a British asylum. Crichton-Browne refers to this pioneering appointment, which took place in 1872, in his annual report to the Visiting Committee for 1873:

> "The appointment of a pathologist, which you have thus sanctioned is, I believe, a somewhat momentous step in the march of scientific progress in the Lunatic Asylums of this country. As far as I am aware, no other Asylum is yet provided with such an officer, but there can be little doubt that the example here set will be followed before long in other Counties, with the result of rapidly expanding our knowledge of brain disease, and of the means by which it may be averted or controlled. It is proposed that our Pathologist should perform all post-mortem examinations, should have the care of the Museum which we are endeavouring to form, should undertake any special enquiries or experiments that may be deemed desirable by the Medical Director, and should by microscopic and chemical research seek to elucidate some of the dark points which are still so numerous as to make a Cimmerian gloom of cerebral pathology."

Crichton-Browne summarised the results of McDowall's research in his book *Victorian Jottings* (1926):

> "My colleague, Dr. T. W. McDowall, at my suggestion carried out an inquiry as to the power of perceiving colours possessed by the insane. He examined 531 patients in the West Riding Lunatic Asylum, all suffering from some form of cerebral disorder or disease, but all sufficiently clear-headed to be subjected to the Helmholtz test. Of 207 men 13, or about 6 per cent, were found to be colour-blind more or less, and of 324 women only 9, or a little under 3 per cent, were affected. Wilson's calculation is that in the community at large there are 2 per cent who are colour-blind, and if his estimate is correct, it would appear that the defect is much more prevalent amongst those who suffer from any nervous disturbance or decay."

All too often, intriguing research projects of this nature are never followed up, and it is doubtful if McDowall's work was ever repeated. He eventually became medical superintendent of the Northumberland County Asylum, Morpeth, and in 1910 Professor of Psychological Medicine at Durham College of Medicine, Newcastle upon Tyne. He was elected President of the Medico-Psychological Association for 1897.

Charles Aldridge

Dr Charles Aldridge followed in the footsteps of Allbutt, in that he published three papers in the *Medical Reports* based on ophthalmoscopic studies carried out on patients at the asylum. These included the state of the retina in epileptics, general paralytics, and shortly before and after death. His three papers were entitled "The ophthalmoscope in mental and cerebral diseases" (1871, vol. 1, pp. 71–128), "Ophthalmoscopic observations in general paralysis, and after the administration of certain toxic agents" (1872, vol. 2, pp. 223–253) and "Ophthalmoscopic observations in acute dementia" (1874, vol. 4, pp. 291–306).

In his second paper, which concerned general paralytics, Aldridge underlined the sinister prognosis (at that time) of this disease:

> "Dr. Allbutt, of Leeds, has published the results of his examinations of the eyes of 51 cases of this disease. Most of his observations were made upon patients in this asylum, but as they occurred four years ago, I have not been able to find one patient alive who was then examined."

Charles Frederick Newcombe, MD

Newcombe's paper "Epileptiform seizures in general paralysis" (1875, vol. 5, pp. 198–226), published in the *Medical Reports*, was written when he was an assistant medical officer at Rainhill, near Liverpool, but he had collected most of his data while working as an unpaid clinical clerk at the West Riding Lunatic Asylum, during the last three months of his final year as an undergraduate of Aberdeen University. Newcombe also wrote a paper for the journal *Brain*, entitled "Case of locomotor ataxy", published in 1879. Crichton-Browne's annual report of 1874 stated that: "Mr. C. E. Watson and Mr. C. F. Newcombe are at the present time faithfully following the excellent example which their predecessors have set them".

In 1874, Newcombe graduated MB, CM, with distinction, and spent the next four years as an assistant medical officer at Rainhill asylum, during which he proceeded MD. He spent the next six years in general practice at Windermere and in "reconnaissance" visits to the United States and Canada, before deciding to emigrate in 1884 to Hood River, Oregon, USA. After five years in general practice there, Newcombe took his family to Victoria, British Columbia, afterwards engaging in medical practice and psychiatry in a dilettante fashion and with diminishing enthusiasm. He had become increasingly interested in collecting geological and botanical specimens, as well as primitive carvings of the native Haida tribe and other palaeontological collections that he obtained from many parts of Canada. He became recognised as the leading authority on the natural history and ethnology of British Columbia (Low, 1982) and became famous not as a physician or alienist, but as a naturalist. He died on 19 October 1924. Newcombe's anonymous obituary in *Nature* (1924) portrays the loss to anthropology and palaeontology, and especially to students of the Haida tribe, occasioned by his death: "and to those who are interested scientifically in the Pacific Coast of Canada, the closing of so rich a storehouse of knowledge of a dying race is an unparalleled disaster."

The Medical Reports

Two other contributors to the *Medical Reports* were Major and Bevan Lewis, both of whom were members of the staff and both of whom later became medical directors of the asylum. Their respective papers heralded an era of neurohistological and neuropathological research in the pathological laboratory, which was to add considerably to the international renown of the hospital. Major contributed six papers: "On the minute structure of the cortical substance of the brain, in a case of chronic brain wasting" (1872, vol. 2, pp. 41–53), "A new method of determining the depth of the grey matter of the cerebral convolutions" (1872, vol. 2, pp. 157–176), "Observations on the histology of the brain in the insane" (1873, vol. 3, pp. 97–112), "Observations on the histology of the morbid brain" (1874, vol. 4, pp. 223–239), "On the morbid histology of the brain in the lower animals" (1875, vol. 5, pp. 160–170), and "The histology of the island of Reil" (1876, vol. 6, pp. 1–10). Bevan Lewis contributed three papers, entitled "On the histology of the great sciatic nerve in general paralysis of the insane" (1875, vol. 5, pp. 85–104), "Calorimetric observations upon the influence of various alkaloids on the generation of animal heat" (1876, vol. 6, pp. 43–64), and, in collaboration with Dr Robert Lawson, "Clinical notes on conditions incidental to insanity" (1876, vol. 6, pp. 120–149). In later years, Crichton-Browne must have congratulated himself on his foresight in appointing Major and Bevan Lewis to the staff, since his protégés' pioneering researches proved to be an important milestone in our knowledge of the histological structure of the cerebral cortex.

No one was more assiduous in the support of his *Medical Reports* than Crichton-Browne himself, as he contributed a total of six papers: "Cranial injuries and mental diseases" (1871, vol. 1, pp. 1–26, and 1872, vol. 2, pp. 97–136), "Nitrite of amyl in epilepsy" (1873, vol. 3, pp. 153–174), "Acute dementia" (1874, vol. 4, pp. 265–290), "The functions of the thalamic optica" (1875, vol. 5, pp. 227–256), "Notes on chronic mania" (1875, vol. 5, pp. 284–292), and "Notes on the pathology of general paralysis of the insane" (1876, vol. 6, pp. 170–231).

In their 62nd report, covering 1907, the Commissioners in Lunacy paid tribute to Crichton-Browne and his *Medical Reports*, some 30 years after the last volume had been published:

> "The character of the scientific work carried on in Asylum laboratories is admittedly of a high order, nor is it of recent date. It is gratifying to recall that many important contributions to neurological science were published in the West Riding Asylum Reports (1871–76), based primarily, but by no means exclusively, on work done at the Wakefield Asylum, under the superintendency of Dr. (now Sir) James Crichton-Browne."

The conversaziones

In addition to editing the *Medical Reports* (volume 6 was co-edited with Major), Crichton-Browne organised increasingly well-attended annual conversaziones at the asylum, at which a principal speaker read a paper on some important topic. The invited speakers were all outstanding authorities in their specialty and included Dr Francis Anstie, Physician to Westminster Hospital; Professor (later Sir William) Turner, the Edinburgh anatomist; Dr William Carpenter, the University College naturalist; Dr (later Sir John) Bucknill, the distinguished alienist; and Dr (later Sir William) Broadbent, a physician from St Mary's Hospital, London.

These conversaziones were elaborate affairs in which the principal speaker's paper was supported by demonstrations and by stalls, on which were displayed pathological specimens and photographs of unusual interest, derived from the asylum or (on loan) from other sources. The conversazione of 1872 illustrates well the arrangements that Crichton-Browne made at these popular meetings. The principal speaker, Professor Turner, spoke on "The convolutions of the cerebrum considered in relation to the intelligence". In addition, Stall 'A' contained pathological specimens obtained from the asylum's own collection, supplemented by specimens borrowed from the Leeds School of Medicine and elsewhere. This was presided over by Dr Wilkie Burman, who announced his intention of performing some physiological and pharmacological experiments on rabbits, cats, and frogs, illustrating the inhibiting power of the vagus nerve over the action of the heart, reflex, and galvanic action, and the action of conia, pricrotoxine, strychnia, and hydrate of chloral when subcutaneously injected. These experiments of Burman would probably have been prohibited by the Cruelty to Animals Act 1876. On Stall 'B', run by Dr Charles Aldridge, were exhibited photographs, stereoscopes, paintings, and drawings of insane patients, as well as oleographs; Stall 'C' (Dr Oscar Woods) had a display of surgical instruments; on Stall 'D', Dr Herbert Major demonstrated microscopical preparations from the asylum's own collection and others; Stall 'E' had drugs and medicinal preparations. Refreshments were on Stall 'F', and the asylum band played selections of music.

The speaker for the 1871 conversazione was Dr Francis Anstie, on "The hereditary connexion of certain nervous diseases with each other", and in 1873, Dr W. B. Carpenter on "The physiological import of Dr. Ferrier's experimental investigations into the functions of the brain". Dr J. C. Bucknill's lecture, "Responsibility for homicide", was delivered at the 1874 conversazione, and Dr W. H. Broadbent's subject for 1875 was "On the theory of construction of the nervous system".

Other professional activities

Crichton-Browne's reputation while he was medical director can be judged from the fact that he was not only consulted by Hughlings Jackson about the manifestations of epilepsy in the insane, but also by Charles Darwin, who was anxious to obtain information about the expression of emotions by insane persons, required for his book *The Expression of the Emotions in Man and Animals* (1872). Darwin explains there how his problem of obtaining such information was solved:

> "I had, myself, no opportunity of doing this, so I applied to Dr. Maudsley, and received from him an introduction to Dr. J. Crichton-Browne, who has charge of an immense asylum near Wakefield, and who, as I found, had already attended to the subject. This excellent observer has with unwearied kindness sent me copious notes and descriptions, with valuable suggestions on many points; and I can hardly over-estimate the value of his assistance."

Crichton-Browne's endeavours on behalf of postgraduate doctors were matched by those as a teacher of medical students. The prospectus of the Leeds School of Medicine for the Session 1875/76 stated that: "Mental Diseases. – Systematic and Clinical Lectures are given by Dr. J. Crichton-Browne, FRSE, Medical Superintendent of the West Riding Asylum, during the Summer Session." The systematic lectures were given at the school and the clinical lectures at the asylum. These sessions for medical students based in Leeds started a tradition, in that responsibility for teaching psychiatry was largely entrusted to the medical directors of the Wakefield asylum until 1934.

In 1875, Crichton-Browne found time to write an elegant paper, criticising Skae's classification of mental diseases (Crichton-Browne, 1875), but the versatility of his talents is well illustrated by an operation performed by him on a patient's leg. His account (cited by Shaw Bolton, 1928) of the operation appeared in the *Medical Director's Journal* in January 1873:

> "On the 11th of the present month after consultation with Mr. Wheelhouse one of the surgeons to the Leeds Infirmary I amputated the leg of a male patient, Stephen Pickles, who was sinking rapidly under caries of the bones of the ankle. The operation was successful and the stump has healed in the most satisfactory manner. It is a remarkable fact that not only has the patient's bodily health improved greatly since the operation, but his mind which had previously been a wreck for six years has cleared up marvellously, so there is now every prospect of his complete recovery."

Crichton-Browne's further activities as administrator of the asylum

One of the first problems to which Crichton-Browne had to direct his energies was the ever-recurring one of overcrowding. Further massive expansion of the asylum itself, exceeding substantially the total of 1124 patients in 1866, was regarded as generally undesirable. Nevertheless, the pressure to admit more and more patients was so strong that the population rose to 1487 during his term of office. The need for an additional asylum to provide for the growing problems in the south of the Riding had long been felt, and in July 1866 the first steps were taken to secure land for one at Wadsley Bridge, Sheffield. In December of that year, Crichton-Browne reported to the Committee of Visitors to the asylum the urgent need to obtain further accommodation before the Wadsley asylum became available. At Wakefield, the Isolation Hospital had been opened in 1866, with a block which was designed to accommodate 120 'working-class males'. The Lunacy Commissioners were impressed with this new ward, observing in their report of July 1867 that, "The accommodation here is of the very best description, and all the fittings and arrangements are most complete and convenient".

In 1868, a further increase in the asylum's capacity was obtained by conversion of the former weaving shed into day rooms and dormitories, and by the acquisition of Mount Pleasant House at Sheffield as an auxiliary establishment to provide for the temporary accommodation of 190 patients of a "comparatively quiet and harmless class" (unpublished annual report). Dr Samuel Mitchell, Crichton-Browne's senior assistant medical officer, was placed in charge of Mount Pleasant House, and it was intended that this should be managed as a pilot scheme for the later operation of Wadsley asylum. It was administered and provisioned from the parent asylum at Wakefield, and was visited at first twice, and later once a week by Crichton-Browne. When the transport problems involved in visiting and provisioning so distant an establishment are considered, this was an impressive achievement, and the major part played by Mitchell in the care of the patients there was rewarded by his appointment as the first superintendent of the Wadsley asylum when it was opened in August 1872. Mount Pleasant House was then closed.

That Crichton-Browne was from the outset disinclined to accept any dilution of his authority as medical director is evident from the retirement of Mrs Zillah Paige, the matron, within a few months of his own appointment. The requirement that the director must be accompanied by the matron or her nominee whenever he visited the female wards had been found irksome by Alderson, and doubtless Crichton-Browne was likewise resentful of this and any other limitation of his powers. Mrs Paige's retirement was commented upon by the Committee of Visitors in their report of July 1867:

> "Mrs. Zillah Paige, who was appointed Matron of the Asylum on the 23rd of September, 1853, finding that failing health interfered with the discharge of her duties, placed her resignation in the hands of the Committee in March last, and was recommended to the Sessions for a retiring pension. The Committee considering the altered circumstances of the Institution, resolved not to continue the office of Matron, but to appoint instead a Chief Female Officer in a more subordinate position, at a reduced salary, giving her also the assistance of a Head Nurse."

Although Mrs Paige was ostensibly retiring on the grounds of ill-health, an observer at the time said that "Crichton-Browne could not put up with her and soon got her pensioned". The chief female officer was directly answerable to Crichton-Browne, an arrangement that accorded well with his belief that, for an asylum to operate efficiently, "paramount authority" should be "entrusted to one guiding and controlling Head" (unpublished annual report).

Another example of his determination to have the administration of the asylum firmly in his own hands was his deliberate failure to respond to the wishes of both the Visiting Committee and the Lunacy Commissioners in the matter of the use put to a new, two-floor building. It had been the firm intention of the Committee and Commissioners that the lower floor should be used as a dining hall, and the upper as dormitories for female patients. However, the "temporary' conversion of the lower floor into a spacious and attractive ward, as an emergency measure to relieve the pressure on beds, had appeared to offer such a ready solution to the asylum's accommodation problem that Crichton-Browne decided to turn an obdurate 'deaf-ear', first to pleas, and eventually to explicit directives from the Commissioners to bring it into service as a dining hall. In the event, the only occasions on which it was ever used as a dining hall were for special functions such as fancy-dress balls and annual dances, and for these it proved invaluable.

But Crichton-Browne was not one to drag his feet when what he judged to be a wise proposal was made by the Commissioners, who stated in their report dated 1865 that: "We have suggested to Mr. Cleaton that it would be found desirable to employ married Attendants and their wives in some of the male wards, and more especially in the male Infirmary". Cleaton left the asylum before he could put this suggestion into practice, but in his report of January 1868, Crichton-Browne was able to describe the beneficial influence of a female nurse introduced into a male ward.

> "How to provide suitable and trustworthy attendants is certainly the great problem of the day in the management of our lunatic asylums, and anything which may assist even in its partial solution, is deserving of consideration. Such an auxiliary seems to be found in the appointment of female nurses to male wards, an arrangement which tends to inspire the male attendants with gentleness and self-command, and confers great benefits upon the patients. One such appointment has taken place here during last year. A female nurse, the wife of an attendant, was placed in April, in one of the largest male wards, containing 70 epileptic and suicidal patients. Her presence

in the midst of these lunatics, many of whom are of impulsive or depraved character, has been productive of the most excellent and pleasing effects, which have transcended even the most sanguine anticipations that led to her appointment. The ward has become quieter and more orderly under her influence, and a marked change for the better has taken place in the personal neatness and general deportment of the patients. A singular power of self-control seems to have been awakened in them, so that they are enabled to suppress those outbursts of violence, that abusive language, and those offensive habits, to which they used formerly to give way. Their whole nature seems to have been softened, and their tone of feeling ameliorated by the simple expedient of introducing a kind-hearted female amongst them. It is in the male sick wards, however, that female nurses will be found most useful. There they may prove invaluable; for it is open to doubt whether the high mortality which prevails amongst male lunatics, which is about one-third greater than that which obtains amongst females similarly afflicted, may not be *in some slight degree* due, to defective nursing, to the absence of those sick-room comforts and attentions, which women alone, are capable of offering."

In the same report (1868), Crichton-Browne made an invidious comparison between the female and male infirmaries: "An air of wholesome cleanliness and hopeful solicitude pervades the one, which has no parallel in the dismal precision, or dreary apathy of the other." Encouraged by the success of introducing a female nurse into a male ward, Crichton-Browne continued with the experiment on a larger scale, and refers to the results in his report of January 1869:

"The experiment of introducing wives of attendants, as nurses in the male wards, adverted to in my last report, has been continued during the past year with the best results. Five women are now thus employed with satisfaction to themselves and benefit to their charges."

His views on nursing staff and their management in the same report (1869) comment on the paramount importance of strict discipline to protect patients from harshness, oppression, and neglect, and of the temptation to abuse their position, as they were "placed like petty autocrats in their respective wards 'dressed up in a little brief authority'". He conceded that the nurses were "as a rule, so patient, just, and industrious", despite "frequent annoyances, taunts and trials", but still felt that action was required to obtain additional guarantees of their fidelity and kindness. This could only be done by making the service more attractive and more efficiently managed. To this end, he recommended: (1) increased remuneration; (2) the certainty instead of the mere possibility of a retiring pension; (3) a minimum standard of education; (4) cultivation of *esprit de corps*; (5) the employment of the attendants' wives as nurses and the provision of good and inexpensive married quarters; (6) unremitting supervision by well paid and independent officers; (7) careful inquiries by the director into *all* complaints; (8) summary dismissal where acts of cruelty had been established; and (9) prosecution where conviction was likely.

Crichton-Browne's report of January 1872 showed that he was not only pleased with the efficiency and kindness of his nurses and attendants, but had succeeded in obtaining for them an increase in salary and the right to a pension. He wrote:

"Several instances of the advancement of Nurses and Attendants trained here to more responsible and remunerative situations in other Asylums, have

> tended to stimulate the staff generally to strive after a high standard of efficiency. My conviction is that the Nurses and Attendants now employed here are unsurpassed for kindness and skilfulness in the treatment of patients confided to their immediate care, and for steadiness and propriety of conduct. I rejoice that you have been able to make an increase in the rate of both Nurses' and Attendants' wages, and I believe that this, with your unhesitating recommendation of a pension, whenever by age and length of service it becomes due, will greatly contribute to contentment and good feeling throughout the establishment."

However, in return for the attention he paid to the problems and welfare of the nurses and attendants, Crichton-Browne insisted on the maintenance of a high standard of behaviour: "a firm resolution has been formed vigorously to repress everything approaching insubordination, or organised discontentment amongst them". He expressed a need for domiciliary nurses and for a nurse training school, an opinion that showed him to be ahead of his time.

Bolton (1928) has drawn attention to the downgrading in 1866 of the role of the consulting physicians, whose number was reduced from two to one, and whose duties were governed by new rules:

> "He only attends when requested and only visits the asylum if required. If no physician is appointed the medical superintendent can call in to his assistance any physician practising in the neighbourhood."

These changes were probably suggested by Crichton-Browne, who presumably felt that his team of resident doctors, headed by himself, was sufficiently competent to handle most medical problems, and that the asylum needed less outside medical support than hitherto. Until the 1960s operations were often carried out in the operating theatre. The patients of Stanley Royd Hospital (previously the West Riding Pauper Lunatic Asylum) requiring major operative procedures were, with effect from 1940, transferred to Pinderfields General Hospital, which had been built within the grounds of the asylum in 1900 as the asylum's acute hospital, but became an Emergency Medical Services Hospital in 1939, thenceforth remaining as a general hospital.

Because of the lamentable physical condition of a high proportion of newly admitted patients, the Visiting Committee issued a directive in 1870, doubtless prompted by Crichton-Browne, that all reception orders for the admission of patients must have attached medical certificates confirming that the patient was free from, and had no contact with, epidemic disease, and was in a fit state to be moved. This latter reassurance must have been lightly given, though, in view of the number of moribund patients admitted each year! An earlier recommendation by the Commissioners in 1866 that every patient should be examined on admission, and the presence of any bruises or other injuries reported to the senior medical officer or director, was shrewd, since nursing and medical staff could otherwise be subsequently accused of having caused injuries which in reality had been sustained before admission.

In his report of January 1868, Crichton-Browne referred to the "formation of classes for instruction in reading, writing and arithmetic" in addition to teaching appropriate trades to selected patients. These new classes were eagerly joined by convalescent patients, some of whom "carried away from the Asylum not only restored reason, but new acquirements. In addition the habits of chronic

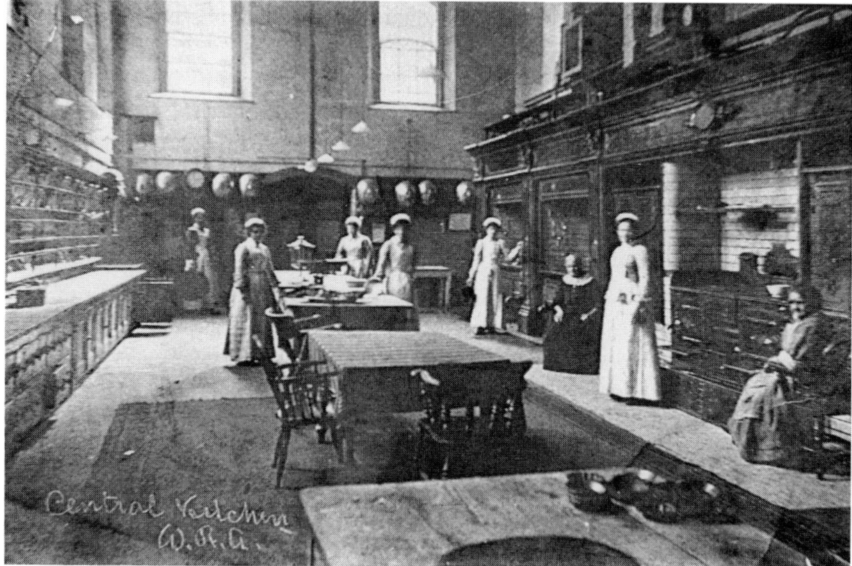

Fig. 25.2. The central kitchen at Wakefield asylum, circa 1900, with the patients seated and the staff standing.

inmates and imbeciles seemed to improve with their spelling.'' A schoolmaster was employed full time, and systematic educational classes remained a feature of the hospital life until the 1930s, being conducted in the final years by nurses. In a further comment on these educational classes, Crichton-Browne wrote in the report of 1874:

> ''The classes for elementary instruction are still thronged by attentive if not apt scholars. Their educational results are not perhaps such as would satisfy an Inspector of Schools, but their moral influence is very salutary.''

Not content with having unskilled male patients taught useful trades, Crichton-Browne initiated classes for tuition in domestic cookery in 1874. The kitchens are pictured in Fig. 25.2.

> ''There are always on our wards passing through various stages of convalescence many wives whose accomplishments in this direction are not all that could be desired – and many girls – future wives, who would be puzzled to boil a potatoe in a creditable manner. It is thought that it would be highly advantageous if these can be sent back to their homes not merely with restored reason but with new culinary acquirements which will tend to make their homes more comfortable and attractive.''

Taken in conjunction with the encouragement of patients to use their skills as musicians and artists during the Crichton-Browne era, these cookery classes confirm the point made by Yellowlees (1953) that ''such recently rediscovered and re-christened forms of treatment as 'Occupational Therapy', 'Group Therapy', 'Play Therapy', 'Music Therapy', 'Art Therapy', physiotherapy, organized games, community singing, dancing, and all the rest of it, were being carried on in the psychiatric dark ages with considerably more enthusiasm and personal interest than is shown – except on paper – today.''

The condition of patients on admission, so deplored by Crichton-Browne's predecessors, had improved little by 1866: 296 of the 371 admissions in the first year of his office were in a feeble state. Many died, directly or indirectly, of alimentary diseases contracted before admission. Referring to the social conditions under which the majority of the population lived, he wrote: "The fact that a large proportion of our inmates is derived from large towns where hygienic principles are much neglected – where the barest necessities of healthy existence, fresh air, pure water and bright light are scarcely to be had, and where excitement and dissipation prevail, will in some measure explain the cachectic conditions with which we have to contend and account for the excess of our mortality over some other Asylums". His report for 1873 stated that: "The physical and mental condition of the 466 patients admitted during 1872, may be said to have been deplorable and to have occasioned incessant anxiety to the medical and nursing staff". However, he opposed a defeatist attitude towards the prognosis of patients admitted to the asylum, and looked to earlier admission and medical science to provide means whereby mental illness could eventually be cured or prevented: "We cannot be content with a system which would imply providing convenient storage of heaps of social debris". He felt that delay in admission had a malign influence on outcome, expressing the opinion in 1872 that, "Procrastination is the thief of reason as well as of time," and that, "Were all persons afflicted by insanity immediately placed under appropriate treatment many would be saved alive who now drift hopelessly into that bourn of chronic madness from which few travellers return".

Crichton-Browne would not countenance restraint, and had recourse to seclusion but sparingly. Nevertheless, it is interesting to note the mild rebuke of the Lunacy Commissioners over his failure to record the packing of patients in wet sheets as 'restraint'. Their report of November 1871 stated:

> "In the female division, three patients have been treated by being packed in wet sheets for maniacal excitement. The facts are duly recorded in the Case Books only, but should also be entered under the head 'restraint' in the Medical Journal, which Dr. Browne, upon our pointing out to him the omission, at once undertook should in future be done."

In 1867, he asserted that the barbaric practice of secluding destructive patients during the night in a naked condition, which was apparently customary at some asylums, had never been adopted at Wakefield.

The extraordinary drive displayed by Crichton-Browne as the asylum's medical director is admirably illustrated by the impressive list of structural improvements and increased facilities since their previous visit, in the Commissioners' report of November 1871. These included the formation of a fully equipped fire brigade, the construction and fitting up of rooms for pathology and photography purposes, the removal of the boundary wall near the hospital and the substitution of good palisading with stone coping, the planting of 1500 trees in the airing courts and plantations, the extension of the farm to take more cows, and an increased supply of carpets, curtains, and furniture for the wards.

Crichton-Browne doubted the wisdom of discouraging visitors, a policy favoured by many asylums of the day. In his report of January 1872, he had this to say about the exclusion of visitors:

> "The presence of strangers in the Wards instead of exciting the patients, or wounding their sensibilities, has soothed and benefited them by varying the monotony of their lives, creating incentives to self-restraint, and persuading them that they are not buried alive and forgotten by the great world without, but that there are many who take an interest in them and in the institution in which they are immured. At the same time, the opening of the Asylum to free inspection has inspired confidence in its management. Many of the prejudices against lunatic asylums grew up simply because they were made closed corporations. Whatsoever is hidden is suspected, and 'No admission except on business' over any doorway suggests animosity and doubt. Dark furtive deeds are presumed to thrive behind high walls, and hence much of the clamour about broken ribs and wrongful detentions."

It is not surprising that Crichton-Browne was in favour of admitting visitors to the asylum, as in 1868 he had expressed serious misgivings about the public's misconceptions and ignorance regarding mental illness, affirming that:

> "The erroneous notions of insanity, and that hostile feeling towards its victims, which led to the iniquities practised upon lunatics in former days, still exists in the lower strata of the public mind. The humane system is only maintained by the constant and earnest labours of an enlightened few. Were the Commissioners . . . and other guardians of the insane . . . to relax their exertions for a single year, it would be as if Pinel and Conolly had never lived."

He went on to illustrate this point by citing some examples of the naive and out-moded notions of visitors to the asylum: "Numbers of intelligent visitors to our Asylums now, are under the impression that corporal punishment is one of the correctives employed and ask to be shown the strait jackets, which they believe to constitute a permanent feature of Asylum costume."

In his report of January 1872, Crichton-Browne drew attention to the fact that the provision of porous pillows for epileptics would not necessarily prevent them from suffocating, as they sometimes slid off the pillow during a fit. He therefore insisted that these patients should be provided with an additional safeguard of continuous observation by attendants and nurses during both day and night. The report of the Lunacy Commissioners dated July 1872 shows that during Crichton-Browne's administration, beer was provided for the male patients, in addition to ample and well served meals for all: "We saw 360 of the men at dinner, in the great hall, their demeanour was excellent, and the dinner consisting of meat and potatoe-pie, ample in quantity, and good in quality, was well served; each man had his pint of beer."

Bearing in mind that smallpox has been eliminated from the United Kingdom (and elsewhere), the Visiting Committee's report of April 1872 serves as a reminder that in Crichton-Browne's time, this dangerous and disfiguring malady was prevalent in Britain. In this report, attention is drawn to the fact that all the patients had been vaccinated on instructions from the Lunacy Commissioners, as smallpox had been rife in the district and as "cases of the disease have occurred at the very gates". This wise precaution proved successful in protecting the inmates and staff from the disease (there had been two outbreaks of smallpox affecting patients in the asylum during Cleaton's regime as superintendent).

In his 1872 annual report, Crichton-Browne also described the murder of an attendant, Thomas Lomas, by George Lawton (an epileptic patient). Lomas had forgotten to lock away a poker which Lawton used to attack the attendant, who was momentarily off guard. Lawton armed himself with the poker and approached the attendant who, in the words of Crichton-Browne,

> ''Secure in his own strength and activity, stood looking out of the window at his charges exercising in the airing court below, when his assassin with no grudge or animosity, but stirred by a pure homicidal impulse, an analogue of epilepsy convulsing the mind instead of the muscles, stole behind him, and dealt a blow, which was fatal in itself, but which was followed by others that reduced the head to a shapeless pulp . . . . The murderer afterwards describing his crime, and praying for his victim, still prided himself on the ferocity of its perpetration – 'I struck him', he said, 'and you know I could strike, for I'm a striker by trade'.''

Commenting on this tragic happening, Crichton-Browne referred to ''the difficulty of combining safety with domestic comfort and freedom in an establishment like this, and of ensuring due care and vigilance even from experienced Attendants, and where their lives are at stake.'' Lawton was arrested, tried and transferred to the Asylum for Criminal Lunatics at Broadmoor. The attendant's wife was awarded a gratuity of £100, to be spent at the discretion of one Committee member and Crichton-Browne.

In his report of January 1871, Crichton-Browne gave a favourable view of the response of epileptics in recent years to certain drugs. He wrote that: ''The material diminution which is observable in recent years, in the number of deaths in this Asylum, reported as due to epilepsy and convulsions, is to be ascribed to the remarkable success of the modern treatment of these affections, by the Bromide of Potassium, Atropine and Ergot of Rye''. However, such unqualified optimism is not supported by his report of January 1873: ''Of the 13 patients who were carried off by epilepsy – 6 died in the *status epilepticus*, a condition of coma induced by a rapid series of fits, 3 died from exhaustion after seizures of unwonted severity accompanied by mental excitement, and 1 from the rupture of a blood vessel on the surface of the brain during a fit''.

Fortunately, the addition of chloral hydrate (discovered by Liebreich in 1868) to the asylum's pharmaceutical armamentarium was to bring about a significant improvement in the prognosis of status epilepticus. Bromide was routinely used in the treatment of epilepsy for many years and was of some value in preventing fits.

The patients' quality of life had improved steadily during Cleaton's administration of the asylum, and Crichton-Browne made further contributions to their welfare. Not only were the meals ample in quantity and well served, but also the patients were supplied with good blankets and reasonably comfortable beds, although the Commissioners recommended sacking bases in lieu of wood. In 1872, the introduction of wire beds was so successful an innovation that samples were requested by St Thomas's Hospital in London, where wire beds were also adopted.

The policy of preserving the asylum's high degree of self-sufficiency, started by Ellis, was vigorously maintained by Crichton-Browne. In 1867, joinery, painting, shoemaking, tailoring, weaving, brewing, and employment in the laundry, kitchen, bakehouse, wards (cleaning), and workroom kept no fewer than 261 patients fully occupied, while a further 206 women were employed on ward needlework and 236 men on the land. All footwear, all the patients' clothing and attendants' uniforms, all necessary linen and linsey-woolsey, were made or woven in the asylum. The balance of a total workforce of 875 were engaged in various other kinds of employment, such as book keeping and clerical duties. A stocking machine, installed in 1870 and operated by only one patient, produced 500 stockings that year.

The employment of patients on a project requiring considerable skill was described by Crichton-Browne in his report dated January 1872. It had been decided to extend a sanitary spur to Ward 2 by the addition of a cross wing, containing a Turkish bath and many other baths and douches. The report makes enthusiastic references to this endeavour, which he clearly regarded as a *tour de force* and a "most important addition to the resources of the Asylum". He continued:

> "Lined with encaustic tiles, lighted by diaphanie windows and with doorways ornamented with stone arches in the Moorish style, the Turkish Bath house is divided into six chambers. The first is used as a dressing-room and is furnished with couches, looking-glass, etc. The second is the mild room generally kept at a temperature of 110°F and is supplied with suitable wooden reclining boards and hot and cold taps with basins for bathing the head. The third is the hot room and can be kept at any temperature that may be required up to 190°F. It is also supplied with reclining boards and out of it opens the rain and drizzle bath, a coil of pipes with innumerable minute perforations, in the midst of which the person to be operated upon stands, so that miriads of little jets of water of any required temperature may be directed upon every aspect of the body. Adjoining the drizzle is the fountain bath, from which a forcible stream of water may be applied to the rectum or anus. The third chamber or hot room may be at any time filled with steam and so converted into a Russian Bath. The fourth chamber is kept at the ordinary temperature of the air, and contains the shampooing table and basins, as well as the Wave Bath from which a broad sheet of cold water can be made to sweep over the body. In the fifth chamber is the weighing machine, a common porcelain bath for alkaline fluids, and the entrance to little recesses devoted to sitz, hip and douche baths. In the sixth chamber are arrangements for the medicated vapour baths, iodine, mercurial, sulphur, each of the three compartments being connected with flues which when required can convey away offensive fumes. With each bath the hot and cold water are made to mingle in an iron box in the centre of which is the bulb of a thermometer, the scale of which projects externally so that the temperature of the water in the box can always be read off."

Crichton-Browne concluded with forgivable pride:

> "I believe there are no baths in this country, not even those of University College Hospital, constructed under the immediate and sagacious supervision of Dr. Tilbury Fox and which formed a model for our imitation, which are more complete or more pleasing in their general effect than those of the West Riding Asylum. The baths have already proved singularly useful in relieving that terrible despondency under which so many patients labour, and in the treatment of skin diseases, rheumatism and other bodily ailments."

The Commissioners in their annual report were hopeful that provision of additional bathing facilities would render unnecessary the bathing of two patients in the same bathwater!

However, the finest individual artistic achievement was doubtless that of the patient who in 1870 carved a most sophisticated and elegant lectern representing an eagle perched on a pillar. It is said that a penknife was the only tool used by the sculptor, and that he tried to destroy his handiwork as soon as it was finished (Ashworth, 1975). The lectern still enhances the hospital's church. In addition to the extension to the laundry and the erection of a new boiler house, a considerable amount of ancillary building work was completed during the early years of Crichton-Browne's superintendency. New workshops, many of which are still in use, were provided for the shoemaker, tailor, upholsterer, tinsmith, plumber, and blacksmith. In addition, a house and offices were built for the engineer: the latter is still in use as the engineer's office. From the beginning, the asylum authorities, not least the director, had operated with one eye firmly on the cost on the county rate, and Crichton-Browne was no exception. His influence was exerted even in the field of engineering, and in 1873 he recommended the fitting of Green's Economisers to the two Lancashire boilers, recently purchased for £250 each, because of what was considered to be the high cost of coal at the time. The heat used in the manufacture of gas was also utilised by passing it through Galloways boilers.

The well established pattern since the days of Ellis was for each successive director to interest himself in the unending problem of the asylum's contaminated water supply and defective drains, with a varying degree of dedication, to identify and eliminate supposed faults, and then take an overoptimistic view of the success of his endeavours. The stimulus for these activities was the recurrent outbreaks of diarrhoea, dysentery, and typhoid (and one serious outbreak of cholera). Obnoxious fumes from defective drains (miasma) were still regarded as the cause of much disease, and Crichton-Browne repeatedly warned the Committee of Visitors of this apparent danger. He insisted that epidemics of typhoid and diarrhoea were a result of emanations from open drains and that "infectious diseases are a result of improper sewer ventilation", but also recognised that the impure state of the water, overcrowding, and poor hygiene were also matters of grave concern. The exceptionally high incidence of diarrhoea in 1867 was, he thought, due to impure drinking water; a patient had for some inexplicable reason contracted cholera in the same ward as the first case in the dreadful epidemic of 1849. Fortunately, he now had the advantage of a new isolation hospital in which to nurse this and other sufferers from epidemic diseases.

In their report of January 1867, the Lunacy Commissioners commented on this serious outbreak of diarrhoea:

> ". . . the large number of Patients reported to have died from Diarrhoea, which it appears became epidemic during portions of the past year. Every effort seems to have been made to ascertain the cause of the prevalence of this malady, and the drains have been carefully attended to, but Dr. Browne is distinctly of the opinion that much of the evil is to be attributed to the water, which upon analysis has been found to contain much organic matter and other impurity. Dr. Odling by whom the analysis was conducted, states that the samples submitted to him 'contain Ammonia, and Nitrates in such relatively large quantities, as to show considerable contamination with

> drainage or something similar', and he does not consider either of them suitable for drinking purposes."

Discussing the unsatisfactory nature of the asylum's water supply, Crichton-Browne mentioned the unhealthy condition of a certain well, the use of which had been forbidden because it had seemingly been contaminated by drainage. Referring to this source of tainted water, he wrote in 1868: "The well thus interdicted had long enjoyed a high [but false] reputation for purity and excellence of its water, and Mr. Cleaton pointed out to me, after its evil qualities had been detected, that the nurses who as a body suffered from typhoid fever during its prevalence here in much larger proportion than the patients were in the habit of sending to it for their drinking water". The patients, on the other hand, had consumed water supplied by the Wakefield Company, which "though far from pure was pronounced less pernicious". Because the samples of water examined by Professor Odling had been taken after a snowstorm, and while the filter beds were undergoing repairs, it was decided that the tests may not therefore "accurately represent its ordinary character". Accordingly, he was asked to carry out further tests, but the results obtained proved to be unsatisfactory, as he declared that the water being used in the asylum was "unfit for drinking purposes". Although Crichton-Browne was given permission to install a new "magnetic Carbide filter", the asylum's water supply from the River Calder remained contaminated.

Having therefore reached – at least temporarily – an *impasse* in his attempts to procure a safe water supply, yet worried by recurrent outbreaks of dysentery, diarrhoea, and erysipelas, Crichton-Browne decided to make a determined effort to improve the condition of the asylum's drains and sewage disposal systems. Experiments with an anemometer had proved that a constant current of foul air was ascending into the asylum drains from those of Wakefield. A large trap was therefore fitted to the asylum's main drain. The age, faulty construction, courses, constant flow of hot water, diversions, extensions, and "ill balanced ramifications" were all formidable obstacles in the way of a thoroughly safe and satisfactory drainage system. Nevertheless, a resolute effort was made to eliminate sources of trouble, and in his report dated January 1871, he stated that:

> "two old and most malignant-looking cesspools, or precipitating tanks as they were called, have been filled in and abolished. A barrel drain of brick, excoriated, rat-eaten, presenting subsidence in certain places, and of exorbitant dimensions has been replaced by a line of pot pipes, ventilating tubes have been fixed at new points and charcoal trays introduced into some manholes that had not before been protected in this way."

The following year, Crichton-Browne described how he had become aware of an unpleasant smell while exploring the underground passages beneath the 1818 building, and had succeeded in identifying as the source a hole in the ground, up which, he wrote:

> "a strong current of mephitic air streamed to be carefully distributed through certain wards by flues which were as if constructed for the purpose. On applying my heel to the neighbourhood of the hole the ground fell in, a rotten plank of wood, the only covering of the drain, having given way, and there

> was the drain itself two feet in breadth with a flat bottom and little or no fall, half filled with sediment – in short, a cess pool 'long drawn out'. This drain has been removed at considerable cost as it passes under the building at a great depth. As a result of these and other changes I anticipate that the health of the inmates will be placed on a more secure basis and that epidemic disease will be banished from among us."

However, there was unexpectedly another opportunity to improve the quality of the water supplied to the institution. In 1874, the asylum authorities were able to seek the inclusion of a clause in a bill, then being promoted by the Wakefield Waterworks Company, providing for the asylum to share in a new source of water that had become available (Ashworth, 1975). Their endeavours were crowned with success, but Crichton-Browne had left the asylum before the new supply was brought into service.

One of the most distressing occurrences in a psychiatric hospital is for a patient to succeed in committing suicide, and Crichton-Browne certainly had his share of these during his term of office. In his report of 1869, he recorded the suicide of a patient in the asylum's slaughterhouse.

> "Only one case of death requires any special mention, that of J. M., who succeeded in committing suicide on the 4th of September last, by cutting his throat. This man, who was at work on the land, and who was not at the time suspected of dangerous propensities, suddenly entered the slaughter-house, near the door of which he happened to be passing, and there, in the presence of the butcher, and another patient, and within a few yards of the farm bailiff, and several attendants, perpetrated the fatal act with a knife, which the butcher had just been using. The suddenness of the whole affair rendered interference impossible."

The part played by the sudden impulse seems to have been a feature of this and another case described by Crichton-Browne in his report dated 1874:

> "One distressing case of suicide has to be deplored. A patient who had been for four years in the Asylum, and who was fast recovering from a recurrent attack of melancholia, was permitted by one of the Medical Officers to visit the family residing at the Porter's lodge with whom he had long been on friendly terms. He took dinner with them and was apparently cheerful and contented, when suddenly possessed as it were by some uncontrollable impulse, he seized a knife which was lying upon the table, ran into an adjoining room, and, before he could be laid hold of, inflicted a wound on his throat from which he soon afterwards died."

Crichton-Browne's own comments on suicide attempts in asylums are in his report of January 1868:

> "It is to be remembered that if an attempt at suicide is occasionally successful in an institution of this kind, a vast number of similar attempts are daily baffled. The inventive cunning of the proceedings of suicidal lunatics, and the obstinate determination with which they follow up their purposes, render them at all times a most anxious charge, but especially so when their number is materially augmented by the presence of what can only be looked upon as an epidemic of suicidal propensities."

One of Crichton-Browne's aims was to ensure that the patients were not subjected to an 'all work and no play' regime. His first report, covering the year 1866, commented on the music provided for and by the patients, the facilities for reading, dances, games, country walks, visits, etc. The Commissioners' report of February 1869 listed some additional recreational amenities, which included regular meetings in the hall, dramatic performances, magic-lantern shows, exhibitions of conjuring, marionettes, juggling, gymnastics, and "Readings from Shakespeare by Miss Glynn". In his report of January 1874, Crichton-Browne stated that the "weekly ball is attended by about 600 patients, a great proportion of whom join in the dancing". But the *pièce de résistance* of his efforts to entertain the patients was surely the performance of *Pygmalion and Galatea* in the hall in April 1875, W. S. Gilbert himself taking the part of Leucippus; it is believed that this was the only occasion on which Gilbert participated as an actor, as well as personally coaching the company of gifted amateurs. The reporter of the *Medical Times and Gazette* of 17 April 1875 was impressed by the brilliance of the acting and the splendour of the actors' raiment, observing that they were "equipped in costumes far exceeding in value the properties of the real stage, and designed by one whose name is a sufficient guarantee of taste and appropriateness – the artist Alma Tadema". The reporter interpreted the performance of the play before an audience of patients as being "one of the finest evidences of that humane method of treatment which contrasts so brilliantly with the former system, by which solitary confinement, mechanical restraint, and culpable negligence, impelled each miserable lunatic into a greater depth of degradation". Six hundred patients and 100 nurses and attendants watched the play "with great delight" (Crichton-Browne, 1926).

Crichton-Browne was appointed Lord Chancellor's Visitor in 1875, and hence the tenure of his appointment as medical director of the asylum at Wakefield came to an end. Regrettably, the famous *West Riding Asylum Medical Reports* and the annual conversaziones also terminated with the departure of their creator. This appointment and Crichton-Browne's consequent departure from the asylum attracted the attention of the *Medical Times and Gazette*; an editorial on 18 December 1875 read as follows:

> "The appointment of Dr. Crichton-Browne cannot fail to give satisfaction to the members of the medical profession. He has already secured for himself a high place in the general literature of medicine, and the special literature of lunacy. He has made the West Riding Asylum a model institution for the treatment of the insane, and an independent school for the prosecution of scientific research."

Crichton-Browne was accorded a farewell dinner at the Bull Hotel, Wakefield, on 18 April 1876, and the menu shows how handsomely the sponsors rose to the occasion. The Bull Hotel is still in existence.

Crichton-Browne's further activities and honours

Crichton-Browne's career after he had left the Wakefield asylum was one of uninterrupted success. Orator, wit, raconteur, and intellectual as he was, he used his talents to give many lectures and write books, based mainly on his own experiences; these included *Victorian Jottings* (1926), *Stray Leaves from a Physician's Portfolio* (1927), *What the Doctor Thought* (1930), and *The Doctor's Second Thoughts* (1931). He was one of four members of the initial editorial staff of the neurological journal *Brain*, which began publication in 1878, his co-editors being Ferrier, Jackson, and Bucknill. Following the cessation of the *West Riding Asylum Reports*, Ferrier suggested that a neurological journal should be started in London to continue their work (Sherrington, 1928). The intimate connection of *Brain* with the *Medical Reports* is shown by the fact that all the members of the editorial staff had strong links with the Wakefield Asylum, and that nine of the contributors to the first volume had had papers published in the *Medical Reports*. Crichton-Browne had some dominant ideas, such as the beneficial effect of the open-air treatment of tuberculosis, the importance of early treatment of mental illness, and the baneful results of the (alleged) overpressure of work in public elementary schools. His report concerning the last-named was considered to be so important that the House of Commons ordered it to be printed.

During his career, he was awarded honorary degrees by the Universities of Edinburgh, Leeds, St Andrews, and Aberdeen; and at various times he was elected President of the Medical Society of London, the Neurological Society, the National Health Society, the Sanitary Inspectors' Association, and the Medico-Psychological Association (in 1878). In 1883, he was elected Fellow of the Royal Society, becoming its treasurer and vice-president, and was knighted three years later; in 1920, he was paid the compliment of being invited to deliver the first Maudsley Lecture.

In his Ferrier Lecture to the Royal Society of London in 1938, after discussing the paper of Fritsch & Hitzig (1870) describing the effect of the electrical stimulation of the brain, Lord Adrian said:

> "David Ferrier (1873) developed the full possibilities of the new method of research. He was then a man of thirty working in the laboratory maintained at the West Riding Asylum by James Crichton-Browne. Many of us have seen these two eminent Victorian physicians in their old age and will be glad to keep the memory of Ferrier's slight, alert figure and Crichton-Browne's dignified vitality. It is a memory which links us to a classical period in the history of medicine, the period when neurology became a science."

Crichton-Browne died in 1938, aged 97. In the words of Sir Arthur MacNalty (1965), "The debt that modern neurology owed to this pioneer is immense", and the same is even truer of psychiatry.

Conclusion

The influence of Crichton-Browne on research at the Wakefield asylum was to remain vibrant for many years after his departure. His enthusiasm infected his protégés Herbert Coddington Major and William Bevan Lewis with an eagerness for further research, their example being followed by Joseph Shaw Bolton in the next century.

Dr Major succeeded Crichton-Browne as director in January 1876. His chief researches were on the role of alcohol in the aetiology of mental illness and on the neurohistology of the brain in man and animals. Much of his work was done at the instigation of Crichton-Browne, and that which earned him his MD, on "Histology of the brain in apes" (for which he also received a gold medal), was undertaken in the main at the asylum.

When he resigned in 1884 to take up a post as honorary physician at the Bradford Infirmary, Major's post was filled by the appointment of Crichton-Browne's second protégé, Dr (later Professor) William Bevan Lewis. Against much opposition from many in the mental health field, he pioneered out-patient treatment at the asylum, and realised his ambition of establishing a specially built acute asylum some distance from the old one, in 1900. He also introduced a private nursing scheme, with the purposes of providing care in the community at a cost to the family more reasonable than that available at a private asylum. Profits from the scheme were used for the purchase of experimental medical equipment and to assist staff and patients in financial distress. Bevan Lewis deplored the presence in the asylum of young, mentally handicapped patients, and in 1899 persuaded the county council to purchase a mansion adjacent to the asylum, where these patients could receive separate treatment.

Bevan Lewis's researches were chiefly in the field of neurohistology, much of his work awaiting years for its recognition. He was the first alienist to be given, in 1908, a chair in psychiatry at the University of Leeds. He was elected President of the Medico-Psychological Association for 1909/10, choosing for the subject of his Presidential Address "The biological factor in heredity". He retired in 1910.

Dr (later Professor) Joseph Shaw Bolton was appointed medical director in 1910. Following the tradition established by Crichton-Browne, he also undertook extensive research. His contributions included "The exact histological location of the visual area of the human cerebral cortex" in 1900, "A contribution of localization of cerebral function" (Goulstonian Lecture, 1910), "The myth of the unconscious mind" (*Journal of Mental Science*, 1926), "The role of mental confusion in prognosis" (Mott Memorial Volume, 1929), and "The cortical localization of cerebral function" (Henderson Fund Lecture, University of Edinburgh, 1933). Professor Shaw Bolton continued the practice, first established by Crichton-Browne, of encouraging visits to the asylum of students from the Leeds Medical School. He was appointed to the Chair of Psychiatry at the University, and, in 1928, as President of the Royal Medico-Psychological Association, he welcomed the delegates at the hospital to the 87th Annual Meeting. His address was "The evolution of a mental hospital, Wakefield 1818–1928" (Bolton, 1928). Professor Shaw Bolton retired in 1933.

The loss of the acute hospital, with its many facilities for research, in 1939 to make way for an Emergency Medical Services Hospital (later to become Pinderfields General Hospital) and the resulting stagnation of the mental hospital during the years of World War II discouraged further research. The 'golden years' initiated by Crichton-Browne were at an end.

Addendum

Shortly after compiling much of this chapter, Dr John Todd, sadly, died. While the bibliography might not be as complete as the late Dr Todd would have wished, his son, Mr James Todd, is gratefully acknowledged for his help in this direction. The contribution of Dr Trevor Turner is also gratefully acknowledged.

References

ALLBUTT, T. C. (1871) *On the Use of the Ophthalmoscope in Diseases of the Kidney and Certain Other General Disorders*. London: Macmillan.

—— (1896–99) *A System of Medicine*. London: Macmillan.

ASHWORTH, A. L. (1975) *Wakefield Mental Hospital – 150 Year History*. Obtainable from Stanley Royd Hospital.

BOLTON, S. (1928) Presidential address. *Journal of Mental Science*.

BROWNE, W. A. F. (1837) *Being the Subject of 5 Lectures before the Managers of the Montrose Lunatic Asylum*. London: Adam Black & Charles Black.

CRICHTON-BROWNE, J. (1871) Preface. In *West Riding Lunatic Asylum Medical Reports*. London: Churchill.

—— (1875) Skae's classification of mental diseases. A critique. *Journal of Mental Science*, **21**, 339–365.

—— (1895) Lecture to the West London Medico-Chirurgical Society 1895. In *Stray Leaves from a Physician's Portfolio*. London: Hodder & Stoughton.

—— (1926) *Victorian Jottings*. London: Etchells & MacDonald.

—— (1931) *The Doctor's Second Thoughts*. London: Ernest Benn.

DARWIN, C. (1872) *The Expression of the Emotions in Man and the Animals*. London: Murray.

DEWHURST, K. (1982) Paper on chlorpromazine. *Irish Journal of Medical Science*.

DICTIONARY OF NATIONAL BIOGRAPHY (1921/22) J. M. Fothergill (obituary). *Dictionary of National Biography*, vol. 7. Oxford: Oxford University Press.

ELLIS, W. C. (1815) *Letter to Thomas Thompson, M.P.* London: Longman & Hirst.

FOTHERGILL, J. M. (1871) Hastings Prize Essay on Digitalis. *British Medical Journal*, *ii*, 5–27, 27–90.

LOW, J. (1982) C. J. Newcombe, the alienist who became collector of the native art and treasures of the Pacific Northwest. *The Beaver*, spring, 32–39.

MCNALTY, A. (1965) Some pioneers of the past in neurology. *Medical History*, **9**.

NATURE (1924) C. J. Newcombe (obituary). *Nature*, **114**.

ROLLESTON, H. D. (1929) *The Honorable Sir Thomas Clifford Allbutt – A Memoir*. London: Macmillan.

SHERRINGTON, C. (1928) D. Ferrier (obituary). *Proceedings of the Royal Society of London, Series* B, **103**, 8–16.

TAYLOR, *et al* (1931) *Selected Writings of Hughlings Jackson, Vol. 1, On Epilepsy and Epileptiform Convulsions*. London: Hodder & Stoughton.

TUKE, S. (1819) *Hints on the Construction & Economy of Pauper Lunatic Asylums*. London: Longman & Hirst.

VIETS, H. R. (1938) *Bulletin of the Institute of Historical Medicine*, **6**, 446–487.

YELLOWLEES, H. (1953) *To Define True Madness*. Harmondsworth: Penguin.

26 Adolf Meyer and his influence on British psychiatry

MICHAEL GELDER

Although Adolf Meyer's influence on the practice of psychiatry in Britain was great, it is now quite difficult to discern. This is because his ideas have become so much part of the basic structure of British clinical psychiatry that it is easy to forget that there was a time when things were different. Whenever we take a case history, make a life chart, write a formulation, or work in a multidisciplinary team, we are likely to be using some of Meyer's ideas – and yet he worked in America, not in Britain. To understand why his ideas were so influential, it is necessary to know something about Meyer's life, understand the essence of his ideas, and find out how they were carried to Britain. Before turning to these matters, however, it is worth considering how Meyer appeared to others towards the end of his career.

A description of Meyer in old age has been written by Jerome Frank (1980), who worked with him shortly before Meyer's retirement at the age of 74. Meyer is described as a short, stocky man with bushy eyebrows, a goatee beard, and a moustache (Fig. 26.1, p. 425). In manner, he was unassuming, dignified and courteous. Although he had lived in the United States for nearly 50 years, he still spoke with a strong Swiss-German accent. At work, Meyer could be a rather intimidating figure, partly because he was widely read and could quote at length both from the literature of psychiatry and the work of philosophers. Outside work, however, he could be warm and friendly.

Like many great men, Meyer had boundless energy and enthusiasm. In his early 70s, he was still in charge of the Phipps Clinic where he held daily staff meetings, saw patients, taught students, and worked in a neuropathology laboratory. How did this remarkable man come to be the most influential American psychiatrist of his generation? To answer this question, it is necessary to consider some of the important events in his long career.

Meyer's career

There have been many accounts of Adolf Meyer's life (e.g. Betz, 1981*a*,*b*; Mora, 1980). The following outline does not seek to review his life in detail, but only to provide a basis for understanding his ideas and his influence on British psychiatry.

Meyer was born in Niederwenigen near Zurich in November 1866. His father was a Zwinglian minister, and one of his uncles was a doctor. Meyer studied medicine in the University of Zurich, where one of his teachers was August Forel. He enjoyed Forel's teaching of psychiatry, but at that time did not think of it as a career; instead, he was interested in neurology. He qualified in medicine in 1890, at the age of 24, and won a travel scholarship, which he was able to supplement with a small inheritance from his grandfather (Betz, 1981*a*). The combined funds enabled him to travel, beginning with four months in Paris, where he attended lectures given by Dejerine and Charcot (Meyer, 1891), followed by six months in Britain, first in Edinburgh then London. It is clear that this experience made a lasting impression. Thus, more than 40 years later, in his Maudsley lecture (1933), Meyer recalled how much he had learned from the Edinburgh physicians. At Forel's suggestion, he also found out about the organisation of psychiatric services in Scotland. In London, Francis Caird, a young surgeon, had arranged introductions to the staff of the neurological hospital at Queen Square, through his friend, Dr James Taylor. In this way, the young Meyer was able to observe the work of Hughlings Jackson, Horsley, Ferrier, and Gowers.

On his return to Switzerland, Meyer decided to pursue his interest in neurology by undertaking research in neuropathology, as a preliminary to clinical training. This research, which was supervised by Forel – a neuropathologist as well as a clinician – was concerned with the forebrain of reptiles (Betz, 1981*a*); the work progressed well and Meyer completed the final draft of his thesis in 1892. Forel, who had previously encouraged Meyer to study psychiatry, again suggested this career, but Meyer rejected the advice because he felt that psychiatry would require "much more ability than I had for verbal expression" (Meyer, 1933, p. 439). Instead, he decided to set off for America, thinking that the career opportunities would be better there than in Switzerland.

On his way to America, Meyer stopped in Britain to attend the meeting of the British Medical Association in Nottingham, and the International Congress of Psychology in Edinburgh, and this brief visit left a second lasting impression on his mind (Meyer, 1933). In Nottingham, he was introduced briefly to Osler, and at the psychology meeting was able to listen to many famous men, including Galton, William James, Stanley Hall, Janet, Tichener, Bernheim, and Lombroso. During his stay in Britain, he also visited London to take further advice about opportunities in America, and decided to go to Chicago (Betz, 1981*b*).

Meyer's actions when he arrived in Chicago throw light on his character. He wrote at once to the Medical Faculty of Rush College, offering to start a neuropathology laboratory. However, as he had only limited experience as a neuropathologist, it is not surprising that the offer was rejected (Betz, 1981*b*). He was not deterred by this rebuff, but wrote instead to the University of Chicago, again inquiring about work in neuropathology. This time the response was a little more favourable: an appointment was offered, but it was to be unpaid. Meyer accepted this offer and set to work as a general practitioner to earn enough money to live. Meanwhile, he continued his attempts to obtain the kind of job that he was seeking by writing again to the University of Chicago, this time to its president. In this letter, Meyer suggested that the University should set up a 'brain institute', in which he would work. Predictably, his suggestion was rejected (Betz, 1981*b*).

Although Meyer was disappointed by these rebuffs, he persisted with his inquiries and eventually obtained a post, again unpaid, as attending physician to the Neurology Department of the College of Physicians and Surgeons in Chicago. In this post, he was able to teach medical students, see patients, and meet local neurologists. It seems that Meyer did not always get on well with the other members of the College, and that he mentioned this problem in his letters to his family. His younger brother Hermann's reply (in German) to one of these letters contains an interesting comment:

> "I should like to remind you of one thing. You have always been accustomed to assert your opinions and your views as if you considered them the only correct ones without troubling very much how others would take them . . . . When Professor Forel spoke to me of your dissertation, almost his first remark was: 'He must still learn to deal with people more gently'. How then will a Chicago Professor or Doctor react if you lay down your plans to him?" (Betz, 1981*b*, p. 29)

This was not a happy time for Meyer. Not only did he have difficulty in obtaining satisfactory paid work, but he was also receiving worrying news about his mother. Soon after he left Switzerland, she had become increasingly tired and depressed, and he was concerned that, by leaving home, he had contributed to her unhappiness. Eventually, the family persuaded Frau Meyer to see Professor Forel, who diagnosed melancholia and arranged for her admission to the Burghöltzli Hospital. Frau Meyer became increasingly depressed and began to express delusional ideas of poverty. Meyer was particularly concerned about these ideas because his mother had provided security for a loan that he had taken out to pay for his travel to America: he worried that the responsibility for his debt might have caused her deteriorating state (Betz, 1981*a*, p. 38). He must have expressed this concern in a letter to his brother Hermann, for he received the following reply (written originally in German):

> "You are convinced that worry about you was an actual cause of the worsening of Mama's condition, if not the very root of it. Even though I know Mama was very concerned about you, I know just as well that no single cause brought her to the state in which she now is. Mama bore the illness of Papa and Anna relatively well but they could not have passed over her without deep effect . . . since you know Mama's condition you can no longer believe that through the removal of some situational factor which with many others has affected her, any kind of easing of her condition can be accomplished." (Betz, 1981*a*, p. 38) (Anna was Meyer's sister who died of tuberculosis soon after he qualified in medicine.)

It is interesting to consider whether this thoughtful reply prepared the ground for Meyer's subsequent ideas about the multifactorial aetiology of mental illness.

In May 1893, when Meyer was thoroughly discouraged by these events, he had an unexpected offer. The Illinois Eastern Asylum was looking for a pathologist: Meyer accepted and, at the age of 26, went to work in his first psychiatric hospital. The asylum was in Kankakee, a town of 10 000 people situated 60 miles south of Chicago; although the town was small, the hospital was not – there were 3000 patients. Despite this, the duties of the pathologist were not onerous, consisting mainly of autopsies and urine examinations, and the pay was adequate. Although appointed as a pathologist, Meyer took stock of the clinical services of the hospital; he was not impressed by what he saw, and he decided to write a report to the governor of the state of Illinois to suggest reforms. The nature of the report can be inferred from the following passage:

> "The ideal asylum or hospital for the insane should furnish the patients most of the advantages of home. . . . The attendants should be nurses not supervisors, they should live like patients, eat the same food . . . and share the recreations and amusements with the patients with as little bossing as possible. Everything that suggests detention in prison must be strictly avoided." (Meyer, 1895*a*, p. 45)

It was a confident statement from someone with so little experience of psychiatric practice.

Meyer seems to have been as unimpressed by the quality of the staff of the hospital as he was in the care they provided. Thus, in the same report, he commented that "whereas the medical man in Germany and other countries has the highest and widest education, we find here the capacity of the average business-man. More than any other physician the alienist must have a broad education" (Meyer, 1895*a*, p. 58). He tried to remedy matters by teaching the staff the things he knew best: neuroanatomy, neuropathology, and neurology. Before long, however, he realised how remote these subjects were from the problems of the patients in Kankakee and decided to add a course of lectures on the psychoses.

Meyer based these additional lectures on the teaching he had received from Forel and from his reading of the fourth edition of Kraepelin's textbook (Meyer, 1927). It is striking that although most of Meyer's own knowledge of psychiatry at that time must have been theoretical, his first lectures emphasised the study of patients. The introduction to the series, which has survived, contains the following statement:

> "We are going to study patients. Those of us who have a talent for observation will have the preference over those who have perhaps a good memory for literature. . . . The observer who can subdue his book learning and his brilliancy will have the best chances for clinical work." (Winters, 1966, p. 452)

As he continued to work with psychiatric problems, Meyer became increasingly dissatisfied with the emphasis Kraepelin and other authors of the time placed on heredity as a cause of mental illness, and began to think instead about environmental influences. He joined the Illinois Association for Child Study (Meyer, 1933*b*, p. 455) and developed his ideas in three papers (Meyer, 1895*b*,*c*,*d*) about the disorders of children – a subject on which he seems to have had no special experience at the time. In the second of these papers, Meyer wrote: "we shall, I hope, arrive at a result which will show that heredity is only to a limited extent as baneful a curse on a family as many writers would make us believe" (Meyer, 1895*b*, p. 325). This passage was written at a time when Meyer's mother was still suffering from a depressive disorder, and he commented subsequently that "I was personally sensitized concerning the blending and differentiation of possible hereditary and constitutional factors with definitely psychogenic ones by an account of an attack of depression in my mother shortly after my emigration" (Meyer, 1933*b*, p. 455).

The year 1895 was a better one for Meyer. His mother's health improved, and he was becoming known both locally and – after presenting his ideas at the annual meeting of the American Medico-Psychological Association – to a wider audience. Moreover, he was offered a new and more important post.

The new work was as pathologist to the Worcester Lunatic Asylum, with the possibility of a link with the nearby Clark University. Meyer accepted the offer and began work at Worcester in November 1895, three and a half years after he had arrived in the United States. One of the attractions of the new post was that, in addition to work as pathologist, Meyer was given responsibility for the training of the psychiatrists. Moreover, he was able to give a wide interpretation to his duties as pathologist and to include the study of living patients as well as pathological specimens (Meyer, 1913).

In order to prepare for his work as a teacher of psychiatry, Meyer was given leave to study in Europe, where he visited Kraepelin and Lombroso. Although impressed by their work, he continued to question the emphasis they laid on heredity and neuropathology as sources for the understanding of psychiatric disorders. His viewpoint was expressed in words written three years later, as part of an official report:

> "psychiatry is undoubtedly one branch of medicine in which pathology in the sense of pathological anatomy and bacteriology has done very little and promises little. Here the pathology of clinicians, the broad enquiry into disease processes, must come first." (Meyer, 1898, p. 21)

Meyer worked hard at Worcester: he published papers on neuropathology and clinical psychiatry, and his reputation grew. Indeed, in 1901 at the surprisingly young age of 35, he was chosen to represent Clark University at the 450th anniversary celebrations of the University of Glasgow, and was one of those awarded the honorary degree of LLD (Henderson, 1964, p. 155). In the following year, Meyer's growing reputation led to the offer of the post of Director of the New York State Pathological Institute, a position previously held by Van Gieson, the neuropathologist. The purpose of the Institute was to improve the standards of medical work in the state institutions of the state of New York, and Meyer threw himself into his new task with great enthusiasm. His experience at Worcester convinced him that to achieve the purpose of the Institute, he needed to do more than provide neuropathology. To raise standards, clinical practice would have to improve. In a report written soon after his appointment, Meyer expressed these convictions in the following words:

> "We need a crusade against empty utterances of opinion when facts are available, against the use of diagnostic terms which have no definite medical meaning. This can be achieved . . . by requiring that the records put the facts into prominence . . . we set the assistants a poor example if we slur over defects in records, where indeed we ought to force [them] to give us more concise and accurate facts, or a statement of why they were not obtained." (Meyer, 1902, p. 101)

Although Meyer understood the value of Kraepelin's system of diagnosis (Meyer, 1927), he campaigned against what he saw as the unthinking use by others of these diagnostic categories. This conviction was expressed in another report: "The superstition about the value of diagnosis of a disease is that once made it puts the doctors in a position to solve the queries about the case not with the facts presented by it . . . but by a system of rules'' (Meyer, 1906*a*, p. 154).*

Meyer's influence in New York grew steadily. He was appointed Professor of Psychopathology at Cornell University Medical College, he organised the first out-patient clinic in the city of New York, and he published many papers. Of these, one, on schizophrenia, is particularly notable; it was delivered in 1906 before the annual meeting of the British Medical Association, held in Toronto. The subject was dementia praecox, and in it Meyer expounded his ideas about aetiology:

> ''Every individual is capable of reacting to a wide variety of situations by a limited number of reaction types. . . . In psychiatry the facts occur in very complex combinations, and therefore one-word diagnosis is almost sure to fall short of what it ought to do. . . . Etiologically, the constitutional make-up counts for a great deal but not in the vague sense of hereditary and degeneracy merely.'' (Meyer, 1906*b*, pp. 757, 758)

Meyer's emphasis on clinical standards led him to propose a change of name for the Pathological Institute, which became the New York State Psychiatric Institute. In a report written subsequently, he summed up his approach in the following words:

> ''The Institute was not to be a sideshow such as so many pathologists in State Institutions have been forced to maintain . . . it was to create standards . . . to establish a spirit of co-operation and a sane view of specific problems, rather than introduce uncritically the fads and methods of other departments of medicine. . . . The plan decided upon was to begin with a period of instruction and the creation of a system of standards. . . . The plans and methods of examination of the patients, the standard of accuracy about the facts of the development of disorder as well as about the actual nature of the disorder . . . [and] the system of control by staff meetings, these are matters on which a safe and profitable routine is established in all our hospitals . . . that which figured in the past as routine, the history taking, the physical and mental examination of patients, have been imbued with a never failing interest.'' (Meyer, 1909)

In June 1908, Meyer again received the offer of a new position, this time at Johns Hopkins University Medical School in Baltimore, where a new psychiatric clinic was being established with an endowment from Henry Phipps, a wealthy financier. Meyer soon accepted the post of director of the new clinic, but there were many delays before the project was completed, and the clinic did not open until five years later, in April 1913. The opening was a grand occasion, marked by speeches from Welch and Cushing, as well as from Osler and Bleuler, who had travelled from Europe. Meyer now had a position of great influence, and he worked hard to exploit it. He demanded high standards of clinical work from his staff and was active in teaching medical students, while at the same time continuing pathological work of his own. The reputation of the clinic grew,

* In this and in several subsequent quotations, several phrases have been removed. This is made necessary by Meyer's discursive style of writing, in which the main thrust of a sentence is often obscured by elaborations and asides.

and many young psychiatrists went there to improve their training and observe its activities.

Meyer remained in charge of the Phipps Clinic until his retirement at the age of 74. During these years, he achieved much and received many honours, but his ideas did not develop in important ways after the first years in Baltimore. For this reason, it is appropriate to leave Meyer's career at this point and turn to an outline of his ideas.

Meyer's ideas

Meyer's ideas on clinical psychiatry can be summarised under five headings: psychobiology, the classification of mental disorders, treatment, hospital reform, and teaching (Fig. 26.2) and training.

Psychobiology

Meyer used the term 'psychobiology' to indicate an approach to psychiatry that attended to the whole person and considered a wide range of factors in the

Fig. 26.1. Adolf Meyer in 1936 (courtesy of the Alan Mason Chesney Medical Archives of the Johns Hopkins Medical Institutions)

Fig. 26.2. Adolf Meyer teaching a class of students in 1935 (courtesy of Alan Mason Chesney Medical Archives of the Johns Hopkins Medical Institutions)

aetiology of mental disorder. The ideas are now so widely accepted that they have to be seen against the beliefs prevailing at the time. When Meyer began to advocate this approach, most psychiatrists regarded psychoses as disorders with a predetermined and generally unfavourable course; in considering aetiology, they concentrated attention on hereditary factors, and in treatment they advocated custodial care. They also spent much time in debates about the relationship between mind and brain.

Psychobiology was set up in opposition to these ideas. The mind/brain problem was rejected as insoluble, the two being regarded as equally essential aspects of the person. Each person was mainly a product of social forces and other life experiences, and heredity was relatively less important. Each healthy person was unique, and he remained unique when ill; the psychiatrist had to understand his patients as individuals by studying their biographies – it was not enough to assign them to diagnostic categories. Psychiatric disorders were reactions of the person to cumulative events in his life, each person having a limited number of ways of reacting. No elaborate theory was needed to understand the relationship between events in people's lives and their abnormal ways of responding: common sense was enough. By common sense, Meyer did not mean the uninformed ideas of a layman, rather a professional judgement based on medical knowledge, but dealing with actual experiences, not speculative unconscious processes. (Although Meyer was interested in Freud's work – and was an honorary member of the New York Psychoanalytic Society – he considered that the psychoanalytic approach embodied an excessive use of theory.)

Psychobiology required a detailed assessment of patients' life experiences, and this could be assisted by the drawing up of a 'life chart'. The chart had columns for life problems and for periods of psychiatric disorder, each of which was shown against the year that it began and ended. The resulting information had to be capable of providing answers to the following questions. What are this person's faults and failings? What are his resources and assets? What was he like at his best? How can his difficulties be modified?

Classification: the 'ergasias'

Meyer's view of psychiatric disorders as particular kinds of reaction to circumstances led him to propose a new system of classification. Although basically simple, the scheme was made unnecessarily difficult to understand by the terms chosen by Meyer to denote each type of reaction. These terms shared the suffix 'ergasia', a word chosen by Meyer to indicate "mentally integrated behaviour or functioning" (Meyer, 1933*b*, p. 1112). There were seven types of ergasia: (a) *anergasias* – a group broadly corresponding to chronic organic psychiatric disorders; (b) *dysergasias* – corresponding to acute organic syndromes; (c) *thymergasias* – the affective disorders; (d) *parergasias* – schizophrenia and paranoid states; (e) *merergasias* – the neuroses; (f) *kakergasias* – behaviour disorders; and (g) *oligergasias* – mental deficiency.

This scheme was never taken up widely; even in the Phipps Clinic, it was used in only 12% of in-patients diagnosed up to the time of Meyer's retirement (Stephens *et al*, 1986). However, with the substitution of the words 'reaction type' for Meyer's term 'ergasia', the scheme was to become incorporated in an important British textbook and to influence the first edition of the American Psychiatric Association's classification scheme (DSM–I).

Treatment

Meyer taught that treatment began with the first interviews with patients, in which their assets and strengths were to be assessed, as well as their illnesses and handicaps. He called this assessment a "distributive analysis"; the aim was to help the patient find out for himself, not to impose a conclusion on him. Distributive analysis was followed by a "distributive synthesis", in which patients were helped to build on their strengths, overcome their handicaps, and adapt better to their circumstances. As well as these psychological components, treatment included measures to improve sleep and nutrition, and a regular routine of living was encouraged. Problems were dealt with at a conscious level, beginning with the most immediate and accessible, and avoiding speculation about unconscious processes. Free association (Meyer preferred the term 'spontaneous association') was encouraged in these interviews, but psychoanalytic interpretation was not. Meyer stressed the need for 'habit training', by which he meant guidance, re-education, and other measures to help patients deal better with the stresses in their lives. Treatment was the work of a team; nurses were involved fully, and visits to the home were made by social workers. Meyer also valued and encouraged the work of occupational therapists.

Meyer applied methods of this kind as much to schizophrenia as to the neuroses. At a time when physical treatments had little beneficial effect and when the diagnosis of schizophrenia often led to therapeutic nihilism, Meyer's therapeutic confidence was important. However, a recent analysis has shown that 43% of patients admitted to the Phipps Clinic during Meyer's time had not improved at the time of discharge (Stephens *et al*, 1986).

Hospital reform

Meyer was one of the pioneers of the reform of American psychiatric hospitals. However, he was not the first to see this need, nor was he the first to emphasise the importance of improving the quality and training of psychiatrists. For example, in 1894, the year after Meyer arrived in the United States, Weir Mitchell, the neurologist, had this to say to the annual meeting of the American Medico-Psychological Association:

> "You were the first specialists and you never came back in line. It is easy to see how this came about. You soon began to live apart, and you still do so. Your hospitals are not our hospitals; your ways are not our ways. You live out of range of critical shot; you are not preceded and followed in your ward work by clever rivals, or watched by able residents fresh from learning from the schools. I am strongly of the opinion that the influences which for many years led the general profession to the belief that no one could, or should, treat the insane except special practitioners, have done us and you, and many of our patients lasting wrong." (Mitchell, 1894, p. 414)

Meyer's interest in social factors in mental illness led him to an interest in the care of patients after they left hospital, and in prevention. After initial caution, he supported the "mental hygiene" movement started by Clifford Beers, an energetic layman who had described unfortunate personal experiences of psychiatric treatment in a book, *A Mind That Found Itself* (Beers, 1908). Meyer was at first critical of Beers' optimistic views about prevention and his expansive ways of working, but he saw the value of an influential movement of this kind and took a practical interest in its progress (Winters, 1969). He was also a strong supporter of the development of psychiatric social work and occupational therapy. Indeed, in the early days of his clinical career, his wife helped him by visiting the families of his patients, becoming in effect the first psychiatric social worker (Lidz, 1966, p. 328).

Teaching and training

Meyer believed that medical students should not learn only about mental disorders, but should also understand personality and its development. At first, he thought that this understanding would be increased by lectures on academic psychology, and in 1914 introduced the first course on psychology for medical students at Johns Hopkins Medical School. The teaching was shared with J. B. Watson, the well known behaviourist, and with Knight Dunlap (Leys, 1984, p. 134), but the course was not a success. Despite the efforts of the teachers, the students failed to see the relevance of academic psychology to their work with patients. For this reason, Meyer took over all the teaching himself, concentrating on the study of personality through clinical examples, and, in this form, the course became established (Lief, 1948, p. 371).

Meyer believed that postgraduate training should emphasise the detailed study of individual patients. He stressed the need to assess courses of instruction – a point he made as early as 1895 in a report to the governor of Illinois (Meyer, 1895*a*, p. 55) – and to examine the trainees' attainments. Indeed, when President of the American Psychiatric Association in 1928, he made a strong plea for the specialist certification of psychiatrists, and referred approvingly to the diplomas in psychological medicine which already existed in Britain.

Meyer believed that postgraduate training in psychiatry should be wide in its scope. Psychoanalysis was to be part of it, but as "an incident in a broader training to be limited to specially talented clinicians and well chosen patients; it is not to figure as the all-pervading principle of actual psychiatric practice" (Meyer, 1933*b*, p. 116). Psychiatrists were to learn neurology and neuropathology, but their teaching was to be by people who also had some experience of clinical psychiatry; otherwise, Meyer warned, the subject matter might not be put across in the most appropriate way.

Influences on British psychiatry

Any reader who works as a psychiatrist in Britain is likely by now to have recognised Meyer's influence on the teaching and practice of clinical psychiatry. The extent of this influence is considerable and, arguably, greater than that on American psychiatry. Indeed, when Shepherd visited Baltimore in the mid-1950s, expecting to see the legacy of Meyer, he discovered that "the Meyerian spirit appeared to be alive and flourishing in a number of off-shore islands within Johns Hopkins' territorial waters – for example in the laboratories of Dr Kurt Richter and Dr Horsley Gantt in the Harriet Lane Clinic – but it was difficult to detect in the mainland of the Phipps Clinic" (Shepherd, 1986). Although a visitor to the Phipps Clinic in the 1980s would have had a very different impression, thanks to the efforts of Professor Paul McHugh, who revived the Meyerian approach at Johns Hopkins, Shepherd's observations were valid at the time and they applied more widely than just to this one hospital. Professor McHugh began his training in psychiatry with Sir Aubrey Lewis at the Maudsley Hospital and Lewis adopted Meyer's psychobiological approach (see below). Thus the wheel was to come full circle.

The post-war American view of Meyer's influence was aptly summed up in the article on Meyer in a leading American textbook: "from the historical perspective, the importance of Meyer's psychobiology lies in the first place in being a trend of thought that paved the way for the acceptance of psychodynamic concepts . . . [and is] relevant today to the current movement in community mental health" (Mora, 1980). While the second part of this statement draws attention to one of Meyer's important legacies, the first points to the reason why so much of what he left was cast aside. For some time, American psychiatry was dominated by psychoanalysis: since psychoanalysis has been less influential in Britain, this statement also suggests why Meyer's ideas survived there. However, before that issue can be considered usefully, it is necessary to understand how Meyer's teaching took root in Britain.

Meyer's writings on psychiatry are difficult to read because, although he lived in the United States for many years, he never mastered a clear style of writing in English. Even when his ideas are known to the reader, it is not easy to follow them in his convoluted prose, and the volumes of his collected papers remain largely unread. It is unlikely, therefore, that Meyer's influence was transmitted through his writings; instead, it seems to have been carried to Britain by psychiatrists who worked with him. Of these people, the two most influential were Sir David Henderson and Sir Aubrey Lewis.

Henderson went to New York to work with Meyer in 1908, the year after he graduated in medicine. At the time, Meyer was in his early 40s and at the height of his powers, and the young Scot was immediately impressed by the forceful personality of his new teacher. Henderson subsequently described Meyer at this time as:

> "a dark complexioned, trimly-bearded man, dignified and serious, thoughtful, a man who looked you straight in the eye with a gaze which pierced your innermost thoughts. . . . He was a leader and he commanded attention; though sensitive and shy he was far more approachable than was generally realized. . . . There was a magnetism about him which created the feeling of being with a great man." (Henderson, 1966)

Henderson stayed at the New York Psychiatric Institute for three years, returning to Scotland in 1912 after a visit of several months to Kraepelin's clinic in Munich to become Junior Physician to Gartnavel Royal Hospital. Soon after his return, he read a paper to the Scottish Division of the Medico-Psychological Association on "Catatonia as a type of mental reaction". This paper shows clearly the influence of Meyer's teaching on Henderson's development as a psychiatrist. In it, he sought to show how Meyer's psychobiological approach could be applied to catatonic patients, commenting for example that "as pointed out by Meyer, the individual who tends to develop dementia praecox is not a well-balanced person, but on the other hand is usually one who throughout life has been in the habit of meeting difficulties in an inadequate way'' (Henderson, 1916, p. 559).

Before Henderson had time to settle in Glasgow, he received an invitation from Meyer to join him once more, this time as Senior Resident in the new Phipps Clinic in Baltimore. Henderson accepted and set off for Baltimore in the autumn of 1912 to take up his resident post. When he arrived, he found that building work was behind schedule and the resident's flat not ready; consequently, he had nowhere to stay, and the Meyers generously invited him to live with them. Henderson remained with the Meyers for six months, and during that time his admiration for Adolf Meyer and his wife increased (see Henderson, 1938, 1966). This experience, coupled with the pioneering task of helping Meyer set up the new clinical service in the Phipps Clinic, made a deep and lasting impression on Henderson, so that when he returned to Scotland again, he was steeped in Meyer's ideas and practices.

In 1915, Henderson went back to Glasgow to work in the Royal Mental Hospital at Gartnavel, where he was to become Physician Superintendent and Lecturer in Psychological Medicine at the University of Glasgow. At that time, none of the current textbooks of psychiatry set out the kind of clinical approach that Henderson had learnt from Meyer, and he decided to join with another of Meyer's pupils to produce a new textbook. His collaborator was R. D. Gillespie, who had worked as Henderson's assistant at Gartnavel, and then (at Henderson's suggestion) with Meyer in Baltimore and who subsequently became physician in psychological medicine at Guy's Hospital. The new psychiatry textbook appeared in 1927. It was dedicated to Adolf Meyer and the preface contained the following statement:

> ''the biological viewpoint of Adolf Meyer and his followers of the American School has seemed to us to shed fresh light on the nature of mental illness, and to offer new hope for its prevention and treatment. This biological hypothesis regards mental illness as the cumulative result of unhealthy reactions of the individual mind to its environment, and seeks to trace in a given case all the factors that go to the production of these reactions.''

The new textbook was notable for four features. Firstly, unlike other current textbooks, the chapter on methods of examination emphasised history-taking as much as the examination of the mental state, and the scheme for recording this information was closely similar to that which Meyer had developed at the New York Psychiatric Institute. Secondly, the system of classification was Meyer's, although the term 'reaction type' was used rather than Meyer's obscure terminology of the 'ergasias'. Thirdly, the book contained many illustrative case histories, constructed on psychobiological lines, to illustrate the importance of understanding the patient as a unique individual. Lastly, aetiology was presented in psychobiological terms, emphasising the interplay of causes. For example, the chapter on schizophrenia included the following statement:

> ''schizophrenia is not a disease, but a congeries of individual types of reaction having certain general similarities. The individual may be loaded in various ways – by inheritance, by physical defects of an endocrine disorder or some grosser kind, by intellectual deficiency, or what not – but none of them is itself a sufficient cause for schizophrenia. It is

> only when the subject, handicapped or not, has to face the usual concrete problems in his journey through life, that reactions can appear which cumulatively lead to one of the numerous conditions which have been included under the designation of 'dementia praecox' or 'schizophrenia'." (p. 188)

Henderson & Gillespie's new textbook was well received. The reviewer in the *Journal of Mental Science* (1928, p. 123) wrote that the authors "are to be congratulated upon the production of an evenly balanced, consistent, judicious and comprehensive textbook" and went on to comment favourably on the case histories, a feature which "invests the book with an atmosphere of vitality which is lacking in the formal description of the symptoms of the various kinds of morbid reaction". With no clear rival, the new book was soon established as the standard text for those sitting postgraduate examinations in psychiatry. A second edition appeared in 1930, and many others followed; indeed, the book was continued into its tenth edition, after Sir David Henderson's death in 1965, by his former pupil Sir Ivor Batchelor. It was finally withdrawn in the late 1970s, more than 50 years after its first appearance.

Sir Aubrey Lewis introduced Meyer's ideas to Britain in an altogether different way. He spent a shorter time than Henderson had done in working with Meyer, and was less strongly influenced by his teacher's powerful personality. Also, while Henderson joined Meyer immediately after qualifying in medicine, Lewis arrived in Baltimore after a year studying psychiatry in Boston. Furthermore, on leaving Baltimore, Lewis went on a long visit to Germany, where he visited Beringer in Heidelberg and Bonhoeffer in Berlin (Shepherd, 1986). Perhaps as a result of these varied experiences, Lewis was able to see Meyer's contribution in a balanced way, relating it to other approaches. Lewis respected Meyer's wide general knowledge of literature and philosophy, and his scholarly approach to psychiatry. He was also strongly impressed by Meyer's personal and professional integrity – a quality that he valued very much (Lewis, 1960).

After his study tour in Europe, Lewis returned to Australia, but in 1928 left again, this time to work with Mapother at the Maudsley Hospital. Forty years later, he summed up his first impressions of the hospital as follows:

> "I expected from what I was told that at the Maudsley I might have to re-adjust my modes of thought to a somewhat insular, rigid, materialistic and old fashioned model, of which Mapother would be the exponent. In fact I found it quite otherwise. The fundamental standpoint of Meyer was very close to that of Mapother, though more profound and less intelligible; the clinical principles of Bonhoeffer and the brilliant group around him – such men as Kronfeld, Birnbaum, Thiele – were readily adaptable to the Maudsley climate, allowance being made for the greater erudition of the Germans." (See Shepherd, 1986, p. 11)

Three aspects of Meyer's thought were particularly influential in Lewis' teaching and practice of psychiatry: his clinical method; the psychobiological approach with its emphasis on multiple causes and on the study of each patient as a unique individual; and the idea of a research centre in which clinicians could work closely with basic scientists. Thus Lewis passed Meyer's teaching on to very many pupils, but while Henderson had an effect on the training of psychiatrists before the war through the textbook he wrote with Gillespie, Lewis' influence did not develop fully until the post-war period. This was because, although Lewis was Clinical Director of the Maudsley Hospital from 1936, there were few trainees at the hospital at that time. It was the expansion of psychiatric training after the war and Lewis' appointment to the Chair of Psychiatry in 1945 which enabled him to exert influence. In this role, he shaped the training of the many psychiatrists who passed through the Maudsley between 1945 and Lewis' retirement. These trainee psychiatrists learnt a clinical method which emphasised extensive history-taking, leading first to a diagnosis and then to an understanding of the individual patient. Life charts were used to show relationships between social or psychological changes, and episodes of mental disorder. Cases were formulated in a way that reflected Lewis' amalgamation of the best of Meyer's ideas with Kraepelin's diagnostic system. Thus a diagnostic formulation was made first, followed by an aetiological statement in which the evolution of the personality and that of the illness were traced along psychobiological lines.

Of all the aspects of Lewis' clinical teaching, perhaps it was the 'admissions and discharges conference' which exemplified Meyer's influence most clearly. After explaining the general sequence of treatment, the doctors taking part in the conference were required to make statements about the part to be played by relatives, nurses, social workers, and occupational therapists. Physical treatment was described, and in every case a statement had to be made about the use of psychotherapy. For the latter, the doctor had to choose between five methods, of which the first was Meyer's distributive psychotherapy. At discharge, further clear statements were required about the patient's living conditions and personal relationships, and about the prospects for resuming work and leisure activities. In structuring the meetings in this way, Lewis had extracted the essence of Meyer's clinical approach and presented it more clearly than its originator had ever done.

Meyer's influence was seen not only in Lewis' teaching: his plan for the Institute of Psychiatry also embodied ideas that can be traced to Meyer. Just as the staff of the Phipps Clinic included basic scientists such as Horsley Gantt and Kurt Richter, so when Lewis established the new Institute, he introduced departments of psychology and physiology as well as a more traditional neuropathology department. In Lewis' conceptual scheme, of which Meyer's ideas formed only a part, a productive amalgamation was soon achieved between basic science and psychiatry; indeed, it can be argued that the formula worked better in the new Institute than it had done in the Phipps Clinic.

Henderson and Lewis were not the only British psychiatrists to work with Meyer. Gillespie's visit to Baltimore has been referred to already; Desmond Curran went in 1930, and Ian Skottowe followed. Both wrote textbooks (Curran with Eric Guttmann) and although these books contain fewer references to Meyer's ideas than appear in Henderson's influential text, both made use of Meyer's concept of reaction types. Indeed, Curran & Guttmann (1943, p. 36) wrote in the first edition of their book that: "in modern psychiatry the old conception . . . of disease entities has been replaced by the broader and more elastic concept of reaction types".

There was another reason why Meyer's teaching took root in Britain: many of his ideas had originated there. Although Meyer was influenced by Swiss thinkers (see Bleuler, 1962) and by American psychologists and philosophers such as James, Peirce, and Dewey, the ideas of British writers on biology and medicine were of great importance to him. It is clear that his visit to Britain as a newly qualified doctor in 1890 made a lasting impression on his mind. Thus in his Maudsley lecture, Meyer expressed "real personal indebtedness to British medicine and British psychiatry" (Meyer, 1933*a*, p. 435) and referred to the influence on his thinking of Huxley's writings and especially of three ideas: first, "his definition of science as organized common sense; second his presentation of the theories of Darwin and the critical philosophy of Hume . . . ; and third, his extreme version of parallelism which made mind a mere epiphenomenon" (Meyer, 1933*a*, p. 438). Meyer also referred to the influence of "Hughlings Jackson's capacity for observation; his use of the principles of evolution and dissolution rather than of a narrower concept of structure and function, and his caution in the use of psychological terms and concepts" (p. 445). He remarked that his own ideas on psychobiology "would not have had an easy development . . . without the influence of the British understanding of biology" (p. 443). In the same paper, Meyer commented on the influence of the teachers he encountered during his stay in Edinburgh; "John Wyllie, then a physician at the Royal Infirmary, keen on sound and clinical methods . . . Alexander Bruce, then beginning to make his mark in neurology, and to some extent Byron Bramwell, of specific note both as a general physician and a neurologist". He went on to comment on the importance to him of hearing the second of Thomas Clouston's lectures on "The neuroses of development", and of hearing a case discussion by Sir Thomas Grainger in which the development of temperament and constitution was considered (p. 451). Meyer was commissioned by his Swiss colleagues to find out about the organisation of mental health services in Scotland, and he reported about this on his return (Meyer, 1893): the report appeared in 1893 as his second published paper (the first was a more general account of his time abroad concerning medical practice in Paris, Edinburgh, and London (Meyer, 1891)).

Having considered why Meyer's teaching took root in Britain, it is appropriate to return to the question of why his influence has continued here while in America, where he worked, it has waned. One reason has been mentioned already. In America during the post-war years, a wave of enthusiasm for psychoanalysis swept through the medical schools, and Meyer's less spectacular ideas became neglected. In Britain, psychoanalysis never achieved the same influence.

The second reason for the decline in America of the Meyerian approach is that as the tide of psychoanalysis receded, it was soon replaced by another enthusiasm. This influence, which continues to gain strength, is known as 'biological psychiatry', a name which suggests a relationship with psychobiology but which is in reality very different. Biological psychiatry uses an illness model which is different from Meyer's notion of reaction types. Also, the biological approach is associated with a system of diagnosis that relies more heavily on the present state of the patient than on the evolution of personal problems. Finally, with the biological approach, treatment relates more closely to the diagnosis than to the unique features of the individual patient. In Britain, with its more conservative approach, the ideas of biological psychiatry have been absorbed into previous teaching and practice. Nevertheless, there are continuing pressures to return to an approach to psychiatry which focuses on the illness at the expense of the ill person, and in which the doctor thinks that the investigative work is done when a diagnosis has been made. It is appropriate, therefore, to end by repeating Meyer's warning about this kind of approach: the person who follows it has, he said, "no use for the actual study of cases beyond the hunting up of a few diagnostic signs and asks 'what is the use of any special study of the case if the diagnosis is [already] made?' " (Meyer, 1906*b*). These words were written in the first decade of this century, and if Meyer could have lived to see American psychiatry as it enters the last decade, he would certainly have repeated them. If British psychiatry can retain the best of Meyer's teaching within its traditionally eclectic approach, it will be the better, and Meyer, who admired so much in British medicine, would be well pleased.

Acknowledgements

I am extremely grateful to Professor Michael Shepherd, who helped me understand the part that Sir Aubrey Lewis played in incorporating Meyerian ideas in British psychiatry. Dr Charles Webster and Dr David Millard also made helpful comments on a draft of this chapter.

References

BEERS, C. (1908). *A Mind That Found Itself*. New York: Longmans Green.

BETZ, B. J. (1981*a*) Adolf Meyer: youth and young manhood 1866–1896: part II. *American Journal of Social Psychiatry*, **1**, 34–40.

—— (1981*b*) Adolf Meyer: youth and young manhood 1866–1896: part III. *American Journal of Social Psychiatry*, **1**, 32–40.

BLEULER, M. (1962) Early Swiss sources of Adolf Meyer's concepts. *American Journal of Psychiatry* (September).

CURRAN, D. & GUTTMANN, E. (1943) *Psychological Medicine: A Short Introduction to Psychiatry* (1st edn). Edinburgh: Livingstone.

FRANK, J. D. (1980) Adolf Meyer in retrospect. Unpublished manuscript.

GROB, G. N. (1963) Adolf Meyer on American Psychiatry in 1895. *American Journal of Psychiatry*, **119**, 1135–1142.

HENDERSON, D. K. (1916) Catatonia as a type of mental reaction. *Journal of Mental Science*, 556–572.

—— (1938) Tribute to Adolf Meyer. In *Contributions Dedicated to Dr. Adolf Meyer by his Colleagues, Friends and Pupils* (ed. S. Katzelenbogen). Baltimore: Johns Hopkins Press.

—— (1964) *The Evolution of Psychiatry in Scotland*. Edinburgh: Livingstone.

—— (1966) Adolf Meyer: a tribute from abroad. *American Journal of Psychiatry*, **123**, 322–324.

—— & GILLESPIE, R. D. (1927) *Textbook of Psychiatry* (1st edn). London: Oxford University Press.

LEWIS, A. J. (1960) The study of defect (the Adolf Meyer Lecture). *American Journal of Psychiatry*, **117**, 289–304.

LEYS, R. (1984) Meyer, Watson, and the dangers of behaviourism. *Journal of the History of the Behavioural Sciences*, **20**, 128–149.

LIDZ, T. (1966) Adolf Meyer and the development of American psychiatry. *American Journal of Psychiatry*, **123**, 320–332.

LIEF, A. (1948) *The Commonsense Psychiatry of Dr. Adolf Meyer*. New York: McGraw-Hill.

MEYER, A. (1891) Medizinische Studien in Paris, Edinburgh und London. *Correspondenz-blatt für schweizer Ärzte*, **21**. (Reprinted in *Collected Papers*, vol. 2, pp. 237–255.)

—— (1893) Die Irrenpflege in Schottland. *Correspondenz-blatt für schweizer Ärzte*, **23**. (Reprinted in *Collected Papers*, vol. 2, pp. 27–36.)

MEYER, A. (1895*a*) *Report to the Governor of Illinois*. (Reprinted (1948) in *The Commonsense Psychiatry of Dr. Adolf Meyer* (by A. Lief), pp. 53–60. New York: McGraw-Hill.)

—— (1895*b*) On the observations of abnormalities of children. *Child Study Monthly*, **1**, 1–12. (Reprinted in *Collected Papers*, vol. 4, pp. 321–328.)

—— (1895*c*) Mental abnormalities in children during primary education. *Transactions of the Illinois Society for Child Study*, 48–58. (Reprinted in *Collected Papers*, vol. 4, pp. 329–336.)

—— (1895*d*) Schedule for the study of mental abnormalities in children. *Handbook of the Illinois Society for Child Study*, 53–57. (Reprinted in *Collected Papers*, vol. 4, pp. 337–340.)

—— (1898) Special report of the Medical Department. *Annual Report of the Trustees of the Worcester Lunatic Asylum*, **66**, 20–27. (Reprinted in *Collected Papers*, vol. 2, pp. 62–66.)

—— (1902) Aims and plans for the Pathological Institute for the New York State Hospitals. Privately printed. (Reprinted in *Collected Papers*, vol. 2, pp. 90–104.)

—— (1906*a*) *Report of the Pathological Institute of the State of New York.* (Reprinted (1948) in *The Commonsense Psychiatry of Dr. Adolf Meyer* (by A. Lief). New York: McGraw-Hill.)

—— (1906*b*) Fundamental concepts of dementia praecox. *British Medical Journal*, **2**, 757–759.

—— (1909) Report of the Psychiatric Institute of New York State Hospitals. *Annual Report of State Commission in Lunacy*, **21**, 96–106. (Reprinted in *Collected Papers*, vol. 2, pp. 157–162.)

—— (1913) Foreword. *Worcester State Hospital Papers 1912–1913.* (Reprinted in *Collected Papers*, vol. 2, pp. 58–62.)

—— (1927) Emil Kraepelin: in memoriam. *American Journal of Psychiatry*, **73**, 749–755.

—— (1933*a*) British influences in psychiatry and mental hygiene. *Journal of Mental Science*, **79**, 435–463.

—— (1933*b*) Preparation for psychiatry. *Archives of Neurology and Psychiatry*, **30**, III.

MITCHELL, S. W. (1894) Address before the 15th Annual Meeting of the American Medico-Psychological Association. *Journal of Nervous and Mental Disease*, **21**, 413–437.

MORA, G. (1980) Adolf Meyer. In *Comprehensive Textbook of Psychiatry* (3rd edn) (eds H. I. Kaplan & B. J. Sadock). Baltimore: Williams and Wilkins.

SHEPHERD, M. (1986) A representative psychiatrist: the career, contributions and legacies of Sir Aubrey Lewis. *Psychological Medicine Monograph* (suppl. 10).

STEPHENS, J. H., OTA, K. Y., MORE, W. W., *et al* (1986) Inpatient diagnoses during Adolf Meyer's tenure as director of the Henry Phipps Psychiatric Clinic 1913–1940. *Journal of Nervous and Mental Diseases*, **174**, 747–751.

WINTERS, E. E. (ed.) (1951) *The Collected Papers of Adolf Meyer*. Baltimore: Johns Hopkins Press.

—— (1966) Adolf Meyer's two and a half years at Kankakee. *Bulletin of the History of Medicine*, **40**, 441–458.

—— (1969) Adolf Meyer and Clifford Beers 1907–1910. *Bulletin of the History of Medicine*, **43**, 414–443.

27 Erwin Stengel. A personal memoir

F. A. JENNER

Some people are dull, apathetic, and uninspired. Others make up for them; they are larger than life, full of wit and energy, delighted by and amusing in repartee, and somehow indestructible. So it seemed was Erwin Stengel. Such a man with a carcinoma of the colon, could chuckle at his own predicament: ''only a semi-colon, not a full stop''. This is the ambience that a world expert on suicide brought to everything. On his appointment as the Professor of Psychiatry in Sheffield, everyone was gathered together and was told that we were to be like a family; the telephone rang, and Stengel went to answer it. When he came back, he burst out: ''Heavens above, how can a psychiatrist talk about being like a family? Let us all be happy together''. While every item of business tended to be associated with humour, there was also a very practical aspect and a missionary zeal for psychiatry.

Distinguished immigrants from Austria and Germany brought a rich intellectual tradition to Britain. Stengel knew Freud and had worked with Wagner-Jauregg (Nobel Laureate for his discovery of the malarial treatment of general paralysis of the insane); Paul Schilder (of Schilder's disease, encephalitis periaxialis diffusa); von Economo (famed for his definitive description of encephalitis lethargica); Gerstmann (of Gerstmann's syndrome – thought then to be due to lesions of the angular gyrus); and with Potzl (of agnosia and aphasia fame). Stengel felt that the enthusiasm in Viennese psychiatry arose from Wagner-Jauregg's therapeutic success, and from the intellectual vigour which resulted from the immigration to its capital from the vast Austro-Hungarian Empire: Freud, von Economo, and Gerstmann, for example, were all immigrants.

The linking of psychiatry with neurology, he felt, was a factor influencing psychiatry in Vienna, but this influence had been over-rated. He compared Austria with Switzerland, where psychiatry had a high profile but was not allied to neurology. He also felt that the surplus of trained doctors and associated unemployment in Austria had led to intense competition and so to high standards. On the other hand, the distance of most British mental hospitals from academic centres had made Britain the leader in social concern for the patient: the delivery of service was less lost in arid academic issues.

Stengel was a contemporary medical student with Manfred Sakel, who later introduced insulin coma therapy into the university clinic while an outsider in private practice, and believed Sakel had been able to do this on the crest of the wave of therapeutic optimism started by Wagner-Jauregg. Sakel, who died still believing in its efficacy, observed that the comas worked best if performed by an enthusiastic team who had seen schizophrenics recover. Stengel felt it was the same 'organic enthusiasm' that led Hoff and Potzl to perform cerebral surgery for schizophrenia, by setting lesions in the medial nuclei of the thalamus, with the purpose of severing their connections with the frontal lobes, three years before Egas Moniz (Chapter 11).

He contrasted the optimism of Vienna with the pessimistic theoretical studies of Heidelberg, and this Austro-German conflict was re-enacted in Sheffield, when Mayer-Gross came. The then registrars understood little of it, but remember Mayer-Gross' comment: "Stengel, you ought to read Jaspers!" Stengel served Sheffield well by inviting his famous friends to his department (he sometimes forgot which day they were coming), among them Konrad Lorenz, Anna Freud, E. B. Straus, Ernest Jones, Denis Hill, Morris Carstairs, E. W. Anderson, Frank Fish, Max Hamilton, and Henri Ey (a fellow admirer of Hughlings Jackson).

He emphasised (1963) the influence of Hughlings Jackson on Freud in the pre-analytical phase, when the imminent eruption of psychoanalysis was already discernible. The concept of higher activities repressing lower functions was the central principle, and the reason for strengthening the ego; Ey held a similar position. For Stengel, psychoanalysis was, after medicine, the enthusiasm of his youth. In 1954 he translated Freud's *Aphasie*, which is not in the collected works. Wagner-Jauregg had little time for such speculation, nor did Jaspers, Kraepelin, Schneider, Mayer-Gross, or others from Heidelberg. However, Wagner-Jauregg was a liberal and encouraged Stengel in his adventurous desire to explore the mysteries of IX Berggasse 19. When Freud's maid came to the out-patient department, Stengel took her under his wing, to approach Freud. When she got better, Freud gave Stengel one of his imitation Graeco-Egyptian pots. Stengel treasured it and gave it to me before he died; I hope this otherwise valueless trinket will remain in the Sheffield Department of Psychiatry, which Stengel founded in 1957.

Anna, Stengel's wife, always supported him. She was originally a Catholic and he a Jew; she had been encouraged to leave him when the *Anschluss* seemed imminent. However, he believed he would be all right, as did Wagner-Jauregg, who told him the situation would soon settle down! She knew better and smuggled the unwilling Erwin to Paris and then, helped by British psychoanalysts, to England, where for a time he was interned and later lived with the Bishop of Bath and Wells. Anna worked as a technician, while Erwin had to study medicine again, finally gaining the Scottish triple qualification. He already had a long list of publications, three written as a student; there is a complete collection of them in Sheffield, as well as letters and notes, though, unfortunately, he burnt many letters and files when he left the department.

Reading Stengel's lecture notes, one gets the impression that on arrival in Britain, he intended to remain or perhaps become a psychoanalyst. It is reputed that Sir Aubrey Lewis said of him, "Stengel was only singed", as he had had analysis for only one year. Stengel's psychoanalytical thinking is striking in his notes for a lecture to psychoanalysts, at Edward Glover's request, entitled "Considerations on some experiences during a short period of internment". In it, he refers to the Home Secretary as "that primal father who deceived and devoured his weakest and most devoted children, which was a constellation bound to create profound satisfaction to the struggling and suffering ego''. He was writing about the happiness the prisoners enjoyed in the camp.

> ''The internees had nothing more to do than to satisfy the representative of the totemistic father. They enjoyed the regression towards a stage of infantile development when the parents were satisfied with a certain amount of cleanliness and good behaviour. They were prepared even to accept castration as a price for the return to that happy period of childhood. . . . I sometimes felt . . . that we were not behind barbed wire but that the outer world was.''

For this psychoanalytical audience he reported, too, a slip of the tongue (so much better in German, *Fehlleistung*): when his wife visited, he apparently said, ''how good to see my wife behind barbed wire''. This lecture is interesting in revealing Stengel's view of the male ego's fear of the testing responsibility of sexual performance and of the pleasure of the release of still unconscious latent homosexuality, in the absence of female distractions. The interned gentile, he wrote:

> ''thanked the commanders of the camp for their real understanding and compassion, doing indeed all that they themselves could. . . . The Jews are a small group. They can only hope to survive if the superegos of those who surround them do not fail. Hence their God of justice. The other virtues – love, grace, and mercy amongst them – are much too unstable to guarantee security . . . for the eternal minority.''

After his death, his wife told me they had agreed to stand together outside divisive delusory systems. However, his Jewish background could not be totally escaped, not least because he was understandably a popular speaker to Jewish societies, and so left notes for his lectures on anti-Semitism. He suggested that this is at its height during crises of Christian belief.

> ''The mechanism of projection makes us hate those on to whom we have unconsciously projected our own feelings and ideas. The Jew is, for the reason I have mentioned, not only a suitable object of projecting aggressive instincts but he also is for the Christian the most suitable object of projection of his disbelief in Christianity.''

On the other hand, Stengel felt that Judaism survived in Europe because:

> ''Christians have been ambivalent; when one part of Christendom rejected, another offered refuge. The history of migration between Poland and Germany, and between Britain and the Continent, illustrates the working of Christian ambivalence quite clearly.''

Like Freud, Stengel had little hope for a utopian solution to man's problems, and certainly not to this particular one, from which they had both suffered. He was devoted to an objective psychodynamic and empirical analysis. Judaism and Christian theology are nonsense in intellectual terms, but psychologically dynamite for men who, as he put it, ''are products of what they used to have as children for breakfast'' (then in particular referring to the Scots and porridge). Speaking on ''Freud on Religion'', Stengel said that ''Freud would have written *The Future of an Illusion* differently, had he known the Church of England''.

From the mass of Stengel's German publications and notes, it is difficult to encapsulate their essence. Throughout, though, despite considerable neurological sophistication, there is a struggle to find humanistic explanations. In, for example, his *Studien über Psychologies des induzierten Irreseins* (induced psychoses) with

Hartmann (1932), he explained how Wagner-Jauregg noted the inadequacies of genetic theory and emphasised the role of the environment, *Milieufaktoren*. He pointed out how genetics fails to explain the content of delusions (*Wahninhalt*). He quoted Freud's *Massenpsychologie und Ich-Analyse*, with the central role of identification and suggestion in the psychology of the masses (*Massenpsychologie*), which is of great importance for understanding the outlook of recent history. He tried to illustrate his views by extensive studies of some families with a sort of folie à deux, and in particular of powerful paranoid women with submissive, somewhat impotent, cowering husbands, whose madness is induced.

In a number of notes Stengel left, there is a simplistic assertion of his faith in three basic principles discovered by Freud: the unconscious, psychic determinism, and the overwhelming influence of childhood experience on psychological development. He refers to monthly meetings in Freud's house, stating that "it was not his [Freud's] fault that as a rule at the end of the discussion his point of view proved more convincing than that of the opponent . . . he was nearly 80 and looking his age . . . but he appeared the youngest of all. . . . He never showed any signs of weakening in spiritual power". In his lecture notes Stengel, who despite everything liked Britain and in some ways became more English than the English, wrote about Freud's affection for this country. Of course, even psychoanalysts oscillate between spirituality, love, hate and determinism; we are doomed to paradox.

In all this written material, Stengel's adulation of Freud is striking, but as young assistants to him, we learned neither to extol nor attack psychoanalysis: to do so was to touch a tender spot and to be corrected. Perhaps it was really the 'God that Failed', for despite great zeal for psychiatry, Stengel was not a therapeutic optimist. Freud's assertion that psychoanalysis would prove so successful that philosophical problems would disappear did not convince him. He was more of a thinker than a therapist, sharing with Sir Aubrey the pessimism he despised. None of his papers are reports of successful treatments. Some contrast Stengel, the optimist, with Aubrey Lewis, the negativist, but neither believed psychiatry really achieved much, although Stengel hoped it would do so soon, and gave young people the feeling they could help it to do so. Sir Aubrey felt psychiatry would and could advance when it became scientific, rigorously critical, and logical. When would-be appointees said they would only make scientific decisions, Stengel asked, "How did you choose your wife and make other important decisions in living?"

It did not take Stengel long to become Reader at the Institute of Psychiatry, and then Professor in Sheffield, but it was difficult for him to live as understudy to Sir Aubrey Lewis. Neither liked the other. Sir Aubrey was a distant, logical, acerbic, critical, erudite, meticulous, trenchant iconoclast. Stengel was a serious scholar, but his academic virtues were Viennese – intuitive, spontaneous, anxious to capture the idiom not the details, absolutely intent on being creative, and always painting impressionistically on a broad canvass. Sir Aubrey discussed Kant's constipation, Hume's scepticism, Locke's empiricism, the intellectual difficulties of separating anxiety and depression. Stengel spoke about the obvious difference between the helpless and hopeless. Life and clinical practice were central for him: a line between medicine and other disciplines was therefore impossible, although imperative for Sir Aubrey. Asked, when he started the Sheffield department, whether he wanted Sir Aubrey's Maudsley-type case histories to be carried out, he replied, ''We could, if we only open on Mondays''.

The antipathy of these two giants was pathetic. Stengel owed much to Sir Aubrey for his position as Reader in the Institute of Psychiatry, but Stengel had difficulties with the fastidiously pedantic, as well as with any siblings or peers not allowing him room to stretch his wings. I felt a little between the two, being always told by Stengel that I was the crown prince, and simultaneously being encouraged by Sir Aubrey, who always discussed John Locke with me. Stengel recorded his ire in his review (1968) of Lewis' *Inquiries in Psychiatry: Clinical and Social Investigations* and *The State of Psychiatry: Essays and Addresses*. In fact, Stengel had shown the review to me and, with unusual temerity, I told him it was a mistake. He wrote that ''One could not recommend a young doctor who thinks of taking up the discipline to read *The State of Psychiatry* as an introduction. It might put him off for two hundred years!'' Stengel was furious with me, and told me how pleased people would be with it. He subsequently showed me letters from Eliot Slater, William Sargant, and many, many others, proving that he was correct, even if there was also a protest letter from the junior staff at the Maudsley. Before this, Sir Aubrey had asked me, a junior, ''Do you think Stengel is a reliable person?'' There was, in fact, an obsessional streak in his make-up. He had no understanding of statistics, and chi-squared results that challenged his views merely ''demonstrated the problem with that approach''. On the other hand, Stengel was a serious scholar with a touch of the artist and in no sense was he fraudulent.

Single-handed, Stengel founded the Sheffield Department of Psychiatry and produced Professors for Adelaide (I. Pilowsky), Glasgow (M. Bond), London, Ontario (H. Merskey) and two for Sheffield (C. P. Seager and F. A. Jenner). He influenced, cajoled, and converted many people into psychiatry, as he influenced everyone who met him; all tend to have stories about his sayings. He produced the ''Sheffield Plan'' (1961), at that time pioneering undergraduate medical teaching of psychology and of psychiatry throughout the medical course: there was associated psychiatry teaching during medical, obstetric, and surgical assignments. Indeed, he took the Sheffield Medical School by storm.

Stengel was an early and ardent supporter of the case for freedom of the homosexual, being outspoken when that was less acceptable than it is now. He noted junior doctors of the period laughing about his advocacy, and felt scornful of their inhumanity and narrow-mindedness. There was also a degree of left-wing politics in Stengel's make-up; he subscribed to the *New Statesman and Nation*, for instance. However, he was delighted to join the protest about Soviet psychiatry, saying ''psychiatrists must comment on totalitarian politicians'', and that ''As one would expect, the right wing resist the protest''. He had been even more concerned to abolish legislation making suicide a crime, having great respect for Swedish honesty about suicide and being critical of all the cryptic devices by which some societies produced inaccurate data. He struggled to believe that psychiatric intervention following attempted suicide helped; he pressed for all attempts to be referred to psychiatrists (and overwhelmed us with consultations). Stengel's work on suicide is well known, and some of his central points are best summarised by himself:

> "Human behaviour usually has multiple motivations, not all of them obvious and some antagonistic to each other. People, according to some psychiatrists, either want to die or to live. That most people who commit suicidal acts want to do both at the same time, and that these suicidal acts may also serve as punishment for others, seems difficult to grasp. Yet there is ample evidence that this commonly happens. To divide people who commit suicidal acts into those who want to kill themselves and those who do not, with a sprinkling of those who do not know, is as justified as to divide married people into those who love and those who hate each other, or parents into those who love and those who hate their children. In fact, the main reason why human relations, and psychiatry, are so complicated and confusing, is that most people love and hate, want to die and to live, and to kill and preserve life at the same time. Why should we expect those people who commit suicidal acts to behave as if they knew exactly what they wanted and to act accordingly? Only rarely is human behaviour governed by one tendency only. The outcome of most human actions, especially of most irrational actions such as suicidal acts, depends on the quantitative relationship of conflicting tendencies and on many other factors, some of them unpredictable. Only in a small minority of people who commit suicidal acts is the self-destructive urge so overwhelming that it completely submerges those tendencies which aim at human contact and preservation of life.
>
> Another kind of dangerous simplification of the suicide problem springs from accepting the patients' explanations of their actions at their face value. The patients are not always aware of all the reasons for their conduct or they may not wish to disclose them. Many doctors too readily accept a patient's denial of suicidal intentions which his actions clearly indicate. Such details are not always conscious lies, but manifest suicidal behaviour is more revealing and a more reliable guide to the truth than the patient's statements. There are many reasons why patients should deny suicidal attempts are carried out without a clear awareness of self-destructive tendencies."

He saw much of attempted suicide as a gamble.

Stengel was a supporter of epidemiological studies in psychiatry and particularly of suicide and attempted suicide. He was therefore anxious to develop an international taxonomy, and produced his seminal classification of classifications for the World Health Organization (1959). Yet he saw the problem that successful classifications depend on real evidence of their value: the argument that they make communication easier does not mean that they make the discussions meaningful. He tried to resolve the dilemma by making us as aware as possible of other people's meanings. At heart a sceptic, he oscillated between trying to bring order to the chaos he accepted was there, and having a personal identification with the preservation and advance of psychiatry: "If we agree that mental illness is a myth we are finished".

Among the many interesting papers Stengel produced was "On learning a new language" (1939), in which he combined his knowledge of aphasia with psychoanalytical theory and his own struggle to learn English. Yet though he had only been in England for about a year, the syntax in no way reveals any struggle. He was interested in the libidinal attachment to objects and words, and in the superego's watch over their strict relationship. "The obsessional personality has the greatest doubts about the accuracy of his statements and is plagued by guilt over possible errors and their consequences. . . . The child is more fortunate and is not so impeded because the superego is less developed." He asserted that the "synonym in the new language will actually elicit different visual images of objects because there will be a different libidinal attachment".

Stengel was also interested in the idea that obsessions defend the individual from schizophrenia and gave a lecture on it to the International Congress of Psychiatry in Zurich in 1957. Unfortunately, this idea was not very fully explored by him (cf., however, Stengel, 1937).

Stengel stimulated many workers to study the psychology of pain and illness behaviour (Merskey, Pilowsky, Bond, and Spear, who is still in Sheffield). His papers show a continuous interest in pain, starting with joint studies with Schilder on pain asymbolia in 1928 (two years after qualifying); this was published in English in 1931. In 1970, he published "Pain and psychological illness" and in 1964 gave the Maudsley lecture "Pain and the psychiatrist" (Stengel, 1965). That led to correspondence in the *British Journal of Psychiatry* (1966) which perhaps illustrates something about the editor, Eliot Slater, and about Stengel. Slater, a great friend of Stengel's, favoured a physiological definition of pain in terms of the nervous pathways involved. However, Stengel wanted to use Merskey's definition, or a variation of it, in which pain was an unpleasant sensation of the type we tend to associate with tissue damage. Stengel's motive was to defend the reality of psychogenic pain, and to assert that the large number of patients attending psychiatrists and complaining of pain experienced it, and yet did not have tissue damage. He asserted that it is a common feature of endogenous depression, disappearing with improved mood, and is more frequent in lower socio-economic groups. He thought pain was a feature of hostility and resentment, and played a role in psychological adaptation. It could be elicited by identification with a close person who had, for example, a coronary occlusion. "Pain and psychological illness", leaning on work of Devine, Merskey, and Spear, all his one-time assistants, was written with Slater in mind. In the 42 years between it and the original study with Schilder, there had been several other studies by him, and the work has been continued by his trainees since then. Slater, though, was opposed to attempts to emphasise hysterical mechanisms.

Stengel sometimes quoted the views of Mannheim and Scheler that only the intellectual could hope to see beyond his circumstances. In later years, he was analytical enough to know that the intellectual would not see reality for long, as there was a need to understand "the dehumanisation needed to be an intellectual". Strangely, though, he was too ambivalent to say that only the analysed could see reality.

However, the intellectual power which drove him gave a moment of inertia to his intentions, which he saw as arising from sibling rivalry with his twin brother. Whatever processes led to his decisions, they acted quickly, and reversals of them were difficult to achieve, even if he was mistaken. Near him, one sometimes felt an unnecessary intrusion in his thought processes. But he could let others speak, as many Austrian refugees who had had appalling experiences in concentration camps and were referred to him learnt; seeking Austrian pensions they came on Saturday mornings by special arrangement, and had been led to hold Stengel in great awe. They were wretched, destroyed persons whose disturbance was as obvious as their once privileged social position, which left them indelibly branded with the inappropriate niceties of a bygone age and place; they were far too refined to breathe the wholesome Yorkshire air. I was always anxious to be allowed to sit in on the interviews, and Stengel found me useful as a note-taker. He shared a cocoon, at a distance, with his patient, and they spoke together in German; I only half understood. He extracted pellucid accounts from these patients of their *Mutti,*

Vati, Die Geschwistern – the house in the country – and then perhaps their failures *in der Schule* and *bei der Arbeit*. They had never done any work, they had always been delicate. Having demonstrated to himself the vulnerability of the child, he compassionately allowed the adult to tell a story about the Nazis, and then about the bleakness of existence alone in a flat in Birmingham or London. The story came to an end; doctor and patient looked at each other, one perceiving the other as miraculously powerful. The doctor was aware that he had focused a little light on reality; he had revealed, as only he could, that even National Socialism was not to blame for everything. Life could still be different, but it was not going to change. The patient and he knew that she (they were mainly women) was going to return to an unhealthy, chosen world of childhood which never existed. Nevertheless, she would do so, cherishing the helpful talk with Erwin Stengel, which had achieved nothing, but perhaps all that was possible. Farewells were invariably profuse, but made in English. The delicate creature left, the robust Stengel snatched my notes; he never commented on them, but marched home for his lunch.

In his final year as Professor at Sheffield, Stengel was President of the Royal Medico-Psychological Association (Fig. 27.1), and was a founding member of

Fig. 27.1. Erwin Stengel, President of the Royal Medico-Psychological Association, 1966/67

the Royal College of Psychiatrists that it was to become, and for which he had struggled. In his Presidential address, he tried to soothe wounds and bring together the advocates and the conservatives. "We cannot have it both ways – live in a society whose stability is still the envy of the world and have change easily." Stengel had worked in Vienna, Bristol, Edinburgh, Dumfries, Chichester, London, and Sheffield, and had a good overview of British psychiatry and of life. He felt at home in Sheffield, where he and his wife were cherished and are buried.

For Stengel, *avoir toujours le mot pour rire* was mandatory. He was proud of his English, and when his prejudices and verbal agility could be allied, neither was treacherous to the other. He effervesced as he perceived the collusion developing within, and those who knew awaited the birth of a new gem of 'Stengalia'. The table at which he sat in the doctors' mess would be alive with laughter, even while discussing suicide. Faculty meetings were less to Stengel's taste: "English and Scottish aggression, checked by respectability and inarticulate silences." He repeatedly declared that "you have no idea what it was like to work for a middle European Professor". We thought otherwise, but do not complain about the experience we enjoyed – usually!

I hope this critical homage has been paid in a way he would have respected.

References

HARTMANN, H. & STENGEL, E. (1932) Studien zur Psychologie des induzierten Irreseins. *Jahrbücher für Psychiatrie und Neurologie*, **2**, 164–183.

MERSKEY, H. (1970) On the development of pain. *Headache*, **10**, 116–123.

SCHILDER, P. & STENGEL, E. (1931) Asymbolia for pain. *Archives of Neurology and Psychiatry*, **25**, 598–600.

SLATER, E. (1966) Pain and the psychiatrist (letter). *British Journal of Psychiatry*, **112**, 329.

STENGEL, E. (1937) Über die Bedeutung der prämorbiden Personlichkeit für Verlauf und Gestaltung der Psychose. *Archives Psychiatricia und Nervenkranken*, **106**, 535–553.

—— (1939) On learning a new language. *International Journal of Psycho-Analysis*, **20**, 1–8.

—— (1954) A re-evaluation of Freud's book on "aphasia", its significance for psycho-analysis. *International Journal of Psycho-analysis*, **35**, 1–5.

—— (1959) Classification of mental disorders. *Bulletin of the World Health Organization.*

—— (1961) The Sheffield Plan. *Lancet*, *ii*, 418–419.

—— (1963) Hughlings Jackson's influence in psychiatry. *British Journal of Psychiatry*, **109**, 348–355.

—— (1965) Pain and the psychiatrist. The 39th Maudsley lecture. *British Journal of Psychiatry*, **111**, 795–802.

—— (1966) Pain and the psychiatrist (letter). *British Journal of Psychiatry*, **112**, 329–331.

—— (1968) Review of *Inquiries in Psychiatry. Clinical and Social Investigations* and *The State of Psychiatry. Essays and Addresses* by Sir Aubrey Lewis. *British Journal of Psychiatry*, **114**, 127–136.

—— (1970) Pain and psychological illness. *Topical Problems in Psychiatry and Neurology*, **10**, 173–177.

28 Samuel Gaskell

HUGH FREEMAN and DIGBY TANTAM

The benefaction for the award of an annual medal and prize to a member of the Royal Medico-Psychological Association was made by Mrs Elizabeth Holland, in memory of her brother, Samuel Gaskell. She was herself a remarkable woman who married a banker, had ten children, translated poetry from the German, began a social club for unemployed men, founded a cottage hospital, and was well known for her wit, conversation, and unflappability. However, she also came from a remarkable family. Her older brother, William, was a noted Unitarian minister, philanthropist, and writer, while his wife, her sister-in-law, was Mrs Elizabeth Gaskell, author of *North and South, Wives and Daughters*, and a celebrated and for a season notorious *Life of Charlotte Brontë*, as well as several other novels and short stories.

The Gaskell family came from Warrington, a town which in the latter part of the 18th century had become a centre of learning, scientific education, and printing; it also had a strong tradition of Dissenting Christianity, with a Unitarian Chapel founded in 1745. Its academy was founded by Unitarians in 1757 as an alternative to university for those who would not swear to conform to the Thirty-nine Articles: Joseph Priestley had been an early teacher there – but of the British constitution rather than chemistry. Warrington also became a manufacturing centre which for a time rivalled Birmingham and Manchester; it was famous for its sail canvas, and half the British ships at Trafalgar had sails made in the town.

The Gaskells were one of the principal Nonconformist families in the north-west, and among the staunchest members of the Warrington Unitarian Chapel, as well as being involved in the foundation of the academy and public library. They were part of a complicated network of inter-related families, all Dissenters, including the Darwins, Wedgwoods, and Hollands, who were active in all humanitarian concerns.

Samuel's father, William Gaskell (1777–1819), was a successful sailcloth manufacturer with a business in Buttermarket Street in the centre of the town. His mother, *née* Margaret Jackson, the "handsomest and best lady married in Leyland Church for some time", according to a contemporary newspaper, had seven children, of whom Samuel was the second. All of them were baptised in the Cairo Street Chapel; two, Margaret and John, died in infancy and were buried with their parents in the Chapel yard. William Gaskell died at the age of 42, when Samuel was 12. Margaret remarried three years later, her second husband being a Unitarian minister, the Reverend E. R. Dimmock; she was said to have shown much self-denial and good sense in ensuring that her children received the best education possible locally. Samuel and his elder brother had tuition at home from an Anglican minister, the Reverend Joseph Saul.

From an early age, Samuel Gaskell (Fig. 28.1) had wanted to become a doctor, partly in response, perhaps, to the death of his sister, but the family doctor discouraged this because an attack of measles had caused a weakness in his eyes. Therefore – perhaps paradoxically – he was bound for an apprenticeship to William Eyres, a publisher and bookseller in Liverpool, where he continued to study in his spare time. When any important news arrived from America, he was employed to take it to London by post-chaise, and is said to have used these long journeys for studious reading, which included medical textbooks.

His drive to enter medicine did not diminish and, being recognised by his master, resulted in several years of his apprenticeship being remitted, so that he became free to follow his original bent. At the age of 18 he moved to Manchester, which by then had become an outstanding centre of both science

Fig. 28.1. Samuel Gaskell

and industry; there, he became apprenticed to Mr Robert Thorpe at the Manchester Royal Infirmary. In 1831, he moved to Edinburgh and returned the following year, having obtained the LRCS and MRCS. In that year, cholera – which had been travelling westwards across Europe – arrived on the east coast of England. Gaskell was appointed resident medical officer at the Cholera Hospital, Stockport, one of two special hospitals for it in the Manchester area. He continued to be interested in cholera subsequently, and even after he was appointed Commissioner in Lunacy was recommended by his sister-in-law Liza to Parthenope Nightingale as being ready to give her sister Florence "any information in his power" about the disease.

In 1834, Gaskell was appointed resident house apothecary at the Manchester Royal Infirmary, in succession to Lloyd, and he became increasingly involved in the lunatic division of the hospital, which had been opened in 1766 with 22 beds. The many references to him in the minutes of the board meetings include his initiative in starting a library in 1839; he was also said to have never lost his temper with the apprentices (which was presumably unusual). Meanwhile, his brother William had been appointed minister of the Cross Street Chapel and had married Elizabeth.

Although he had been criticised by the coroner for the death of a patient who drowned herself in the hospital pond before he left the Infirmary, he was fully exonerated and received a glowing reference from his superior, Dr Bardsley, who wrote, "I can most conscientiously state that it is impossible for any public Medical Officer to have excelled him in the exercise of these qualities" (Renaud, 1898) – these qualities being talent, diligence, application to duty, practical knowledge, and moral conduct. After he left, the pond was drained without the consent of the hospital authorities, on instructions from the police commissioners. His successor at the Infirmary was Joseph Holland, who became the superintendent of the second asylum to be built in Lancashire, Prestwich Hospital.

In 1840, Gaskell became resident surgeon at the Lancaster County Lunatic Asylum, which had been opened in 1816, following the County Asylums Act 1808. Its resident population had grown rapidly from 60 in the first year to 406 in 1836, and, in the absence of a medical superintendent, the management of patients was increasingly custodial. Twenty-nine patients were in handcuffs, leg locks, or strait-waistcoats when Gaskell took up his appointment, and 30–40 more were chained to boxed seats in heated rooms over a permanent sewer, which did away with the need for them to move even to the toilet (Lancaster Moor Hospital, 1966).

Gaskell set himself to remedy this situation as soon as he could, expressing the hope "to follow in the steps of Pinel and Esquirol". Restraints were minimised, games and slide-shows in the winter were introduced, and meat and tea appeared on the menu. Dances were organised at which one of the patients would play the violin. The situation at Lancaster improved so rapidly that Gaskell became well known as a reformer. He was invited to assist in the plans for the new hospital (Cheadle Royal Infirmary) to replace his old workplace, the Manchester Lunatic Asylum, and his work was recommended by a visiting French psychiatrist as better than anything else he had seen in England. The Lunacy Commission, established in 1828, had been granted more extensive powers of hospital visitation in 1845, and, in 1847, Lord Shaftesbury and other Commissioners visited the Lancaster asylum. They were impressed by Gaskell's achievements, by his development of a library for the patients, by the institution of work for them, by the encouragement of patients to help each other, and by the disappearance of the more unpleasant methods of treatment such as purging and bleeding. He placed great importance on the selection and instruction of attendants, and assigned to 40 female patients the exclusive care of an equal number of orphan children, "to develop in the women the great principle of maternal love". The Commissioners reported in 1843 that "the tranquility and orderly conduct are remarkable" at the Lancaster asylum. Gaskell also introduced the practice of routinely toiletting incontinent patients at regular intervals, thus reducing the filth and stench often associated with the wards at night, but also having the added advantage of ensuring that the night attendants were awake and active. This resulted in a reduction of the night-time suicides, violence, and disturbance which had previously not been uncommon in asylums.

Gaskell had read widely in psychiatry. Books preserved from the hospital library of that period include Cullen's *Practice of Physic*, Esquirol's *Maladies mentales*, and books by Willis, Reid, and Bell. There was also an autobiographical account of an episode of psychiatric disorder by John Perceval, son of the assassinated Prime Minister Spencer Perceval, who had been confined in 1830 in conditions which the book protested about strongly. It is likely that these works further encouraged Gaskell's philanthropy, but also stimulated his scientific interest. His first report for the Lancaster asylum, in 1841, contains an interesting section on the causes of insanity; no cause could be found in 69% of the women and 60% of the men. Where a cause was alleged, the commonest cited in women were childbirth, death of friends, or disappointment in affection, with intoxication, epilepsy, or religion in the case of men.

In 1841, Gaskell had been one of six superintendents who responded to a circular letter from Dr Samuel Hitch, and met at the Gloucester asylum to discuss setting up a professional association. As a result, the first meeting of the Association of Medical Officers of Asylums and Hospitals for the Insane was held at Nottingham, later the same year; this later became the Royal Medico-Psychological Association, and eventually the Royal College of Psychiatrists. Although Gaskell found difficulty in managing on his salary of £400 per annum and thought the matter of expenses "most hateful", he arranged for the second meeting of the Association to be held at his hospital in 1842.

In 1843, the FRCS was conferred on Gaskell. He also became interested in the increasing number of admissions of mentally handicapped children from the Lancashire and Yorkshire dales. He visited the Hôpital Bicêtre in Paris, publishing in *Chambers' Edinburgh Journal* an account of this visit, in which he advocated the separation of the care of the mentally ill and mentally handicapped, long before that principle was widely accepted. In 1846, in collaboration with John Conolly and a lay philanthropist (Andrew Read), Gaskell founded the first special school in Britain for mentally retarded children – Park House, Highgate, London (Chapter 16).

Gaskell was anxious to prevent the number of patients in the hospital from rising uncontrollably, but there was a constant pressure of new cases and of mentally ill paupers transferred from workhouses, and in spite of these efforts, the population of the asylum increased from 559 to 758 during his period of office. No doubt, therefore, his appointment as a Lunacy Commissioner would have been welcome to him, since the growing problem of long-stay patients must have been becoming a burden. On his appointment, he moved to London, and began a round of regular visits to asylums, where he earned a reputation for "being a remarkably well-informed and painstaking official". His obituarist in the *British Medical Journal* goes on:

> "Proprietors and superintendents who did not look too greatly into details for themselves were greatly surprised, and not greatly pleased, to find that dignified Commissioner looking into beds and cupboards, and all manner of uninvestigated places. It should never be forgotten that what is called the non-restraint asylum is not alone the abolition of mechanical restraint, but that it connotes a revolution in the treatment of the insane in a great number of particulars, the neglect of which would render non-restraint, standing by itself, of comparatively little value. One of the more important adjuncts to non-restraint was the improved night-nursing, instituted by the late Mr. Gaskell." (*British Medical Journal*, 1886)

The attentions of the Lunacy Commissioners sometimes met with criticism not unknown to similar bodies today. After a visit by Gaskell and two of his colleagues, the management committee of the Colney Hatch Asylum (now Friern Barnet Hospital) "observed with much regret that the more they have, from feelings of courtesy, listened to the representations of the Commissioners in Lunacy, the more that body has attempted to encroach on the functions of the Committee of Visitors, and to assume a tone of dictation" (Hunter & Macalpine, 1974). Nor was this the only hazard of the job. One of Gaskell's colleagues on this visit was a lawyer, R. W. S. Lutwidge, who died after being attacked by a patient on an inspection of Fisherton House, Wiltshire, in 1873.

As a Commissioner, Gaskell visited nearly every workhouse in England and Wales, as well as the asylums, since Poor Law authorities tended to ignore their legal responsibilities for the mentally ill. In 1852, he was appointed to the Royal Commission on Lunacy in Scotland and, in 1859, gave evidence to the Select Committee on Lunatics, drawing attention to the lack of provision for non-violent mentally ill people, who were deliberately overlooked by the authorities required by the Poor Law to provide them with accommodation, in order to save costs. He continued to urge the need for the separation of different types of patients, and this was helped by the opening of Broadmoor Hospital in 1863. His practical experience as a psychiatrist added much weight to his efforts to improve standards of care, in which he strongly supported Lord Shaftesbury.

The obituary in the *Journal of Mental Science* records of his work as Commissioner that

> "he was highly esteemed, both by his colleagues in office and by the superintendents of the institutions of the insane, although the latter were at times disposed to resent his very thorough and minute examination of the institutions he inspected from floor to ceiling. His influence, however, was excellent [and he gave] sound advice . . . to assistant medical officers to associate familiarly with patients, and accompany them in their walks. . . . In no particular matter did he effect so great a change in asylums as in the matter of dirty bed-linen, which he maintained from his own experience could be reduced to a very small item if the superintendents insisted upon proper precautions being taken with dirty patients before they retired to rest, and their being systematically roused in the night to attend to the calls of nature."

A surprising reference to Gaskell's work as a Commissioner is to be found in the fiction of the period (Ross, personal communication). In 1862, Charles Dickens engaged the novelist Charles Reade to contribute a serial to his magazine, *All the Year Round*; Reade had condemned the barbarity of the prison system in *It's Never Too Late to Mend* (1856) and now wanted to do the same for private lunatic asylums, but, as Kathleen Jones (1960) points out, the sensational though isolated scandals of this kind had in fact been rooted out some years before. The story came out in serial form during 1863 and was then published as a three-volume novel under the title *Hard Cash*. It concerns a young man who is wrongfully confined because his father wants to gain control of his money; he is visited by two Lunacy Commissioners, 'Mr Abott' and 'Dr Eskell', and though he is eventually released, this is after so much bureaucratic delay that the Commissioners emerge with little credit. 'Dr Eskell' appears patient and kindly, but ineffective, and it seems that informed readers

> "quickly identified Eskell with the Commissioner Samuel Gaskell, and Wyecherly [the asylum doctor] with John Conolly. . . . It is not clear why Reade chose two of the most progressive workers in the field of mental health to travesty . . . and to give [them] names which had a similar ring to their real names." (Ross, ibid)

Dickens clearly became concerned about this, and in the part where 'Dr Eskell' appears in a less than flattering light, added a footnote expressing his confidence in the actual Commissioners. Hunter & Macalpine (1961) considered that Gaskell had been portrayed in a thinly disguised form as being "incompetent and bumptious", but did not have any explanation for Reade's action in doing this.

Apart from the annual reports of the Lancaster asylum and contributions to the reports of the Lunacy Commissioners and on mental defectives in *Chambers' Journal*, his only published work was an article, "On the want of better provision for the labouring and middle classes when attacked or threatened with insanity", which appeared in the *Journal of Mental Science* in 1860. However, this was a remarkably progressive piece, proposing for the first time that voluntary admission should be possible and that there should be public hospitals for milder cases of psychiatric disorder which would be acceptable to those who were not paupers but could not afford private care. In fact, it was not until 1930 that voluntary admission to public hospitals became possible, and not until the 1950s that any substantial number of psychiatric beds were provided outside mental hospitals.

Samuel Gaskell never married, but remained close to Elizabeth Gaskell and her family, as well as often visiting his sister Elizabeth (Holland) in Wallasey. In 1865, while crossing a street, he was knocked down by a vehicle. It was stated that from that time, he "experienced so much discomfort in the head that it was not only impossible for him to pursue his work, but painful to enter into social life. Consequently, he became, to a great extent, a recluse, although he maintained his mental faculties to the close of his life". He died on 17 March 1886 at his home in Weybridge, Surrey, at the age of 79.

Gaskell's career is an illustration of the increasing professionalisation of British society in the early 19th century, and of the corresponding loss of marginality by the Dissenting middle class. Desmond (1990) points out that following some modest reform of the royal colleges and teaching hospitals, as well as the establishment of a non-sectarian university in London, a new consensus emerged in science and medicine. This bourgeois elite slowly replaced not only the gentlemen amateurs, strongly identified with Toryism and the Anglican Church, but also the independent teachers of medicine and anatomy who, like the apothecaries, were more tradesmen than professionals. The new professional men, though, were not only meritocratic, but of the utmost respectability; they were anxious to improve society and reform abuses, but had abandoned the political radicalism of the 1820s.

Gaskell was not an innovator of the first rank, such as William Tuke or John Conolly; however, he was certainly an outstanding figure in the early development of British psychiatry. He can best be regarded as one of that group of supremely energetic mid-Victorians whose administrative and lobbying skills, together with an insatiable drive to discover the facts, laid the foundation for a modern and humane system of health care in Britain. As such, his name deserves to stand beside those of Edwin Chadwick, Florence Nightingale, and Lord Shaftesbury; it is commemorated in the publishing imprint of the Royal College of Psychiatrists.

Acknowledgements

HF would like to thank Manchester University Press for permission to reproduce some material from his contribution to the book *Some Manchester Doctors*.

DT is grateful for assistance from: Miss Reddy, Librarian, Manchester Royal Infirmary; the medical librarians of the John Rylands Library, University of Manchester; Dr Berrios, Librarian of the Royal College of Psychiatrists; the Archives Department, Warrington Borough Library; and the Administrator, Lancaster Moor Hospital. He is also grateful to Mr Guest-Gornall for permission to use his father's unpublished paper on Samuel Gaskell, and to the editors of the *Psychiatric Bulletin* and the *Transactions of the Unitarian Historical Society*, in which journals some of the material in this paper has previously been published.

The authors are also grateful to Alastair K. Ross, Esq., formerly a Commissioner of the Board of Control, for drawing their attention to the material relating to Charles Reade.

References

British Medical Journal (1886) Obituary of Samuel Gaskell. *British Medical Journal*, *i*, 720.

Desmond, A. (1990) *The Politics of Evolution: Morphology, Medicine and Reform in Radical London*. Chicago: University of Chicago Press.

Hunter, R. & Macalpine, I. (1961) Dickens and Conolly: an embarrassed editor's disclaimer. *Times Literary Supplement*, 11 August, p. 534.

—— & —— (1974) *Psychiatry for the Poor: 1851 Colney Hatch Asylum to Friern Hospital 1973*. London: Dawson.

Jones, K. (1960) *Mental Health and Social Policy*. London: Routledge & Kegan Paul.

Lancaster Moor Hospital (1966) *150th Anniversary 1816–1966*. Lancaster: North Lancashire & South Westmorland Hospital Management Committee.

Perceval, J. (1840) *Perceval's Narrative*. London: Effingham Wilson. (Reprinted 1962 (ed. G. Bateson). London: Hogarth Press.)

Renaud, F. (1898) *A Short History of the Manchester Royal Infirmary*. Manchester: Manchester Royal Infirmary.

Index

Compiled by **STANLEY THORLEY**